P. Ireland

DESK COPY

POLYMER PRODUCTS DEPARTMENT

EXPERIMENTAL STATION

Troitzsch · International Plastics Flammability Handbook

Jürgen Troitzsch

International Plastics Flammability Handbook

Principles – Regulations – Testing and Approval

with contributions by

Dipl.-Ing. Hans-Joachim Bönold
Dr. Martin Rieber
Dr. Hans-Wilhelm Schiffer

Translated by
John Haim in conjunction with David Hyatt

Distributed in the United States of America by
Macmillan Publishing Co., Inc., New York
and in Canada by
Collier Macmillan Canada, Ltd., Toronto

Dr. Jürgen Troitzsch
Chemische Werke Hüls AG
Postfach 1326
D-4370 Marl 1

Translated by
Dr. John Haim
3 Charleston Cort, Fornace Green
Crawley Sx, RH10, 6PT, GB

Distributed in USA by
Scientific and Technical Books
Macmillan Publishing Co., Inc.
866 Third Avenue, New York, N.Y. 10022

Distributed in Canada by
Collier Macmillan Canada Distribution Center,
539 Collier Macmillan Drive, Cambridge, Ontario

Distributed in all other countries by
Carl Hanser Verlag
Kolbergerstr. 22
D-8000 München 80

CIP-Kurztitelaufnahme der Deutschen Bibliothek

Troitzsch, Jürgen:
International plastics flammability handbook:
principles, regulations, testing and approval/
Jürgen Troitzsch. With contributions by
Hans-Joachim Bönold . . . Transl. by John Haim in
conjunction with David Hyatt. – München; Wien:
Hanser, 1983.
Dt. Ausg. u. d. T.: Troitzsch, Jürgen: Brand-
verhalten von Kunststoffen
  ISBN 3-446-13571-5

  ISBN 0-02-949770-1 Macmillan Publishing Co., Inc., New York

  Library of Congress Catalog Card Number 81-85877

Cover design: C. A. Loipersberger

Copyright © Carl Hanser Verlag München Wien 1983
Printed in Germany by Courier Druckhaus, Ingolstadt

Foreword

It is a measure of the inexact nature of fire science and engineering that a book of this size is required to enumerate the various fire test methods and regulations in use around the world. Add to this welter of confusion the large number of commercially significant synthetic and natural polymers and you have a recipe for an encyclopedia of no small proportions. Herr Troitzsch compiled such an encyclopedia for his German-reading audience in 1981. Now his publisher is bringing the work to us in English. It is a handy addition to the shelf for those who seek to develop products with improved fire properties.

Public concern about fire safety has ancient origins. In the last three centuries considerable public effort has been expended to control the ravages of unwanted fire. Beginning with the Great London Fire of 1666 and ending, roughly, with the San Francisco fire of 1906, these efforts were bent to developing the means to prevent major conflagrations. The work was focused on providing fire departments, adequate water supplies, and building separation and orientation to reduce the likelihood of spread from one building to another. By and large this effort met with success – we rarely lose more than one building in a given fire.

Beginning in the latter half of the nineteenth century serious efforts were made to prevent the total loss of individual buildings. Studies of fire disasters and of experimental fires produced test methods, building code provisions, and concepts for containing a fire, once started, long enough for the fire services to arrive and combat the blaze. Sprinklers, fire-rated structural components, enclosed stairways, exterior fire escapes, and other measures became commonplace. Buildings erected since about 1930 or so generally do not burn out and collapse; rather, the fire is contained to the area or floor of origin.

Despite these successes we still have a high rate of fire loss in many countries; the United States is a leader in these statistics. Careful study of the details of our fire experience shows the following:
- most fire deaths occur in residences
- most major fire disasters in public buildings involve serious violations of existing codes
- spread and growth of fatal fires involve furnishings and interior finishes, not structural members.

Fire officials are therefore focusing more of their attention on ways and means to control fires in the largely unregulated interiors of family residences. Inevitably much of this attention will be paid to the behavior of materials in fire. This book will help those who are dealing with this concern by providing in one volume information on behavior, tests, and regulations. Used as a reference work the book should prove helpful in many ways. One hopes that fire research will provide a more quantitative and rational basis for deciding questions of fire safety in the future and that this will markedly reduce the number of items to be included in a book of this kind twenty years hence. In the meantime we can only be grateful that we have people like Jürgen Troitzsch and his colleagues willing to assemble the vast array of information with which we currently have to struggle.

John W. Lyons
National Bureau of Standards
Washington, D.C.
August 1982

Foreword to the English Edition

The lively interest in the flammability of plastics was confirmed soon after publication of the German edition of this book by numerous reviews, letters and discussions. Foreign colleagues and specialists active in the field asked repeatedly for an English edition. A translation seemed particularly relevant in view of the international nature of the second part covering regulations and test methods.

The present English version differs only slightly from the original German edition. The sections on mining and on an assessment of plastics in fire insurance have been omitted as they related largely to the situation in the Federal Republic. Only minor revisions have been made to the text in order to bring the work up to date. The principal changes to the Appendix are to the addresses of manufacturers and suppliers of flame retardants and smoke suppressants in 10.1 which have been revised to make the list more suitable for international use.

No work is perfect and any comments from readers on shortcomings and how to deal with them will be welcome (please send correspondence to me via Carl Hanser Verlag, Postfach 860420, D-8000 Munich 86, FRG).

I should like to express my particular thanks to Dr John Haim who translated this book with such enthusiasm. He has eliminated various ambiguities and other deficiencies present in the German edition.

My co-authors deserve thanks for the speed in which they read through the translation and for their advice on the use of technical terms.

Finally, I should like to thank again the staff of Hanser Publishers for their customary rapidity and efficiency in producing the English edition.

Jürgen Troitzsch
Marl
October 1982

Preface to the German Edition

None of the many publications on the flammability of plastics provide a comprehensive review of the fundamentals as well as of the relevant regulations and test methods. In order to fill this gap, plans were made in the autumn of 1978 to issue a pocketbook in time for the K '79 International Plastics and Rubber Exhibition. The complexity of the subject became apparent on closer acquaintance and it was soon realised that the project could not be completed within the original constraints. Discussions with the publisher led to the decision to cover the field in depth by issuing a handbook.

The expertise and time available to one person were clearly insufficient to cope with the abundance of information on the subject. Consequently publication on a reasonable time-scale and in the present form was feasible only with the cooperation and support of the experts who have contributed to this book. I should like, therefore, to express my gratitude to my co-authors D. I. *Hans-Joachim Bönold* (BASF AG) for the section on "Transportation", Dr. *Hans-Wilhelm Schiffer* (Bayer AG) for "Electrical engineering" and Dr. *Martin Rieber* (Hoechst AG) for "Textiles".

The book consists of two parts. The first describes the basic principles of the combustion process, the burning behaviour of plastics with and without flame retardants and of smoke development. It is hoped that this will facilitate the readers' introduction to this complex subject and also provide the background to a better understanding of the fire test procedures, regulations and approval criteria covered in the second part. Special thanks are due to my colleagues Dr. *Klaus Burzin* and Dr. *Günther Maahs* (both of Chemische Werke Hüls AG) for their valuable comments on the manuscript of this part of the book.

The second part, aimed at the expert, describes fire protection regulations, the test methods introduced to satisfy them and product approval procedures for plastics components in various applications. The development of fire tests, the estimation of fire hazard on the basis of differing "fire philosophies" and related terminology are also considered.

The most extensive section in the book is devoted to the building sector for which numerous regulations and test methods have been developed in all the industrialised countries. I should like to thank the experts from over twenty countries who read through the manuscript and provided up to date information, which served to clarify the bewildering number of regulations and test methods:

D. I. *W. Becker* (Federal Republic of Germany)
Dr. ir. *P. Vandervelde* (Belgium)
Ir. *H. Zorgman* (Netherlands)
G. *Touchais* (France)
Mrs. *R. Ramaprasad* and *H. L. Malhotra* (Great Britain)
Dr. *L. Turri* (Italy)
D. I. *W. Höhnl* (Austria)
Dipl.-Chem. HTL *R. Hoffmann* (Switzerland)
E. *Danø* (Denmark)
P. *Loikkanen* (Finland)
Architect *O. H. Jónsson* (Iceland)
Dr.-Ing. *P. J. Hovde* (Norway)
U. *Wickström* (Sweden)
Prof. Dr. *Helff* and Prof. Dr. *Hildebrand* (GDR)
the Department of External Relations of the Ministry of the Interior and the GOST Standards Organisation (USSR)
Dr. *K. Pál* (Hungary)
V. *Kmoch* and *P. Smilek* (ČSSR)

W. A. Haas (USA)
Mrs. *M. Crainey* (Canada)
G. H. Blödorn and *K. G. Martin* (Australia) and
Dr. *H. Suzuki* (Japan).

Further sections deal with the fields of transportation and electrical engineering in which international harmonisation of regulations and test methods has made greater progress. Their number and variety is thus less extensive. The field of textiles is reviewed generally while the section on furnishings concentrates on developments in the USA and Great Britain. My thanks to Ing. (grad.) *T. Denk* (Siemens AG) and D. I. *F. H. Prager* (Bayer AG) who checked the sections on "Electrical engineering" and "Furniture and furnishings", respectively.

The secondary fire effects, smoke development and toxicity and corrosivity of fire gases, which are of increasing public interest, are also covered in some depth. I should like to thank Dr. *G. Johannson* (Röhm GmbH) who made many valuable suggestions on the section on "Smoke development of fire gases" and Dr. *P. Mürmann* (Chemische Werke Hüls AG) who checked the medical content of "Toxicity of fire gases".

I hope that this book will help to clarify the numerous problems of fire protection and lead to a better understanding and meaningful discussion of its many interactions.

At this point I should like to express my gratitude to Chemische Werke Hüls AG for their comprehension and generous support.

Last but not least, my hearty thanks to the personnel of Hanser Publishers and their managing director, *Joachim Spencker,* who approached this project with such enthusiasm and expertise and Dr. *Wolfgang Glenz* who was always ready to advise and assist.

Jürgen Troitzsch
Marl
September 1981

How to use this book

Structure

The book commences with a historical synopsis on the topic of fires and an account of the present situation in fire protection. Subsequently the basic principles of the burning process and the combustion of individual plastics are considered. The thermal properties and burning behaviour of plastics are examined in the light of the physical and chemical processes taking place. Methods of rendering plastics fire retardant and reducing smoke emissions are introduced and the modes of action of flame retardants and smoke suppressants are explained.

The second part is aimed at the expert. An introduction to the methodology of fire testing is followed by a discussion of national and international fire protection regulations and test methods for plastics. Structural fire protection occupies the largest part of the book and is arranged according to a uniform scheme for all 22 countries dealt with in Sections 8.2.2 to 8.2.17. Each of these sections commences with an account of the statutory regulations and continues with a summary of the relevant test methods in the form of diagrams and tables of test specifications. The reader is thus able to grasp the essentials at a glance. Further details should be taken from the original standards listed in the bibliography at the end of each section.

Officially recognised test institutions and procedures for obtaining official product approval are enumerated under the heading "Official approval". Each section terminates with a look at future developments in the relevant country.

Sections 8.3 to 8.6 are arranged in a similar fashion except that the divisions are according to subject rather than country. Secondary fire effects are dealt with together in Chapter 9 for the sake of clarity. "Smoke development of fire gases" thus contains all the test methods relevant to building, transportation and electrical engineering. The relatively new field of testing toxicity of fire gases and the subject of corrosivity of fire gases complete Chapter 9.

The Appendix contains various lists including a suppliers' index for flame retardants, addresses of standards organisations and electrical engineering organisations. The glossary of technical fire protection terminology and the English, German and French equivalents of the most important terms will be extremely useful to workers in the field. The Appendix terminates with a list of all the standards and guidelines mentioned in the book and a comprehensive name and subject index.

References

A bibliography will be found at the end of each chapter or section and the principal journals and books on the subject are listed in the Appendix.

Illustrations and tables

Illustrations and tables are numbered consecutively in each chapter. Diagrams of test equipment include only those features necessary for understanding the method.

The tables of test specifications summarise details of test specimens, specimen position, ignition source, test duration and conclusions.

Contents

1 Introduction

1.1 Historical review

Few discoveries have had as much influence on the development of mankind as the skill of generating and using fire. This capability is a basic requirement of all civilisations since it enabled Man to reduce his dependence on a hostile environment. With the aid of fire he learned to prepare meals, fire pottery and extract metals from their ores. Gradually mankind ceased to be nomadic and built settlements which developed into large towns with the advent of the first great cultures. There is, however, another side to fire, namely a deadly uncontrolled natural force against which Man is helpless.

Historically, fires, wars and epidemics were considered to be the principal scourges of the human race. Due largely to urban design, towns and cities were frequently reduced to ash and rubble by catastrophic fires. Houses were built extremely close to each other in a veritable maze of streets and, particularly in the Middle Ages, were constructed almost entirely of wood.

Some of the catastrophes which have achieved particular notoriety are listed here as examples of the vast number of fires which have occurred throughout history:

- In A.D. 64, during Nero's reign, Rome burnt down in eight days. Ten of the fourteen districts were completely destroyed.
- In 1666 the Great Fire of London destroyed 13,200 houses, 94 churches and countless public buildings in the space of three days.
- In 1812 the Russians set fire to Moscow to repel Napoleon's army. The conflagration raged for five days and destroyed 90% of the city.
- In 1842, 4,200 buildings were destroyed in Hamburg by a fire which cost 100 lives and rendered 20% of the population homeless.
- In 1906, following an earthquake, fire almost totally destroyed San Francisco and killed 1000 persons. The fire extended over an area of almost 10 km^2.
- In 1923, Tokyo and Yokohama were almost completely devastated by fires following earthquakes.

The Second World War added a new dimension to fire, the fire storm:

- In 1945 the allied attack on Dresden resulted in the most devastating fire catastrophe on record. Approximately 300,000 people were killed in the fire storm unleashed by the bombardment and the city was completely devastated.

Throughout history attempts have been made to limit this uncontrolled aspect of fire in two ways:

- On the one hand, fire fighting has been organised using fire fighters or brigades: An example of the latter existed in Ancient Egypt and the 'Cohortes Vigilum' in the Rome of the Caesars can be considered as forerunners of the modern fire service.

- On the other hand, preventive fire protection has also been practised. Various methods are used: fire regulations are passed [1] and, in addition, attempts are made to protect materials more effectively against attack by fire, for example with flame retardants. Examples of the latter have been known since ancient times and a few are mentioned in the résumé below [2−4].

In 360 B.C. a treatise on fortifications recommended that timbers should be protected against fire by painting with vinegar. In the battle for the town of Piraeus in 83 B.C., wooden siege towers were impregnated with alum to prevent them being set alight by the Romans and were successfully used without catching fire. In A.D. 77 *Pliny the Elder* described asbestos table cloths which could be cleaned by heating to red heat.

In 1638, *Nicolas Sabbatini* suggested that clay and gypsum could be used as flame retardants for theatre scenery made of painted canvas. The first patent (no. 551) in which textiles and papers treated with fire retardants are described was published in England in 1735. The mixture used consisted of alum, borax and vitriol (probably impure iron sulphate). In 1783, the *Montgolfier* brothers used a flame retardant coating of alum on the envelope of their hot air balloon.

Gay Lussac was commissioned in 1786 to reduce the flammability of textiles used in French theatres following several fires. In 1820 he suggested the use of mixtures of ammonium phosphate, ammonium chloride and borax. These proved highly effective and are still used on occasion.

Towards the middle of the 19th century numerous flame retardants for textiles were tested. Ammonium phosphate, ammonium sulphate and a mixture of ammonium phosphate and chloride were found to be the most effective.

At the beginning of the 20th century, *William Henry Perkin* carried out fundamental research into flame retarding textiles. He was the first person to study systematically the mechanisms of flame retardance. Modern flame retardants for wood, cotton, paper and especially plastics are based on his studies.

1.2 The present situation

Today the probability of a catastrophic fire razing an entire town in peacetime is remote.

Technical advances such as powerful water jets and fire engines have considerably improved the effectiveness of fire fighting. Due to the plethora of mainly governmental legislation fire protection today plays an extremely important role in reducing fire risk. Housing areas, for example, are separated from each other by open spaces; individual buildings have outer walls built of fire resistant materials (so-called fire walls): only building materials and components which have passed certain fire tests and therefore meet fire performance requirements are used. Many buildings are protected by fire alarms and sprinkler systems.

One would think, therefore, that Man has mastered the uncontrolled aspect of fire. Nothing could be further from the truth. Major fires occur daily and, although they are not on the same scale as earlier catastrophes, they are nevertheless, increasing in size and frequency as the following examples show:

- On 22. 5. 1967, the "A l'Innovation" department store in Brussels burnt down leaving 270 dead.
- In a discotheque fire in Saint-Laurent-du-Pont in France on 1. 11. 1970, 146 young people met their death.
- The huge fire which destroyed the "Summerland" entertainment centre on the Isle of Man on 2. 8. 1973 caused 49 fatalities.
- In February 1974, the Cresiful Building in São Paulo, Brazil was consumed by fire and 200 people died.

– The fire at the Ford Spare Parts Centre in Cologne in the Federal Republic of Germany on 20. 10. 1977 luckily did not involve any fatalities. The fire damage, however, amounted to some DM 240 million (total damage was estimated at DM 425 million). Damage of this order was a new experience in Germany in peacetime.

This trend has its roots in the turbulent development of science and technology. As a result, we are confronted with unfamiliar circumstances.

– One of these is scale. Houses and storage sheds are being replaced by high rise buildings or skyscrapers and huge warehouses. There is an unprecedented development in the size and number of methods of transport.
– The second is the vast increase in gross national product of the industrialised nations which has resulted in increased wealth and living standards.

Both these aspects and a range of related factors have resulted in an increase in the risk of fire [5]:

– Houses and apartments are luxuriously furnished. Carpeting, furnishings, equipment, oil and gas for heating, all increase the fire load in a building.
– In industry and commerce, ever increasing amounts of goods are manufactured and stored in larger and larger buildings.
– The concentration of people in towns due to the availability of jobs in itself attracts new industries, increases consumption and results in a further concentration of population and materials.
– Technology, new processes and applications introduce many new fire hazards (e.g. new ignition sources such as welding sparks and short circuits).
– New technologies increasingly involve new types of material since traditional materials do not meet certain technical requirements.

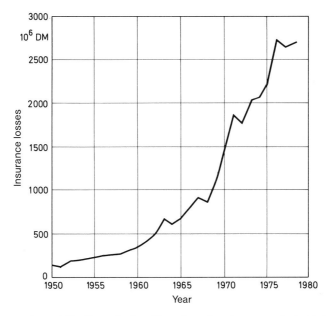

Fig. 1.1 Compensation paid by fire and related loss of earnings insurances in the Federal Republic of Germany.

The exponentially increasing cost of fire damage is a further factor [6, 7]. Fig. 1.1 shows the increase in the compensation paid by insurance underwriters in the Federal Republic of Germany since 1950. As mentioned earlier, this is largely due to increasing scale and prosperity. Prosperity could be said to be characterised on the one hand by the availability of sophisticated and therefore expensive products such as machines and, on the other, by the increasing use of combustible materials.

The combination of scale, high value products and combustible materials is encountered with increasing frequency in fires with ensuing high financial losses. The often expressed opinion that the type of combustible material involved is the sole factor in determining the extent of losses is unfounded.

References for Chapter 1

[1]   *H. Bub:* DIN-Mitt. 57 (1978) 10, p. 555.
[2]   *W. Hornung:* Kleine Feuerwehrgeschichte. Die roten Hefte, No. 21, W. Kohlhammer Verlag, Wiesbaden, 1972.
[3]   *J. W. Lyons:* The Chemistry & Uses of Fire Retardants. Wiley-Interscience, John Wiley, New York, 1970, p. 166.
[4]   *J. J. Pitts,* in *W. C. Kuryla, A. J. Papa* (Ed.): Flame Retardancy of Polymeric Materials. Vol. 1, Chap. 2, p. 134, Marcel Dekker, Inc., New York, 1973.
[5]   *O. Herterich, P. G. Seeger:* Denkschrift zur Lage der Brandschutzforschung. Issued by Vereinigung zur Förderung des Deutschen Brandschutzes e. V. (VFDB), Hamburg, 1973.
[6]   *O. Herterich:* VFDB Z., Forsch. Techn. Brandschutz 23 (1974) 4, p. 135.
[7]   *H. D. Beenken:* Wirtschaftliche Bedeutung des Brandschutzes. Fire Protection Seminar, Technische Akademie Wuppertal, 12–14. 3. 1979.

2 Market Situation

Plastics have made a decisive contribution to the present high living standard of the industrialised countries. Historically, plastics have developed in several stages. Those based on natural products appeared first with vulcanised fibre in 1859 followed by celluloid and artificial horn in 1870 and 1897, respectively. The development of thermosetting plastics commenced in the early part of the 20th century with the introduction of Bakelite in 1910. The real breakthrough occurred with the event of polymerisation plastics in 1930 [1].

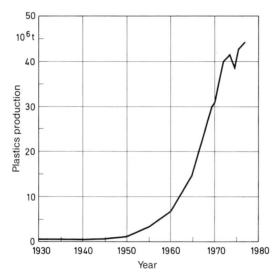

Fig 2.1 Estimated World production of plastics (excluding synthetic rubber and fibres)

Table 2.1 Apparent consumption (production + imports – exports) and per capita consumption of plastics 1977 to 1979 [4−6]

Country	Apparent consumption [1000 t]			Per capita consumption [kg]		
	1977	1978	1979	1977	1978	1979
Federal Republic of Germany	5 450	5 849	6 454	89	95	105
France	2 410	2 555	2 730	48	48	51
Great Britain	2 439	2 190	2 326	40	41	42
Italy	2 221	2 490	2 880	42	44	51
Japan	4 628	5 537	7 256	41	48	62
USA	14 009	15 934	17 091	64	73	77

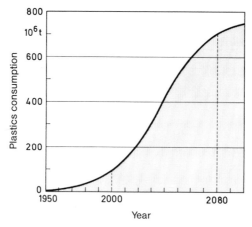

Fig 2.2   Growth in World consumption of plastics after [3]

After the Second World War development was vigorous and production of plastics increased exponentially until 1973 when a slump due to the first oil crisis occurred. Growth subsequently resumed its previous rate (Fig. 2.1) and is expected to continue in a similar fashion in the coming decades [3].

The world consumption of plastics in 1979 stood at some 50 million tonnes. Production figures for the years 1977–1979 for the principal Western industrialised countries are shown in Table 2.1.

The consumption of the standard plastics is headed by polyethylene followed by PVC, polystyrene, polypropylene and polyurethane (Table 2.2). These five plastics make up 55–75% of the total plastics consumption in the countries listed.

Table 2.2   Consumption of selected plastics in 1979 [6]

Country	Plastics consumption in 1979 [1000 t]						
	PVC	PS	LDPE	HDPE	PP	PUR	total*
Federal Republic of Germany	1 039	na	← 1 442 →		na	na	6 454
France	720	205	619	205	146	na	2 730
Great Britain	440	166	495	176	243	94.5	2 326
Italy	570	340**	725	180	200	150	2 880
Japan	1 492	785	1 194	675	934	na	7 256
USA	2 630	1 705	3 128	1 991	1 379	864	17 091

*   total consumption incl. engineering plastics and thermosets
**   incl. ABS and SAN
na = not available

An analysis of plastics consumption according to application is given in Table 2.3.

The fire performance requirements demanded of materials frequently necessitate the addition of flame retardants. This is particularly true of plastics used in building and electri-

Table 2.3 Plastics consumption in various fields of application in 1978 and 1979 [5, 6]

| Country | Plastics consumption, market share [%] | | | | | | | | | | | | | |
| | Building/Construction | | Packaging | | Electrical/Electronic | | Transport | | Furnishing | | Household | | other | |
	78	79	78	79	78	79	78	79	78	79	78	79	78	79
Federal Republic of Germany	25	25	21	21	14	15	6	7	5	5	2.5	2.5	26.5	24.5
France	18	–*	29	–*	6	–*	–*	–*	5	–*	4	–*	38	–*
Great Britain	21	18	30	32	8	11	5	5	7	7	5	2.5	24	24.5
Italy	10.5	10.5	30	30	9	9	5.5	6	5.5	5.5	5.5	5.5	34	33.5
Japan	14	14	22	25	11	11	6.5	8	1	1	6	6	39.5	35
USA	20	19.5	26	27	8	8	6	5	5	5	10	10	25	25.5

* not available

Table 2.4 Consumption of flame retardants for plastics in the USA 1970–1980 [7]

| Type of flame retardant | Consumption [1000 t] | | | | | | | | | | |
	1970	1971	1972	1973	1974	1975	1976	1977	1978	1979	1980*
Additives											
Aluminium oxide hydrates	na	na	na	72	50	60	64	80	90	75	80
Antimony oxides	6.5	7	8	8.5	11	8.5	14	13	15	15	16
Boron compounds	1	1	2	2	4	4	5	5	5	5	5
Bromine compounds	na	na	3	5	6	9	10	8	13	15	17
Chloroparaffins and chlorinated cycloaliphatics	8	10	19	27	31	30	15	16	17	19	20
Phosphate esters, halogen-free	26	22.5	24.5	31	10	19	16	17	18	19	19
halogenated	2.5	3	7	11	29.5	13.5	8	9	10	12	13
Other	3	4	4.5	7	7	5	6	7	7	9	9
Total	47	47.5	68	163	148.5	149	138	155	175	169	179
Reactive systems for											
Epoxies	2	1	2.5	3.5	4.5	3	5	5	5	5	5
Polycarbonates	na	na	0.5	1	1	0.5	1	1	2	2	2
Polyesters	10.5	12	5	6.5	7	5	6	7	7	8	8
Styrene derivatives	na	na	na	1	0.5	0.5	1	1	2	2	2
Polyurethanes, flexible foams	5	7	8	11	2	0.5	1	1	3	4	4
rigid foams	5	7	8	2	7	7	6	7	9	11	12
Other	2.5	3	3.5	4	4	2.5	3	3	3	4	4
Total	20	24	19.5	29	26	19	23	25	31	36	37

* estimated
na = not available

cal applications, in transportation and, increasingly, in furniture and furnishings. It is difficult to quote exact figures on the consumption of fire retardant plastics since they are not listed separately in official statistics while other sources are incomplete. The consumption figures for flame retardants used in plastics provide an indirect indication. These amounts vary considerably in the individual countries since they depend on several factors such as legislation (building regulations, decrees, guidelines, etc.), local regulations, insurance recommendations and voluntary restrictions imposed by manufacturers themselves.

A summary of the consumption of flame retardants in the USA between 1970 and 1980 is given in Table 2.4 and it is interesting to examine how the factors have affected the consumption of flame retardants in the USA during this period [7]:

1971 – consumption of flame retardants shows an increase of 16% over the 1970 figure as a result of the newly introduced Small Carpets and Rugs Standard and the growing influence of Consumer Organisations demanding more stringent safety requirements for manufactured goods.

1972 – consumption of flame retardants increases by some 40% due to further legislation; the introduction of FMVSS 302 (cars) and FAA (aircraft) regulations results in increased fire performance requirements for materials used in these sectors, a new Carpet Standard is also introduced.

1973 – a further 40% increase in the demand for flame retardants (excluding $Al(OH)_3$) is registered following legislation on mattresses by the Department of Commerce and the State of California.

1974 – a small rise in flame retardant consumption due to lack of manufacturing capacity especially of phosphate esters.

1975 – consumption of flame retardants decreases sharply at first due to the recession but almost catches up by year's end due to new regulations (TV Cabinet Standard, Californian Regulation for Upholstered Furniture).

1976 – turnover in flame retardants stagnates in anticipation of the TCSA (Toxic Substances Control Act) coming into force in 1977. Other factors include numerous manufacturers' liability law suits and less strict application of fire regulations due to economic considerations.

1977 – stagnation continues due to withdrawal of flame retardants such as Dechlorane and Tris [tris (2,3-dibromopropyl) phosphate] from the market following controversy. Demand is stimulated by underwriters pressing for incorporation of flame retardants in polyurethanes.

1978 – consumption increases intermittently due to the TCSA and further pending legislation.

1979 – the economic situation and the wait-and-see attitude of the plastics processing industry relative to planned toxicity regulations causes a further small reduction in flame retardant consumption.

1980 – a forecast of slight growth based on the necessity of complying with existing and planned fire regulations (particularly in the furniture sector) which will more than counteract the effects of the downturn in the economy.

Predictions for the next five years are optimistic. According to a forecast by Business Communications Co. (BCC), consumption of flame retardants led by bromine and phosphorus compounds will show an annual increase of 8% up to 1985 [8]. Growth rates of individual flame retardants are shown in Table 2.5.

The Western European market for flame retardants was approximately 26,000 t in 1978 and is estimated at some 37,500 t for 1980. Table 2.6 shows the breakdown of flame retardant consumption in Western Europe.

The consumption of bromine compounds used mainly as additive flame retardants in the standard plastics (thermoplastics) in the principle European countries, Japan and the USA is

Table 2.5   Estimated consumption of flame retardants in the USA up to 1985 (after BCC [8])

Flame retardant	Consumption [1000 t] 1980	1985	Annual growth [%] 1980–85
Antimony oxides	14	18	4.7
Aluminium hydrates	136	191	7.0
Phosphorus compounds	96	158	10.4
Bromine compounds	15	25	11.4
Chlorine compounds	36	46	5.0
Boron and miscel-laneous compounds	18	23	5.0
Total	315	461	7.9

Table 2.6   Consumption of flame retardants in Western Europe in 1978 and 1980 [9]

Flame retardant	Consumption [t] 1978	1980*
Bromine compounds	6 000	11 000
Chloroparaffins	4 500	5 500
Other chlorine compounds	4 500	6 000
Phosphate esters	3 000	5 000
Antimony trioxide	8 000	10 000
Total	26 000	37 500

* estimated

Table 2.7   Estimated consumption of bromine compounds in the principal Western industrialised countries in 1978 and 1980

Country	Consumption of bromine compounds [t] 1978	1980
Federal Republic of Germany	2 800	6 000
Great Britain	1 150	2 500
Italy	600	1 000
France	500	500
Belgium	400	600
Total Western Europe	6 000	11 000
USA	15 000	40 000
Japan	3 000	10 000

summarised in Table 2.7. This analysis clearly shows the huge lead of the USA over Western Europe and Japan in the use of bromine compounds as flame retardants in plastics. In fact the position is unchanged if all flame retardants are taken into account and is predicted to continue in the short term (Table 2.5).

The figures quoted in Tables 2.5–2.7 are not directly comparable since they are based on estimates. Taken together, however, they reflect in general terms the development of flame retardant consumption and associated trends.

Further information on the flame retardant situation is given in various papers [10–13].

The principal manufacturers of flame retardants are listed in Appendix 10.1.

References for Chapter 2

[1]   *H. Saechtling:* Kunststoff-Taschenbuch. 21. Ed., Carl Hanser Verlag, München, 1979, p. 4.
[2]   Kunststoff-Verarbeitung 1979/80 Jahresbericht. Gesamtverband kunststoffverarbeitende Industrie, e. V. (GKV) (Publisher), Frankfurt, 1980, p. 41.
[3]   *H. Teitge:* Kunststoffe 70 (1980) 5, p. 299.
[4]   *A. Camani:* Kunststoffe-Plastics 25 (1978) 9, p. 20.
[5]   *A. Camani:* Swiss Plastics 2 (1980) 4, p. 6.
[6]   *A. Camani:* Swiss Plastics 3 (1981) 7/8, p. 40.
[7]   *Anon.:* Flame Retardants. Mod. Plast. Intern. 1 (1971) 9, p. 66; 2 (1972) 9, p. 72; 3 (1973) 9, p. 53; 4 (1974) 9, p. 52; 5 (1975) 11, p. 66; 6 (1976) 9, p. 42; 7 (1977) 9, p. 46; 8 (1978) 9, p. 54; 10 (1980) 9, p. 42.
[8]   *Anon.:* C & EN, Nov. 17, 1980, p. 26.
[9]   *H. Jenkner:* in *R. Gächter, H. Müller* (Eds.): Taschenbuch der Kunststoff-Additive, p. 387, Carl Hanser Verlag, München, 1979.
[10] *K. Ikeda:* Chem. Econ. Eng. Rev. 9 (1977) 12, p. 31.
[11] *R. C. Kidder:* Mod. Plast. Encyclopedia 1977/1978, p. 192.
      D. Condit: Mod. Plast. Encyclopedia 1978/1979, p. 192.
      L. O. Raether: Mod. Plast. Encyclopedia 1979/1980, p. 179.
[12] *D. P. Miller:*Plast. Engn. 36 (1980) 2, p. 29.
[13] *A. von Hassell:* Plast. Technol. 26 (1980) 7, p. 71.

3 The Burning Process

In order to be able to comment on the phenomenon of fire it is convenient first to describe its macroscopic form. It is apparent that a fire proceeds in various stages which depend on certain parameters. If additional information on the actual burning process is required, the microscopic region in which the physical and chemical processes controlling it take place must be considered.

3.1 Fire

The course of a fire can be split into several phases as explained below, using a fire in a building as an example [1, 2].

The initiating fire

An ignition source such as a cigarette ignites combustible matter (for instance, the contents of a wastepaper basket). This material burns and generates heat, heating up and igniting additional combustible matter (e.g. a curtain near the basket). The additional heat released and resultant rise in the temperature of the surroundings speed up the rate at which the fire develops. At this stage radiant heat and the temperature have increased to such an extent that the fire load (i.e. all the combustible matter such as furnishings, carpets, etc.) decom-

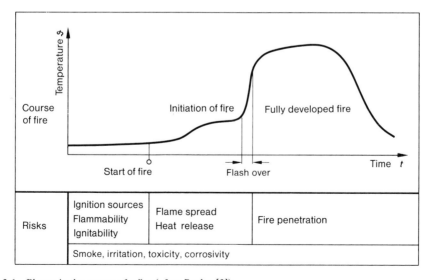

Fig. 3.1 Phases in the course of a fire (after *Becker* [3])

poses with the evolution of a flammable gas mixture. The ignition of the gas causes an extremely high, even explosive, rate of fire spread over the entire area. This point in time is termed "flash-over" and leads to the fully developed fire which constitutes the second phase.

The fully developed fire

The fire penetrates doors, walls, ceilings and windows and spreads to neighbouring rooms until the whole building is in flames. The room temperatures exceed 1000 °C and the entire fire load in the building burns. At this point the fire has reached its peak.

The decreasing fire

Depending on the size of the fire load and the ventilation conditions, the fire passes its climax and enters the decreasing phase in which the building is more or less rapidly burnt out. These three phases and associated risks are illustrated in Fig. 3.1.

3.2 Fire determining parameters

In order for a fire to start, three components – fuel, oxygen and energy – are necessary. The combustion process cannot take place without them. *Emmons* has illustrated this clearly in a fire triangle (Fig. 3.2) [4]. The extraordinary complexity of a fire springs from these three components which are themselves affected by a multitude of variables. It is therefore impossible to describe a fire quantitatively or to predict its course exhaustively. Selected parameters which influence the above components are discussed in the following summary [5, 6].

- Energy can be transferred to the fuel by radiation, sparks and flames. Of special importance for the continuation of the fire are the intensity (distance of the energy source from combustible matter) and duration of the ignition source.
- Oxygen is necessary for the actual burning process, i.e., for chemical reaction of the fuel. It must be present in sufficient quantities (e.g., through ventilation) at the site of the fire.
- The fuel itself influences the fire situation in several ways. Parameters of primary importance affecting the behaviour of fuel in a fire include position in the fire room, "built-in" state, form (shape, thickness, surface characteristics, distribution, density, etc.) and finally physical and chemical properties (ignition and flash points, thermal conductivity, specific heat and heat of combustion, etc.).

This variety of parameters demonstrates that the fire performance of a fuel is only partially characterised by its chemical and physical properties and is therefore not an intrinsic property of the material – contrary to frequently stated opinions.

The instant at which flash-over occurs is of prime importance for the fire situation since it leads, as can be seen from Fig. 3.1, to the fully developed fire. At this stage the fire situation can no longer be controlled and one must be content with preventing the fire from spreading to other parts of the building or, indeed, to other structures. Prior to flash-over, the fire can be effectively fought in the vicinity of the initiating fire and extinguished. Suitable measures at this point, such as the use of flame retardants, can effectively and permanently influence processes such as ignition, flame spread and heat release. These terms are discussed in Chapter 7: "Methodology of fire testing".

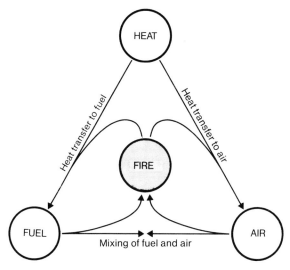

Fig. 3.2   Fire triangle (according to *Emmons* [4])

3.3 The flame

In order to gain a deeper understanding of the combustion process, it is useful not only to consider its macroscopic manifestation, but also to examine the microscopic or molecular region where material properties play a determining role. While fire is the external manifestation of an uncontrolled combustion process and therefore cannot be exactly defined, the flame may be considered as the expression of controlled combustion and can thus be described.

Basically, two types of flame exist: the *premixed flame* in which the gas composition is fixed prior to combustion (e.g. as in the Bunsen burner) and the *diffusion flame* – so called because the oxygen necessary for combustion diffuses into the gas mixture from the surrounding atmosphere.

The best known example of a diffusion flame is the candle flame. An illustration detailing the individual phenomena of the combustion process in such a flame is shown in Fig. 3.3 [7].

Wax melted by radiated heat migrates up the wick by capillary action and is pyrolysed on its surface at temperatures between 600−800 °C. The pyrolysis gases migrate further and either remain in the inner part of the flame, the flame nucleus, or reach the external flame mantle.

A reducing atmosphere exists in the flame nucleus owing to the lack of oxygen. The hydrocarbon fragments from pyrolysis migrate to regions in which temperatures reach 1000 °C. Generation of conjugated double bonds followed by cyclisation and aromatisation leads to the formation of soot particles. The latter are transported further and start to glow, causing luminescence of the flame. They are consumed in the luminescent region of the flame by reaction with water and carbon dioxide to form carbon monoxide.

The pyrolysis gases are carried to the exterior and encounter oxygen diffusing inwards. In this flame mantle reaction zone, high energy, primarily oxygen-containing radicals are generated at temperatures around 1400 °C. These maintain the combustion reaction. If the

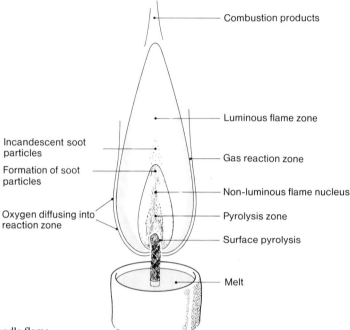

Fig. 3.3   Candle flame

process is uninterrupted and an adequate supply of oxygen is maintained, the end products of combustion of the candle flame are carbon dioxide and water. The processes which take place during the combustion of plastics are, in principle, similar to those of the candle flame.

This subject will be discussed further in the following chapter, but some of the relevant terms are explained here. Further details and an introduction to this field are given in review articles by *Fristrom* [8], *Stull* [9] and *Hastie* [10].

Combustion is a catalytic exothermic reaction maintained by internally generated free radicals and radiant heat. If the supply of free radicals and heat exceeds the energy required for combustion, the reaction proceeds at an increasing rate until an explosion occurs. If the energy supply is constant and equals the demand, a stationary equilibrium occurs, i.e., the rate of combustion is constant. If the available energy is less than required to maintain equilibrium, the rate of combustion decreases until extinction occurs.

The radicals, oxygen and thermal energy necessary for combustion are brought to the site of combustion by various transport mechanisms [8]:

By mass transfer:

- Flow processes such as eddy diffusivity; mass transport in turbulent flow.
- Molecular diffusion: mass transport due to concentration gradients.
- Thermal diffusion: mass transport due to temperature gradients.

By energy transfer:

- Thermal conduction: heat transfer due to temperature gradients.
- Radiation: energy transfer due to radiation.

The flame is a combustion process which takes place exclusively in the gas phase. It represents, however, only one aspect of combustion since other types exist. An example is provided by a system in which reaction components are present in gaseous and solid phases.

If the volatilisation temperature of a solid is higher than its combustion temperature, the combustion process occurs directly on its surface. At low temperatures in the presence of sufficient oxygen, incandescence occurs, i.e. flameless combustion takes place. With an insufficient oxygen supply, smouldering occurs and neither flames nor incandescence appear.

References for Chapter 3

[1] *H. Seekamp:* Materialprüfung 45 (1963), p. 5.
[2] *W. Becker:* VFDB-Z. Forsch. Techn. Brandschutz 24 (1975) 1, p. 4.
[3] Bauen und Brandschutz (Building and fire protection conference). VdS and VFDB, May 1979, p. 15.
[4] *H. W. Emmons:* Heat Transfer (1973), p. 145.
[5] *S. Steingiser:* J. Fire & Flammability 3 (1972), p. 238.
[6] *R. Thater:* Brennverhalten von Plastformstoffen. VEB Deutscher Verlag für Grundstoffindustrie, Leipzig, 1968, p. 11.
[7] *J. Walker:* Sci. American 235 (1978) 4. p. 154.
[8] *R. M. Fristrom:* J. Fire & Flammability 5 (1974), p. 289.
[9] *D. R. Stull:* Fundamentals of Fire and Explosion. AIChE Monograph Series 10. Vol. 73. 1977, Chap. 5, p. 45.
[10] *J. W. Hastie:* J. Res. nat. Bur. Standards 77 A (1973) 6, p. 733.

4   The Burning of Plastics

4.1 The combustion process

The combustion of plastics is a process comprising many steps, some of which are still uninvestigated. It therefore cannot be described quantitatively, although it is possible to describe it qualitatively. A simplified schematic representation of the various phenomena which take place during the combustion of plastics is shown in Fig. 4.1.

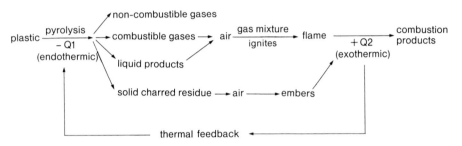

Fig. 4.1   The combustion process (schematic)

Three stages are necessary to initiate the actual combustion process: heating, decomposition and ignition of the polymer.

4.1.1 Heating

The solid plastic is heated by thermal "feedback" as shown in Fig. 4.1 or by an external heat source (e.g. radiation or flame). In this initial phase thermoplastics tend, on account of their linear molecular chains, to soften or melt and start to flow. Thermosetting plastics have a three-dimensional cross-linked molecular structure which prevents softening or melting. The polymers do not pass as such into the gas phase if further energy is supplied, but decompose before vaporising.

4.1.2 Decomposition

Decomposition is an endothermic process in which sufficient energy must be provided to overcome the high binding energies of the bonds between individual atoms (between 200 and 400 kJ/mol) and to provide any necessary activation energy. As the individual plastics differ in structure, their decomposition temperature-ranges vary within certain limits. Table 4.1 gives the range of decomposition temperatures for some plastics, and for the natural product, cellulose.

In most cases decomposition occurs via free radical chain reactions, initiated by traces of oxygen or other oxidising impurities which are trapped in all plastics during manufacture. This oxidative degradation of polymers usually proceeds via the formation of hydroperoxide

Table 4.1   Range of decomposition of some plastics [1]

Plastic	T_d [°C]	Plastic/natural product	T_d [°C]
Polyethylene	340–440	Polymethyl methacrylate	180–280
Polypropylene	320–400	Polyacrylonitrile	250–300
Polystyrene	300–400	Polyamide 6	300–350
Polyvinyl chloride	200–300	Polyamide 66	320–400
Polytetrafluoroethylene	500–550	Cellulose	280–380

groups whose decomposition leads to highly reactive species such as H and OH radicals and thus to chain branching. These free radicals are responsible for flame spread (see below) in the combustion process. The formation of such high energy radicals has been illustrated by *Hawkins* [2] using the thermal oxidation of polyolefins as an example.

Start	(polyolefin) RH	$\longrightarrow$	R· + H·	(1)
Growth	R· + O_2	$\longrightarrow$	ROO·	(2)
	ROO· + RH	$\longrightarrow$	ROOH + R·	(3)
Branching	ROOH	$\longrightarrow$	RO· + ·OH	(4)

The radical R formed in equation (1) reacts with oxygen to give ROO· (2), which together with further polyolefin forms hydroperoxide (3). In the branching step the hydroperoxide decomposes to give RO· and the highly reactive species ·OH (4).

These radicals cause degradation and give rise to various decomposition products depending on the constitution of the polymer:

(a) Almost exclusively gaseous products are formed; e.g., the depolymerisation of polymethyl methacrylate results in the formation of over 90% monomer and the degradation of polyethylene leads to the formation of saturated and unsaturated hydrocarbons.
(b) Gaseous products and carbonaceous residues are formed; for instance in the pyrolysis of polyvinyl chloride hydrogen chloride is eliminated in the first step and the remaining polyene sequence forms aliphatics and aromatics in a second step. These escape as gaseous products or remain as solid carbonaceous residues as a result of cross-linking reactions.
(c) Almost exclusively carbonaceous residues are formed; for example in the case of polyacrylonitrile or high temperature resistant plastics such as polyimides.

Madorsky [3], *Kamiya* and *Niki* [4], *Rabek* [5], *van Krevelen* [6] and other workers [7] have investigated the thermal and oxidative degradation of polymers in great detail.

4.1.3 Ignition

The flammable gases formed by pyrolysis mix with atmospheric oxygen, reach the lower ignition limit and are either ignited by an external flame or, if the temperature is sufficiently high, self-ignite. The flash-ignition and self-ignition temperatures of various polymers determined to ASTM D 1929 are given in Table 4.2 together with those of cotton for comparison [1,8]. These values hold only under the conditions of this Standard and should not be considered as intrinsic properties of the material.

Table 4.2   Flash-ignition and self-ignition temperatures of various plastics by ASTM D 1929

Plastic/natural product	FIT* [°C]	SIT** [°C]
Polyethylene	340	350
Polypropylene	320	350
Polystyrene	350	490
Polyvinyl chloride	390	450
Polytetrafluoroethylene	560	580
ABS	390	480
Polymethyl methacrylate	300	430
Polyacrylonitrile	480	560
Polyamide 6	420	450
Polyamide 66	490	530
Polyurethane (rigid foam)	310	415
Cotton	210	400

  * FIT = Flash-ignition temperature
** SIT = Self-ignition temperature

Ignition depends on numerous variables such as oxygen availability, temperature and the physical and chemical properties of the polymer. The reaction of the combustible gases with oxygen is exothermic and, if sufficient energy is available, overrides the endothermic pyrolytic reaction and initiates flame spread.

4.1.4 Flame spread

The exothermic combustion reaction reinforces pyrolysis of the polymer by thermal feed-back (see Fig. 4.1) and fuels the flame at an increasing level. The hydrocarbon diffusion flame in which the following reactions take place can be taken as a simple model [9]:

Growth:

$$CH_4 + OH\cdot \longrightarrow CH_3\cdot + H_2O \tag{5}$$
$$CH_4 + H\cdot \longrightarrow CH_3\cdot + H_2 \tag{6}$$
$$CH_3\cdot + O \longrightarrow CH_2O + H\cdot \tag{7}$$
$$CH_2O + CH_3\cdot \longrightarrow CHO\cdot + CH_4 \tag{8}$$
$$CH_2O + H\cdot \longrightarrow CHO\cdot + H_2 \tag{9}$$
$$CH_2O + OH\cdot \longrightarrow CHO\cdot + H_2O \tag{10}$$
$$CH_2O + O \longrightarrow CHO\cdot + OH\cdot \tag{11}$$
$$CHO\cdot \longrightarrow CO + H\cdot \tag{12}$$
$$CO + OH\cdot \longrightarrow CO_2 + H\cdot \tag{13}$$

Branching:

$$H\cdot + O_2 \longrightarrow OH\cdot + O \tag{14}$$
$$O + H_2 \longrightarrow OH\cdot + H\cdot \tag{15}$$

The chain branching step in which extremely high energy H and OH radicals are formed is particularly important. These radicals confer a high velocity on the flame front. *Schmidt* [10] has illustrated the avalanche-like proliferation of these OH radicals particularly vividly (Fig. 4.2).

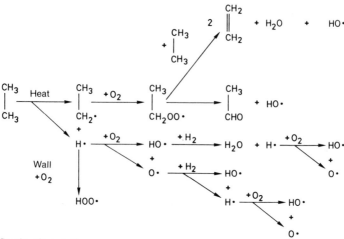

Fig. 4.2   Combustion of ethane

According to more recent investigations, however, the H radicals appear to be at least as important as the OH radicals. A phenomenological description of flame spread along a polymer surface is given in Fig. 4.3 according to *Akita* [11]. The diffusion flame advances over the decomposed polymer surface. As with the candle flame, the surface temperature of the polymer (500°C) is lower than that of the diffusion flame and of the edge of the flame, where reaction with oxygen occurs (1200°C).

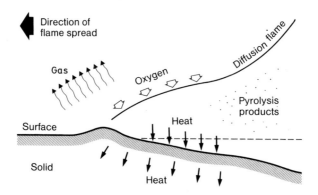

Fig. 4.3   Flame spread (schematic) after *Akita* [11]

A further factor which determines the extent of flame spread is the heat of combustion of the polymer. The heats of combustion of various polymers are compared with those of cotton and cellulose in Table 4.3.

One should not, however, try to relate the heat of combustion to the combustibility of individual materials, as the example of extremely flammable celluloid, with a heat of combustion of only 17,500 kJ/kg, clearly demonstrates.

Table 4.3   Heats of combustion of various plastics and natural products [12]

Plastic	$\triangle H$ [kJ·kg^{-1}]	Plastic/natural product	$\triangle H$ [kJ·kg^{-1}]
Polyethylene	46 500	Polyamide (6 or 66)	32 000
Polypropylene	46 000	Polyester resin	18 000
Polyisobutylene	47 000	Natural rubber	45 000
Polystyrene	42 000	Cotton	17 000
ABS	36 000	Cellulose	17 500
Polyvinyl chloride	20 000	Celluloid	17 500
Polymethyl methacrylate	26 000		

Concurrent with the extremely rapid gas phase reactions controlled by diffusion flames, various slower, oxygen-dependent reactions also take place. These give rise to smoke, soot and carbon-like residues and take place partly in a condensed phase with glow or incandescence.

Comprehensive descriptions of the combustion of polymers have been given by *Fristrom* (see ref. [8] Chapter 3 "The Burning Process"); *Akita* [11], *Hindersinn* and *Wagner* [13], *Learmonth* et al. [14], *Wall* [15] and *Stuetz* et al. [16].

4.2 Thermal properties and burning behaviour of the most important plastics

This section deals with the thermal properties and burning behaviour of the most important thermoplastics, foam plastics, thermosets and high temperature resistant plastics. Firstly, the so-called material properties: i.e. the physical and chemical properties which are specific to each plastic, are described. These include temperature resistance, decomposition temperature, mode of decomposition (statistical chain rupture, depolymerisation, crosslinking and charring). Secondly, other complex phenomena such as burning behaviour, smoke development and odour are described. A phenomenon such as burning behaviour is not determined solely by the physical and chemical properties of the plastic but by many other variables, such as its geometry, form, the applied ignition source and ventilation. The burning behaviour of a plastic is thus not an intrinsic property of the material. However, if the majority of the above variables are fixed by defined conditions and if investigations take place on a small scale (e.g. with small test pieces and a small burner as a low intensity ignition source), then the physical and chemical properties of the plastic become more important and make certain characteristics stand out for each plastic (e.g. burning with "blue" flame, formation of soot particles, fruity smell). These can be helpful in characterising the material. These characteristics enable qualitative statements to be made with the above provisos. They should not, under any circumstances (and contrary to frequent practice) be used to predict the performance of a plastic in a real fire. The material properties can only partially influence the complex fire system which is affected by countless other variables.

The next section contains information drawn from the following sources: Kunststoff-Taschenbuch [17], Polymer Handbook [12], Handbook of Plastics and Elastomers [18], Flammability Handbook for Plastics [19], Brennverhalten von Plastformstoffen ([6] see literature references for Chap. 3), Chemistry and Uses of Fire Retardants [20], Fire Safety Aspects of Polymeric Materials [21].

The thermal and oxidative degradation of a range of plastics has been described in detail by *Madorsky* [3], *Conley* [7], various authors in [15] and *Doležel* [22].

Literature which refers to specific plastics or groups of plastics is listed in the relevant subsections.

The abbreviations for plastics used in the following conform, as far as possible, to DIN 7728 Part 1, April 1978 edition. They are tabulated in Section 10.2 of the appendix.

4.2.1 Thermoplastics

Thermoplastics consist of threadlike or thermolabile cross-linked macromolecules. Under the influence of heat they soften and flow and can then be formed into any desired shape. They harden again on cooling. This process can be repeated as often as required unless chemical degradation due to excessive temperatures occurs. When exposed to an ignition source, thermoplastics tend to soften and melt. Depending on their chemical structure, they burn with differing intensity, smoke emission and formation of residue.

It should be noted that the material properties described here apply only to the "raw" plastics and not to the formulations (with stabilisers, processing aids, flame retardants, etc.) frequently found in practice.

The most important properties of thermoplastics are summarised in Table 4.4.

4.2.1.1 Polyolefins

The most important polyolefins used as standard plastics are low density polyethylene (LDPE), high density polyethylene (HDPE) and polypropylene (PP). Polybutene and polymethylpentene are less frequently encountered examples of this class of material.

$$\left[CH_2 - CH_2 \right]_n \qquad \left[\begin{array}{c} CH - CH_2 \\ | \\ CH_3 \end{array} \right]_n$$

polyethylene   polypropylene

Polyolefins burn hesitatingly at first with a small bright blue flame (LDPE, HDPE) and subsequently with a bright yellow flame which continues to burn after removal of the ignition source. The fire gases and smoke vapours smell of wax and paraffin; this odour is pungent in the case of polypropylene. After the flame is extinguished a smell of dead candle remains.

In the absence of oxygen, polyethylene starts to degrade thermally at about 300 °C. In the presence of oxygen thermal degradation sets in at 150 °C with the colour changing from white through brown to black. Polypropylene undergoes thermal degradation more easily than polyethylene particularly when oxygen is present [22].

The degradation of polyolefins involves statistical chain rupture, resulting in a multitude of short, medium and long chain fragments. These consist mainly of olefins, paraffins and

Table 4.4 Thermal characteristics of various thermoplastics.

Polymer	Bulk density [g/cm³]	Temperature resistance [°C]		Vicat-softening point B [°C]	Decomposition range [°C]	Flash-ignition temperature³ [°C]	Self-ignition temperature³ [°C]	Heat of combustion³ ΔH [kJ/kg]
		short term	long term					
Polyethylene LD¹	0.91	100	80	–	340–440	340	350	46 500
HD	0.96	125	100	75	330–410	350–370	390–410	46 000
Polypropylene	0.91	140	100	145	300–400	345–360	490	42 000
Polystyrene	1.05	90	80	88	–	390	480	36 000
ABS	1.06	95	80	110	–	390	455	–
SAN	1.08	95	85	100	–	370	455	20 000
PVC rigid	1.40	75	60	70–80	200–300	390	>530	10 000
Polyvinylidene chloride	1.87	150	–	–	225–275	>530	580	4 500
Polytetrafluoroethylene	2.20	300	260	–	510–540	560	450	26 000
Polymethyl methacrylate	1.18	95	70	85–110	170–300	300	450	32 000
Polyamide 6	1.13	150	80–120	200	300–350	420	480	21 500
Polyethylene terephthalate	1.34	150	130	80	285–305	440	480	31 000
Polycarbonate	1.20	140	100	150–155	350–400	520	2)	17 000
Polyoxymethylene	1.42	140	80–100	170	220	350–400	ca. 400	

¹ LD = Low density
  HD = High density
² no ignition
³ by ASTM D 1929

cyclic hydrocarbons. The long chain fragments and the soot-like products formed by cyclisation and dehydrogenation contribute to smoke development. Carbon oxides and water are also formed during combustion.

Information on the degradation of polyolefins can be found in *Hawkins* [2] and *Hansen* in [7] (Chap. 8).

4.2.1.2 Styrene polymers

The most important representatives of this group are transparent polystyrenes (PS), SAN (styrene-acrylonitrile copolymer) and the opaque multiphase high impact copolymers based on SB (styrene-butadiene), ABS (acrylonitrile-butadiene-styrene) and ASA (acrylonitrile-styrene-acrylate).

$$\left[\begin{array}{c} CH - CH_2 \\ | \\ C_6H_5 \end{array} \right]_n$$

polystyrene

All styrene polymers burn with a luminous yellow flame, smoking strongly, and continue to burn after removal of the ignition source. The combustion gases have a sweet smell which in the case of SAN is reminiscent of burnt horn. The high impact types also smell of burnt rubber.

Thermal degradation of polystyrene occurs by depolymerisation; in the main, monomers, dimers and trimers are formed. Depolymerisation is also the principal mechanism in the case of the styrene copolymers. The decomposition and combustion products are, however, of a more complex nature due to the additional acrylonitrile, butadiene and acrylic ester components.

Degradation of styrene polymers is described in detail in [3] (Chap. 3).

4.2.1.3 Polyvinyl and polyvinylidene chlorides

Polyvinyl chloride (PVC), polyolefins and styrene polymers make up the group of the so-called "standard" plastics. PVC is the most versatile of the thermoplastics as regards processability and range of applications. With suitable additions its properties can be made to range from those of rigid to those of plasticised PVC.

$$\left[\begin{array}{c} CH - CH_2 \\ | \\ Cl \end{array} \right]_n \qquad \left[\begin{array}{c} Cl \\ | \\ C - CH_2 \\ | \\ Cl \end{array} \right]_n$$

polyvinyl chloride   polyvinylidene chloride

Rigid PVC burns with charring and a green-edged flame which extinguishes immediately the ignition source is removed. The fire gases have a pungent smell due to hydrochloric acid liberated during combustion. Plasticised PVC may continue to burn with a smoky flame depending on the type and quantity of plasticiser incorporated. Hydrogen chloride is eliminated in the decomposition of PVC at temperatures between 200 °C and 300 °C. This gives rise to conjugated double bonds in the carbon chain while elimination of water and cyclisation result in a charred residue. Both elimination of HCl and charring cause the flame to extinguish:

- Hydrogen chloride interferes in the gas phase radical chain mechanism of flame spread by removing energetic H and OH radicals which support combustion. The non-combustible HCl dilutes the mixture of combustible gases and covers the condensed phase shielding it from further attack by oxygen.
- The charred layer formed on the PVC surface prevents the ingress of oxygen and radiant heat, thus protecting the underlying polymer from further degradation.

Aliphatics, aromatics and condensed aromatic systems are further products of the pyrolysis and combustion of PVC. The latter products, together with HCl, contribute to smoke emission during the burning of PVC. The end products of the combustion of PVC are HCl, CO and CO_2; it should be noted that phosgene and chlorine are not liberated.

Like rigid PVC, polyvinylidene chloride (PVDC) and chlorinated polyvinyl chloride (PVCC) burn with an almost smokeless green-edged flame. Due to their high chlorine content, they extinguish immediately if the ignition source is removed.

The pyrolysis of PVC, PVCC and PVDC is described in detail by *Conley* and *Malloy* in [7] (Chap. 8), *Doležel* [22] (p. 346), *Wessling* [23], *Braun* in [24] (Chap. 2) and *Boettner* et al. [25].

4.2.1.4 Fluorocarbon polymers

The most important fluorine-containing polymers are polytetrafluoroethylene (PTFE), tetrafluoroethylene-hexafluoropropylene copolymer (FEP), ethylene-tetrafluoroethylene copolymer (ETFE), polyvinyl fluoride (PVF), polyvinylidene fluoride (PVDF) and polychlorotrifluoroethylene (PCTFE).

polytetrafluoroethylene   polyvinyl fluoride   polychlorotrifluoroethylene

Polytetrafluoroethylene melts and decomposes at elevated temperatures (> 500 °C). At red heat there is a pungent smell of hydrofluoric acid. PTFE cannot be made to burn by low intensity ignition sources.

Pyrolysis of PTFE at about 500 °C results in depolymerisation to tetrafluoroethylene. At higher temperatures toxic gases such as perfluoroethylene, perfluoroisobutylene, and carbonyl fluoride are formed. The latter results from the reaction of the monomer with oxygen and easily hydrolyses on contact with atmospheric moisture to hydrofluoric acid and carbon dioxide.

The degradation of fluorocarbon polymers is described by *Wright* in [7] (Chap. 9).

4.2.1.5 Poly(meth)acrylates

Polyacrylates and polymethacrylates are composed of acrylic or methacrylic ester units. The most important plastic in this group is polymethyl methacrylate (PMMA).

$$\left[\begin{array}{c} CH_3 \\ | \\ -C - CH_2 - \\ | \\ COOCH_3 \end{array}\right]_n$$

polymethyl methacrylate

PMMA burns with a luminous yellow, slightly crackling flame with slight smoke development. The material melts and volatilises on pyrolysis so that no residue remains. The fire gases have a sweet fruit-like smell.

PMMA undergoes over 90% depolymerisation to the monomer which burns in the gas phase. The oxygen of the ester group results in almost complete combustion of the pyrolysis products and is the reason for the low smoke development of the burning polymer.

The degradation of poly(meth)acrylate plastics is described by *Madorsky* [3] (p. 176) and *Conley* and *Malloy* in [7] (p. 225).

4.2.1.6 Polyamides

The most important polyamides (PA) are polyamide 6, polyamide 66, polyamide 610, polyamide 11 and polyamide 12. They contain linear polymer chains of carboxylic acid amide groups, –CONH–, which may consist either of one component such as aminocarboxylic acids or their lactams (PA 6: ε-caprolactam; PA 11: 11-aminoundecanoic acid, PA 12: 12-aminododecanoic acid)

$$\left[NH - (CH_2)_x - CO \right]_n$$

or of two components such as hexamethylene diamine with adipic acid (PA 66) or sebacic acid (PA 610).

$$\left[NH - (CH_2)_6 - NH - CO - (CH_2)_y - CO \right]_{n/2}$$

Polyamides burn with a bluish yellow-edged, somewhat crackling flame during which the polymer bubbles, forming a charred mass from which threads can be drawn. The polymer extinguishes rapidly outside the immediate range of action of the ignition source. The combustion gases smell of burnt horn.

Thermal decomposition of polyamides occurs via statistical chain scission giving rise mainly to carbonaceous residues and volatile products such as ammonia, nitriles, amines, cyclic ketones, esters, carbon monoxide and carbon dioxide and water.

Reviews of the thermal decomposition products of polyamides are given by *Madorsky* [3] (p. 236) and *Conley* and *Guadiana* [7] (p. 347).

4.2.1.7 Polyalkylene terephthalates

Polyalkylene terephthalates are linear thermoplastic polyesters available commercially as polyethylene terephthalate (PETP) and polybutylene terephthalate (PBTP).

polyethylene terephthalate   polybutylene terephthalate

Polyalkylene terephthalates burn with a luminous sooty, spitting flame, melting and charring slightly. The wisps of smoke are light blue, smell vaguely sweet and have an irritating effect. Thermal degradation occurs via statistical chain scission. The main products of pyrolysis of PETB are acetaldehyde, terephthalic acid, carbon monoxide and carbon dioxide and water.

The degradation of PETB is described by *Conley* and *Guadiana* in [7] (p. 401) and *Madorsky* in [3] (p. 272).

4.2.1.8 Polycarbonate

Polycarbonate (PC) is a linear thermoplastic polyester. The commercial product is based on the reaction of bisphenol A and diphenyl carbonate or phosgene.

polycarbonate

Polycarbonate burns with a sooty, dark yellow spitting flame, foams up and chars. It extinguishes away from the ignition source. Polycarbonate can be made to incandesce under pyrolytic conditions. The decomposition products smell initially slightly of and later strongly of phenol. Besides charred residues, pyrolysis results in gaseous products such as aldehydes, ketones and carbon oxides.

4.2.1.9 Polyacetals

Commercial polyacetals are polymers and copolymers of the cyclic trimer of formaldehyde which usually contain stabilising terminal ester groups. They are designated as polyoxymethylene (POM).

polyoxymethylene

Polyoxymethylene burns with a hot, smokeless blue flame. Its burning behaviour resembles that of "meta". Even in an oxygen deficient atmosphere, its oxygen content of over

50% ensures almost smokeless combustion. The combustion gases smell strongly of form-aldehyde.

POM depolymerises almost completely to formaldehyde. Thermal degradation begins at temperatures as low as 90 °C if terminal OH groups are unprotected by esterification and at 230 °C if terminal groups are esterified. The principal combustion products are water, carbon dioxide with small quantities of carbon monoxide, formaldehyde and hydrogen. Further details are given by *Conley* and *Guadiana* in [7] (p. 413).

4.2.2 Foam plastics

Since it is possible to obtain foams from practically any plastic, there is a vast range of these materials although only a few have achieved real importance. They can be divided into thermoplastic, thermosetting and elastomeric foams depending on the polymer on which they are based. The most important examples of thermoplastic foams are polystyrene, polyvinyl chloride and polyethylene. Phenolic and urea foams are the most important ther-mosetting foams. Mechanically frothed foams such as natural and styrene-butadiene rubbers as well as expanded rubber produced with the aid of blowing agents constitute the main elastomeric foams. The latter process is applicable to practically all elastomers. Poly-urethane foams occupy a special position since they can be classified in any of the above groups depending on formulation.

A further range of foams derived from high temperature resistant plastics exists. Due to their high cost they have not achieved any great practical importance. They include poly-imides and polybenzimidazoles and are used, for example, for sound proofing jet engines (see [27] Chap. 14).

A distinction is made between rigid and flexible foams. The former usually have a closed cell structure while the latter are mainly open celled. The closed cell structure results in very low thermal conductivity and rigid foams are thus used principally for thermal insulation. Flexible foams are unsuitable for this purpose since they are poor insulators on account of their open cell structure. They are used as fillers in pillows, upholstery, mattresses and, on an increasing scale, in the automotive industry.

The burning behaviour of foams differs somewhat from that of the solid polymer from which they are derived for several reasons. The combustion of a polymer is a surface process so that the total surface available determines the scale of burning. Due to their low bulk density (down to 15 kg/m³) foams possess a high surface per unit mass. This results in almost complete pyrolysis of combustible material in the vicinity of radiation and flame while the material is in immediate contact with atmospheric oxygen. Consequently foams have a greater tendency to burn than solid material. In the case of closed cell foams, heat build-up also occurs on the surface due to low thermal conductivity. This contributes significantly to pyrolysis and burning.

To put the matter into perspective, it should be remembered that foams usually contain only 2 to 3 Vol % of combustible matter and therefore only represent a minimal fire load compared to compact materials. They thus make only a limited contribution to, for example, heat radiation. Furthermore, non-flammable foaming agents such as carbon dioxide and halogenated hydrocarbons reduce combustibility by diluting the flammable gases and shield-ing the combustion zone from oxygen.

Just as in the case of solid polymers, the burning behaviour of thermoplastic and ther-mosetting foams varies according to their chemical structure:

– Thermoplastic foams such as polystyrene foam withdraw rapidly from the flame zone due to melting and shrinking so that frequently ignition does not occur.

– Thermosetting foams do not withdraw from the flames on account of their three dimensional cross-linked structure and do not usually ignite. Rapid charring occurs and the carbonised layer protects the underlying foam from further attack by flames and causes extinction.

The following section deals in greater detail with the burning behaviour of the two most important foams, expanded polystyrene and polyurethane, as well as of further thermoplastic (polyvinyl chloride) and thermosetting (phenol and urea resins) foams. Elastomers and high temperature resistant plastics are not discussed.

Reviews of the burning behaviour of foam plastics are given by *Burgers* and *Hilado* in [27] (Chap. 18), *Thater* (see p. 154 of ref [6] in Chap. 3) and in [21] (p. 91). Elastomeric foams are briefly described by *Zimmerman* and *Bailey* in [26] and *Fabris* and *Sommer* [28].

4.2.2.1 Polystyrene foam

Polystyrene foam is a tough, closed cell thermoplastic foam. It is available as moulded-bead foam (bulk density $15-30$ kg/m^3) or extruded foam ($25-60$ kg/m^3). Polystyrene foam is used mainly for thermal insulation in buildings or for packaging.

In the vicinity of a flame, polystyrene foam fuses and burns like solid polystyrene with a luminous yellow, sooty flame and a sweetish odour. It continues to burn after removal of the ignition source. Frequently, polystyrene foam shrinks away so rapidly from the flame that it does not ignite. It is resistant to short exposures to temperatures up to 100 °C and decomposes at approximately 300 °C.

4.2.2.2 Polyvinyl chloride foams

As with solid PVC both rigid and plasticised products are available. Rigid PVC foam is a tough, closed cell material manufactured with bulk densities varying between $50-130$ kg/m^3. It is used in small quantities, e.g. as a structural core in sandwich panels and moulded components utilised in the construction of ships, planes and vehicles.

Rigid PVC foam is resistant to temperatures up to 70 °C. It decomposes and shrinks above 220 °C but burns only if an external flame is applied colouring the flame green and charring completely. The charred material glows, incandesces and burns up. Flash- or self-ignition only occur at elevated temperatures in contrast to solid PVC due to the lower density of the shrunken material which liberates correspondingly less heat.

Plasticised PVC foam is available as a closed cell and also as an open cell flexible foam. It is supplied with bulk densities of $40-130$ kg/m^3 (closed cell) or $70-130$ kg/m^3 (open cell).

Plasticised PVC foams usually have a high plasticiser content and thus continue to burn with a sooty flame after removal of the ignition source. Due to the differing amounts of plasticiser and other additives in individual grades, it is impossible to generalise on the burning behaviour of plasticised PVC foams.

4.2.2.3 Polyurethane foams

The chemistry of the polyurethanes is extraordinarily versatile due to the almost unlimited choice of starting materials. With suitable formulation, thermoplastic, thermosetting and elastomeric foams in rigid, semi-rigid and flexible types can be manufactured. In order to appreciate this potential a short résumé of polyurethane chemistry is given below.

Polyurethanes are produced by the reaction of di- or polyisocyanates with di- or polyols. The isocyanates most commonly used in the manufacture of foams are toluene-2,4-diisocyanate (TDI) or a mixture with its isomer, toluene-2,6-diisocyanate (TDI 80/20 and 65/35)

toluene-2,4-diisocyanate   toluene-2,6-diisocyanate

and diphenylmethane-4,4′-diisocyanate (MDI) or polymethylene polyphenylisocyanate (crude undistilled MDI).

diphenylmethane-4,4′-diisocyanate   polymethylene polyphenylisocyanate
(MDI)   (crude MDI)

The polyols used as the second reaction component are extremely numerous although the following are preferred in practice:

- Polyether alcohols based on polyethylene oxide or polypropylene oxide. Depending on chain length and functionality, these are used to manufacture rigid (short chain tri- and multi-functional alcohols) or flexible foams (long chain, trifunctional alcohols).
- Polyester alcohols, manufactured by polycondensation of di- or polycarboxylic acids with di- or polyalcohols, are used particularly for elastomeric foams.
- Various polyols such as glycerol, hexanetriol pentaerythritol, sorbitol, raw sugar, phenols or aminoplastics containing OH groups, modified natural products such as castor oil and tall oil are used for various purposes (chain lengthening, cross-linking, increasing elasticity, increasing heat resistance, etc.).

The main reaction in polyurethane chemistry is that of isocyanate with alcohol to give urethane:

$$-N=C=O \quad + \quad HO- \quad \rightleftharpoons \quad -N-\underset{\underset{O}{\|}}{\overset{}{C}}-O- \qquad (16)$$
$$\overset{|}{H}$$

This reaction is thermally reversible; no urethane linkage is stable above 250 °C.

Manufacture of foams can be carried out using carbon dioxide as a blowing agent. This is achieved by using excess isocyanate in the urethane reaction and reacting the former with water or a carboxylic acid to give an amine or amide.

$$-N=C=O \quad + \quad HOH \quad \longrightarrow \quad -NH_2 \quad + \quad CO_2 \qquad (17)$$

$$-N=C=O \quad + \quad HO-\underset{\underset{O}{\|}}{C}- \quad \longrightarrow \quad -\underset{\underset{H}{|}}{N}-\underset{\underset{O}{\|}}{C}- \; + \; CO_2 \tag{18}$$

A further important reaction is the catalytic trimerisation of an isocyanate to form an isocyanurate ring:

$$3 \; -N=C=O \quad \longrightarrow \tag{19}$$

This results in an extremely stable three-dimensional network with increased rigidity and thermal stability and reduced flammability.

Rigid polyurethane foam is tough with approximately 5% of the cells being open and is usually available in bulk densities of $30-35$ kg/m^3. It is used as thermal insulation in the building industry. It burns with a light yellow luminous flame, froths and continues to burn after removal of the ignition source. It is resistant to temperatures up to 120 °C and starts to decompose at 220 °C by depolycondensation to the monomeric isocyanates and alcohols. At higher temperatures the principal products are carbon oxides, water and a black charred residue.

If excess isocyanate is used, isocyanurate rings (see above) can be incorporated in the polyurethane by catalytic trimerisation. The spatial cross-linking which occurs results in a more thermally stable system, the temperature resistance of which can lie some $20-50$ °C above that of polyurethane. Due to the higher degree of cross-linking, only slight depolycondensation takes place. Only small quantities of gaseous products are thus liberated and smoke production during combustion is low. Polyisocyanurates extinguish away from the ignition source leaving a charred residue which frequently afterglows.

Pure polyisocyanurate foams (PIR) are extremely brittle on account of their high degree of cross-linking and are easily abraded. In order to counteract these deficiencies, polyurethane-modified PIR foams are used in practice. They are less brittle than PIR and exhibit better heat stability and lower combustibility than polyurethane foams.

Similar effects can be achieved with highly branched polyols (e.g. novolac or dextrose) and polymeric isocyanates. These also give rise to highly cross-linked products with increased thermal dimensional stability.

Flexible polyurethane foam is open celled and is commercially available in bulk densities ranging from 20 to 45 kg/m^3. It is stable to temperatures up to 100 °C. In contrast to rigid foam, it is only slightly cross-linked and tends to melt and undergo depolycondensation. It burns with a similar appearance to but more intensely than rigid foam.

Comprehensive descriptions of polyurethane foams are given by *Vieweg* and *Höchtlen* [29], *Backus* and *Gemeinhardt* in [27] (Chap. 9), *Hardy* and *Saunders* in [27] (Chap. 14) and *Gmitter, Fabris* and *Maxey* [26]. The burning behaviour of polyurethanes is described by *Frisch* and *Reegen* in [30] (Chap. 7) and *Papa* [31]. *Ballistreri* et al. summarise recent work on the thermal degradation of polyurethanes in [33].

4.2.2.4 Phenolic foams

Phenolic foams (PF foams) are hard, brittle mixed cell (at least 25% open cell) materials supplied in bulk densities ranging from 40 to 100 kg/m^3. Their principal application is as thermal insulation in buildings. Temperature resistance extends to 130 °C although they will withstand short exposures to temperatures up to 250 °C. Decomposition sets in at 270 °C. Under the influence of an open flame, they burn for a few seconds due to the emission of volatiles. Above 400 °C however, they only incandesce and glow. Flaming or self-ignition does not occur. PF foam continues to smoulder and glow for some time after removal of the ignition source. There is minimal smoke development and, due to its high degree of cross-linking, PF foam chars almost completely.

The lower combustibility compared to solid phenolic resin probably occurs as a result of liberation of volatiles below the flash point of the resin due to the cellular structure and low mass of the foam. An extremely stable carbonaceous residue is left. Since no further combustible gases are generated, this continues to incandesce until it is completely consumed. The flammability of PF foams is described by *Papa* and *Proops* [27] (Chap. 11).

4.2.2.5 Urea foams

Urea foams (UF foams) are hard and brittle with bulk densities of 5–15 kg/m^3 and limited heat resistance (50–90 °C). Depending on the blowing agent used, they can be open or closed cell. Brittleness and abrasion can be reduced by modifying with additives such as polyethylene glycol. This results, however, in an increase in flammability. UF foams decompose in the range 250–300 °C. Slow progressive charring occurs in the vicinity of an ignition source. The charred frothy layer shields the underlying foam from further attack by flames. In contrast to PF foam no visible incandescence or afterglow occurs probably due to the nitrogen content of the polymer suppressing the surface oxidation processes responsible for glowing. Some surface abrasion of UF foam always occurs due to its friability. This can cause brief ignition of the entire surface. The flammability of UF foams is described by *Frisch* in [27] (Chap. 12).

4.2.3 Thermosetting plastics

Due to the irreversible curing reaction thermosets are, in contrast to thermoplastics, rigid and cannot be plastically formed even at elevated temperatures. Curing causes three dimensional cross-linking of the linear, fusible, soluble starting products. These can incorporate various fillers such as minerals, wood flour, organic fibres, chips, glass fibres, glass mats, etc., resulting in materials with the most diverse properties. The product characteristics can also be altered by varying the monomer, countless numbers of which exist. This is particularly true of polyester and epoxy resins.

As a result of their three dimensional cross-linked structure, thermosets do not soften or flow when burning. The tendency to form gaseous decomposition products is also less marked than with thermoplastics. Indeed, heat may cause surface charring which can prevent ignition.

Incandescence and glow frequently occur on the charred surface probably due to the strongly exothermic decomposition of peroxides formed on the surface as a result of reactions with atmospheric oxygen.

4.2.3.1 Phenolic resins

Phenolic resins (PF) are manufactured by the acidic or basic condensation of phenol or formaldehyde to form novolac or resols. Novolac can be converted to resol by adding hexamethylene tetramine which decomposes on heating to ammonia and formaldehyde. On applying heat, curing takes place via three dimensional cross-linking to form the insoluble, inflexible resin.

Phenol-formaldehyde resin

Phenolic resins have densities of 1.25 to 1.34 g/cm^3 and, depending on formulation, are resistant to temperatures up to 120−175 °C. Decomposition occurs at about 300 °C with charring and an odour of phenol and formaldehyde. Phenolic resins burn with a bright sooty, yellow flame and extinguish if the ignition source is removed. There is little tendency to emit smoke. Flaming occurs only with material previously thermally decomposed. Further heating causes the material to incandesce; there is afterglow if the ignition source is removed.

The flammability of phenolic resins is reduced by the addition of mineral fillers such as asbestos, stone powder and glass fibre and increased by the addition of organic additives such as wood flour, chopped paper, etc.

Phenolic resins decompose on heating by statistical chain rupture. Thermal and oxidative degradation at 350 °C to 400 °C generates formaldehyde, phenols, carbon monoxide, methanes, acetone and propanols. Approximately 15% of the products are volatile at 450 °C rising to a maximum of 50% at 1200 °C. The combustion products consist of oxides of carbon and water. Phenolic resins have a great tendency to char thus reducing the formation of volatiles.

The thermal and oxidative degradation of phenolic resins is described by *Conley* in [7] (Chap. 11) and [30] (Chap. 8).

4.2.3.2 Unsaturated polyester resins

Unsaturated polyesters (UP) are manufactured by polycondensation of polyalcohols (usually C_2 to C_4 diols) with unsaturated acids (fumaric acid, maleic anhydride) and saturated acids (phthalic acid and its derivatives). The unsaturated polyester is obtained as a linear polycondensation product. The second step, curing, is carried out by adding styrene which undergoes radical copolymerisation with the polyester. A cross-linked resin with short polystyrene bridges (2−3 styrene units) results. Countless products can be obtained by varying the starting materials. For example, vinyl ester resins, for continuous high temperature service, (up to 150 °C) originate from bisphenol A, dichlorohydrin and acrylic acid.

UP resins have a density of 1.2 g/cm^3, can be subjected to temperatures up to 120 °C and start to decompose above 140 °C. They burn with a sooty luminous yellow flame with a sharp, sweet smell leaving a charred residue.

UP resin is degraded by statistical chain rupture in which styrene is the primary product. Other degradation products are phthalic anhydride, carbon dioxide and C_2 to C_4 alkenes.

unsaturated polyester resin

Temperature resistance can be increased to 200 °C by modification with mineral fillers such as glass fibres. The literature on the thermal degradation of unsaturated polyester (*Alt* in [34] Chap. 7) is not very extensive. Usually only the degradation of the thermoplastic polyesters (see below under polyalkylene terephthalate) is described.

4.2.3.3 Epoxy resins

Epoxy resins (EP) are manufactured by the reaction of polyols with epichlorohydrin. The most frequently used polyols are bisphenol A and novolac. The resultant linear polymers are cross-linked with hardeners. In principle any compound with active H atoms such as amines, alcohols, acids and acid anhydrides can be used for curing. These react with the epoxide groups by polyaddition.

diglycide ether of bisphenol A

polyglycide ether of a novolac resin

Epoxy resins have densities of about 1.20 g/cm^3. Their combustibility is greater than comparable thermosetting plastics since they have a reduced tendency to carbonise on account of their chemical structure. They are thermally stable up to 130–140 °C and start to decompose in the range 240–350 °C depending on their structure. They burn with a luminous yellow, sooty, blue-edged flame. After removal of the ignition source they continue to burn on their own. The smoke smells of phenol, formaldehyde and hardener.

EP resins with mineral fillers such as stone powder or glass fibres and densities of 1.80 g/cm³ are available commercially. They are temperature resistant up to 130–155 °C and are less combustible than unfilled EP resins.

Novolac-based EP resins are more thermally stable than those based on bisphenol A. Thermal decomposition (250–450 °C) produces mainly oxides of carbon, formaldehyde, phenol and water as well as lower saturated and unsaturated hydrocarbons (C_1 to C_3) and oxidised products such as aldehydes and ketones. The combustion products are oxides of carbon, formic acid and water. The thermal degradation of EP resins has been described by *Conley* in [7] (Chap. 11) and in [30] (Chap. 8).

4.2.3.4 Urea and melamine resins

Urea (UF) and melamine (MF) resins are manufactured by the condensation of formaldehyde with urea or melamine. The resultant primary product is reacted with an acid hardener and, depending on the application, mixed with various fillers such as cellulose, wood flour or stone powder, followed by curing under pressure and heat. The chemistry of condensation is largely unexplained. The structure of UF and MF resins can be schematically represented as follows:

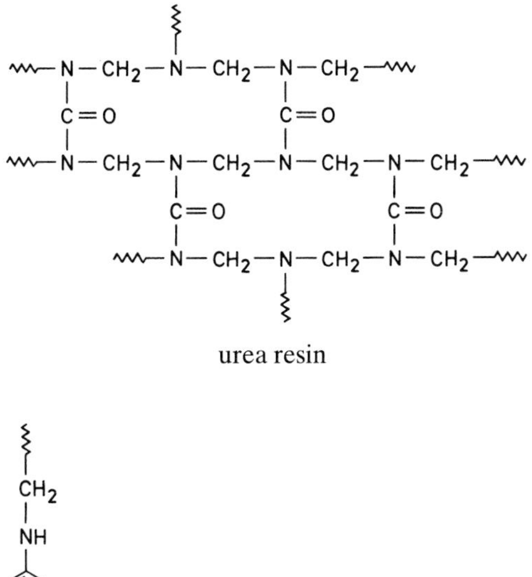

urea resin

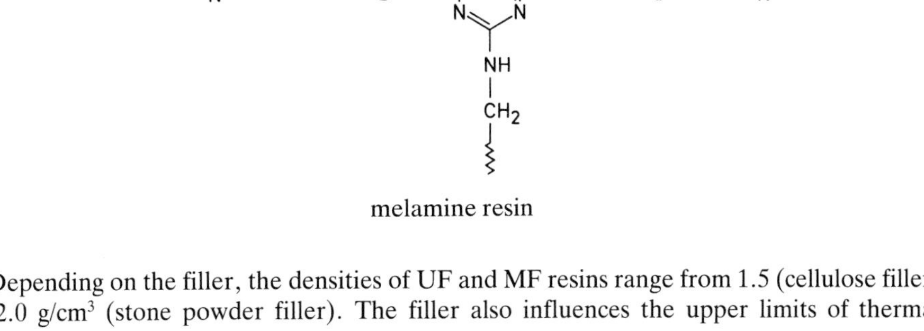

melamine resin

Depending on the filler, the densities of UF and MF resins range from 1.5 (cellulose filler) to 2.0 g/cm³ (stone powder filler). The filler also influences the upper limits of thermal stability which vary between 120−150 °C (UF) and 200 °C (MF). Decomposition sets in between 200−250 °C (UF) and above 300 °C (MF). The high nitrogen content of these resins acts as an inherent flame retardant so that unfilled melamine resin does not flame below 600 °C. MF resins have even less tendency to burn than UF resins. Both char with minimal smoke development when a flame is applied. They colour the flame yellow, burst, crack, swell and exhibit white edges. The decomposition gases smell of ammonia and form-aldehyde and an odour of burnt milk and fish is apparent. A charred residue with no afterglow remains.

Cellulose or wood flour filled resins decompose at about 300 °C; the filler afterglows.

There has been only limited research into the thermal degradation of UF and MF resins. The decomposition products include ammonia, methylamine, oxides of carbon, water and a carbonaceous residue. The combustion products are oxides of carbon and ammonia. Short descriptions of the thermal decomposition of these resins have been given by *Sunshine* in [32] (Chap. 4) and *Conley* in [30] (Chap. 8) and [7] (Chap. 11).

4.2.4 High temperature resistant plastics

The systematic development of high temperature resistant plastics started at the end of the fifties with the event of space travel. They are relatively difficult to manufacture and process and their resultant high cost has precluded most of them from finding practical application and large scale production.

Polymers are designated as high temperature resistant plastics if they are suitable for continuous service above 150 °C. There are several ways of synthesizing such materials. Starting from a carbon-containing framework, the molecular chain can be stiffened by incorporating ring systems in the case of chain or ladder polymers. Alternatively the CH linkage in the macromolecule can be partially or wholly replaced with inorganic atoms such as fluorine. A further method is to use inorganic polymers with chains consisting of inorganic components and organic side groups such as silicones and polyphosphazenes.

The temperature resistance of standard plastics can be considerably improved at the processing stage by the use of stabilisers and cross-linking agents or the incorporation of structural materials such as glass and graphite. Nevertheless, such products usually have a considerably lower temperature resistance than synthesized high temperature resistant poly-mers. Plastics with temperature resistance improved by variations in processing are not dealt with here.

In the following section the aromatic and heterocyclic polymers are discussed in greater detail. A few of the best known examples of the many polymers which have been synthe-sized are presented and their combustion behaviour described. Organic polymers with heteroatoms such as the fluoropolymers have already been discussed in Section 4.2.1.4. Of the inorganic polymers, the polyphosphazenes have become the increasing centre of interest over the last few years. As the most recent examples of this group, they are dealt with here.

4.2.4.1 Aromatic and heterocyclic polymers

The temperature resistance of linear polymers increases with rigidity, i.e. with the loss of free rotation of the thread-like macromolecule. This can be achieved by incorporating aromatic or heterocyclic rings. Rigidity increases as the spatial separation between the rings diminishes. It is further increased if the rings are tied to rigid systems such as semi-ladder or ladder polymers (see [7] p. 34). The various types of linkage in linear polymers are illus-trated in Fig. 4.4.

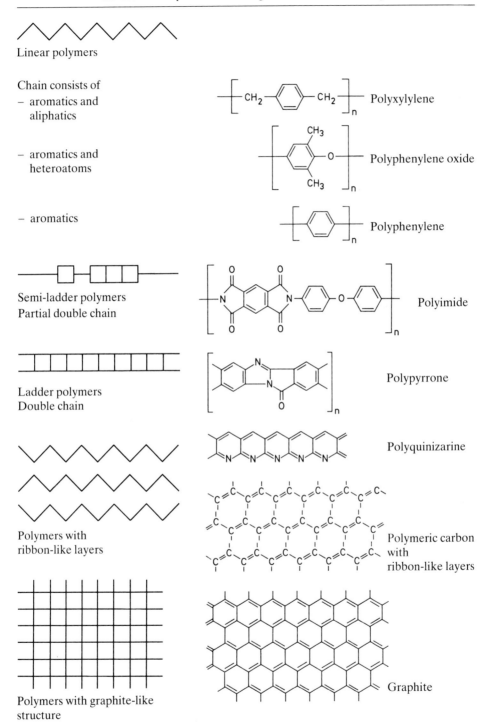

Fig. 4.4   Types of linkage in linear polymers

With increasing rigidity there is a loss in thermoplastic properties and thus these polymers cannot be processed. Furthermore, they are inflexible and insoluble. Polymerisation and forming must therefore be carried out in a single operation. Alternatively two stages may be used: firstly, soluble pre-polymers are processed followed by "curing" to bring them into their final form.

Due to their high ring content and the strong binding forces between the rings, the high temperature resistant plastics tend to form residues on heating in which their basic structure is retained. Use is made of this characteristic in the manufacture of so-called polymer carbons by polymer pyrolysis. Depending on the original polymer and treatment, carbon fibres or glassy carbon are obtained. This polymeric carbon material possesses the ribbon-like structure shown in Fig. 4.4 and not as previously assumed the lattice arrangement of graphite.

Glassy carbon is obtained by the pyrolysis of polyfurfuryl alcohol, phenolic resin or of polyacenaphthylene. The best known is the pyrolysis of polyfurfurylalcohol which results in polymeric carbon via the intermediate steps shown in Fig. 4.5 [35].

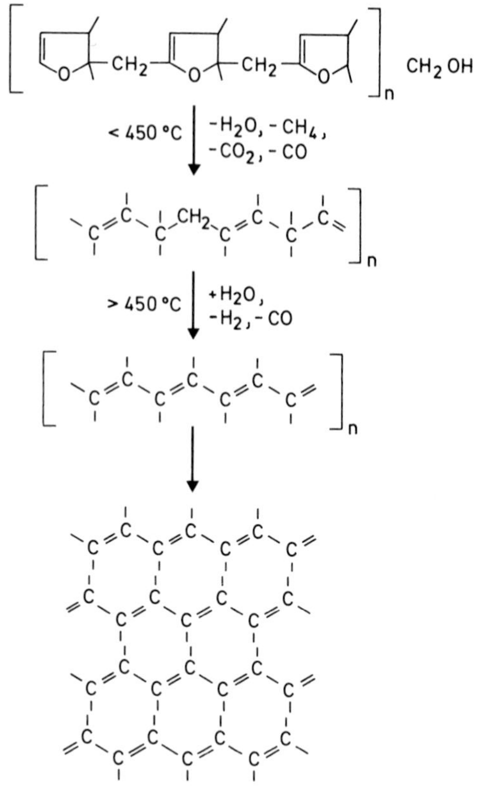

Fig. 4.5 Intermediates in the degradation of polyfurfuryl alcohol and formation of polymeric carbon with ribbon-like structure (after [35] Fig. 3)

The best known and first carbon fibre is produced by the pyrolysis of polyacrylonitrile via the steps shown in Fig. 4.6.

Polymeric carbon can be manufactured from a range of other starting materials such as p-polyphenylene and polyimide. Recently silicon carbide fibres have been produced from

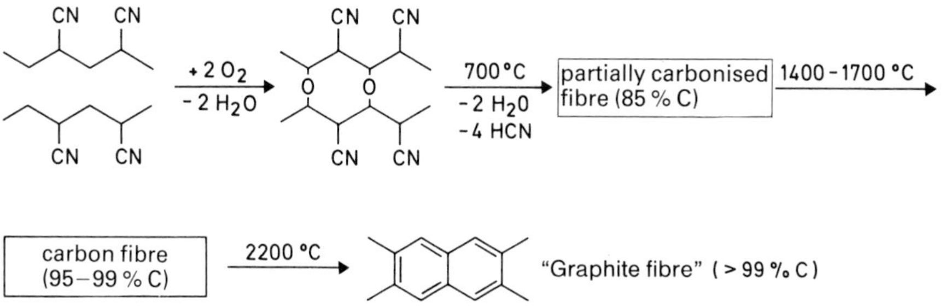

Fig. 4.6   Manufacture of carbon fibre from polyacrylonitrile

dimethyldichlorosilane [36]. Polymeric carbon is extremely resistant to high temperatures so that, for example, carbon fibres can be used to filter molten iron (see [17] p. 404).

The tendency of high temperature resistant plastics to char increases with their degree of linking. The formation of gaseous decomposition products and the tendency to burn with an open flame diminish in consequence. Polyimides, for example, cannot be ignited and application of a flame causes them to incandesce.

Many of these plastics are resistant to high temperatures only if air is excluded, otherwise strongly oxidative degradation often sets in quickly. The latter is related to peculiarities in the chain structure such as easily attacked CH bonds or incomplete linkage reactions (ladder polymers). Polyxylylene, (for structure see Fig. 4.4) for example, shows no change in properties up to 220 °C in the absence of air. It is, however, only resistant to temperatures up to 95 °C in air.

Due to their high cost and difficulties in handling, high temperature resistant polymers have found acceptance only in specialised applications. For example, aramide fibres, manufactured by polycondensation of terephthalic acid with phenylene diamine, are used for fire protective clothing and as textiles in the aero industry. Polyimides, polyaryl ethers, polyphenylene sulphides, etc. are utilised in the aerospace and electrical/electronic industries as sheet laminates, foamable resins and binders.

The combustion characteristics of a few examples of the huge range of these polymers are described below. Their properties range from thermoplastic and flammable to infusible and non-ignitable. Further details of these plastics and of the whole field of aromatic and heterocyclic plastics are given in a series of comprehensive monographs [37–42] while recent developments are given in [43] and [44]. *Schulman* [7] (Chap. 13) and *Wright* [24] (Chap. 3) report on the thermal and oxidative degradation of this class of polymers.

Polyphenylene oxide

2,6-dimethylpolyphenylene oxide (PPO) is usually modified with polystyrene (PS) in order to achieve better processability. In this form it is commercially the most important of all high temperature resistant plastics.

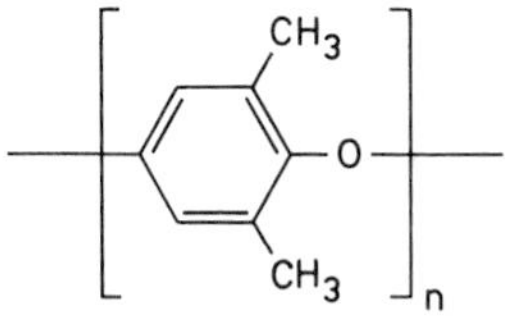

2,6-dimethylpolyphenylene oxide

Pure PPO has a density of $1.06 \ g/cm^3$. It can be ignited only with difficulty and burns with a bright, sooty flame, melting and charring. After the flame is removed it continues to burn. The decomposition products smell slightly of phenol. The PS modified products burn with a luminous yellow sooty flame.

Pure PPO is temperature resistant up to approximately 110 °C and even up to 190 °C in the absence of air. Decomposition in air sets in at 200 °C and is approximately 50% complete within 90 minutes at 250 °C. The decomposition products consist mainly of acetone, phenol and higher crosslinked structures.

Polyphenylene sulphide

Polyphenylene sulphide (PPS) has a density of $1.36 \ g/cm^3$, is highly crystalline and melts in the range 270−285 °C. It is resistant to temperatures up to approximately 260 °C. It burns with a luminous orange-yellow flame and grey smoke, swelling up and forming a black carbonised residue but extinguishes immediately if the ignition source is removed. The decomposition products smell slightly of styrene and hydrogen sulphide.

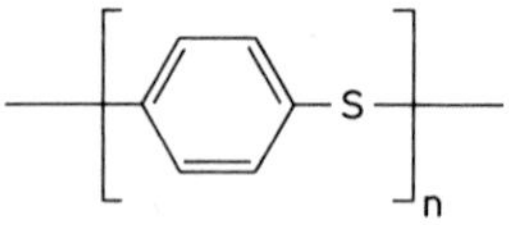

polyphenylene sulphide

PPS is fairly resistant to oxidative decomposition: no volatile products are formed up to 500 °C. Degradation to hydrogen, methane and carbon oxides sets in above 700 °C. In a nitrogen atmosphere almost 40% remains as a carbonaceous residue at 1000 °C.

Polyether sulphones

The most important example of these linear polymers are the polyether sulphones (PES) themselves and polyaryl sulphones and polysulphones (PSO).

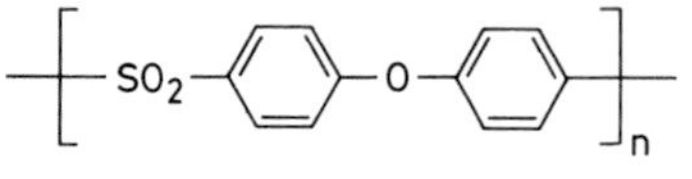

polyether sulphone 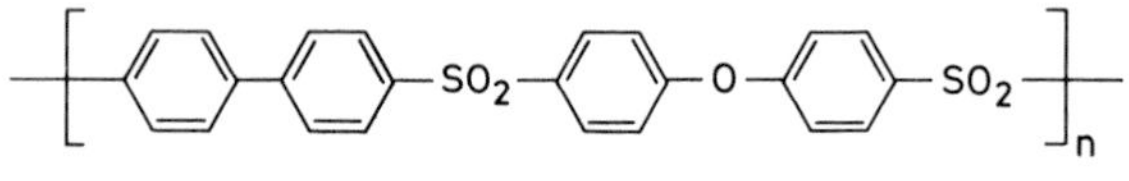   polyaryl sulphone

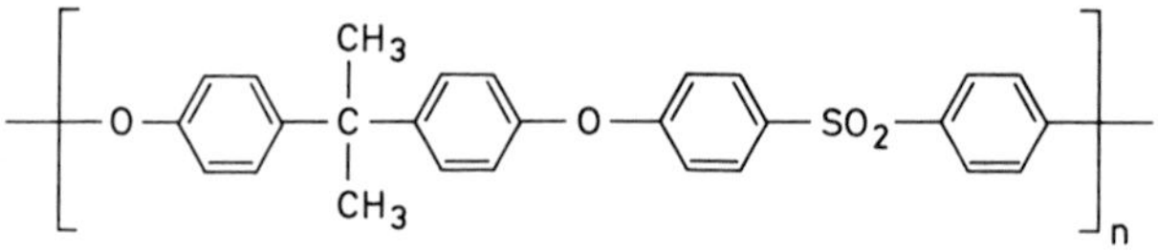

polysulphone

Depending on their structure, polyether sulphones have densities of 1.24 to $1.37 \ g/cm^3$. They possess very good temperature resistance even with respect to thermal-oxidative degradation and can be exposed for long periods to temperatures up to 160−250 °C. They are difficult to ignite and burn with a yellow, sooty flame even after removal of the external flame. When burning they melt down to a brown residue which turns black. The decomposition products smell slightly of hydrogen sulphide. Above 380 °C degradation of bisphenol-

A-based-polysulphones (see the structural formula above) gives rise to sulphur dioxide, methane, oxides of carbon, hydrogen and phenol or its derivatives.

Polyimides

Polyimides (PI) are the most important examples of heterocyclic and semi-ladder polymers. They are obtained by the reaction of tetracarboxylic anhydrides (usually pyromellitic anhydride) with aromatic diamines (e.g. diaminodiphenyl ether).

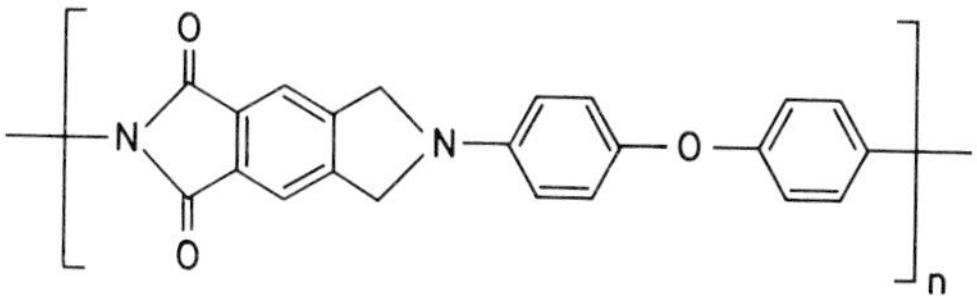

polyimide

Polyimides have a bulk density of 1.42 g/cm^3. They cannot be ignited by an external flame, do not melt, but turn brown, incandesce and char almost without generating smoke. A slight smell of phenol occurs.

Depending on type, polyimides are temperature resistant up to 260–320 °C. They can be subjected for short periods to temperatures up to 500 °C. The small number of hydrogen atoms in the polyimide chain renders it highly stable to thermal-oxidative degradation. Water is initially eliminated during thermal decomposition.

At higher temperatures, oxides of carbon, ammonia, small amounts of hydrogen, aromatics such as aniline, phenol, benzene and higher condensed products are liberated leaving a carbonaceous residue which has 60% of the weight of the original material.

Polyimides are used in the most diverse applications. They can be reinforced with glass fibre or graphite and foams and fibres can be manufactured from them. Due to their exceptional electrical properties over the whole range of service temperature, they are widely used in components in the electrical and electronics industries. A whole range of polyimides, of which the polyamide-imides and polyester-imides are the best known, can also be made.

Miscellaneous

Of the semi-ladder polymers, the polybenzimidazoles (PBI) are of particular interest. Depending on their structure, their colour varies from yellow to orange-black. They are particularly stable thermally. Their continuous temperature resistance in air lies in the range 300–350 °C. In nitrogen this increases to 480–500 °C.

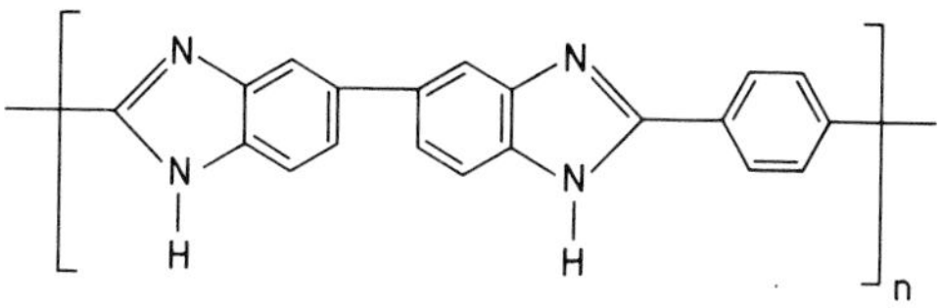

polybenzimidazole

PBI cannot be ignited by a flame but char and incandesce. Pyrolysis liberates hydrogen, hydrogen cyanide, ammonia, water, methane, nitrogen, traces of aromatics such as benzene, aniline and phenol, while 70–80% by weight of the polymer remains as a carbonaceous residue.

Further semi-ladder polymers include the polyoxazoles and polybenzothiazoles which also distinguish themselves by high temperature resistance and low combustibility.

Ladder polymers with a double chain structure have already been briefly mentioned. The polyimideazopyrrolones ("pyrrones", see Fig. 4.4) which combine the properties of the polyimides and the polybenzimidazoles are of great interest.

4.2.4.2 Inorganic polymers

Silicones and polyphosphazenes are the inorganic polymers with elastomeric and thermoplastic properties closest to those of organic plastics. They are inorganic linear polymers with organic side chains. The polyphosphazenes are discussed here since they are relatively new linear polymers with thermoplastic characteristics.

Various monographs deal with inorganic polymers [38, 40, 42, 45] and their degradation [7] (Chap. 14). Polyphosphazenes are mentioned in [42] and [45] and are described in detail by *Allcock* [46] who first synthesized them.

Polyphosphazenes

Polyphosphazenes are linear polymers with a backbone composed of phosphorus and nitrogen and side chains usually of alkoxy and aryloxy groups. The best known are the polyaryloxyphosphazenes which are colourless, flexible, film-forming thermoplastics.

$$\left[\begin{array}{c} \text{OR} \\ | \\ -\text{P} = \text{N}- \\ | \\ \text{OR} \end{array} \right]_n$$

polyphosphazene

Polyphosphazenes are thermally stable up to approximately 200 °C. They have limited combustibility since their inorganic framework acts as an additional flame retardant due to the phosphorus and synergistic nitrogen components. Polyphosphazenes are, depending on their side chains, either non-ignitable or extinguish after removal of the flame. With polyaryloxyphosphazenes, the aromatic side chain groups cause softening, dense smoke evolution in some cases and charring. Aluminium hydroxide filled formulations and foams have more favourable burning behaviour. In both cases, combustibility and smoke development are usually reduced. Little is known at present on the decomposition and combustion behaviour of the polyphosphazenes. Investigations on the combustibility and smoke development of polyphosphazenes have been carried out by *Quinn* and *Dieck* [47].

References for Chapter 4

[1] *H. F. Mark* et al., in *M. Lewin, S. M. Atlas, E. M. Pearce* (Eds.): Flame-Retardant Polymeric Materials. Vol. 1, Chap. 1, p. 1, Plenum Press, New York, 1975.

[2] *W. L. Hawkins,* in *G. Geuskens* (Eds.): Degradation and Stabilisation of Polymers. Chap. 4, p. 77, Applied Science Publishers Ltd., London, 1978.

[3] *S. L. Madorsky:* Thermal Degradation of Organic Polymers. Interscience Publishers, John Wiley & Sons, New York, 1974.

[4] *Y. Kamiya, E. Niki,* in *H. H. G. Jellinek* (Ed.): Aspects of Degradation and Stabilization of Polymers, Chap. 3, p. 79, Elsevier Scientific Publishing Company, Amsterdam, 1978.

[5] *J. F. Rabek,* in *C. H. Bamford, C. F. H. Tipper* (Eds.): Chemical Kinetics. Vol. 14, Degradation of Polymers. Chap. 4, p. 425, Elsevier Scientific Publishing Company, Amsterdam, 1975.

[6] *D. W. van Krevelen:* Properties of Polymers. Chap. 21, p. 459, Elsevier Scientific Publishing Co., Amsterdam, 1976.

[7] *R. T. Conley* (Ed.): Thermal Stability of Polymers. Vol. 1, Marcel Dekker, Inc., New York, 1970.

[8] *G. A. Patten:* Mod. Plast. 39 (1961) 7, p. 119.

[9] *P. C. Warren:* SPE Journal 27 (1971) 2, p. 17.

[10] *W. G. Schmidt:* Inst. Plast. Ind., Trans. (1965) 12, p. 247.

[11] *K. Akita,* in *H. H. G. Jellinek* (Ed.): Aspects of Degradation and Stabilization of Polymers. Chap. 10, p. 514, Elsevier Scientific Publishing Company, Amsterdam, 1978.

[12] *J. Brandrup, E. H. Immergut* (Eds.): Polymer Handbook. 2. Ed. John Wiley & Sons, New York, 1975.

[13] *R. R. Hindersinn, G. M. Wagner:* Encyclopedia of Polymer Science and Technology. Vol. 7, p. 1, Interscience Publishers, John Wiley & Sons, New York, 1967.

[14] *G. S. Learmonth* et al.: Brit. Polym. J. 1 (1969), p. 149.

[15] *L. A. Wall* (Ed.): The Mechanisms of Pyrolysis, Oxidation, and Burning of Organic Materials. Nat. Bur. Stand (U.S.), Spec. Publ. 357, 1972.

[16] *D. E. Stuetz* et al.: J. Polymer Sci. Chem. Ed. 18 (1980), p. 967 and p. 987.

[17] *Hj. Saechtling:* Kunststoff-Taschenbuch. 21. Edition. Carl Hanser Verlag, München, 1979.

[18] *C. A. Harper* (Ed.): Handbook of Plastics and Elastomers. Mc Graw-Hill Book Comp., New York, 1975.

[19] *C. J. Hilado:* Flammability Handbook for Plastics. 2. Edition. Technomic Publ. Co., Inc., 1974.

[20] *J. W. Lyons:* The Chemistry & Uses of Fire Retardants. Wiley-Interscience, John Wiley, New York, 1970.

[21] National Materials Advisory Board (Ed.): Fire Safety Aspects of Polymeric Materials. Vol. 1. Materials: State of the Art. Technomic Publ. Co., Inc., Westport, 1977.

[22] *B. Doležel:* Die Beständigkeit von Kunststoffen und Gummi. Chap. 3, Thermischer und thermisch-oxidativer Abbau von Polymeren. Carl Hanser Verlag, München, 1978.

[23] *R. A. Wessling:* Polyvinylidene Chloride. Gordon and Breach Science Publishers, New York, 1977.

[24] *G. Geuskens* (Ed.): Degradation and Stabilisation of Polymers. Applied Science Publishers Ltd., London, 1978.

[25] *E. A. Boettner, G. L. Ball:* Thermal Decomposition of Polyvinyl Chloride: An Overview. Third International Symposium on PVC, 10–15. 8. 1980, Cleveland, USA.

[26] *K. C. Frisch, J. H. Saunders* (Eds.): Plastic Foams. Part I. Marcel Dekker, Inc., New York, 1973.

[27] *K. C. Frisch, J. H. Saunders* (Eds.): Plastic Foams. Part II. Marcel Dekker, Inc., New York, 1973.

[28] *H. J. Fabris, J. G. Sommer:* Rubber Chem. Technol. 50 (1977) 3, p. 523.

[29] *R. Vieweg, A. Höchtlen* (Eds.): Kunststoff-Handbuch Vol. VII. Polyurethane. Carl Hanser Verlag, München, 1966.

[30] *M. Lewin, S. M. Atlas, E. M. Pearce* (Eds.): Flame-Retardant Polymeric Materials. Vol. 1. Plenum Press, New York, 1975.

[31] *W. C. Kuryla, A. J. Papa* (Eds.): Flame Retardancy of Polymeric Materials. Vol. 3. Chap. 1, Marcel Dekker, Inc., New York, 1973.

[32] *W. C. Kuryla, A. J. Papa* (Eds.): Flame Retardancy of Polymeric Materials. Vol. 2. Marcel Dekker, Inc., New York, 1973.
[33] *A. Ballistreri* et al.: J. Polymer Sci. Chem. Ed. 18 (1980), p. 1923.
[34] *R. Vieweg, L. Goerden* (Eds.): Kunststoff-Handbuch. Vol. VIII. Polyester. Carl Hanser Verlag, München, 1973.
[35] *E. Fitzer:* Angew. Chem. 92 (1980), p. 375.
[36] *J. Tanaka:* Chem. Econ. Eng. Rev. 12 (1980) 9, p. 40.
[37] *H. Lee, D. Stoffey, K. Neville:* New Linear Polymers. Mc Graw-Hill Book Company, New York, 1967.
[38] *A. H. Frazer:* High Temperature Resistant Polymers. Interscience Publishers, John Wiley & Sons, New York, 1968.
[39] *E. Behr:* Hochtemperaturbeständige Kunststoffe. Carl Hanser Verlag, München, 1969.
[40] *V. V. Korshak:* Heat-Resistant Polymers. Israel Program for Scientific Translations, Jerusalem, 1971.
[41] *R. D. Deanin* (Ed.): New Industrial Polymers. ACS Symposium Series 4, Washington, D.C., 1972.
[42] *H. G. Elias:* Neue Polymere Werkstoffe 1969−1974. Carl Hanser Verlag, München, 1975.
[43] *D. A. Kourtides:* Polym.-Plast. Technol. Eng. 11 (1978) 2, p. 159.
[44] *H. G. Elias:* Kunststoffe 70 (1980), p. 699.
[45] *N. H. Ray:* Inorganic Polymers. Academic Press, London, 1978.
[46] *H. R. Allcock:* Angew. Chem. 89 (1977), p. 153.
[47] *E. J. Quinn, A. L. Dieck:* J. Fire & Flammability 7 (1976), p. 5 and p. 358; ibid. 8 (1977), p. 412; J. Cell. Plastics 13 (1977), p. 96.

5 Fire Retardant Plastics

5.1 Flame retardants

5.1.1 Mode of action

A flame retardant should inhibit or even suppress the combustion process. Depending on their nature, flame retardants can act chemically and/or physically in the solid, liquid or gas phase. They interfere with combustion during a particular stage of this process, e.g. during heating, decomposition, ignition or flame spread. The various ways in which a flame retardant can act physically or chemically are described below. They do not occur singly but should be considered as complex processes in which many individual stages occur simultaneously with one dominating (e.g. in addition to an endothermic reaction, dilution of the ignitable gas mixture, due to the formation of inert gases, may also occur). The dominating features can change and it is therefore difficult to make definitive statements on the mode of action of a flame retardant. Elucidation is also rendered difficult by the dependence of flame retardance on the chemical structure of the plastic involved. The modes of action of flame retardants described below refer mainly to the solid and gas phases.

It is almost universally accepted that flame retardants which inhibit the combustion process by chemical action are more effective than those which act by physical means. In many cases, however, the boundary between chemical and physical effects is so indistinct that it is difficult to evaluate their respective contributions.

5.1.1.1 Physical action

There are several ways in which the combustion process can be retarded by physical action:

a) By cooling. Endothermic processes triggered by additives cool the substrate to a temperature below that required for sustaining the combustion process.
b) By formation of a protective layer (coating). The condensed combustible layer can be shielded from the gaseous phase with a solid or gaseous protective layer. The condensed phase is thus cooled, smaller quantities of pyrolysis gases are evolved, the oxygen necessary for the combustion process is excluded and heat transfer is impeded.
c) By dilution. The incorporation of inert substances (e.g. fillers) and additives which evolve inert gases on decomposition dilutes the fuel in the solid and gaseous phases so that the lower ignition limit of the gas mixture is not exceeded.

5.1.1.2 Chemical action

The most significant chemical reactions interfering with the combustion process take place in the solid and gas phases:

a) Reaction in the gas phase. The radical mechanism of the combustion process which takes place in the gas phase is interrupted by the flame retardant. The exothermic processes are thus stopped, the system cools down and the supply of flammable gases is reduced and eventually completely suppressed.

b) Reaction in the solid phase. Here two types of reaction can take place. Firstly, breakdown of the polymer can be accelerated by the flame retardant causing pronounced flow of the polymer and, hence, its withdrawal from the sphere of influence of the flame which breaks away. Secondly, the flame retardant can cause a layer of carbon to form on the polymer surface. This can occur, for example, through the dehydrating action of the flame retardant generating double bonds in the polymer. These form the carbonaceous layer by cyclizing and cross-linking.

5.1.2 The most important flame retardants

A distinction is made between reactive and additive flame retardants. Combinations of flame retardants may produce a synergistic effect of great importance for practical use.

Reactive flame retardants serving as the reactive component are built chemically into the polymer molecule, together with the other starting components. This prevents them from bleeding out of the polymer and volatilising and their flame retardance is thus retained. In addition, they have no plasticising effect and do not affect the thermal stability of the polymer. They are used mainly in thermosets (especially polyesters, epoxy resins and poly-urethanes) in which they can be easily incorporated. They are, however, normally more expensive than additive retardants since their manufacture involves more extensive equipment.

Additive flame retardants are incorporated in the plastic either prior to, during, or, more frequently, following polymerisation. They are used especially in thermoplastics. If they are compatible with the plastic they act as plasticisers, otherwise they are considered as fillers. They are often volatile or tend to bleed so their flame retardance may be gradually lost. The development [1] of high molecular weight products (oligomeric and polymeric flame retardants) enables plastics to be made permanently fire retardant by the additive method.

Combinations of additive or reactive flame retardants can produce an additive, synergistic or antagonistic effect. While the additive effect is the sum of the individual actions, the effects of synergism and antagonism are higher and lower, respectively, than this sum. When used alone, synergists show no or only negligible effectiveness. The synergistic effect occurs when they are used together with specific flame retardants. Synergists have achieved great importance in practical use because they are less expensive than the actual flame retardants and the additions of the latter can be greatly reduced in the presence of the synergist, without any reduction of the flame-retardant effect.

Surveys of the general mode of action of flame retardants and synergists are given in the literature [1] to [18] (and in particular in [6, 10, 13, 14, 16 and 17]).

5.1.2.1 Halogen-containing flame retardants

The effectiveness of halogen-containing flame retardants increases in the order F $\ll$ Cl $<$ Br $<$ I. Fluorine- and iodine-based flame retardants are not used in practice because neither type interferes with the combustion process at the right point. Fluorine cannot become effective as a radical interceptor in the gas phase because of its strong bond to carbon. Iodine in contrast is attached to carbon so loosely that it is liberated by even a negligible energy supply; as a result, the polymer properties (e.g. light stability) are affected and the flame-retardant effect is already lost in the temperature range of pyrolysis.

Of the two remaining halogens, bromine is the more effective since its weaker bonding to carbon enables it to interfere at a more favourable point in the combustion process. It is assumed, moreover, that the effective agent, HBr, is liberated over a narrow temperature range so that it is available at a high concentration in the flame zone. HCl, which is formed over a wider temperature range and is present at lower concentrations, is thus less effective [6].

Halogen-containing flame retardants act by interfering with the radical chain mechanism taking place in the gas phase. The high-energy OH and H radicals formed by chain branching:

$$H + O_2 \longrightarrow OH + O \tag{1}$$
$$O + H_2 \longrightarrow OH + H \tag{2}$$

are removed by the halogen-containing flame retardant. At first the flame retardant breaks down to

$$RX \longrightarrow R + X \tag{3}$$

where X is either Cl or Br.

The halogen radical reacts to form the hydrogen halide:

$$X + RH \longrightarrow R + HX \tag{4}$$

which in turn interferes with the radical chain mechanism:

$$HX + H \longrightarrow H_2 + X \tag{5}$$
$$HX + OH \longrightarrow H_2O + X \tag{6}$$

The high-energy H and OH radicals are removed by reaction with HX and replaced with lower-energy X radicals. The actual flame retardant effect is thus produced by HX. Previously the decisive stage of inhibition was believed to take place according to Eq. (6) but more recent studies suggest the reaction according to Eq. (5) to be responsible. Further details are given by *Petrella* in [13, p. 186] and *Dixon-Lewis* [19].

The hydrogen halide consumed is regenerated by reaction with hydrocarbon:

$$X + RH \longrightarrow R + HX \tag{7}$$

Thus HX ultimately acts as a catalyst. The radical interception mechanism is questioned by *Larsen* [20, 21] who surmises that a physical mechanism lies behind the flame retardant effect of halogen compounds. After all, as hydrogen halides are non-flammable gases they not only dilute the flammable gases but also form a non-combustible protective layer on the condensed phase interfering with or halting the combustion process.

Several authors, in particular *Hindersinn* und *Wagner* [6], have pointed out that halogen-containing flame retardants are also effective in the condensed phase. Thus, HBr acts as an oxidation catalyst forming oxidized products with a tendency to cyclize and condense to yield carbonaceous products which protect the condensed phase below the flame zone against attack by oxygen and radiant heat.

The reaction energy released in the gas phase is additionally reduced by the carbonaceous products formed by the hydrogen halide; these escape as soot and smoke in the gas phase. They also contribute to cooling of the system by "wall effects".

Halogen atoms can be bound aliphatically or aromatically in flame retardants. The more effective aliphatic halogen compounds are easier to break down and hence are less temperature resistant than aromatic retardants. Their suitability depends on the plastic and the method of incorporation.

Halogen/antimony synergism

Sb_2O_3, almost the sole antimony compound used commercially, shows no perceptible flame-retardant action on its own. Together with halogen-containing compounds, however, it produces a marked synergistic effect. No entirely satisfactory theoretical interpretation has been offered up to now. It is believed, however, that the most important reactions take place in the gas phase and are the result of an influence on the radical chain mechanism.

According to a theory proposed by *Pitts* et al. [7, p. 163] and [22], $SbCl_3$ is formed via the intermediate SbOCl, which is actually the effective agent. Sb_2O_3 and HCl first yield SbOCl, which gives off $SbCl_3$ over a relatively wide temperature range:

$$Sb_2O_3 + 2\,HCl \xrightarrow{\sim 250\,°C} 2\,SbOCl + H_2O \tag{8}$$

$$5\,SbOCl \xrightarrow{245\ to\ 280\,°C} Sb_4O_5Cl_2 + SbCl_3\uparrow \tag{9}$$

$$4\,Sb_4O_5Cl_2 \xrightarrow{410\ to\ 475\,°C} 5\,Sb_3O_4Cl + SbCl_3\uparrow \tag{10}$$

$$3\,Sb_3O_4Cl \xrightarrow{475\ to\ 565\,°C} 4\,Sb_2O_3 + SbCl_3\uparrow \tag{11}$$

The consequence of these reactions is that $SbCl_3$ is given off stepwise in the temperature range from 245 to 565 °C. The individual endothermic stages ensure that the system is cooled. $SbCl_3$, as the actual flame retardant, acts as a radical interceptor like HCl or HBr. It is thought that the trivalent antimony facilitates the formation of halogen radicals which affect the radical chain reaction of flame spread.

Other authors suggest that SbOCl or $SbCl_3$ reduces the rate at which the halogen leaves the flame zone thus increasing the probability of reaction with the reactive species. $SbCl_3$ probably evolves heavy vapours which form a layer over the condensed phase, stop oxygen attack and thus choke the flame. It is also assumed that the liquid and solid $SbCl_3$ particles contained in the gas phase reduce the energy content of the flames by wall or surface effects.

Recently *Hastie* has suggested a different mechanism [18], assuming a twofold flame retardant effect of the SbX_3 (where X = Cl or Br):

– on the one hand, SbX_3 breaks down to form HX, which in turn interferes with the radical chain mechanism in the familiar way:

$$SbX_3 + H \longrightarrow HX + SbX_2 \tag{12}$$

$$SbX_2 + H \longrightarrow HX + SbX \tag{13}$$

$$SbX + H \longrightarrow HX + Sb \tag{14}$$

– on the other hand, SbO and SbOH are formed (Eqs. 15 and 16), which together with HX produce the inhibition reaction (Eqs. 17 to 19):

$$Sb + OH + M \longrightarrow SbOH + M \tag{15}$$

$$SbOH + H \longrightarrow SbO + H_2 \tag{16}$$

$$SbO + H \longrightarrow SbOH \tag{17}$$

$$SbOH + H \longrightarrow SbO + H_2 \tag{18}$$

$$HX + H \longrightarrow H_2 + X \tag{19}$$

Condensed phase processes also play an important role. In some polymers, combinations of antimony-halogen compounds cause a pronounced tendency to char. The antimony halides SbX_3 and SbOX are assumed to have a dehydrating, dehydrohalogenating and dehydrogenating effect, depending on which polymer they are used in. These reactions are utilised to influence the pyrolytic processes by formation of a carbon layer on the polymer phase.

Sb_2O_3 and other antimony compounds are described in detail by *Avento* and *Touval* in [16] (p. 355) and *Waddell* and *Touval* [23].

"Synergism" between halogens and radical initiators

This synergism is set in quotation marks because it is currently felt that the increased flame-retardant action produced by radical initiators is of a non-synergistic nature.

In 1964 *Eichhorn* [24] and *Jahn* and *Vanderhoff* [25] reported that the level of bromine compounds in polystyrene could be drastically reduced, without affecting the original flame-retardant effect, by adding radical initiators such as dicumyl peroxide to bromine-containing flame retardants. The synergistic effect was assumed to result from the bromine being split off and removed from the flame retardant quantitatively by the peroxides over a short period, thereby reaching the gas phase in one thrust and interfering very effectively with the radical chain mechanism of the combustion process.

Later *Gouinlock* et al. [26] dealt with this problem and found a different explanation which is generally accepted today: within the range of the flame zone, the peroxides cause extremely rapid breakdown of the polymer in the condensed phase. As a result, the polymer viscosity decreases suddenly and the material starts to flow and drip, thus withdrawing from the flame front. Where dripping and flowing-away are obstructed by the addition of glass fibres, the "synergistic" effect of the peroxide is reduced or eliminated.

5.1.2.2 Phosphorus-containing flame retardants

While halogen-containing flame retardants act in the gas phase, phosphorus-containing flame retardants mainly influence the reactions taking place in the condensed phase. They are particularly effective in materials with high oxygen content, such as cellulose. This classic application is considered here.

The flame retardant is converted by thermal decomposition to phosphoric acid which in the condensed phase extracts water from the pyrolysing substrate, causing it to char. *Lyons* [27] as well as *Hindersinn* and *Witschard* [10] (p. 68) have described the individual reaction steps as follows:

Thermal decomposition leads to the formation of phosphoric acid:

$$R-CH_2-CH_2-O-\overset{\overset{O}{\uparrow}}{\underset{|}{P}}- \xrightarrow{\Delta} R-CH=CH_2 + HO\overset{\overset{O}{\uparrow}}{\underset{|}{P}}- \tag{20}$$

$$2\,HO\overset{\overset{O}{\uparrow}}{\underset{|}{P}}- \xrightarrow{\Delta} -\overset{\overset{O}{\uparrow}}{\underset{|}{P}}-O\overset{\overset{O}{\uparrow}}{\underset{|}{P}}- + H_2O \tag{21}$$

The phosphoric acid formed according to Eq. (21) esterifies, dehydrates the cellulose and causes charring:

$$-CH_2-CH_2-OH + -\overset{\overset{O}{\uparrow}}{\underset{|}{P}}-O\overset{\overset{O}{\uparrow}}{\underset{|}{P}}- \longrightarrow -CH_2-CH_2-O-\overset{\overset{O}{\uparrow}}{\underset{|}{P}}- + -\overset{\overset{O}{\uparrow}}{\underset{|}{P}}-OH \tag{22}$$

$$-CH_2-CH_2-\overset{\overset{\displaystyle O}{\uparrow}}{\underset{|}{O P}}- \quad \xrightarrow{\Delta} \quad -CH=CH_2 \;+\; \overset{\overset{\displaystyle O}{\uparrow}}{\underset{|}{-P}}-OH \quad \longrightarrow \quad \text{charring} \qquad (23)$$

A second possibility of forming unsaturated compounds with subsequent charring is the acid-catalysed elimination of water from cellulose:

$$R-CH_2-CH_2-OH \quad \xrightarrow{H^+} \quad R-CH_2-CH_2-\overset{+}{O}H_2 \qquad (24)$$

$$\longrightarrow \quad R-CH=CH_2 \;+\; H_2O \;+\; H^+$$

The above mechanisms are considered valid for all oxygen-containing polymers (e.g. polyurethanes and polyester resins). Nevertheless, no uniform theory (even less than for halogen-containing flame retardants) yet proposed adequately explains the flame retardant action of phosphorus compounds.

The following processes probably take place in the condensed phase:

– The non-volatile, polymeric phosphoric acids just formed inhibit the pyrolysis reactions by providing the simultaneously forming carbonaceous layer with a glassy coating. This protective layer is resistant to even high temperatures and shields the underlying polymer from attack by oxygen and radiant heat.
– Pronounced charring is promoted by compounds such as phosphines, some of which are highly reducing, that have been formed in addition to the phosphoric acid in the pyrolysis zone. The phosphines reduce the formation of CO and CO_2 in favour of C. They probably also suppress afterglow in the solid phase because this phenomenon is caused by the oxidation of carbon to CO and CO_2.

There is evidence that phosphorus-containing flame retardants can also be effective in the gas phase. *Hastie* [18] and *Granzow* [28] have reported that compounds such as triphenylphosphine oxide (TPPO) break down into fragments such as HPO (Eqs. 25 to 27), which could be detected in the gas phase. These fragments catalyse the recombination of H atoms to H_2 (Eq. 28), thus reducing the energy of the flame:

$$(C_6H_5)_3PO \quad \longrightarrow \quad PO, P, P_2 \qquad (25)$$

$$H + PO + M \quad \longrightarrow \quad HPO + M \qquad (26)$$

$$OH + PO \quad \longrightarrow \quad HPO + O \qquad (27)$$

$$HPO + H \quad \longrightarrow \quad H_2 + PO \qquad (28)$$

Weil [16] gives a comprehensive review of the field of phosphorus-containing flame retardants up to 1980. An adjacent contribution in [16] by *Drake jr.* covers phosphorus compounds in textiles.

Phosphorus/halogen synergism

There is considerable doubt about the synergistic effect of phosphorus and halogens as flame-retardant components in polymers. The various facts suggesting synergism in the gas phase can be explained by the following assumptions:

a) Phosphorus halides and oxyhalides are good flame coolers in the gas phase. It has been proven experimentally that they are better radical interceptors than hydrogen halides. In addition, they have high-boiling points and higher specific gravities than HX and therefore remain longer in the flame zone. This increases the probability of their reaction with the radicals supporting the flame.

b) Halogen-containing flame retardants do not give off their entire halogen content as HX in the gas phase; phosphorus halogen compounds give off HX quantitatively because the P-X bond is weaker than the C-X bond.

c) On account of their higher molecular weight, the phosphorus halides form a layer over the condensed phase, thus shielding it from the air required for combustion.

These assumptions have been evaluated critically by *Weil* [9] and by *Hindersinn* and *Witschard* [10]. Due to lack of experimental evidence, phosphorus/halogen synergism is still unproven. Whether the reactions in the gas phase exert any major influence on the combustion process and whether or not the decisive role is played by the condensed phase charring reactions (as in the reaction solely with phosphorus compounds) is open to debate.

Phosphorus/nitrogen synergism

The synergistic effect of phosphorus and nitrogen compounds has been definitely proven for their use in cellulose. Nitrogen compounds, such as urea, added together with phosphorus compounds are assumed to facilitate the phosphorylation of cellulose with phosphoric acid. They accelerate the formation of polyphosphoric acid, which is considered the actual dehydrating agent. Dehydration then leads to charring of the substrate.

It is further assumed that the charred zone can be covered

a) by a layer of liquid polyphosphoric acid,
b) by a glassy, temperature-resistant layer of polymeric PNO (described in the literature),
c) by a layer of cross-linked polyphosphazenes.

The nitrogen compounds can promote the formation of a layer of frothy coal by forming gaseous decomposition products which protects the substrate very effectively against the intense radiant heat from the combustion zone. The nitrogen compounds prevent the phosphorus compounds from escaping by pyrolysis into the gas phase, where they are less effective than in the condensed phase. The nitrogen compounds themselves form acids (HNO_2, HNO_3) which produce the dehydration of the polymer via a carbonium ion mechanism. The nitrogen compound pyrolyses to form volatile constituents which reach the gas phase and act as radical interceptors.

With the exception of the effect in cellulose, all the statements made above are conjectural and largely unproven experimentally. It is believed, however, that the mechanisms involved take place chiefly in the condensed phase, as is the case when phosphorus compounds are used alone. A detailed discussion of these problems is given by *Weil* [9].

5.1.2.3 Inorganic flame retardants

Few inorganic compounds are suitable for use as flame retardants in plastics, since such compounds must be effective in the range of decomposition temperatures of the plastic. This range lies between 150 °C and 400 °C.

Apart from antimony trioxide, which interferes with the combustion process chemically in combination with halogen-containing flame retardants, the most widely used inorganic flame retardants such as aluminium hydroxide and boron-containing compounds affect the combustion process via physical means.

Unlike organic compounds, inorganic flame retardants do not evaporate under the influence of heat; rather they decompose, giving off non-flammable gases like H_2O, CO_2, SO_2, HCl, etc., mostly in endothermic reactions. In the gas phase, these act by diluting the mixture of flammable gases and by shielding the surface of the polymer against oxygen attack.

The inorganic flame retardant acts simultaneously on the surface of the solid phase by cooling the polymer via the endothermic breakdown process and reducing the formation of pyrolysis products.

In addition, as in the case of the inorganic boron compounds, a glassy protective layer can form on the substrate, fending off the effect of oxygen and heat. Detailed descriptions of inorganic flame retardants are given by *Pitts* in [7] (p. 133), *Woycheshin* and *Sobolev* in [23] (p. 237), *Milewski* and *Katz* in [23] (p. 250) as well as *Avento* and *Touval* in [16] (p. 361).

Aluminium hydroxide

Currently, aluminium hydroxide is the most widely used flame retardant; it is low cost and easy to incorporate into plastics.

Aluminium hydroxide starts to break down in the temperature range from 180 °C to 200 °C, conversion to aluminium oxide taking place in an endothermic reaction with release of water vapour.

$$2\,Al\,(OH)_3 \xrightarrow{\Delta} Al_2O_3 + 3\,H_2O - 298\ kJ/mol \tag{29}$$

In the combustion zone, this reaction triggers various processes which affect the combustion process [29, 30]:

– As a result of the endothermic breakdown of the aluminium hydroxide, the polymer is cooled, and thus fewer pyrolysis products are formed.
– Together with the charring products, the Al_2O_3 formed on the surface of the substrate acts as an insulating protective layer.
– The water vapour liberated has a diluting effect in the gas phase and forms an oxygen-displacing protective layer over the condensed phase.

All these processes are of a purely physical nature. Chemical reactions such as interruption of the radical chain mechanism of the gas phase combustion processes have not been detected. The physical effect theory is also supported by the fact that, unlike chemically effective flame retardants, plastics containing aluminium hydroxide evolve little smoke and soot.

Boron-containing compounds

Boron-containing compounds can be effective in the condensed phase, and in some cases, in the gas phase as well. A major application of borates is the use of mixtures of boric acids and borax as flame retardants for cellulose. Boron-containing compounds act by endothermic, stepwise release of water and formation of a glassy coating protecting the substrate:

$$2\,H_3BO_3 \xrightarrow[-2\,H_2O]{130\ to\ 200°C} 2\,HBO_2 \xrightarrow[-H_2O]{260\ to\ 270°C} B_2O_3 \tag{30}$$

On heating, the mixture dissolves in its own water of hydration, swells to form a frothy substance, loses water and finally fuses into a clear melt. The B_2O_3 forming the melt softens at 325 °C and starts to flow above 500 °C. Additionally in cellulose, boric acid – similar to the polyphosphoric acid resulting from phosphate esters – shows dehydrating action by acid-catalysed elimination of water resulting in pronounced charring of the substrate. These two effects – the glassy coating and the pronounced tendency to char – protect the substrate successfully against oxygen attack and heat. The formation of flammable decomposition gases is thereby reduced.

No consensus of opinion exists as yet on the processes in the gas phase. *Cowan* and *Manley* [31] hold the view that zinc borate together with antimony trioxide show a synergistic effect in plasticised PVC. They attribute this synergism to the formation of zinc chloride and zinc oxychloride which, similarly to the antimony compounds, interfere with the radical chain mechanism by stepwise release of hydrogen chloride. *Hilado* et al. [32] have found only an additive rather than synergistic effect when using zinc borate and PVC in rigid polyurethane foam.

Other boron compounds such as barium metaborate or calcium borate show only negligible flame-retardant properties. Compounds such as sodium and potassium tetrafluoroborate are supposed to act by releasing boron trifluoride in the gas phase; however, experimental evidence is still lacking.

Boron compounds probably act in the solid phase by forming a glassy coating and in oxygen-containing substrates by simultaneous, pronounced charring. There is still controversy about their action in the gas phase.

Other inorganic compounds

Of the many inorganic compounds studied as potential as flame retardants in plastics, only a few materials in addition to those mentioned above are of real interest. The phosphates and sulphates (cf. *Pitts* [7], p. 133 ff) are hardly suitable for use in plastics.

In the last few years, the hydrated basic carbonates of aluminium with magnesium (Hydrotalcite) or sodium (Dawsonite) have attracted increasing attention. Used in PVC these compounds act as flame retardants and smoke suppressants of limited effectiveness. Dawsonite breaks down endothermically at about 300 °C [33]:

$$NaAl(OH)_2CO_3 \xrightarrow{\Delta} NaAlO_2 + H_2O + CO_2 \tag{31}$$

This higher decomposition temperature, (cf that of $Al(OH)_3$ decomposition from 200 °C upwards), may be of advantage in the processing of plastics. Moreover, the fibrous structure of Dawsonite reduces the tendency of thermoplastics to drip. The flame-retardant mechanism of Dawsonite corresponds to that of aluminium hydroxide.

This product has, however, been withdrawn since it has recently come under suspicion as being carcinogenic on account of its asbestos-like structure.

Chalk, a filler which some also consider as a flame retardant, acts purely by the diluting effect of highly filled plastics materials reducing the amount of combustible material available per unit volume and thus reducing combustibility. Since chalk does not break down below 900 °C, flame-retardant action, i.e. reaction in the temperature range of plastics pyrolysis (150 °C to 400 °C), does not take place.

For completeness, we mention here that the action of elemental red phosphorus as a flame retardant in various plastics has been investigated and described in detail by *Peters* in [11] (p. 113 ff). *Piechota* [34] was the first worker to investigate polyurethane foams and found red phosphorus to be very effective as a flame retardant. In many other plastics, however, this effectiveness has not been clearly demonstrated.

The actual flame retarding effect is due, in all probability, to the oxidation of elemental phosphorus during the combustion process to phosphoric acid or phosphorus pentoxide. The latter acts, as described in 5.1.2.2 by the formation of a carbonaceous layer in the condensed phase. The formation of fragments which act by interrupting the radical chain mechanism is also likely [35, 36].

5.1.3 Intumescent coatings as flame retardants for plastics

Intumescent coatings are systems which puff up to produce foams. Because of this characteristic they are used to protect materials such as wood and plastics which are combustible and those like steel which lose their strength when exposed to high temperatures.

Intumescent agents have been available commercially for some 20 years and are used foremost as fire protective coatings. In recent times they have been used as "flame retardants" for plastics by incorporating the intumescent components in the polymer matrix.

Intumescent coatings are always formulated according to the same principles whether they are used as a coating or as a flame retardant. The intumescent effect is achieved by using the following components:

– *Acid source.* This usually consists of the salt of an inorganic non-volatile acid such as boric, sulphuric or phosphoric acid. Salts of phosphoric acid like ammonium phosphate or ammonium polyphosphate which liberate the acid on which they are based at temperatures above 150 °C are nearly always used. The acid generated initiates the first of a series of reactions, which begins with the dehydration of the carbonific compound and its subsequent charring.
– *Carbonific compounds.* These are polyhydroxy compounds which dehydrate and char due to acid attack which proceeds via an esterification reaction. Compounds frequently used include pentaerythritol, starch and phenolic or urea resins.
– *Spumific compounds.* Compounds such as chloroparaffins, melamine and guanidine are used. Under the effect of temperature these liberate large quantities of non-combustible gases such as HCl, NH_3, CO_2 and ensure the formation of the carbonaceous foam layer over the substrate. The decomposition products of the blowing agent (e.g. chloroparaffin residues) frequently assist charring.
– *Resin binders.* These cover the foam with a skin which prevents the gases escaping. They should not harden but remain thermoplastic in order to have an optimum effect. Chlorinated rubbers, for example, are highly suitable since they soften and melt at low temperatures, act as blowing agents via formation of HCl, and contribute to charring with their residues.

Intumescent coatings act as follows:

In the first stage the effect of intense heat causes the inorganic salt to decompose to the acid (e.g. ammonium dihydrogen phosphate):

$$NH_4H_2PO_4 \xrightarrow{\Delta} NH_3 + H_3PO_4 \tag{32}$$

The components of the intumescent mixture start to soften. The acid esterifies the polyhydroxy compound to give the polyol ester (e.g. pentaerythritol):

$$C_5H_8(OH)_4 + H_3PO_4 \longrightarrow C_5H_8(OH)_4 \cdot H_3PO_4 \tag{33}$$

The mixture melts and decomposes; the polyol ester breaks down to acid, water and a carbonaceous residue:

$$C_5H_8(OH)_4 \cdot H_3PO_4 \xrightarrow{\Delta} H_3PO_4 + H_2O + C \tag{34}$$

Simultaneously, the compound supplying the blowing agent decomposes and the gases generated expand the molten mass (e.g. chloroparaffin):

$$C_nH_{(2n+1)}Cl \longrightarrow HCl + C \tag{35}$$

The softened resin binder forms a skin over the foam and prevents the gases from escaping. The viscosity of the frothy mass increases and the foam solidifies completely by cross-linking and charring. The foam is some 50 to 100 times as thick as the original intumescent layer resulting in good thermal insulation thus protecting the substrate from the effects of heat and decomposition.

According to *Vandersall* [37] and *Ellard* [38] the foam does not consist of a pure carbon framework but is partially inorganic due to the formation of a phosphate glass. Its composition is, however, not known in detail.

In order to obtain a foam with an optimum protective effect, the components must be selected so that the individual stages such as acid formation, fusion, acid attack and formation of blowing agent occur in rapid sequence. It is therefore important to generate the blowing agent at a point in time wh the viscosity of the melt lies in a range suitable for foam formation. If the viscosity is too low, the gases escape resulting in a weak foam with a damaged surface. If, on the other hand, it is too high, foaming of the melt is impeded. Foam formation is promoted by utilising components which carry out several functions such as generating blowing agents at the same time as charring. Foam formation is influenced to a high degree by exposure to heat and flame. Detailed descriptions of the classic intumescent coatings are given by *Lyons* in [4] (p. 256) *Vandersall* [37], *Chang* et al. [12] (p. 411) and *Hindersinn* and *Witschard* [10] (p. 90). The more recent intumescent agents are no longer used as coatings but incorporated directly in the plastics material. The use of such flame retardants in polypropylene is described by *Brady* et al. [39]. The flame retardant is manufactured by reacting phosphorus pentoxide with dipentaerythritol and melamine. Its polymeric structure is not known and under the effect of heat it causes polypropylene, which normally flows, to char.

5.2 The most important fire retardant plastics

In contrast to other additives, flame retardants can impair the properties of plastics appreciably. The problem is to find a compromise between the decrease in performance of the plastic caused by the flame retardant and the desired improvement in fire safety.

An ideal flame retardant should be easy to incorporate in, and be compatible with, the plastic (i.e. not bleed out), and not alter its mechanical properties. Furthermore, it should be colourless, exhibit good stability to UV and light, and be resistant to ageing and hydrolysis. It should also be matched to the decomposition temperature of the polymer, i.e. its effect must start to act below the decomposition temperature of the plastic and continue over the whole range of decomposition. It must not cause corrosion, must be temperature resistant, effective in small amounts, odourless and without harmful physiological effects. It must also emit only low levels of smoke and toxic gases and finally be as cheap as possible.

In order to approach this unachievable range of properties, countless formulations have been developed for fire retarding each plastic for diverse applications. These may be based on additive and reactive flame retardants to which synergists and fillers may be frequently added.

In practice, the use of flame retardants results in various problems. Attempts are made to solve these by optimum formulation. Thus the effect of most flame retardants depends on acids liberated during their decomposition (e.g. hydrogen halides from halogen-containing, and phosphoric acids from phosphorus-containing compounds). These can cause corrosion of equipment during processing which can be counteracted by choosing suitable stabilisers. Plastics containing flame retardants which decompose only at high temperatures, e.g. compounds with aromatically bonded bromine, can be processed more easily than those containing aliphatically bonded bromine. They are however usually less effective. Their effectiveness can be considerably increased without significantly affecting processability by the addition of synergists like antimony trioxide.

Flame retardants also influence the physical properties of the polymer in as much as they function, for example, as plasticisers. This occurs with many phosphorus compounds.

Additive flame retardants are used almost exclusively in plastics with a pure carbon chain structure such as polyolefins, polyvinyl chloride and polystyrene. Compared to reactive flame retardants, they can be easily and cheaply incorporated into the polymer and do not alter its characteristics significantly. They are also added to plastics with a heterogeneous chain such as polyurethanes, polyesters and polyamides – an indication of their wide range of application. Reactive flame retardants are, however, preferred for this class of plastic since they enable specific formulations with a particular range of properties to be developed at a reasonable cost. The incorporation of reactive flame retardants in the polymer chain also ensures a durable fire retardant effect since they do not migrate or bleed out and are non-volatile.

Flame retardants used on a commercial scale in plastics include organic chlorine and bromine compounds, phosphorus compounds or phosphorus compounds containing chlorine and bromine, synergists such as antimony trioxide or organic radical initiators and inorganic compounds such as aluminium hydroxide which act simultaneously as flame retardants and fillers.

The principal chlorine-containing flame retardants in commercial use are chlorinated hydrocarbons or chlorinated cycloaliphatics. They are distinguished by low cost and good light stability. They suffer, however, from the disadvantage that they have to be utilised in quantities which adversely affect the properties of the plastic in order to provide a sufficient level of fire retardance.

The most commonly utilised aliphatic compounds are chloroparaffins which are available in liquid or solid form depending on their chlorine content (between 30 and 70%). They have semi-plasticising properties, poor thermal resistance (up to a maximum of 220 °C) and tend to bleed out.

Cycloaliphatic chlorine compounds are stable up to 260 °C and have found widespread application as reactive flame retardants. The most widely used is hexachloroendomethylenetetrahydrophthalic acid (HET acid) and its anhydride.

Aromatic chlorine compounds are thermally stable up to about 280 °C but have a less pronounced flame-retardant action. Consequently the more effective bromine compounds are used instead.

Bromine compounds are better flame retardants than chlorine compounds and, since they are used in lower concentrations, affect the properties of the plastic less. They can be readily incorporated and do not bleed; however they exhibit poor stability to light and are expensive. They are used as both reactive and additive flame retardants.

Amongst additive flame retardants, aliphatic bromine compounds, such as hexabromobutene, are the most effective though they possess poor thermal stability.

Cycloaliphatics such as hexabromocyclododecane and pentabromochlorocyclohexane are preferred for commercial use. Whilst providing a high degree of flame retardance they possess superior temperature resistance to aliphatic bromine compounds.

Aromatic bromine compounds such as decabromodiphenyl ether which break down at temperatures above 400 °C are used in plastics processed at high temperatures. Synergists such as antimony trioxide are added in order to improve the flame retardance of such compounds.

The most frequently used reactive flame retardants containing bromine are tetra-bromobisphenol A, tetrabromophthalic anhydride and dibromoneopentyl glycol. Countless other reactive flame retardants tailored to the needs of specific formulations also exist. They lie however outside the scope of this book.

The range of phosphorus-containing flame retardants is extraordinarily versatile since, in contrast to halogen compounds, it extends over several oxidation states. Thus phosphines, phosphine oxides, phosphonium compounds, phosphonates, elemental red phosphorus, phosphites and phosphates are all used as flame retardants. Frequently, the phosphorus compounds also contain halogens, and in particular bromine, which increase the effectiveness of the flame retardant, although it is questionable whether this is a synergistic effect. Many of the phosphorus compounds are liquid and possess plasticising properties.

Phosphoric acid esters, aryl phosphates and their alkyl-substituted derivatives are the additive flame retardants with a plasticising action most commonly used commercially in thermoplastics and in particular in PVC.

Tris(dibromopropyl)phosphate, a highly effective and versatile flame retardant has been withdrawn as it is suspected of being mutagenic and carcinogenic.

The almost limitless range of reactive flame retardants containing phosphorus is confusing. Usually polyols modified with groups containing phosphorus, such as the phosphines, phosphonates, etc. mentioned above are utilised. Other phosphorus-modified reactive components in use include isocyanates, acids, nitrogen-containing and unsaturated compounds.

Fire retardant plastics are discussed in detail by *Lyons* [4] (Chaps. 7 and 8) and in the first three volumes of *Kuryla* and *Papa* [7–9] (a comprehensive list of flame retardants as at 1972 is given in [7] Chap. 1). Other reviews are given by *Lewin* et al. [12] (Vol. 1), *Kirk-Othmer* [16], *Katz* and *Milewski* [23] and various other workers [40–47].

5.2.1 Plastics with all-carbon backbones

5.2.1.1 Polyolefins

For various reasons, flame retardants cannot be simply incorporated in polyolefins. Polypropylene, for example, is usually processed at high temperatures (up to 300 °C) necessitating the use of flame retardants with high thermal stability; suitable aromatic halogen compounds must be used in conjunction with synergists (Sb_2O_3) in order to increase their effectiveness. The incorporation of flame retardants in polyethylene is made more difficult by the crystallinity of the polymer which impedes homogeneous distribution of the flame retardant and reduces its effectiveness.

Additive flame retardants are used in polyolefins almost exclusively. The maximum concentration at which reactive flame retardants can be used without significantly affecting the properties of the polymer is 5%. The fire retardant effect at this low concentration is slight.

In the past, polyolefins were generally flame-retarded with chloroparaffins and antimony trioxide (preferably in the ration 2:1). Frequently PVC or chlorinated polyethylene were also added. Nowadays cycloaliphatic (hexabromocyclododecane) and aromatic bromine compounds such as penta-, octa- and decabromodiphenyl, the corresponding ethers, and in particular decabromodiphenyl ether and compounds such as tetrabromobisphenol A or bis-dibromopropyl ether are preferred. Antimony trioxide is also used here as a synergist [42, 46, 48].

Recently bromine-containing phosphorus compounds with high heat resistance and good resistance to hydrolysis have been described [49, 50]. Phosphorus compounds are seldom used in polyolefins since they are largely incompatible with them and are expensive.

Formulations with red phosphorus have also been developed but have not gained accept-ance due to the intrinsic colour and toxicity of phosphorus [51]. Further possible additives include aluminium hydroxide, magnesium hydroxide [52] and, recently, intumescent coatings [39]. A detailed description of flame retardant polyolefins is given by *Schwarz* in [8] Chap. 2.

5.2.1.2 Polyvinyl chloride

Due to its high chlorine content, rigid PVC is inherently fire retardant and thus meets the usual fire performance requirements for combustible materials. However, this is frequently not the case with modified rigid PVC such as high impact grades. The components respon-sible for the high impact properties burn more easily than the PVC matrix and also reduce the total chlorine content. Antimony trioxide is usually added to high impact PVC as a synergist and additional flame retardants such as zinc borate or barium metaborate are frequently utilised. Finely divided aluminium hydroxide is also readily used since it is cheap and even large amounts do not significantly affect the high impact strength.

Plasticised PVC contains up to 50% plasticiser. The latter burns more easily than pure PVC so that flame retardants must be incorporated for many applications. This is achieved by partly replacing the plasticiser with a flame retardant phosphate plasticiser or chloroparaffin and adding antimony trioxide as a synergist. For many applications, such as cables, large quantities of fillers such as chalk are used. In many cases aluminium hydroxide can be used to advantage in place of chalk since it also acts as a flame retardant [29, 53]. Antimony trioxide can be partly replaced by cheap borates, such as zinc borate and barium metaborate [31].

Phosphoric esters such as tricresyl phosphate are used as plasticisers. They are costly, have poor light stability and diminish cold impact strength [54]. A range of new phosphate plasticisers, the alkylaryl phosphates (isopropylphenyl phosphate), exhibits increased light stability and improved cold impact strength [55]. Other aspects of the fire performance of PVC and related polymers are described by *O'Mara* et al. in [7] Chap. 3 and *Burn* and *Martin* in [56].

5.2.1.3 Polystyrene, styrene copolymers and polystyrene foam

As with polyolefins and PVC, only additive flame retardants are used commercially to make polystyrene fire retardant. As in the case of the polyolefins bromine compounds are increas-ingly replacing chlorine compounds while phosphorus and halogen-phosphorus compounds are used only in exceptional cases due to their cost and low effectiveness. Aromatic bromine compounds such as decabromodiphenyl ether are used with antimony trioxide as a synergist particularly for "non-dripping on combustion" polystyrene grades required, for example, for television backs. Since this combination of flame retardants has good temperature resist-ance it is also utilised in ABS which is processed at temperatures up to 280 °C. PVC is frequently used for flame retarding ABS; in addition, antimony trioxide and inorganic borates are incorporated. Such "polymer alloys" are, however, difficult to process due to their inadequate thermal stability.

Compared to solid polystyrene which is processed at temperatures up to 260 °C, the manufacture of foam polystyrene with physical blowing agents is carried out at approxi-mately 120 °C for bead foam and about 200 °C for extruded foam. These lower temperatures enable the less thermally stable aliphatic and cycloaliphatic bromine compounds to be used. Due to their higher effectiveness as flame retardants they can be used in fairly small amounts (1 to 2%). The level can be reduced still further (<1%) in bead foam by the addition of radical initiators such as organic peroxides. Flame retardants can be added at the start of, or during, polymerisation; however, they must not interfere with the course of polymerisation through chain transfer reactions. Typical flame retardants include hexabromobutene, pentabromochlorocyclohexane, hexabromocyclododecane, pentabromophenylallyl ether etc. Organic peroxides such as dicumyl peroxide or oligomeric compounds like oligomeric diisopropyl benzene are used as "synergistic" (see 5.1.2.1) radical initiators.

A list of flame retardants used in polystyrene and foam polystyrene can be found in [8] Chap. 1.

5.2.2 Plastics with a heterogeneous backbone

5.2.2.1 Polyurethane foam

Polyurethane foam is one of the most widely used foam materials and belongs to the standard plastics. Usage is split between flexible foam and rigid foam in the ratio 3:1. The main areas of application are in building, transportation, refrigeration and in furniture. Certain technical fire protection requirements have to be met for these applications which in many cases necessitate a fire retardant treatment.

Low cost additive flame retardants used to be incorporated in PUR foams. Cheaper, improved methods of manufacturing foams have resulted in the increasing use of reactive flame retardants, particularly, for rigid foams. They have the advantage over additive flame retardants of providing a permanent flame retardant effect.

In contrast to rigid PUR foam, it is difficult to provide flexible foams with a really effective fire retardant treatment since factors such as open cell structure, low degree of cross-linking and chemical structure impair the flame retardant effect. The physical properties of the foam are also adversely affected if incompatible additives such as fillers are incorporated. The most frequently used reactive flame retardants are polyols and isocyanates which have been modified with groups containing phosphorus, halogens (usually bromine) or both. Some of these are, however, extremely susceptible to hydrolysis, so that foam must be manufactured by methods which exclude water completely.

Phosphate polyols, colourless liquids containing approximately 10% phosphorus, are most frequently used. Phosphonate and phosphite polyols are suitable too as starting materials for manufacturing rigid foams. Of the phosphorus/halogen polyols, those based on tetrabromophthalic anhydride-polyol adducts containing phosphorus are usually used in rigids. These products are less suitable for flexible foams since a lower flame retardant effect is achieved.

Halogenated polyols can be used to advantage in flexible foams. A highly effective example is dibromoneopentyl glycol which is relatively stable to hydrolysis and contains aliphatically bound bromine. Flame retardants containing aromatically bonded bromine are of limited effectiveness since they do not decompose in the temperature range of the burning foam.

Polyesters containing hexachloroendomethylenetetrahydrophthalic acid (HET acid) as the flame retardant component are frequently used as polyol components. Antimony trioxide is added to increase the flame retardant effect.

The use of flame retardants introduces a whole series of effects detrimental to the properties of the foam including reduced resistance to heat and hydrolysis and increased smoke evolution. Foams with reduced combustibility can be obtained without adding flame retardants by modification with aromatic (highly aromatic polyols) or cross-linking components such as isocyanurates or carbodiimide. Such foams exhibit a strong tendency to char. They are thus better protected against the effects of flame [57].

Additive flame retardants can be more easily incorporated in PUR foams than reactive retardants. A major disadvantage is that they frequently cause shrinkage particularly in flexible foams where they are preferred. In the case of phosphate esters, they also act as plasticisers.

Phosphorus-containing flame retardants are used in the form of phosphates, phosphonates, phosphines and phosphinic oxides. Because of their lasting fire retardant effect, compounds with high molecular weight are preferred; polymeric phosphorus components are therefore readily used.

An increase in the flame retardant effect is achieved by using halogen-containing phosphorus compounds. Halogen-containing phosphate esters such as bromine and chlorine containing tris(halogenoalkyl)phosphates are particularly popular flame retardants.

The compound, which has, on account of its high bromine content, the best flame retardant effect, tris(dibromopropyl)phosphate, is no longer used as it is suspected of being mutagenic and carcinogenic.

As in other plastics, the more effective bromine compounds are generally used in preference to other halogen compounds. Nevertheless, chloroparaffins and PVC are also used since they are effective as flame retardants due to elimination of HCl and a strong tendency to char. Depending on requirements, aliphatic, cycloaliphatic and aromatic bromine compounds such as tetrabromobutane, hexabromobutene, dibromoneopentyl glycol, hexabromocyclododecane, hexabromobenzene, various highly brominated diphenyls and diphenyl ethers are used. Aromatic bromine compounds are however preferred since they do not impair the activity of the amine catalysts by elimination of hydrogen halide. Antimony trioxide is used in many cases as a synergist to improve the flame retardant effect.

The use of inorganic flame retardants causes problems since they are difficult to incorporate and distribute homogeneously in the foam; furthermore they provide only limited flame retardance. Some fillers can even act as fire promoters due to a wicking effect.

Typical inorganics in use are aluminium hydroxide, red phosphorus and salts such as calcium phosphate. Ferrocene has also proved to be a good flame retardant and smoke inhibitor.

PUR foams are described in detail by *Frisch* and *Reegen* in [12] (Chap. 7) and *Papa* in [9] (Chap. 1). *Frisch* discusses mainly flame retardants containing reactive phosphorus, isocyanurate modified foams and high temperature resistant PUR foams. *Papa*, in contrast, gives a general review of the additive and reactive flame retardants described in the literature and patents up to 1973.

5.2.2.2 Thermosetting resins

Due to their fire performance unsaturated polyester and epoxy resins sometimes require fire retardant treatment in order to meet fire protection requirements. This is seldom required for phenolic, urea or melamine resins due to their high nitrogen content. Melamine resins are even added to other plastics in order to reduce their combustibility.

Polyester and epoxy resins are rendered fire retardant by incorporating reactive and additive flame retardants, synergists and fillers as required. Reactive flame retardants containing halogen to which antimony trioxide has been added as a synergist satisfy the most stringent requirements. Thus tetrabromobisphenol A is frequently used in polyester and epoxy resins. Other flame retardants which can also be utilised in glass fibre reinforced polyesters are hexachloroendomethylenetetrahydrophthalic acid (HET acid) or its anhydride, dibromoneopentylglycol and tetrabromophthalic anhydride. Alkylene oxide addition products of tetrabromobisphenol A are used for corrosion-resistant grades, since unsaturated polyester resins are fairly cheap to produce; the relatively expensive organic phosphorus compounds are seldom used.

Large quantities of additive flame retardants and fillers are frequently incorporated in unsaturated polyester resins. These include chloroparaffins and various bromine compounds such as pentabromotoluene, brominated diphenyl ether or aromatic polymeric bromine compounds such as polytribromostyrene or poly(pentabromobenzyl)acrylate. Antimony trioxide and large quantities of calcium carbonate or aluminium hydroxide are added to the above. The more expensive coated (e.g. with silane) aluminium hydroxide is easier to incorporate in glass fibre reinforced types. Additives such as ammonium polyphosphate and borates are also popular. The inorganic additives named here are also used in epoxy resins. Organic compounds containing phosphorus or phosphorus/halogen as well as bromine compounds such as decabromodiphenyl ether also play their part in epoxies.

In the few cases where phenolic resins require fire retardant treatment, additive or reactive flame retardants have proved effective. Besides familiar flame retardants such as tetrabromobisphenol A and various organic phosphorus compounds used in many plastics, halogenated phenols and aldehydes (e.g. p-bromobenzaldehyde) are specifically utilised as reactive flame retardants. Phosphorus can be introduced by direct reaction of the phenolic resin with phosphorus oxychloride. Likewise inorganic compounds such as boric acid are incorporated into phenolic resin by chemical reaction.

Chlorine compounds (e.g. chloroparaffins) and thermally stable aromatic bromine compounds (e.g. brominated diphenyl ethers) are utilised as additive flame retardants. Antimony trioxide is added as a synergist. Suitable phosphorus compounds include halogenated phosphoric acid esters like tris(2-chloroethyl)phosphate and halogenated organic polyphosphates, as well as large quantities of inorganics such as calcium and ammonium phosphates. Zinc and barium salts of boric acid and aluminium hydroxide also find frequent application.

In order to suppress the afterglow of phenolic resins, use is made of compounds like aluminium chloride, antimony trioxide and organic amides.

A survey of flame retardants used in phenolic resins is given by *Sunshine* in [8] Chap. 4 and *Conley* et al. in [12] Chap. 8. Melamine and urea resins are covered in the same papers.

5.2.2.3 Miscellaneous

The nitrogen content of *polyamides* imparts certain inherent fire retardant characteristics to them. Furthermore, they are usually processed into products which are not subject to fire protection requirements so that flame retardants are only incorporated for certain applications. While reactive flame retardants are seldom used, there are a number of additive flame retardants. Preference is shown for highly halogenated cycloaliphatics (HET acid) and particularly for aromatic compounds such as chlorinated naphthalenes and diphenyls to which antimony trioxide or tin oxide are added. Aromatic bromine compounds such as various brominated diphenyl ethers and hexabromobenzene are also used. Various organic phosphorus compounds (e.g. phosphines, phosphonates, etc.) are also in use. Reinforced flame retarding types are obtained by processing melamine, for example, together with organic halogen compounds and glass fibres. In some cases red phosphorus is added. Fillers are only seldom used.

Only compounds which exhibit high thermal stability can be considered as flame retardants for high temperature resistant thermoplastics such as *polycarbonate* and *polybutyleneterephthalate*. Examples include compounds with aromatically bonded bromine. In polycarbonate for example, tetrabromobisphenol A, which is highly compatible, is incorporated as the reactive component. In polybutyleneterephthalate, hydroxyethylated tetrabromobenzimidazolone or tetrabromophthalic anhydride are incorporated as flame retardants.

Antimony trioxide can be added as a synergist to all these halogen-containing flame retardants to increase their effectiveness.

Polymers such as *polyphenylene oxide, polyphenylene sulphide or polyether sulphone* have
only a slight tendency to burn and consequently do not generally require any additional
flame retardant treatment. Due to their extremely high processing temperatures, "classical"
flame retardants cannot be used.

References for Chapter 5

[1]   R. Burkhardt, E. N. Petersen, N. Vollkommer: Chemiker-Ztg. 102 (1978) 1, p. 11.
[2]   H. Vogel: Flammfestmachen von Kunststoffen. Dr. Alfred Hüthig Verlag, Heidelberg, 1966.
[3]   P. Thiéry: Fireproofing. Elsevier Publ. Comp. Ltd., Amsterdam, 1970.
[4]   J. W. Lyons: The Chemistry & Uses of Fire Retardants. Wiley-Interscience, John Wiley, New
      York, 1970.
[5]   R. Thater: Brennverhalten von Plastformstoffen. VEB Deutscher Verlag für Grundstoffindustrie,
      Leipzig, 1968.
[6]   R. R. Hindersinn, G. M. Wagner: Encyclopedia of Polymer Science and Technology. Vol. 7.
      Interscience Publishers, 1967, p. 1.
[7]   W. C. Kuryla, A. J. Papa (Eds.): Flame Retardancy of Polymeric Materials. Vol. 1. Marcel
      Dekker, Inc., New York, 1973.
[8]   Flame Retardancy of Polymeric Materials. Vol. 2. Marcel Dekker Inc., New York, 1973.
[9]   Flame Retardancy of Polymeric Materials. Vol. 3. Marcel Dekker Inc., New York, 1975.
[10] Flame Retardancy of Polymeric Materials. Vol. 4. Marcel Dekker Inc., New York, 1978.
[11] Flame Retardancy of Polymeric Materials. Vol. 5. Marcel Dekker Inc., New York, 1979.
[12] M. Lewin, S. M. Atlas, E. M. Pearce (Eds.): Flame Retardant Polymeric Materials, Vol. 1.
      Plenum Press, New York, 1975.
[13] Flame Retardant Polymeric Materials. Vol. 2. Plenum Press, New York, 1978.
[14] C. J. Hilado: Flammability Handbook for Plastics. 2nd Ed. Technomic Publishing Co., Inc.,
      Westport, 1974.
[15] National Materials Advisory Board: Fire Safety Aspects of Polymeric Materials. Vol. 1.
      Materials: State of the Art. Technomic Publ. Co., Westport, 1977.
[16] Kirk-Othmer: Encyclopedia of Chemical Technology. 3rd Ed. Vol. 10. John Wiley & Sons, New
      York, 1980.
      J. W. Lyons: An Overview. p. 348.
      J. M. Avento, I. Touval: Antimony and Other Inorganic Compounds. p. 355.
      E. R. Larsen: Halogenated Flame Retardants. p. 373.
      E. D. Weil: Phosphorus Compounds. p. 396.
      G. L. Drake jr.: Flame Retardants for Textiles. p. 420.
[17] I. N. Einhorn: J. Macromol. Sci.-Revs. Polymer Technol. D1, 2 (1971), p. 113.
[18] J. W. Hastie: Molecular Basis of Flame Inhibition. J. Res. Nat. Bur. Stand. A 77 (1973) 6, p. 733.
[19] G. Dixon-Lewis: Combust. & Flame 36 (1979), p. 1.
[20] E. R. Larsen: ACS Organic Coatings and Plastics Chemistry Preprints 36 (1976) 2, p. 310.
[21] E. R. Larsen, R. B. Ludwig: J. Fire & Flammability 10 (1979), p. 69.
[22] J. J. Pitts, P. H. Scott, D. G. Powell: J. Cell. Plast. 6 (1970) 1, p. 35.
[23] H. S. Katz, J. V. Milewski (Eds.): Handbook of Fillers and Reinforcements for Plastics. Van
      Nostrand Reinhold Company, New York, 1978.
      H. H. Waddell, I. Touval: Antimony Oxide. Chap. 13.
      E. A. Woycheshin, I. Sobolev: Alumina Trihydrate. Chap. 14.
      J. V. Milewski, H. S. Katz: Miscellaneous Flame Retardants. Chap. 15.
[24] J. Eichhorn: J. Appl. Polym. Sci. 8 (1964), p. 2497.
[25] H. K. Jahn, J. W. Vanderhoff: J. Appl. Polym. Sci. 8 (1964), p. 2525.

[26] *E. V. Gouinlock, J. F. Porter, R. R. Hindersinn:* J. Fire & Flammability 2 (1971), p. 206.
[27] *J. W. Lyons:* J. Fire & Flammability (1970), p. 302.
[28] *A. Granzow:* Accounts of Chemical Research 11 (1978) 5, p. 177.
[29] *H. Hentschel:* Kunststoffe-Plastics 24 (1977) 7, p. 18.
[30] *I. Sobolev, E. A. Woycheshin:* JFF/Fire Retardant Chem. 1 (1974), p. 13.
[31] *J. Cowan, T. R. Manley:* The Brit. Polym. Journ. 8 (1976) 6, p. 44.
[32] *C. J. Hilado, W. C. Kuryla, R. W. McLaughlin, W. R. Proops:* J. Cell. Plastics 6 (1970), p. 215.
[33] *P. V. Bonsignore:* Plast. Engng., 32 (1976) 10, p. 41.
[34] *H. Piechota:* J. Cell. Plast., 1 (1965), p. 186.
[35] *H. Staendeke:* New Aspects of Phosphorus-Based Flame Retardants. 3rd European Conference on Flammability and Fire Retardants, Rome 28−29. 6. 1979.
[36] *E. N. Peters:* J. Appl. Polym. Sci., 24 (1979), p. 1457.
[37] *H. L. Vandersall:* J. Fire & Flammability 2 (1971), p. 97.
[38] *J. A. Ellard:* 165. ACS Meeting, Dallas, 1973.
[39] *D. G. Brady* et al.: J. Fire Retardant Chemistry 6 (1979), p. 150.
[40] *R. Reichherzer:* Kunststoffberat. Rdsch. Tech. 20 (1975), p. 18.
[41] *R. C. Kidder:* Plast. Engn. 33 (1977) 2, p. 38.
[42] *H. Jenkner:* Kunststoffe 62 (1972), p. 690.
[43] *R. S. Lindstrom* et al.: JFF/Fire Retardant Chem. 1 (1974), p. 152.
[44] *H. E. Stepniczka:* Kunststoff-Journal 10 (1976) 1−2, p. 12.
[45] *R. P. Levek,* in *R. B. Seymour* (Ed.): Additives for Plastics. Vol. 1. State of the Art. Academic Press, New York, 1978, p. 259.
[46] *H. Jenkner,* in *R. Gächter, H. Müller* (Eds.): Taschenbuch der Kunststoff-Additive. p. 387, Carl Hanser Verlag, München, 1979.
[47] *S. Salman, D. Klempner:* Plast. Engn. 35 (1979) 2, p. 39.
[48] *A. Hofmann:* Kunststoffe 61 (1971), p. 811.
[49] *J. A. Albright, C. J. Kmiec:* J. Appl. Polym. Sci. 22 (1978), p. 2451.
[50] *A. Granzow, C. Savides:* J. Appl. Polym. Sci. 25 (1980), p. 2195.
[51] *V. D. Rumyantsev* et al.: Plasticheskie Massy 3, (1977), p. 57; translated in: Int. Pol. Sci. Techn. 4 (1977) 7, T 103.
[52] *S. Miyata* et al.: J. Appl. Polym. Sci. 25 (1980), p. 415.
[53] *P. V. Bonsignore, P. L. Claassen:* J. Vinyl Technol. 2 (1980) 2, p. 114.
[54] *K. M. Bell* et al.: Kunststoffe 59 (1969), p. 272, p. 344, p. 419.
[55] *D. L. Buszard,* in: G.P.C.P., Les Plastiques et le Feu, Journées d'Etude, 24−26. 11. 1976, p. 133, Compagnie Française d'Editions, Paris, 1978.
[56] *L. S. Burn, K. G. Martin:* A Review of Combustion Characteristics of UPVC Formulations. Commonwealth Scientific and Industrial Research Organization (CSIRO), Division of Building Research, Highett, Victoria, Australia.
[57] *E. K. Moss, D. L. Skinner:* J. Cell. Plast. 13 (1977) 7/8, p. 276.

6 Smoke Development

In fire incidents, so-called "secondary fire effects" occur in conjunction with the actual combustion process. Primarily these include the development (i.e. production) of smoke and toxic gases. The level of smoke development depends on numerous factors such as the source of ignition, oxygen availability and the constitution and properties of the combustible material. Smoke poses a danger to human life, particularly in the initial phases of a fire, due to the loss of orientation caused by sight obscuration. This can lead to panic and irrational behaviour which make escape impossible with fatal results. Death rarely occurs as a direct consequence of the effects of smoke, i.e. due to the inhalation of smoke particles, but is generally due to the phenomena accompanying it such as toxic gases (mainly carbon monoxide), lack of oxygen and heat radiation.

Smoke also hinders the fire brigade frequently making it impossible to rescue victims and to locate and effectively fight the seat of the fire.

Smoke development is difficult to describe since it is not a material property and may be influenced by the various factors already listed. The following is an attempt to present the main points of this complex subject which has in fact only been approached in the last decade. The present account reflects the literature consulted and no claim is made as regards completeness.

The scale of smoke production from plastics and its reduction with smoke suppressants vary considerably depending on whether smouldering (pyrolysis) or flaming conditions pertain. The following statements refer mainly to the latter situation.

The rate of smoke emission is a further important parameter not considered here. The ability of people to escape depends on whether a room fills rapidly or slowly with smoke.

The opinion that only aromatics affect the level of smoke development is not necessarily true. For instance, the non-aromatic decomposition products of polyolefins can generate just as much or more smoke under certain conditions.

Finally, the data contained in the literature must be put in perspective since they have been obtained with the aid of test methods based on differing criteria. They are thus strictly only valid for the particular test conditions and do not enable conclusions to be drawn on the processes occurring in a real fire situation (this problem is dealt with in greater detail in Chap. 7).

6.1 Constitution of smoke

Smoke results from incomplete combustion. It is a dispersion of solid or liquid particles in a carrier gas consisting of combustion gases and air. The liquid particles are tar-like droplets or mists composed of liquid products of pyrolysis, or their partially oxidised derivatives, and water. The solids contain carbon flakes, soot beads, ash, sublimed pyrolysis products and oxides of inorganic compounds.

Smoke consists of a conglomerate of liquid and solid spherical aggregates varying in diameter from 0.002 to 0.5 μm depending on their previous history. The larger aggregates result from low temperature pyrolysis and have diameters ranging from 0.05 to 0.5 μm with an average of 0.1 μm. The aggregates formed at higher temperatures are ca. one tenth the size with diameters of 0.01 to 0.08 μm. These "primary particles" form conglomerates which may consist of a few large spheres or of several thousand small or minute spheres which agglomerate very rapidly. They generally reach diameters of approximately 0.6 to 1.1 μm although they can be as much as 10 μm in diameter. Particles larger than 0.05 μm are visible as smoke. Those around 1 μm impair visibility most. The particle sizes quoted here and given by various authors [1–10] provide only a limited description of smoke since little is known about the processes during combustion which lead to its formation. There is thus no generally accepted theory for the origin of smoke since, for example, it is extremely difficult to give details of sizes of primary particles.

6.2 Formation of smoke

As mentioned previously the formation of smoke depends on the incomplete combustion of the mixture of solid and liquid components resulting from pyrolysis. This consists mainly of aliphatic and aromatic components. Depending on the structure of the plastic from which they originate one of the components predominates. At low temperatures, combustion either does not take place or is severely limited. In this case the pyrolysis products frequently condense to fogs which are an important constituent of smoke. In the absence of sufficient oxygen, solid smoke constituents are formed at higher temperatures particularly in the form of soot in the flame zone. Several descriptions of the path of soot formation exist. One of the best known is that of *Lawson* and *Kay* [11] shown schematically in Fig. 6.1.

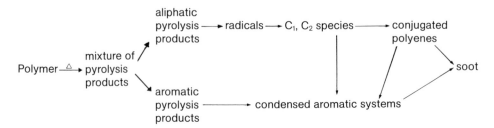

Fig. 6.1 Soot formation from aliphatic and aromatic pyrolysis products

Aliphatic pyrolysis products are split into radical fragments which, in the absence of oxygen, react to form conjugated polyenes or aromatic systems via short chain intermediates. By splitting off hydrogen and condensation they generate soot. The condensed aromatic systems are at present considered as the direct precursors of soot. Recent indications are that the conjugated polyenes which were also considered formerly as direct precursors of soot undergo cyclisation to aromatic systems which then contribute to soot formation [12]. Other theories due to *Seader* and *Chien* [5] and *Lahaye* and *Prado* [4] assume that acetylene is formed as an intermediate which gives rise to soot via polyacetylenes and polyaromatics (see also *Calcraft* et al. [13]).

Similar processes occur with aromatic pyrolysates which give rise to soot from poly-aromatics either directly [11] or via acetylene [5] or both [4]. The conversion of aromatic pyrolysis products to soot is almost quantitative. This is not the case with the aliphatic pyrolysates since the radicals generated may react in more diverse ways so that polyaromatics form only a fraction of the products. It has been demonstrated with premixed flames that benzene flames generate approximately 100 times more polyaromatics than those based on lower aliphatics [14].

According to *Lahaye* and *Prado* [4] the actual soot formation step occurs through condensation of polyaromatic species as a result of ionic or homogeneous nucleation. Fine droplets are formed and later carbonise. Homogeneous nucleation probably commences in the pyrolysis zone since practically no ionised species are present there. As a result of oversaturation, the polyaromatic species condense to fine droplets which act as condensation nuclei and can develop into very large particles by further accumulation of polyaromatics. Ionic nucleation occurs in the flame zone where significant concentrations of ions exist. Charge transfer from lighter ions such as CHO^+ and H_3O^+ to polyaromatics generates nuclei on which further non-ionised polyaromatics condense. The large number of ions provides a multitude of condensation nuclei which prevents excessive growth of individual particles.

Solid particles such as minute carbon particles or inorganic fillers can also act as soot-forming condensation nuclei. In addition to the soot particles, some hygroscopic fillers increase smoke density by triggering condensation of atmospheric water vapour.

Soot is therefore formed in a series of steps initiated by pyrolysis of the polymer to form gaseous decomposition products. The latter are then converted into varying amounts (depending on the substrate) of polycyclic aromatic systems. These soot precursors condense and at the lower temperatures present here can grow into very large tar- or soot-like agglomerates which escape into the surroundings provided they do not enter the flame zone. If they pass into the flame zone they are either entirely consumed or contribute to smoke formation as very small solid soot particles. These processes usually occur with polymers which break down predominantly to aromatic fragments. Polymers which pyrolyse mainly to aliphatic hydrocarbons are less likely to generate soot since their pyrolysis products react to form polycyclic aromatics, not in the pyrolysis zone but later in the vicinity of the flame zone. Their formation is, however, strongly impaired by competing combustion reactions which consume the major portion of the pyrolysis products. Relatively little soot consisting almost entirely of very small particles is thus formed. In this connection the reader is referred to the introductory remarks on smoke production from polyolefins; under certain conditions, high smoke intensities can occur even if only small amounts of soot are formed. Soot should be considered as only one factor in smoke development.

Smoke consists not only of liquid and solid carbon-containing components, such as tar and soot, but also of inorganic constituents such as water vapour and solids which originate, for example, from fillers. Smoke density is itself influenced by parameters such as the shape, size and concentration of smoke particles. It should not, however, be directly equated with obscuring of vision which is limited by a host of further variables such as light conditions, changes in the refractive index of air caused by heat shimmer, background contrast and eye irritation.

6.3 Smoke production from the most important plastics

As described in Section 4.2, the fire performance of plastics is not a material property. This is also true of the secondary effects of fire such as the production of smoke and toxic gases. Smoke development depends on many variables such as availability of oxygen, heat intensity, whether combustion involves flaming or smouldering, geometry of the finished component, etc. Nevertheless material properties and in particular chemical characteristics play an important role in determining smoke levels, hence the widespread efforts to solve this problem with smoke suppressants.

In order to determine the influence of the chemical structure of a plastic on smoke development, other variables are eliminated as far as possible by the use of standardised test methods (e.g., the NBS smoke chamber). This enables a comparative evaluation of the material to be made. Based on the knowledge gained by these tests it is then possible to develop systems specifically for suppressing smoke with some guarantee of effectiveness in real fire situations, i.e. in the presence of all other variables which influence smoke development.

The differing chemical structure of individual plastics results in the formation of decomposition products during pyrolysis which contribute in varying degrees to smoke development. As mentioned previously, the largest contribution is made by aromatics attaining the gas phase which are converted into condensed polyaromatic systems, the direct precursors of soot.

The amount of soot formed from pyrolysis products decreases roughly in the order

naphthalenes > benzenes > diolefins > monoolefins > paraffins.

Thermoplastics which decompose primarily to aromatics in the gas phase and thus give rise to large amounts of soot include polystyrene and its copolymers SAN and ABS; on pyrolysis these depolymerise to styrene monomers and oligomers.

On pyrolysis of PVC, hydrogen chloride is first eliminated from the polymer giving rise to unsaturated structures in the carbon chain. Some of these polyene sequences pass into the gas phase, where they dehydrogenate and cyclise to aromatics which contribute to soot formation. This effect is even greater in the case of plasticised PVC due to the presence of large amounts of aromatic plasticisers.

A wide variety of saturated and unsaturated hydrocarbons results from the pyrolysis of polyolefins due to statistical chain rupture. These products form only limited amounts of aromatics thus giving rise to less soot.

Thermoplastics such as polyacrylates and polyacetals make only a limited contribution to smoke production since, due to their oxygen content, they form almost exclusively oxygen-containing, non-aromatic decomposition products even under smouldering conditions. Polymethyl methacrylate pyrolyses to over 90% monomer which produces little smoke due to the oxygen content of the ester groups. Polyoxymethylene depolymerises almost quantitatively to formaldehyde which has an oxygen content of over 50% and burns almost without smoke.

Polyamides decompose by statistical chain scission to nitrogen-containing and oxygen-containing products which escape into the gas phase as ammonia, nitriles, amines, cyclic ketones and esters. Since practically no aromatics are formed, only small amounts of smoke are evolved.

Polyurethanes undergo depolycondensation to isocyanates and alcohols. Polyisocyanates, which cause strong smoke evolution, are formed in the pyrolysis zone. In polyisocyanurates the isocyanate is cross-linked to form isocyanurate rings and only escapes to the gas phase to a minor degree; consequently smoke development is greatly reduced.

The linear thermoplastic polyesters decompose by statistical chain rupture. In the case of polyethylene terephthalate and polybutylene terephthalate, the main products are aldehydes and terephthalic acid. The latter is responsible for the smoke generated. Pyrolysis of polycarbonate gives rise to smoke-generating aromatic fragments from the bisphenol A contained in it.

In contrast to thermoplastics, pyrolysis and combustion of thermosets results in minimal smoke development. This is due to the cross-linked structure of thermosets which renders them liable to char and liberate fewer decomposition products to the gas phase.

A few thermosetting plastics do tend, however, to develop smoke strongly since they contain aromatic structures which are liberated in the gas phase. These include, in particular, unsaturated polyester resins cross-linked with polystyrene bridges which evolve styrene as the decomposition product of statistical chain scission. This leads to smoke development with suspended soot flakes. Epoxy resins can also make a strong contribution to smoke development particularly if they are based on bisphenol A. Novolac-based epoxies have greater thermal stability and develop less smoke.

Phenolic resins have a lesser tendency to emit smoke since they char intensely and only small amounts of aromatics are liberated in the gas phase. They decompose by statistical chain rupture yielding mainly formaldehyde, phenol and other oxygen-containing fragments such as acetone and alcohols. Nitrogen-containing thermosets such as urea and melamine resins have a very strong tendency to char so that, particularly in the case of the latter, there is practically no smoke development.

High temperature resistant polymers consist mainly of rings and ring systems which retain their structure under the influence of heat and finally char to graphite-like networks. Only limited amounts of gaseous decomposition products are formed so that no significant smoke development occurs.

Among the high temperature resistant polymers, polyphenylene oxide has achieved the greatest practical importance. In order to improve processability, it is usually modified with polystyrene. Pure polyphenylene oxide pyrolyses to acetone, phenol and cross-linked structures. The gaseous aromatic structures generated give rise to soot which in the case of polystyrene modified grades occurs to a pronounced extent.

High temperature resistant polymers such as polyphenylene sulphide and polyethersulphones tend to char and consequently evolve little smoke. As semi-ladder polymers, the polyimides possess overwhelmingly cyclic structures and on decomposition form exclusively charred residues with practically no smoke emission.

Polyphosphazenes, which have an inorganic backbone contribute to smoke development in varying degrees depending on the structure of their organic side chains. In the case of certain aryloxy groups this can be considerable (see 4.2.4.2).

6.4 Smoke suppressants

Like the fire performance of plastics, smoke production is determined by numerous parameters. As a result, no comprehensive theory yet exists to describe the formation and constitution of smoke. Even research into the mode of action of smoke suppressants in plastics has not led to anything like a universally accepted theory on the physical and chemical processes involved. There are however various approaches to this topic which are briefly discussed below.

6.4.1 Mode of action

Smoke suppressants rarely act by influencing just one of the parameters determining smoke generation. Ferrocene, for example, is effective in suppressing smoke by oxidising soot in the gas phase as well as by pronounced charring of the substrate in the condensed phase. It is extremely difficult to split these multifunctional effects into primary and subsidiary actions since they are so closely interwoven. At present, therefore, no uniform theory on the mode of action of smoke suppressants has been established.

6.4.1.1 Condensed phase

Smoke suppressants can act physically or chemically in the condensed phase. Additives can act physically in a similar fashion to flame retardants, i.e. by coating (glassy coatings, intumescent foams) or dilution (addition of inert fillers) thus limiting the formation of pyrolysis products and hence of smoke. Chalk ($CaCO_3$), frequently used as a filler, acts in some cases not only physically as a dilutent but, also chemically, in PVC, for example, by absorbing hydrogen chloride or, in certain other cases, by effecting cross-linking so that the smoke density is reduced in various ways. The processes contributing to smoke suppression can be extremely complex.

Smoke emission may be reduced by chemical means in many ways. In thermosets, it can be reduced by structural measures, e.g. in the case of unsaturated polyesters, pronounced soot-forming aromatic cross-linkers, such as styrene, can be replaced by non-aromatic compounds like ethyl acetate [1].

Smoke can be suppressed by the formation of a charred layer on the surface of the substrate, e.g. by the use of organic phosphates in unsaturated polyester resins. In halogen-containing polymers, such as PVC, iron compounds cause charring by the formation of strong Lewis acids like iron (III) chloride.

Certain compounds such as ferrocene cause condensed phase oxidation reactions which are visible as a glow. There is pronounced evolution of CO and CO_2 so that less aromatic precursors are given off in the gas phase [15].

Compounds such as MoO_3 can reduce the formation of benzene during the thermal degradation of PVC, probably via chemisorption reactions in the condensed phase. Relatively stable benzene-MoO_3 complexes which suppress smoke development are formed [16].

6.4.1.2 Gas phase

Smoke suppressants can also act chemically and physically in the gas phase. The physical effect takes place mainly by shielding the substrate with heavy gases against thermal attack. They also dilute the smoke gases and reduce smoke density. In principle, two ways of suppressing smoke chemically in the gas phase exist, by eliminating either the soot precursors or the soot itself. Removal of soot precursors occurs by oxidation of the aromatic species with the help of transition metal complexes. Soot can also be destroyed oxidatively by high energy OH radicals formed by the catalytic action of metal oxides or hydroxides. Smoke suppression can also be achieved by eliminating the ionised nuclei necessary for forming soot with the aid of metal oxides. Finally soot particles can be made to flocculate by certain transition metal oxides.

A more detailed account of the mode of action of smoke suppressants in plastics is given in the following section. For practical reasons the examples given are those for which the effect of the particular smoke suppressant has been studied most intensively.

6.5 Smoke suppressants in plastics

Much work has been carried out over an extended period on how one can best use smoke suppressants to decrease the strong tendency of certain plastics such as PVC, polystyrene, polyurethanes and some unsaturated polyesters to generate smoke.

PVC has been particularly thoroughly researched, probably because its smoke development can be affected by intervention in both gas phase and condensed phase reactions.

Increasingly stringent fire performance requirements have to be met by plastics. In many cases this can only be achieved by incorporating flame retardants. If these act in the gas phase by interrupting the radical chain mechanism, they almost always contribute to an increase in smoke levels since they suppress the oxidation reactions occurring during combustion and promote soot formation. Flame retardants which are effective in the gas phase are used mainly in thermoplastics and cause dense smoke development even in those polymers which by themselves inherently emit relatively little smoke. The addition of smoke suppressants which are chemically active in the gas phase promotes the oxidation reactions and interferes somewhat with the flame retarding effect. Thus smoke suppressants act in the opposite direction to flame retardants by activating the combustion process. In order to solve this dilemma one can resort to physically acting smoke suppressants which function simultaneously as flame retardants. They suffer from the disadvantage, however, of limited effectiveness.

The way ahead lies with the development of a new generation of materials which act in the condensed phase by, for example, crosslinking or protecting the substrate as a coating. Such systems limit the formation of gaseous decomposition products and act simultaneously as flame retardants and smoke suppressants. They are of particular interest for those thermoplastics which normally do not char. These systems have been shown to be effective in practice by work on high impact polystyrene. Friedel-Crafts alkylation in the presence of Sb_2O_3-chlorine (Lewis acid precursor) leads to catalytic cross-linking and charring of the substrate below the combustion temperature [17].

In the following, the chemical modes of action of the best known smoke suppressants in some plastics, particularly PVC, are dealt with in further detail and the use of smoke suppressants in the most important polymers is reviewed. A compilation of the literature on smoke production from plastics is given by *Hilado* and *Kosola* [18]. *Lawson* and *Kay* [11] give information on the application of smoke suppressants in plastics and *Brauman* et al. [19] have investigated smoke development from various polymers.

6.5.1 Polyvinyl chloride

Polyvinyl chloride is the plastic for which the most research has been done with respect to smoke development and smoke suppression. Basically smoke evolution can be limited by reducing the formation of gaseous decomposition products or by chemically eliminating potential and actual components of smoke.

Smoke generated from the decomposition of polyvinyl chloride consists principally of soot particles formed from aromatic condensed systems. Another contributor is hydrogen chloride liberated during pyrolysis which can form a cloud of hydrochloric acid by reacting with atmospheric moisture. The evolution of hydrogen chloride can be reduced considerably by HCl absorbers such as $CaCO_3$ and $MgCO_3$.

Of the actual smoke suppressants, compounds that reduce the formation of soot, ferrocene and molybdenum trioxide are the best known and most thoroughly researched. In small ($<1\%$) concentrations ferrocene not only reduces the smoke density but also the combustibility of polyvinyl chloride. Its applications are limited by several disadvantages; it has a high vapour pressure, is yellow in colour and cannot be incorporated in plasticised PVC [20]. Ferrocene has been used for some considerable time as a smoke suppressant in fuels especially aviation spirit – an indication that it destroys soot particles in the gas phase.

When used in polyvinyl chloride, ferrocene probably initiates gas phase reactions which result in the formation of high energy radicals such as OH. These oxidise the soot particles to carbon monoxide according to:

$$C_{(solid)} + OH \longrightarrow CO + H \tag{1}$$

It is known that certain metal oxides (Ba, Sr, Ca) remove soot. It is assumed that they contribute to breakdown of molecular hydrogen and water vapour by gas phase catalysis in the zone where soot is formed as a combustion product according to:

$$MO + H_2 \longrightarrow MOH + H \tag{2}$$

$$MOH + H_2O \longrightarrow M(OH)_2 + H \tag{3}$$

$$M(OH)_2 + (X) \longrightarrow MO + H_2O + (X) \tag{4}$$

$$H + H_2O \longrightarrow OH + H_2 \tag{5}$$

High energy OH radicals are formed which oxidise the soot according to Eq. (1) [21]. There are several reasons for believing that this mechanism is also valid for transition metals and especially for oxidised species formed from ferrocene (e.g. α-Fe$_2$O$_3$) (see below).

Ferrocene and other metal compounds probably interfere with the nucleation reactions leading to soot by deactivating the ionised nucleating centres and the growth steps. Attack on the nucleation centres $C_nH_m{}^+$ can take place either by thermal or catalytic ionisation of the metal followed by deactivation of the nucleating centre or by direct reaction.

$$M^\circ \xrightarrow{\ \Delta \text{ or cat.}\ } M^+ + e^- \tag{6}$$

or for ferrocene:

$$Cp_2Fe \longrightarrow Cp_2Fe^+ + e^- \tag{6 a}$$

$$C_nH_m{}^+ + e^- \longrightarrow C_nH_m \tag{7}$$

The direct reaction procedes via:

$$M^\circ + C_nH_m{}^+ \longrightarrow C_nH_m + M^+ \tag{8}$$

Attack by ferrocene and other metal compounds can occur earlier in the combustion process if soot precursors, i.e. condensed aromatic systems, are eliminated by oxidation. This can occur by the conversion of ionic oxygen-containing spieces to OH radicals:

$$M^\circ + H_3O^+ \longrightarrow M^+ + H_2 + OH \tag{9}$$

$$\text{or } M^\circ \xrightarrow{\ \Delta\ } M^+ + e^- \tag{10}$$

$$H_3O^+ + e^- \longrightarrow H_2 + OH \tag{11}$$

Finally ferrocene and other transition metal complexes probably hinder the formation of benzene and aromatics in the pyrolysis phase.

Ferrocene and many other metal compounds act not only in the gas phase but, more importantly, in the condensed phase where they accelerate primarily dehydrochlorination and, simultaneously, cross-linking and charring reactions on the PVC surface.

Lawson [22] describes the formation of ferricenium ions from ferrocene in the condensed phase. This takes place in the presence of HCl and traces of oxygen

The ferricenium ion acts as a Lewis acid and catalyses dehydrochlorination, cross-linking and charring of PVC.

Lecomte et al. [23] assume that, in the presence of HCl and oxygen, ferrocene finally oxidises to α-Fe_2O_3 via ionic intermediates. They surmise that it is not ferrocene itself but its decomposition products which are the species active in suppressing benzene and smoke.

Descamps et al. [15] have described an additional secondary reaction which occurs when ferrocene and other metal compounds such as vanadium (V_2O_5) and copper (CuO) compounds are used. These compounds induce "chemical incandescence" and partially convert the decomposition products, generated during the pyrolysis of PVC, to carbon monoxide. The level of smoke emission is thus reduced.

The second most commonly used compound for reducing smoke production from PVC is molybdenum trioxide. In contrast to antimony trioxide which is effective mainly as a flame retardant in the gas phase, molybdenum trioxide acts as a weak flame retardant and as a smoke suppressant in the condensed phase. The oxychlorides which play a decisive role in the flame retardance of antimony trioxide are of little importance for the less reactive molybdenum trioxide and do not influence smoke emission. The mechanisms for reducing smoke density effect early dehydrochlorination in the condensed phase and reduction in the benzene content of the pyrolysis gases. Molybdenum trioxide acts as a Lewis acid and accelerates heterolysis of the C-Cl bond, accelerating the dehydrochlorination of PVC. Transpolyene segments which do not cyclise to benzene [24] are the main products. Limited catalysed cross-linking occurs simultaneously due to the metal oxide. *Lum* [16] suggests that a reduction in the evolution of benzene or toluene due to chemisorption processes with the formation of relatively stable π-aryl complexes with MoO_3 occurs.

Lattimer and *Kroenke* [25] express doubts on the "Lewis acid mechanism" and suggest a "reductive coupling" mechanism which could take place as follows:

$$R-Cl + Mo^n \longrightarrow \left[R-Mo^{n+2}-Cl\right] \xrightarrow{[R-Mo^{n+2}-Cl]} R-R' + 2Mo^{n+1}Cl \qquad (13)$$

A review of all the present theories on the mode of action of smoke suppressants in polyvinyl chloride has been given by *Fritz* during a seminar on fire performance and fire protection [7]. *Lawson* and *Kay* [11] give a review of the literature and patents covering smoke suppressants up to 1975. Besides ferrocene they mention other heavy metal compounds, cyanides and complex ferrocyanides, various oxides such as Fe_2O_3, V_2O_5, MoO_3 as well as oxidic Mg/Zn mixtures. The influence of metal oxides on the pyrolysis of PVC is described by *Lum* et al. [26] and *Ballistreri* et al. [27]. Reviews on the action of molybdenum trioxide are contained in various papers [28−32]. Compounds such as ammonium di- and octamolybdate and mixtures of MoO_3 with other oxides, e.g. NiO, Fe_2O_3, V_2O_5, Al_2O_3, etc. which act as powerful smoke suppressants are also mentioned. Aluminium hydroxide and zinc borate are further smoke suppressants described in the literature.

6.5.2 Styrene polymers

The aromatic fragments occurring as a result of the decomposition of polystyrene, which determine the amount of soot formed, can be limited by the addition of various smoke suppressants. According to *Deets* and *Lee* [33], when organic metallics like ferrocene or benzoyl ferrocene are used, smoke suppression is related to the amount of metal volatilised. Smoke suppression is achieved primarily by gas phase reactions. Iron acetonylacetonate liberates limited amounts of metal into the gas phase and is therefore of low effectiveness in polystyrene. In ABS, ferrocene and benzoyl ferrocene are ineffective but iron acetonylacetonate, in contrast, is highly effective. In this case smoke suppression mechanisms occur in the condensed phase.

Heavy metal salts (Fe, Mn, Cr) of 8-hydroxyquinoline, copper and lead phthalocyanines and radical initiators like tetraphenyl lead [11] attack the aromatics in the gas phase and contribute to smoke suppression. Of the inorganic compounds, magnesium hydroxide, aluminium hydroxide and/or zinc borate are effective smoke suppressants; magnesium carbonate, however, exhibits no significant effect.

6.5.3 Unsaturated polyester resins

Unsaturated polyester resins are usually cross-linked with short polystyrene bridges which cause high levels of smoke emission in fires. Smoke generation can be significantly reduced by structural measures; e.g. by replacing the polystyrene bridges with non-aromatic bridges based on ethylacrylate or methylmethacrylate [1]. Smoke density may also be limited by the use of certain dicarboxylic acids such as fumaric, maleic and succinic acids.

A further method is the addition of materials which effect pronounced charring of the substrate. Organic phosphates are preferred which dehydrate the substrate and as polyphosphoric acids form an inorganic/organic protective layer inhibiting smoke generation.

Iron compounds such as Fe_2O_3, which convert to iron (III) chloride during pyrolysis, and as strong Lewis acids ensure increased cross-linking, are frequently used in halogen-containing resin systems based on HET acid. Iron (III) chloride acts simultaneously as a Friedel-Crafts catalyst and enables coupling reactions between alicyclic chlorides (HET acid) and aromatic derivatives to take place. As a result, the aromatics are retained in the condensed phase and smoke development is inhibited [1].

Smoke suppression and simultaneous reduction in combustibility is achieved by the synergistic effect of MoO_3 and halogen-containing compounds such as dibromoneopentyl glycol [34]. Systems such as $MoO_3 + Sb_2O_3 + Al(OH)_3$ are incorporated in glass fibre reinforced polyester resins in order to reduce smoke emission. The green colour of MoO_3 due to surface reduction is a disadvantage which can be avoided by using ammonium molybdates [28].

Aluminium hydroxide, frequently used as a filler, cools the pyrolysis zone. Water escaping into the gas phase limits nucleation and agglomeration of the soot particles to large units; consequently smoke from aluminium hydroxide-modified polyester systems is white rather than black [1]. The use of magnesium hydroxide or zinc borate as smoke suppressants is also mentioned in the literature.

6.5.4 Polyurethane foams

An important method of reducing smoke emission from polyurethanes is to introduce structures with greater cross-linking into the polymer. This is achieved for example with isocyanurates, imides and carbodiimides. Such cross-linked structures contribute to pronounced charring of the substrate which is effective in smoke suppression. Solid dicarboxylic acids act similarly. Maleic acid, isophthalic acid, HET acid with phosphorus compounds and derivatives of aromatic carboxylic acids are used [35, 11].

Alcohols, and in particular furfuryl alcohol, have recently been described as effective smoke captors [36]. Smoke suppression is thought to occur by removal of polyisocyanates which cause thick smoke and are generated in the pyrolytic decomposition of urethane and isocyanurate compounds. The alcohol is oxidised to aldehyde which reacts with polyisocyanurate via a Schiff's base and further isocyanate to form a cross-linked structure which remains in the condensed phase.

Charring is also achieved by the addition of phosphorus compounds such as ammonium polyphosphate and countless phosphorus, phosphonium and phosphinic esters.

Compounds such as ferrocene, certain metal chelates and potassium or ammonium tetra-fluoroborate acting as Lewis acids in the condensed phase, also induce strong charring by catalytic processes.

Finally fillers like barium sulphate and aluminium hydroxide should not be forgotten.

6.5.5 Miscellaneous

Flame retardant *polyolefins* which tend to generate large amounts of smoke can be treated with fillers such as aluminium hydroxide or systems like molybdenum trioxide/zinc oxide. Ferrocene or nickelocene are occasionally used in non-flame retardant polyolefins.

Aluminium hydroxide is used with good results as a smoke suppressant in certain *polyaryl-oxyphosphazenes* [37].

References for Chapter 6

[1]   *J. E. Selley, P. W. Vaccarella:* Plast. Engn. 35 (1979) 2, p. 43.
[2]   *J. P. Stone, R. N. Hazlett, J. E. Johnson, H. W. Carhart:* J. Fire & Flammability 4 (1973), p. 42.
[3]   *K. Maries:* Measurement of Smoke; QMC Instruments Ltd., London, 1979.
[4]   *J. Lahaye, G. Prado,* in: G.P.C.P., Les Plastiques et le Feu, Journées d'Etude, 24−26. 11. 1976, Compagnie Française d'Editions, Paris, 1978, p. 85.
[5]   *J. D. Seader, W. P. Chien:* J. Fire & Flammability 6 (1975), p. 294.
[6]   *C. P. Bankston, E. A. Cassanova, E. A. Powell, B. T. Zinn:* J. Fire & Flammability 7 (1976), p. 165.
[7]   *J. A. Fritz:* Dégagements de Fumées. Comportement au Feu et Sécurité Incendie, C.E.M.P., Paris, 16−18. 5. 1978.
[8]   *C. P. Bankston, E. A. Powell, R. A. Cassanova, B. T. Zinn:* J. Fire & Flammability 8 (1977), p. 395.
[9]   *C. P. Fenimore, G. W. Jones:* Combustion & Flame 13 (1969), p. 303.
[10] *I. J. Jagoda, G. Prado, J. Lahaye:* Combustion & Flame 37 (1980), p. 261.
[11] *D. F. Lawson, E. L. Kay:* JFF/Fire Retardant Chem. 2 (1975), p. 132.
[12] *R. J. S. Green, J. Hume, S. Kumar:* Fire and Materials 1 (1976), p. 36.
[13] *A. M. Calcraft, R. J. S. Green, T. S. McRoberts:* Plast. & Polym. (1974), p. 200.
[14] *G. L. Nelson:* J. Fire & Flammability 5 (1974), p. 125.
[15] *J. M. Descamps, L. Delfosse, M. Lucquin:* Fire and Materials 4 (1980), p. 37.
[16] *R. M. Lum:* J. Appl. Polym. Sci. 23 (1979), p. 1247.
[17] *S. K. Brauman:* J. Polym. Sci. Chem. Ed. 17 (1979), p. 1129.
[18] *C. J. Hilado, K. L. Kosola:* J. Fire & Flammability 8 (1977), p. 532.
[19] *S. K. Brauman, N. Fishman, A. S. Brolly, D. L. Chamberlain:* J. Fire & Flammability 7 (1976), p. 41.
[20] *J. J. Kracklauer, C. J. Sparkes:* Plast. Engn. 30 (1974) 6, p. 57.
[21] *J. W. Hastie:* J. Res. Nat. Bur. Stand. 77 A (1973) 6, p. 733.
[22] *D. F. Lawson:* J. Appl. Polym. Sci. 20 (1976), p. 2183.
[23] *L. Lecomte, M. Bert, A. Michel, A. Guyot:* J. Macromol. Sci.-Chem. A 11 (1977)8, p. 1467.
[24] *W. H. Starns, D. Edelson:* Macromolecules 12 (1979) 5, p. 797.
[25] *R. P. Lattimer, W. J. Kroenke:* The Functional Role of Molybdenum Trioxide as a Smoke-retardant Additive in Rigid PVC. Third International Symposium on PVC, Cleveland, USA, 10−15. 8. 1980.
[26] *R. M. Lum* et al.: Effects of Metal Oxide Additives on the Precombustion Pyrolysis Chemistry of Plasticized PVC. Third International Symposium on PVC, Cleveland, USA. 10−15. 8. 1980.

[27] A. Ballistreri et al.: J. Polym. Sci. Chem. Ed., 18 (1980), p. 3101.
[28] D. A. Church, F. W. Moore: Plast. Engn. 31 (1975) 12, p. 36.
[29] F. W. Moore, G. A. Tsigdinos: The Role of Molybdenum in Flame Retardancy and Smoke Retardation. Proceedings of the Climax 2nd Intern. Conf. on the Chemistry and Uses of Molybdenum, New College, Oxford, England, Sep. 1976.
[30] F. W. Moore: Evaluation of Molybdenum Compounds as Smoke Suppressants for Rigid PVC Formulations. Published by Climax Molybdenum Company of Michigan, L-309-13, 1977.
[31] Y. Uegaki, T. Nakagawa: J. Appl. Polym. Sci. 21 (1977), p. 965.
[32] D. Edelson et al.: Combustion & Flame 38 (1980), p. 271.
[33] G. L. Deets, Y. C. Lee: J. Fire & Flammability 10 (1979), p. 41.
[34] G. A. Skinner et al.: Fire and Materials 1 (1976), p. 154.
[35] H. P. Doerge, M. Wismer: J. Cell. Plast. 8 (1972), p. 311.
[36] K. Ashida, M. Ohtani, T. Yokoyama, S. Ohkubo: J. Cell. Plast. 14 (1978), p. 200 and p. 256.
[37] E. J. Quinn, R. L. Dieck: J. Cell. Plast. 13 (1977), p. 96.

7   Methodology of Fire Testing

7.1 Assessment of the fire hazard

Uncontrolled fire is a danger to life and property. A prime cause of this fire hazard is the use of natural and synthetic flammable materials in buildings and vehicles. Materials, semi-finished and finished components are put to use in many ways as furnishings and as integral parts of buildings such as coverings of walls and ceilings, roofing and piping. Uses of such materials in vehicles include seats and upholstery. Different applications have different fire hazards, which although they cannot be eliminated altogether can be reduced to an acceptable level. This "acceptable level" depends on the prevailing fire philosophy and varies considerably from country to country.

Earlier assessments of the fire hazard were largely based on a combination of intuition, guesswork and experience but nowadays attempts are made to approach this problem rationally by determining which parameters affect the fire and characterising them quantitatively. Even such a rational study of the hazard is far removed from allowing a reliable prediction of the potential fire situation because the premises required to include all the determining parameters and their interactions are lacking. Indeed, such a full quantitative description is unlikely to be possible even in the future.

For a given product the hazards in different areas of application (e.g. building, transport, electrical industry, mining, furnishing and textiles) are so different that information cannot be directly transferred from one to another. Even within one area there is little correlation: the fire risk of a motor boat cannot be compared with that of a 300,000 ton supertanker.

Fire hazard can be estimated more precisely and measures taken to reduce it only if the experience already gained with measurement and quantification of fire determining parameters is considered.

In order to include such parameters the course of a fire must be more exactly characterised. As has already been described in Chapter 3, a fire can be divided into three phases: the initiating fire, the fully developed fire and the decaying fire. It is known from experience that plastics, like all other combustible materials, always burn in a fully developed fire and do not make any significant contribution to fire resistance. Thus in estimating the fire hazard only the early stages of combustion up to the flash-over point need to be considered. This phase is composed of several parts: ignition, flame spread, heat release and flash-over; alongside this, various side effects occur such as smoke and toxicity and corrosivity of fire gases.

These phenomena are accompanied by an almost infinite number of parameters which influence each other and make up the totality of the fire. These include the type, duration and intensity of the ignition source, the ventilation and the type, form and properties of the combustible material (see Chapter 3). As it is impossible to measure all the variables in such a complex system, the important parameters must be separated from the unimportant parameters. This is usually achieved by standardised laboratory tests. However, most of these have the disadvantage that they do not allow predictions to be made about an actual fire. Because of this there are other types of test (finished component tests, model fire tests etc.) which are used to try to obtain more realistic measurements of certain parameters. Fire test methods and associated problems will be dealt with in more detail in later sections. Details of fire hazard assessment are given in references [1−13].

7.2 Historical development of fire testing

Awareness of the high potential fire hazard in towns of predominantly wooden buildings led people to carry out ad-hoc fire trials to ascertain the combustibility and hence the fire resistance of buildings. Some of the earliest investigations were made about 1790 in England; one hundred years later in England and the USA building structures were tested for fire resistance by subjecting them to wood fires. The present day test procedure for the determination of the fire resistance of building components has developed from this by a process of standardisation. In the development of standards from ad-hoc investigations the original 1:1 scale has frequently been reduced to a laboratory scale with precisely specified test conditions. For example:

- The present "Spread of Flame" test for building materials in Great Britain, described in BS 476: Part 7, was developed at the beginning of the 1940's with the intention of simulating a fire in a corridor. The specimen is positioned vertically with the longitudinal axes horizontal and simulates the wall of a corridor, while the radiant panel represents a fire at the end of the corridor (for details see Section 8.2.5. A slightly modified form of this test is also used in the Netherlands and in New Zealand).
- Around 1940 *Steiner* developed the Tunnel Test (ASTM E 84; see 'USA' in Section 8.2.14) in order to ascertain the hazard of fire spreading along a wall or ceiling in a room or a corridor. It was known from experience that in many fires participation of cladding decidedly influenced the course of the fire. This led to the development of the 'corridor model' on a reduced scale in which the specimen represents the ceiling covering which is flamed from below at one end.

From "open" tests which were normally performed out-of-doors, there was a move to "closed", scaled-down and standardised test procedures in the laboratory. "Closed" investigations have the advantage that inter alia they take account of the heat which is developed in the course of the fire and which here preheats the material through the "feedback effect" rather than escaping into the environment. This feedback has a decisive influence on the course of the fire.

All ad-hoc investigations and the standardised fire test procedures developed from them were established to examine natural materials such as wood and other cellulose-based materials. For example, in Germany in the 1930's and during the Second World War, test procedures were developed to investigate the fire performance of wood and wood-based materials for the building industry. One of the main reasons for this was to develop appropriate protection for wood against fire bombs (the first version of DIN 4102 – Fire performance of building materials and building components – dates from 1934).

A completely new situation arose after the war with the advent of plastics. Test procedures which had been developed for wood were applied to the new materials but it was often found that the test results no longer enabled reliable predictions to be made. For example thermoplastics and foams can withdraw from the flame by melting, dripping and shrinking. Because of this no empirical correlation existed with an actual fire and hence with the consequent hazard assessment.

In order to counter this uncertainty numerous ad-hoc tests, model fire tests and laboratory test procedures were developed and introduced alongside the classical fire tests. Using these approaches it was intended to build up experience on the fire performance of these materials. Many simple, cheap laboratory methods were developed principally to test the properties of plastics and to screen materials during product development or for quality control. These tests are only intended to compare materials with one another and do not possess any correlation to actual fires. Because of their easy implementation, such tests are widely used and have been introduced as standardised procedures especially in the USA as ASTM, NFPA and Underwriters' Laboratories standards.

7.3 Terminology

Materials tested according to the above standards were classified by such terms as "self-extinguishing" and "difficult to burn". These technical terms are only really defined when they are given together with the test method, e.g. "self-extinguishing to ASTM D 1692". However, in practice, the significance and necessity of this is frequently not recognised. If the test procedure is not specified, the term is devalued and the impression is given, for example, that a self-extinguishing material would under all circumstances extinguish itself, thereby implying a non-existent null risk with possible serious consequences. Even more dangerous is the widespread use of markings which are not based on any test procedure such as "flame-proof", "non-burning", "fire-proof", etc.

This confused situation was suddenly recognised in 1974 when the US Federal Trade Commission banned the use of markings such as "non-burning" or "self-extinguishing" in connection with foam plastics. A terminology began to be considered which was related to real fires and to the hazards connected with them. Since then the hazard has been empha-sised rather than the safety aspects. Tests are used to establish to what extent a particular product poses a fire hazard.

The test results should be given in a non-subjective manner by number and/or letter combinations. In this way one has the guarantee that such markings will not lead to a false judgement of the fire hazard. A list of subjective and objective markings is given in Table 7.1.

Table 7.1 Subjective and objective fire protection terms

Subjective markings Deprecated	Objective markings Allowed
fire-proof	combustibility
flame-proof	flammability
flame-resistant	ignitability
non-ignitable	flame
low combustibility	flame spread
low flammability	glowing combustion
self-extinguishing	incandescence
non-burnable	heat release

The terms "low combustibility" and "low flammability" can be used in conjunction with a standard identification, e.g. "low flammability to DIN 4102 Part 1", or "low combustibility to TGL 10685/11". However, it is better to use formal markings such as number and letter combinations; e.g.

– Class B1 to DIN 4102 Part 1,
– Class M.3 to NF P 92-501,
– Class 2 to BS 476: Part 7.

This confusion in fire terminology is increased by the use of different expressions for example in commerce, by science and administration and in the building, electrical, transport and mining industries. Such problems of terminology occur in many countries and almost impossible difficulties exist in translating such terms from one language into another. In order to resolve these problems the ISO has set up a working party as a subcommittee of the Coordinating Committee for Fire Tests (CCFT). This has already started to coordinate terminology in the field of fire protection. The terminology which emerges will be published as a new edition of ISO 3261 [14] or as a completely new ISO standard. In the Federal Republic of Germany a standard is being developed by the Materials Testing Standards Committee (NMP) in DIN based on the terminology worked out by ISO-CCFT.

The most important terms used in this book are collated in Section 10.3 of the Appendix. For further details on terminology, references [1−3] and [6] may be consulted.

7.4 Test methods for assessing the fire hazard

Fire test procedures are usually carried out to comply with specific regulations or voluntary agreements. Alongside these, however, there are tests which do not in principle simulate a fire situation but only compare, for example, the combustibility of certain materials under fixed conditions. Such tests are applied as screening tests for materials during product development or for quality control. They are usually simple in conception, easily carried out, reproducible and low cost. They seldom, if ever, give trustworthy information about the behaviour of a material in an actual fire. Tests intended for product development and quality control are only given in Chapter 8 of this book if they are an integral part of the regulations, e.g. the oxygen index test in the Norwegian building regulations.

In developing relevant test methods for application by the authorities and other organisations the following points should be noted:

– *Environmental test conditions:* the test environment should be able to be varied, e.g. by altering the orientation of the test specimen to simulate several fire situations.
– *Ability to test finished parts:* the material should be tested in its finished form, that is in the form in which it will later be used.
– *Reproducibility:* the scatter of the results should be sufficiently narrow that a choice of material is possible.
– *Ease of operation:* the test method should be capable of being carried out by a trained person in an acceptable time (ca. 1 hour).
– *Cost:* the test must be economical.

These requirements arise from the aim of being able to describe a real fire and all its parameters quantitatively and thus obtain simultaneously measurements of as many of these parameters as possible. Or, put in another way, we would like the advantages of a precisely specified test which measures some material property and correlates with the results of a full scale test. The numerous tests are naturally far removed from this ideal and all contain more or less satisfactory compromises.

The multiplicity of existing fire test methods can be seen if they are arranged systematically according to the individual steps of the initiating fire (the time following flash-over is not considered here). In a scheme developed by *Seekamp* and *Becker* [15] the individual steps are associated with each other both spatially and temporaly. The different fire test methods can be fitted into this scheme if the time up to flash-over is divided roughly into three periods: about 1 minute, several minutes and ¼ hour, the first being the instant of ignition and the last the time at which the flash-over occurs. The spatial components, that is to say the observed phenomena of ignition, a transition region, flame spread and finally a transition to the point where fire gains the upper hand, can be fitted to these three periods. Arranged in this way the fire test methods are distributed fairly evenly over the scheme. In both spatial and temporal terms they describe point events which differ from each other and, in spite of identical aims such as determination of combustibility, ignitability or flame spread, they do not give any consistent results.

This is certainly the reason for the disappointing results obtained in a joint investigation carried out in the mid 1960's by seven laboratories with 24 materials under the auspices of Working Group (WG) 4 of ISO/TC 92. When the materials were investigated and classified according to the different national fire test methods, it was found that there was scarcely any correlation between the tests and none at all between the different laboratories.

This lack of correlation was clearly demonstrated by *Emmons* [16]. He replaced the test results obtained in the joint investigation by results obtained by a random selection of numbered cards from a box. The results obtained in this way differed from those obtained in the joint investigation only in having a somewhat higher scatter.

Because of these poor results it was decided by ISO/TC 92 not to adopt any of the existing intuitive and/or empirical fire test methods but to develop simple, basic tests which concentrate on one of the parameters determining the course of the initiating fire.

7.4.1 Laboratory-scale tests

Systematic investigations of the events in the initiating fire have established the parameters which form the basis for estimating the hazard in this phase of the fire. The resulting relatively simple fundamental tests conceived by ISO/TC 92 are now in an advanced stage of development. These "reaction to fire" tests allow an estimation of the parameters:

– combustibility
– ignitability
– flame spread
– heat release.

Reaction to fire tests ascertain whether materials take part in a fire, their contribution to flame spread and their tendency to propagate and expand the fire by altering the thermal environment (preheating).

According to the ISO concept, the phenomena accompanying the fire (smoke development and toxicity of the fire gases), which can also be arranged according to "reaction to fire", are not to be equated with the parameters mentioned above as they are not independent quantities but depend on the extent to which a material contributes to the fire. They can be described by their relationship to flame spread [5].

The individual "reaction to fire" parameters are discussed below in relation to the new viewpoint of ISO/TC 92 as represented in [5]. Details of the test rigs and the reasons for them are given in Chapter 8. An exact description of the ISO "reaction to fire" tests follows in 8.2.18.

The test methods which were, and often still are, called "non-combustibility" tests should be designated "*combustibility* tests" since the latter emphasizes the danger of combustion and not the deceptive safety of non-combustibility. These test methods permit the differentiation of combustible (mostly organic) and non-combustible (mostly inorganic) materials. Even so this does not mean that all materials which are considered inorganic are non-combustible. For example, mineral fibre mats may contain small amounts of synthetic resin binders and may not pass a particular test.

Ignition of a material can occur either by convection or irradiation without the influence of a flame (*ignitability*) or by the direct effect of a flame (flammability). Whether and when a material can be ignited depends on whether a flame is present and on radiation intensities. Using a suitable test method it is possible to simulate the propensity of a material to ignite during various stages of the initiating fire up to flash-over. One can thus determine whether or not the material can cause a fire when exposed only to a low intensity ignition source without radiation being applied, or whether it causes the fire to develop to flash-over under high radiation intensities.

Different *flame spread* tests put different demands on the fire performance of the product to be tested. In the simplest case a low intensity flame impinges on the material. Far higher demands are made if, in addition to the ignition source, a heat source reinforces the flame spread. A test of this type can be seen as a special case of a procedure for igniting a material since the radiation intensity at which the flame front does not advance any further is obtained. This point thus corresponds to the radiation intensity necessary for igniting the material which could be determined with one test. In the case of the above ignitability tests a series of investigations at different radiation intensities would be necessary. Some flame spread tests are even more rigorous: they enable the effects of convection and radiation from the flame itself to be taken into account by suitable equipment design. The resulting feedback increases the rate of flame spread.

The *heat release* of a material in a fire situation is the heat liberated by the actual material burned and must not be confused with the calorific potential which describes the quantity of heat which can theoretically be liberated. The rate at which heat is liberated from a product is especially important because of its influence on the initiating fire. Determination of the quantity of heat evolved per unit time allows an estimation of the potential hazard posed by a product: if the rate of heat release is small the fire spread can be influenced but if it is large this is no longer possible as flash-over is quickly reached.

The parameters discussed above occur in chronological order in a fire and are cumulative. In the case of flame spread this means that ignition has already taken place and that a high rate of heat release will lead to a high rate of flame spread. Consequently the test methods for measuring the above parameters make ever increasing demands on the product to be tested.

The secondary fire effects, smoke and toxic fire gases, occur alongside these phenomena, particularly as the rate of spread of flame increases. Together with radiant heat and lack of oxygen they represent the greatest danger to people.

To ascertain the smoke hazard, test methods have been developed which try to simulate the effect of smoke on human vision. These tests are based on highly simplified assumptions and must, if possible, be modified and optimised to a realistic simulation. A full account of the current test methods is given in 9.2.

The development of test methods for estimating the hazard of toxic fire gases is in its infancy. ISO has published a technical report [17] proposing to assess the hazard either by chemical analysis of the fire gases or by their effect on biological systems; the second method is preferred. Two procedures are recommended:

– firstly, identification of the materials which cause an unusually high toxic environment;
– secondly, development of a standard for classifying all commonly used materials with respect to the relative degree of toxicity which they create.

Of the two possible ways of measuring the toxicity of fire gases, the analytical method is considered less desirable because it, inter alia, does not consider the combined effect of several individual components and because a component can show biological activity when present in extraordinarily small (sometimes immeasurably small) amounts. Biological methods enable the total effect of the decomposition gases on the biological system to be investigated and a more realistic estimation of the hazard arising from toxic fire gases to be made.

The laboratory test procedures which describe the "reaction to fire parameters" are frequently termed second generation tests, since they are no longer empirically based but describe independent fire determining processes on a scientific basis. These views are, however, not accepted universally; it has been speculated that there may be more fundamental independent parameters yet to be defined [18].

Regardless of how these laboratory test methods are viewed there is no doubt that laboratory scale fires cannot be extrapolated to characterise a true fire satisfactorily. They can only represent a general trend since the environmental effects (ventilation, heat, geometry, etc.) cannot be quantitatively included simultaneously in specified test conditions. In order to take account of these influences, additional full scale tests must be carried out to allow more realistic assessment of the hazard.

7.4.2 Large-scale tests

In the following discussion the term "large-scale test" is used to denote 1:1 scale tests carried out under conditions which approximate as nearly as possible to reality either in the open air or inside buildings. Such tests are often described as full scale model fire tests. Thus whole buildings or vehicles (or at least the essential parts of them such as a furnished room or the compartment of a train) are tested. Finished parts such as sockets or chairs which can be tested in the laboratory on a 1:1 scale are not considered as they are only single components and not essential parts of the building or vehicle.

Originally large-scale tests were carried out exclusively in an ad-hoc manner to obtain information not already available on the fire performance of a material or finished part under normal operating conditions. Ad-hoc tests are methods which try to simulate a real fire without laying down exact conditions. A typical ad-hoc procedure would be the application of a flame to a material with a match to see if it burns.

According to *Malhotra* [19], ad-hoc tests can be separated into realistic and partially realistic categories. In the first group, design, ignition source, fire load and fire development closely simulate real conditions. In the second group, certain parameters such as fire load, ventilation or the testing of only certain components in a system are specified. The latter should preferably be called "large-scale tests" for the improvisational aspect characteristic of ad-hoc tests is lost by the partial fixing of the experimental conditions.

Large-scale tests are carried out to determine the fire performance of materials and finished parts under more or less normal operating conditions. This is especially necessary for new products for which results obtained in the laboratory must be confirmed in practical application. Such investigations are necessary both for the use of new materials (e.g. a new plastic) in known applications and for new materials introduced into new types of application (e.g. inflatable roofs, wide-bodied jets). Conversely, large-scale tests can indicate if an existing laboratory method is suitable for testing a given material or not. Many laboratory methods had to be altered, extended or developed completely anew after the war due to the increased usage of plastics rather than wood. These changes were based on experience gained from large-scale tests and actual fire incidents.

Large-scale tests for the assessment of the fire hazard of materials are especially important in the fields of building, transport and mining.

In the building field numerous full scale investigations under working conditions have been reported. A literature survey up to 1975 is given in [20], and up to 1978 in [21]. A survey on the topic of building, seen from the American point of view, is given in [22].

Primarily the fire hazard arising from combustible building components such as wall and ceiling coverings and insulation, roofs, windows, floor coverings, air ducts, cable ducts and pipes was investigated (newer German literature can be consulted in [23–26]). Extensive investigations were also made involving combustible goods in warehouses [27] and furnishings and fittings in dwelling houses (see also 8.6).

In the field of transport, large-scale tests have been carried out on aircraft, ships and road and rail vehicles. Here there are often special hazards which can only be described and estimated adequately by such tests. For aircraft three possible fire accident types (on the ground, during the flight and after a crash) must be considered and simulated. For rail vehicles, e.g. underground trains, special hazards like fire during passage through a tunnel must be considered. This topic is fully covered for air travel and road and rail vehicles in [28] and [29]. For further details on the subject of transport, see under 8.3.

Large-scale tests are also carried out in other fields such as electrical engineering and mining. For example, the fire hazards of cables for use in atomic power stations are investigated in conditions close to reality. In mining, underground conditions are simulated and the fire performance of materials and finished parts are tested under working conditions in fire galleries or shafts.

From time to time large-scale tests can be carried out in the open air on complete objects such as dwelling houses and aircraft or on parts of them such as furnished rooms or sections of aircraft cabins (with one or more rows of seats) in fire test houses. Despite the advantages of a large-scale test on the complete object, the enormous costs and massive expenditure of time weigh against such methods. Because of this there are natural limits set on the size of the objects to be investigated: on economic grounds alone one would not set fire to a complete tower block or a large passenger jet; the information obtained would in no way justify the expenditure.

An especially satisfactory information/expenditure ratio is achieved with the "compartment size" test. A compartment is defined as a closed spatial element in which a fire develops and in which flash-over occurs. This closely mirrors the true relationships, for the initiating fire phase always takes place in such a compartment and people spend much of their time in such compartments (e.g. in a room of a building, inside a car, in a ship's cabin or in a train compartment). Large compartments like the cabin of a wide-bodied jet or a large office are not included in the definition as the likelihood of flash-over occurring is small.

"Compartment size" investigations allow the determination of variables similar to those in a laboratory test but without completely losing the relationship to actual fire conditions.

In the USA, in particular, there has been intensive development of compartment fire experiments leading to the publication in 1977 of ASTM E 603-77 [30] relating to the building field. Recommendations are given for carrying out the tests and evaluating the results; numerous observations are made about the optimum room size and the form, type and arrangement of the test specimen, and of the ignition source as well as on methods of obtaining measurements, safety precautions and suitable test conditions. Finally ways of analysing the data (by comparing heat flow, temperature and smoke development with such parameters as ignitability, flame spread and heat release which are determined on a laboratory scale) and of drawing conclusions from the results are given.

In addition to the large-scale tests described above, investigations are also made on a 1:1 scale in which only one type of material or finished part is tested. Such tests have the advantage that they are less expensive and more cost-effective; at the same time they allow certain parameters which constitute a special fire hazard to be more exactly described.

Examples of such test methods are the "corner tests" which are often used in the USA for assessing the fire hazard of linings. Here the ignition source is situated in the corner of the room; this arrangement puts the greatest demands on the material being tested.

Corner tests are applied by Insurance Companies (e.g. Factory Mutual) for estimating the fire hazards of certain materials like foams, in order to determine the size of the premium.

Further part-tests exist, e.g. in the measurement of the fire hazard of rows of seats which are intended for use in passenger aircraft. In the construction field, fire tests are carried out on building elements in various countries. In France outer façades are evaluated on a test stand [25] and in the GDR building elements, such as inner and outer wall claddings, roof coverings, floors etc. are tested in the open air or in a fire room (see 8.2.10).

7.4.3 Correlation of test methods

One of the aims in fire protection is to obtain a correlation between the test results and the actual course of a fire so that the fire hazard can be properly estimated. In general it has been found that the laboratory and pilot scale methods contained in the regulations allow a certain correlation with large-scale tests and with actual fire incidents. Numerous investigations have indicated that materials which satisfy the highest demands according to certain tests (e.g. the German Brandschacht test and the American tunnel test) usually do not contribute to fire spread and fire propagation in large-scale investigations. However, hazards cannot be reliably assessed on the basis of laboratory tests or even large-scale tests since, even in these, the fire situation is only partially reproduced under the given experimental conditions. Experience gained under actual fire conditions must be included as well.

Besides correlating laboratory tests to large-scale tests and then to real life fires (scale-up), it is also useful to apply the reverse procedure. Starting with the real situation, physical models for large-scale tests can be made and then by scaling down, retaining the important chemical and thermodynamic properties and the geometry of the system, a correlation with a laboratory test may be sought. In practice this latter method is used because of financial and time limitations; thus compartment size tests are replaced by geometrically identical, scaled down laboratory versions. Similarly, scaled down corner tests are used for testing only a part of the system for screening materials.

Even today fire hazard assessment is usually based on procedures which arose intuitively and empirically without knowledge of the parameters which influence the course of the fire. Systematic investigations of such parameters are now being made (ISO). These parameters must not be regarded, however, as isolated events or else the fire will be even less well described than by the empirical, intuitive methods. As shown in the following discussion, work is already in progress which no longer regards the events in a fire as isolated, point occurrences but describes the fire as a complete system dynamically and with reference to fundamental parameters and empirical knowledge.

7.5 Fire dynamics and fire scenarios

In order to make meaningful statements on real fires, it is necessary to quantify all the events occurring in a fire. This is not within our ability and it is therefore impossible to develop a universal test method which considers and measures all fire-determining parameters including all the interaction effects. However, especially in the USA, attempts are beginning to be made to research the course of the fire quantitatively using "fire dynamics". Alongside this, investigations are being made using "fire scenarios", in which representative fires are modelled to estimate the fire hazard for the entire system, including people, and not just the hazard arising from the materials alone.

In these methods specifically causal and thus linear thinking is put aside and the complete fire system, with interaction effects, is discussed by linking individual parameters and neglecting irrelevant details. In other words the combination of the magnitudes of the various influences in systems is sought (by "interrelated thinking") rather than studying the magnitudes of the individual influences in isolation (by "linear thinking"). This new mode of thinking is thoroughly described by *Vester* [31]. In the USA such programs have been initiated at for example the Center for Fire Research of the NBS [32] and by the Factory Mutual Research Corporation.

In the USA the term "fire dynamics" is taken to mean the quantitative, scientific description of the phenomena which occur in a fire. In order to approximate to this ideal the following four approaches are used [13] (Chapter 6):

- *Fundamental research:* here the fundamental parameters which constitute the physical and chemical features of combustion are established and quantified. Thus the kinetics of pyrolysis and of combustion reactions, and the transfer of combustion energy by conduction, convection and radiation are studied. These topics are essentially of academic interest but form the bases for the study of fire dynamics.
- *Individual fire events:* here the fire is resolved into a series of topics which are analysed individually. These topics are ignition, flame spread on the surface of a solid body, rate of burning, formation of toxic species, formation of aerosols in a diffusion flame, heat release and extinction by heat loss, lack of oxygen and chemical inhibition.
- *Interaction of parameters:* using fire dynamics attempts are made to describe the interaction of the parameters or of the individual events in a fire. Examples are: the influence of feedback of heat radiation and of the ventilation on the rate of burning, the mutual influence of two burning materials, and the influence of heat radiation on the later fire performance of a material.
- *Interaction between fire and people:* the first three parts of the systematic approach are concerned exclusively with the course of the fire itself and the materials exposed to the fire. The most important influence, however, is that of fire on people and involves problems such as: sight obscuration by smoke or by lacrimatory gases, panic caused by fire phenomena, burns caused by clothes or falling burning debris and the appearance of toxic decomposition products. This final part of the systematic approach is only mentioned for the sake of completeness as the behaviour of people in fires lies outside the scope of this book.

Further details on fire dynamics are contained in [13] (Chapter 6) and [33] (Chapter 3).

The term "fire scenario" means a generalised but detailed description of a fire incident. It must contain the steps which determine the course of the fire such as ignition source, first material ignited, type of propagation, time to flash-over, and the methods of control and extinguishing of the fire. Fire scenario studies can be developed in four different ways (see [33], Chapter 4):

- By an exact representation of a fire incident; this is however impossible as data for all aspects of a real fire are not available.
- By synthesising elements of different fires into a meaningful whole. This method is frequently applied by seeking out fire statistics of significant events and assembling them into a case study.
- By modelling a realistic initiating fire on the basis of fire dynamics (a model means a theoretical or physical analogue of a complex fire system).
- By carrying out realistic 1:1 scale investigations which enable the parameters effecting the fire propagation to be measured.

Fire scenarios can be set up on the basis of these methods and then analysed. Further details about the development and analysis of fire scenarios and their application in specific areas such as building and transport can be found in [33] (Chaps. 5–7).

References for Chapter 7

[1]   *J. M. Kingsland, C. Meredith:* Fire Tests and Fire Hazards. National Technical Conference "Safety & Health with Plastics", Society of Plastics Engineers, 8–10. 11. 1977, Denver, USA, p. 77.

[2]   DD 64: 1979. Draft for Development: Guidelines for the Development and Presentation of Fire Tests and for their Use in Hazard Assessment. British Standards Institution.

[3]   SAA MP 32 – 1977. SAA Guide for the Presentation, Preparation and Application of Fire Tests. Standards Association of Australia.

[4]   ISO Technical Report 3814 – 1975. The Development of Tests Measuring "Reaction to Fire" of Building Materials.

[5]   ISO Technical Report 6585 – 1979. Fire Hazard and the Design and Use of Fire Tests.

[6]   *W. Becker:* DIN-Mitt. 57 (1978) 10, p. 582.

[7]   *H. W. Schiffer:* Chemie-Technik 8 (1979) 9, p. 425.

[8]   *F. H. Prager:* Kunststoffe im Bau 13 (1978) 2, p. 45.

[9]   *J. Troitzsch:* Maschinenschaden 52 (1979) 6, p. 216.

[10] *L. Amy:* Matières Plastiques et Feu; l'Incendie. Commission Feu et Environnement, SFMP (Ed.), 1971.

[11] Norme Expérimentale X 65-010, Sept. 1978. Essais de Comportement au Feu, Principes Généraux. Association Française de Normalisation.

[12] La Sécurité Incendie et les Matériaux de Synthèse dans le Bâtiment, Oct. 1979. Commission Technique du "Syndicat Professionnel des Producteurs de Matières Plastiques".

[13] Fire Safety Aspects of Polymeric Materials. Vol. 2. Test Methods, Specifications and Standards. Technomic Publ. Co., Inc., Westport 1979.

[14] ISO 3261 – 1975. Fire Tests – Vocabulary.

[15] *W. Becker:* VFDB-Z., Forsch. Techn. Brandschutz 24 (1975) 1, p. 4.

[16] *H. W. Emmons:* Scientific American 231 (1974) 7, p. 21.

[17] ISO Technical Report 6543 – 1979. The Development of Tests for Measuring Toxic Hazards in Fire.

[18] *P. Vandevelde:* Comparison between Different Reaction to Fire Test Methods on Wall-Lining and Flooring Materials. Interflam '79, 27–29. 3. 1979, University of Surrey, Guildford, England.

[19] *H. L. Malhotra:* Full-Scale Ad-hoc-Tests: Their Meaning, Limitations and Role. VFDB; 5. International Fire Protection Seminar, Karlsruhe, 22–24. 9. 1976, I, p. 63.

[20] *R. John, P. G. Seeger:* Auswertung des in- und ausländischen Schrifttums über die Durchführung von Brandversuchen in bzw. an Gebäuden im Maßstab 1:1. Forschungsbericht der Forschungsstelle für Brandschutztechnik an der Universität Karlsruhe (available from Documentation Office for Building Technology of the Fraunhofer Gesellschaft, Stuttgart).

[21] *P. Shakeshaft:* A Review of Data on Active Methods of Fire Protection in Residential Premises: Experimental Fires. Building Research Establishment Current Paper CP 21/78, January 1978.

[22] Fire Safety Aspects of Polymeric Materials. Vol. 7: Building. Technomic Publ. Co., Inc., Westport, 1979.

[23] *D. Brein, P. G. Seeger:* Kunststoffe im Bau 14 (1979) 2, p. 51.

[24] *F. H. Prager, H. Zorgmann:* Kunststoffe im Bau 14 (1979) 2, p. 57.

[25] *W. Klöker* et al.: Kunststoffe 67 (1977) 8, p. 438.

[26] *H. G. Klingelhöfer:* VFDB-Z. Forsch. Techn. Brandschutz 27 (1978) 4, p. 102.

[27] *R. K. Dean:* Full-Size Fire Tests of Stored Plastic Commodities. February 1976. Phase II, July 1977. Phase III, February 1978. Factory Mutual Research Corporation, Norwood, Massachusetts, USA.

[28]   Fire Safety Aspects of Polymeric Materials. Vol. 6. Aircraft: Civil and Military. Technomic Publ. Co., Inc., Westport, 1977.
[29]   Fire Safety Aspects of Polymeric Materials. Vol. 8. Land Transportation Vehicles. Technomic Publ. Co., Inc., Westport, 1979.
[30]   ANSI/ASTM E 603 – 77. Standard Guide for Room Fire Experiments.
[31]   *F. Vester:* Neuland des Denkens. Deutsche Verlags-Anstalt, Stuttgart, 1980.
[32]   *B. Miller:* Plastics World (1977) 11, p. 42.
[33]   Fire Safety Aspects of Polymeric Materials. Vol. 4. Fire Dynamics and Scenarios. Technomic Publ. Co. Inc., Westport, 1978.

8 National and International Fire Protection Regulations and Test Procedures

8.1 Preliminary comments

8.1.1 Sets of regulations

The aim of fire protection is to minimise the risk of a fire thus protecting life and possessions. The state, as official custodian of public safety, ensures such protection via relevant legislation which includes laws and statutory orders. Standards and codes of practice based on recognised technical principles are the means of putting the general requirements of fire protection defined in the legislation into practice. Materials, semi-finished and finished products are tested according to methods laid down in the standards and classified according to test results. Such tests are carried out by officially recognised materials testing institutes. A test mark is frequently required as evidence of the suitability of a material. This implies a quality check on production either by the manufacturer or an outside body. In the latter case an agreement must be entered into with a state recognised institution.

Many organisations are concerned with fire protection within the framework of civil law. The regulations and codes issued by such organisations are applied voluntarily, although in practice they must almost always be complied with since products which do not satisfy them have little chance of commercial success. They are also frequently considered as standard technical practice and are referred to in statutory orders and safety regulations.

Organisations operating under civil law can be divided into non-profit and commercial enterprises. The former frequently exist as registered associations, e.g. the Verband Deutscher Elektrotechniker (VDE) e. V. (Association of German Electrical Engineers), which by its charter, operates on a voluntary basis and draws up safety rules independently of any pressure groups. The "not for profit" organisations in the USA are independent and are not permitted to distribute profits to third parties. Any profits must, in fact, be invested in improving and expanding their activities to further their objectives.

The Verband der Sachversicherer (Association of Property Insurers), for example, is an organisation which includes fire insurance underwriters in Germany. These issue fire insurance policies based on the Allgemeine Feuerversicherungs-Bedingungen (General Conditions of Fire Insurance) which expressly assume that the various statutory, official or agreed safety regulations have been complied with. Agreed safety regulations are generally formulated by the Verband der Sachversicherer on behalf of all fire underwriters and are an integral part of the policy. Some of them lay down fire safety requirements for materials, components and manufacturing processes in the insured property. Other regulations cover design, installation and routine maintenance of fire protection systems and lay down testing and approval procedures (e.g. regulations for sprinkler systems , CO_2 fire extinguishers, fire alarms, smoke and heat extractors and also safety regulations in electrical engineering).

Numerous public and private organisations are concerned with the rules and regulations of fire protection. In addition to governmental bodies, these include professional societies and industrial, commercial, technical and insurance associations.

Depending on the field of application, regulations are applied nationally and/or internationally. For example, national codes are encountered almost exclusively in building and mining, because every country possesses its own set of rules and test methods which have developed historically. International harmonisation of regulations would in some cases have major economic implications, primarily negative in the eyes of individual states. The safety concepts or fire philosophies of many countries are in many cases diametrically opposed to internationalisation in certain areas. Even so, vigorous efforts are being made to harmonise building codes. This has already occurred in the case of the Nordic countries (Denmark, Finland, Iceland, Norway and Sweden) where fire testing is practically identical in all 5 countries and test results and test marks are mutually recognised. Unification of national building regulations relating to fire protection is also planned (see Section 8.2.9).

The harmonisation of fire safety standards commenced in the 1960's in the countries of the CMEA* (Council for Mutual Economic Assistance). Due to the uniform centralised executive power in these countries, regulations covering fire protection in buildings, classification and testing of fire performance and fire resistance of building materials and components are governed by Standards. Some are published as CMEA standards which are legally binding on all member states. Nevertheless, methods for testing the fire performance of building materials and structures still differ considerably in each CMEA country (see also Section 8.2.1). Progress, albeit modest, has also been made within the European Economic Community (EEC) and the United Nations Economic Commission for Europe (ECE) in harmonising the technical aspects of building regulations relevant to fire protection (see Section 8.2.1).

European standards are also issued by the European Committee for Standardisation (CEN) (with members from 15 countries) and the European Committee for Electrotechnical Standards (CENELEC). These standards assist in eliminating technical barriers to trade between member states as well as between these and other European countries.

In other fields, regulations exist which are, in the main, internationally valid. This applies in transportation and in civil aviation in particular. The most important new technologies were developed in the USA and thus the US Federal Aviation Regulations (FAR) of the Federal Aviation Administration (FAA) set the criteria for corresponding internationally accepted regulations. Evidence of airworthiness must be furnished with the aid of these regulations which have been partially or totally adopted by most countries.

Sets of regulations in international use also exist in other areas of transportation. For example, the International Convention for the Safety of Life at Sea (SOLAS) is accepted in nearly all countries. The regulations, recommendations and conditions of supply relating to railways are being harmonised within the Union Internationale des Chemins de Fer (UIC) (International Railway Union). Further details on transportation are given in Section 8.3.

International harmonisation of standards and mutual recognition of test results are planned in electrical engineering in order to remove trade barriers. International electrical standards are being developed by the International Electrical Commission (IEC) in order to achieve this aim. The Commission for Certification of Electrical Equipment (CEE) will base mutual recognition of test results by all member countries on these standards (see also Section 8.4).

While the IEC is responsible for international electrical standards, all other technical fields are covered by the International Organization for Standardization (ISO). This organisation aims to promote the worldwide development of standards in order to facilitate the exchange of goods and services and to encourage mutual cooperation in intellectual, scientific and economic activities. ISO member committees (of which there were 71 in 1980) are the national standards organisations. Further details on ISO will be found in Section 8.2.18.

* also known as COMECON

8.1.2 Overview of the subject

The topics discussed below reflect, in the main, those fields in which fire protection requirements are imposed by regulations. These include building, transportation and electrical
engineering. Building is dealt with in particular detail since this is the field where regulations, test methods and approval procedures are most numerous and where the greatest
variations exist from country to country. Furthermore, the use of all plastics as combustible
building materials is dealt with here from the point of view of fire protection. This field
therefore forms the most important part of this book. 14 West European, 4 East European
and 4 non-European countries are covered. In addition the activities of ISO are dealt with in
detail.

In transportation and the electrical industry, regulations and test methods are rather more
international so that they are less numerous and varied. Other subjects discussed in this
book are textiles (Section 8.5) and furniture and furnishings (8.6). An account is given of the
most significant aspects in all of these fields in the Federal Republic of Germany. Where
necessary a selection of further pertinent features of the situation in West European countries and organisations, the USA and internationally is considered.

Textiles for which few regulations relating to fire protection exist are discussed briefly.
The tests are usually used as quality controls rather than for determining fire hazard and are,
in any case, extremely numerous due to the many applications of textiles. The brevity of this
section is also explained by the fact that most textiles are composed of natural materials
which lie outside the scope of this book.

Furniture and furnishings are included since much thought is being given to the question
of fire protection in this area. Few fire protection regulations relating to furniture and
furnishings exist outside the USA and Great Britain at present and the EEC and ISO are in
the process of examining this field more closely.

The various fields covered in the following are dealt with according to a uniform system.
This is intended to help the reader become acquainted with, and to review rapidly, the
various regulations, requirements, test methods and approval procedures for the principal
areas of application of plastics. After a short introduction to the statutory regulations or
codes in force, the classifications and tests necessary for meeting the requirements are
described. The tests are elucidated according to a uniform scheme in which diagrams illus-
trating the principles of the methods and tables of the specifications are given. Further
details are given where necessary for clarity. Only those methods contained in regulations
are discussed here. Most of the tests are applications-related and can be carried out on
laboratory or pilot scales. Full scale tests are seldom required except in certain countries or
in the mining industry. Tests which are not clearly defined such as ad-hoc investigations,
voluntary tests for product development and quality control and methods for determining
the fire resistance of building components (which only contain plastics in exceptional cases)
are not considered.

It is not the aim of this book to evaluate the fire performance of various plastics or of semi-
finished or finished parts on the basis of the test methods discussed in the following. The
reader should consult the literature and in particular "Fire Performance of Plastics" by
Becker [1].

After describing the test methods, a list of appointed and recognised test laboratories
which carry out fire tests is given. The ways of obtaining approval and test or quality marks
are described together with the associated inspection and monitoring procedures.

Test or quality marks on a material signify that it has met performance criteria laid down
in standards or association regulations. Manufacturers' quality control associations, which
have their own technicians and inspectors, are also frequently approved by the state for
testing and inspecting materials. Tests are carried out at materials testing laboratories,

technical organisations or by specially appointed experts. Inspection may be carried out by the manufacturer or independently by an authorised outside party with whom an inspection agreement has been entered into.

All manufacturers entitled to use the quality mark are listed in a directory which is published periodically and is available to the public. The right to use the mark can be withdrawn if the inspection regulations are infringed or if several negative test results are obtained. This may have serious commercial consequences for the manufacturer who is thus motivated to ensure that his product meets the requirements.

Short sections on future developments follow each subject and country dealt with in the following. These cover briefly planned national and international changes or new trends in regulations, testing and approval.

Secondary fire effects such as smoke development, toxicity and corrosivity of fire gases and phenomena such as burning drops from materials in fires are dealt with separately in Chapter 9 in order to present a clear picture of this important subject. A short introduction to each topic is followed by a discussion of the relevant requirements and test methods. The determination of smoke density is dealt with at some length. The techniques for determining the toxicity of fire gases are discussed in the light of the latest knowledge. A general review of the present situation regarding corrosivity of fire gases is given since few established test methods exist.

The fire protection regulations and test procedures enumerated in Chapters 8 and 9 cover the principal areas of application of plastics in the main countries but cannot represent this vast subject exhaustively. They are intended to give the reader a comprehensive review of the most important aspects of this field and enable him to become rapidly acquainted with the intricate field of fire protection.

8.1.3 Test methods

The fire tests discussed below are arranged according to the test criteria on which they are based and their contribution to measuring certain fundamental parameters which affect the initiating fire. These criteria and parameters are, however, presented in a general form since, as mentioned earlier, it is not the aim of this book to evaluate the test methods or the plastics examined by them.

Size is one of the most important factors affecting test procedures. Tests may be carried out on a laboratory scale, pilot scale or full scale. The first two are the most commonly used and are discussed below.

It is usually assumed, particularly with laboratory scale tests, that the test apparatus can be considered as a closed system, i.e. without interaction with its environment. The results are decisively influenced by certain variables in such systems related in particular to the specimen and ignition source. Other variables which are not directly connected such as the ventilation and volume of the test system are disregarded.

The principal variables as regards the specimen are:

– Type of specimen: for practical reasons, panels are usually preferred. Many methods do in fact allow realistic testing as an assembly and with the same thickness as the finished part. However, such finished parts represent only a section of a structure, e.g. inner linings, particularly in the field of building. The electrical sector is an exception since actual complete finished parts such as plugs and switches can frequently be tested on the laboratory scale.
– The specimen can be positioned in many different ways. The preferred orientations of the specimen in the methods described here are: horizontal, inclined at 45° and vertical.

The following ignition source parameters play a prime role:

- Type and intensity: the main ignition sources have flames of varying intensity, e.g. matches, alcohol, gas burners (small burners, Bunsen burners, multiple jet burners), wood cribs, etc. Gas or electric radiators or radiant panels are frequently used, while hot media (e.g. air) are less popular. A pilot flame is also frequently used in addition.
- Positioning: horizontal, inclined at 45° and vertical positions are preferred.
- The results are highly dependent on how the ignition source impinges on the specimen (i.e. edge or surface) and on the length of exposure.

The list of variables above relating to specimen and ignition source illustrate how much individual tests may vary in just two aspects and why test results obtained by different methods seldom agree. Test results can only be correlated empirically with a real fire.

Certain phenomena which decisively affect the initiating fire are defined in the various test methods. They are combustibility, ignitability, flame spread and heat release as well as the various secondary fire effects, i.e. smoke development, toxicity and corrosivity of fire gases. The latter are dealt with in Chapter 9.

Some test methods are designed to measure only one parameter while others are designed to measure several simultaneously. An example of the former case is the ISO 1182 combustibility test and of the latter is the French Epiradiateur test in which heat release, ignitability and flame spread are all determined. These parameters are referred to in many national tests under identical names but, due to differing test conditions, they are not comparable. Eventually, it is hoped to define these parameters by internationally accepted test procedures within the scope of ISO/TC 92 (See 8.2.18). This problem is discussed further in Chapter 7.

The most important fire test methods are summarised in various articles by *Steingiser* [2] and *Booth* et al. [3] up to 1972. A detailed study by *Jagfeld* and *Veil* [4] contains a critical assessment of fire tests.

The addresses of national and international standards organisations are given in Appendix 10.4.

References for Section 8.1

[1] *W. Becker:* Fire Performance of Plastics. Springer Verlag, Berlin - Heidelberg - New York, in preparation.
[2] *S. Steingiser:* A Philosophy of Fire Testing, J. Fire & Flammability 3 (1972), p. 238.
[3] *M. Booth* et al.: Fire Performance of Plastics. Rubber and Plastics Research Association of Great Britain, Shawbury, Shrewsbury, 1972.
[4] *P. Jagfeld, M. Veil:* Kritische Beurteilung bekannter Brandprüfverfahren im Hinblick auf ihre Eignung zur Beschreibung des Brandverhaltens von vorwiegend organischen Werkstoffen. Stuttgart, April 1974.

8.2 Building

8.2.1 Introductory remarks

The statutory regulations and provisions relating to fire protection are furthest advanced in the field of building particularly in the industrialised countries where comprehensive sets of regulations may differ significantly. Most industrialised countries belong to one or other economic grouping. The regulations are then affected by the attempts at harmonisation within such groups in order to eliminate trade barriers. The three major economic groupings in Europe are the European Economic Community (EEC), the Nordic Council and the Council for Mutual Economic Assistance (CMEA). In all of these, attempts are being made to harmonise legal and administrative regulations.

The EEC Commission composed of members from 10 EEC states is working within General Directorate III (GD III) on the draft of a framework directive for construction products which will lay down the conditions for approving new building materials, components and methods of construction. This includes an EEC test for new and existing building materials and components inclusive of designation and quality marks, and the relevant inspection and monitoring procedures. An EEC model test (equivalent to the test certificate from a nationally recognised test laboratory) will suffice for less stringent requirements. GD III has drawn up a programme for harmonising fire test procedures for the following:

– fire resistance,
– fire performance of building materials,
– toxicity of fire gases,
– full scale tests.

It is hoped to introduce the procedures being developed by ISO/TC 92 (see Section 8.2.18) for testing the fire performance of building materials. However insufficient experience of test equipment and of various building materials has been accumulated. Consequently a group of European industrial fire laboratories (I-ILDA) is investigating individual ISO test methods and carrying out round-robin tests with selected building materials. The results of these I-ILDA activities could be incorporated as practical proposals from industry in future EEC codes based on ISO tests.

All these activities are intended to achieve complete harmonisation of building regulations in the EEC although at present this is precluded for economic reasons. "Optional" harmonisation has therefore been put forward as an alternative to existing regulations. Harmonisation in building in the EEC is discussed in several articles [1 to 6].

The countries of the Nordic Council (Denmark, Finland, Iceland, Norway and Sweden) are working on harmonising legislation in member states. The Nordic Committee for Building Regulations (NKB) is pushing forward with harmonisation of fire protection in building. Guidelines for the classification and testing of building materials and components have been issued under the title "Coordinated Nordic Technical Fire Classes". Although the test methods are used in all member countries, national differences still exist in classification and harmonisation of building regulations is still at the planning stage (further details are given in Section 8.2.9).

The CMEA (composed of Bulgaria, Czechoslovakia, German Democratic Republic, Hungary, Poland, Rumania and the Soviet Union) is also attempting to harmonise building regulations and the corresponding standards for fire precautions. Limited harmonisation has already been achieved regarding fire performance requirements and classification of building materials and components [7]. In contrast the corresponding fire tests are mainly carried out as previously, using various national methods.

A list of other organisations concerned with structural fire protection is given in Appendix 10.5.

The countries dealt with in the following sections have been selected on account of their industrial and commercial importance and their comprehensive regulations on fire precautions. Some states have not been included since no information was forthcoming and others because fire protection regulations and test methods are still under development. Some information, on countries not otherwise discussed, is incorporated in the description of the general fire protection situation.

Each country is dealt with according to a uniform scheme:

– statutory regulations,
– classification and testing of fire performance of building materials and components,
– official approval,
– future developments.

It is stressed again that fire resistance is not dealt with in this book. A bibliography for each country is given at the end of each section.

Statutory regulations

Regulations covering fire protection in building are more or less centralised depending on the particular form of government. Countries with centralised regulations include France, Belgium, Italy (where building regulations and test methods for fire precautions have just been introduced), CMEA countries and Japan (where additional local regulations exist). In principle Great Britain also belongs to this group. However, separate regulations apply in England and Wales, the Greater London Area, Scotland and Northern Ireland. The regulations however are gradually being brought into line with those in force in England and Wales. The Nordic countries have centralised national regulations although classifications and test methods have been largely harmonised within the framework of the NKB (see Section 8.2.9).

In countries with a federal structure each province or state usually has its own decentralised building regulations which are generally based on a model building code and framework guidelines in order to maintain some uniformity. The Federal Republic of Germany, Austria, Switzerland, Canada, Australia and the USA all have a federal structure. The execution of regulations is the responsibility of the Länder, Cantons, Provinces or States although in certain cases this function is transferred to institutions such as the Institut für Bautechnik in the Federal Republic of Germany. The situation is almost chaotic in the USA where the individual states are theoretically responsible for building regulations. In practice, however, local authorities determine their application via some 20,000 local regulations.

A special situation exists in the Netherlands where responsibility for enforcing building regulations rests largely with local authorities.

Reviews and comparisons of European and international building regulations are given in several articles [8–10].

Classification and testing of the fire performance of building materials and components

The classification of the fire performance of building materials and components reflects safety concepts in each country. Although national "fire philosophies" differ considerably from one another in certain respects, they are based on the same concepts. As can be seen from Table 8.1, building materials are usually divided into four levels of fire contribution (see also [4])

– minimal
– slight
– normal
– large.

Within the meaning of this safety concept, fire contribution provides a measure of fire hazard.

Minimal (meaning none or very low) contribution to fire of building materials is usually determined by the non-combustibility, or, in newer terminology, combustibility test (for specification of fire hazard see Section 7.3). This is carried out in a furnace at 750 or 825 °C (cylindrical specimen) using a procedure based on ISO 1182 (as ISO/R 1182, ISO/DIS 1182, ISO 1182) or at 750 °C according to ASTM E 136 (cuboid specimen) which is basically similar. Only France does not use this method in the building sector but tests by a calorimetric technique based on ISO 1716. Such calorimetric measurements are used in various countries including the Federal Republic of Germany in addition to the furnace method. As can be seen from Table 8.1, "minimal contribution to fire" is subdivided in some countries such as the Federal Republic of Germany (A1, A2) and Switzerland (VI, VIq). This enables totally inorganic building materials to be differentiated from those with low (usually <1%) organic content such as mineral fibre panels containing binders.

The classifications "low", "normal" and "high" contribution to fire of a building material are a measure of its behaviour in an initiating fire. Materials which make a low contribution to fire usually start to participate in the fire at a later stage of the initiating fire. Those which make a normal contribution resist medium and low intensity ignition sources for a short time (of the order of minutes) and those which make a high contribution are set on fire by practically any ignition source and are therefore generally not permitted to be used as building materials. Many national classification systems contain intermediate classes in order to be able to differentiate materials more clearly.

Test methods simulating all the important phases of an initiating fire, from ignition to flash-over are available, and can provide information on the contribution of building materials to each stage. Roughly 50 methods for simulating the initiating fire and 20 methods for describing secondary fire effects (i.e. smoke development and toxicity of fire gases) exist in the 22 countries covered below. In some cases an additional test is carried out to determine whether materials give off burning drops (further details are given in Chapter 9).

Fire tests using low intensity ignition sources (usually small burners) establish the ignitability of a material and allow the elimination of those with high contributions to fire. Various classes exist based on the demands made on the material. The least stringent case is when the specimen is positioned horizontally. Such methods based on the American ASTM D 635 test are used in the USA, Great Britain, Australia and, in modified form, in France and the Soviet Union. The test is more rigorous if the specimen is inclined (usually at 45°) as for example in Czech and Japanese methods. The toughest demands are made on the material if the specimen is positioned vertically. The igniting flame may be applied to the specimen surface (lower demands) or edge (higher demands) as in the DIN 4102 Part 1 Small Burner Test and in similar tests in Austria, Switzerland and Italy. Tests involving solely surface flame action are used in Great Britain while exclusively edgeing flame action is found in American, Canadian, Swedish, Czech and Soviet procedures.

The above methods are sometimes used to establish whether materials have a normal fire contribution and describe the flame spread which sets in after the material ignites. With further increase in the rate of flame spread, the instant of flash-over is approached and only

Table 8.1 Classification of the fire performance of building materials in national building regulations

Fire contribution of building material	Country 1)																			
	A	AUS 2)	B	CDN 3)	CH	ČS	D	DDR	DK 4)	F	GB	H	I	J	N	NL	S	SF 5)	SU	USA 6)
minimal	A	nc*	nc*	nc*	VI VIq	A	A1 A2	nbr	nc*	MO	O	nc*	O	1	nc*	nc*	nc*	nc*	nc*	nc*
determined by "furnace tests" based on ISO 1182	+	+	+		+	+	+	+	+	+	+	+	+	+	+	+	+	+	+	
ASTM E 136				+																+
slight	B1	O	by F and GB methods	≤25	V	B	B1	sbr	A(1)	M1 M2	1	lc*	1	2	A20	1	1	1(I)	lc*	A(I)
normal	B2	≤7		≤75 ≤150	IV	C1 C2	B2	br-mFA	B(2)	M3	2	mc*	2	3	A30	2 3	2	2(II)	clf*	B(II)
large	B3	>7			III II I	C3	B3	br-gFA		M4 M5	4 5	hc*	4 5		4 5	4 5		chf*	chf*	C(III)

1) Abbreviations, see Appendix 10.6
2) Spread of flame indices
3) Spread of flame classes for linings
4) Classes 1, 2 for linings
5) Classes 1, 2 (flammability) and I, II (fire propagation) for linings
6) Classes A, B, C or I, II, III for linings depending on Model Building Code

* These abbreviations are used only in this Table; in reality words are utilised. nc = non-combustible, lc = low combustibility, mc = moderately combustible, clf = combustible/low flammability, hc = highly combustible, chf = combustible/highly flammable.

materials with a small fire contribution match up to these requirements. For this region some tests also take into account heat release.

Materials with a normal or low fire contribution are tested with the aid of medium or high intensity ignition sources such as naked flames or radiators.

Various test methods involving exposure to flame are used. Normal fire contribution is determined with the "Plattenrahmen" test (GDR), normal and low fire contributions are determined in Scandinavia by test method 004 (box test) or 002 (Schlyter test – also used in a modified form in Austria) and in the USA and Canada by the tunnel test (ASTM E 84). Finally low fire contribution is determined by the "Brandschacht" method in the Federal Republic of Germany, German Democratic Republic and Hungary (here the normal fire contribution is taken into account using less rigorous test conditions).

Radiators are used as ignition sources almost exclusively in the determination of normal and low fire contribution. Such methods include the Epiradiateur (F, B), Brûleur Electrique (F), Surface Spread of Flame (GB, NL, B), Vlamoverslag (NL), DS 1058.3 Panel (DK), Flame Spread Index (SU), ASTM E 162 Radiant Panel (USA), Early Fire Hazard (AUS) and ISO/DP 5658 Spread of Flame (I) tests.

Some methods also take into account heat release; these are the Vlamoverslag test (NL), Nordtest 004 (Box Test, Nordic countries) and the BS 476: Part 6 Fire Propagation Test (GB) which has also been introduced in Japan as the Face Test.

In some countries the test methods relate to finished components such as linings and floor coverings rather than to building materials in general. In certain cases, plastics must undergo additional tests if established methods do not provide unambiguous data, as for example with thermoplastics which can withdraw from the ignition source.

The fire performance of inner linings is evaluated by the Schlyter (NT Fire 002) and Box (NT Fire 004) tests in the Nordic countries, by the TGL 10685/12 Fire Room Test for elements of building structure in the GDR and by the Tunnel test in the USA and Canada (ASTM E 84 or ULC-S 102).

Floor coverings are frequently investigated in tests, separate or complementary to those for building materials, as summarised below:

Federal Republic of Germany:	Small burner – DIN 54 332 and Radiant panel – NBSIR 75-950
France:	Radiant panel – NF P 92-506 (corresponds to small radiant panel in BS 476: Part 7)
Austria:	tested as building materials ÖNORM B 3800 Part 1 – for low combustibility (B1) and normal combustibility (B2) or "waste-paper basket" test
Switzerland:	Small burner – SNV 198 897 (similar to DIN 54 332)
Nordic countries:	NT Fire 007
GDR:	as element of building structure in fire room – TGL 10685/12
USA:	Methenamine tablet – ASTM D 2859 or Radiant Panel – ASTM E 648 (equivalent to the former NBSIR 75-950)
Canada:	Modified tunnel test – ULC-S 102.2 (flame applied downwards)

In a few cases as in Canada, light diffusers and lenses are tested by the tunnel test method (ULC-S 102.3) to see whether they fall from position in a fire. Special tests are carried out for thin building materials, fabrics and sheeting in several countries such as Canada (ULC-S 109), Australia (AS 1530, Part 2) and Japan (JIS A 1322) where a small burner or alcohol flame is used.

In Great Britain and the USA, plastics undergo additional tests to building materials. In the former country they are also tested to BS 2782: Part 5. The rate of burning of plastics is determined by Method 508 A (equivalent to ASTM D 635), the burning behaviour of PVC film by Method 508 C and a further test for burning behaviour, Method 508 D. In the USA, the self-ignition and flash-ignition temperatures are determined by ASTM D 1929. The burning characteristics of horizontally and vertically positioned specimens are tested to ASTM D 635 and ASTM D 568 respectively.

Official approval

The fire performance of building materials is tested in almost all countries, with the notable exceptions of Great Britain, Australia and the USA, by officially recognised test laboratories. In these three countries, private test institutes can also be chosen. Nevertheless the building authorities prefer test certificates issued by institutes recognised by the Department of the Environment in Great Britain and by the National Association of Testing Authorities in Australia. In the USA, large test organisations such as Underwriters' Laboratories Inc. are favoured by the authorities.

When a test has been passed, the test laboratory issues a test certificate. This is usually accepted as sufficient evidence by the authorities although in some cases a committee has to verify and approve it. Some countries require a test mark linked with inspection and quality control for materials subject to stringent fire protection requirements. This applies in the Federal Republic of Germany, Japan, Nordic countries, Canada and Czechoslovakia. In a few cases a quality label indicating quality control and independent inspection is required for certain building materials such as foam polystyrene (e.g. in Austria and the Netherlands). Organisations such as the American Underwriters' Laboratories grant test marks for certain building materials which require internal and independent monitoring. Further information on test marks and inspection will be found in Section 8.1 and the individual country sections, as well as in an article by *Cibula* [11].

Present situation and future developments

The following account relates to the situation in 1980; it is however subject to modification in the light of changes in the regulations covering fire precautions and improvement in test procedures due to advances in technology.

In many countries the building regulations are revised in a regular cycle (on average every 4 years in GB, USA, CDN, AUS, and the Nordic countries). In the Federal Republic of Germany the Model Building Code and DIN 4102 are being revised whilst in Belgium structural fire protection requirements and test methods in the NBN standards are being brought up to date. In Great Britain, the Building Regulations and test methods contained in BS 476 are being partially revised. In Italy new test methods and a new classification for building materials based on them have been introduced by decree. Spain – which is not covered in this book – is in the process of introducing fire protection regulations with associated test and classification standards adopted from ISO and France [12] while the Austrian B 3800 standard is being revised. New building regulations to be introduced by the NKB will be binding on all member states of the Nordic countries.

In the GDR, Hungary and Czechoslovakia some of the standards covering requirements, testing and evaluation in structural fire protection are being reissued.

It is planned to equip a larger number of laboratories for fire testing building materials in Canada which up to now has had only one. The Australian building regulations are being brought into line with a set of model regulations and standard AS 1530 is being revised.

Many countries intend to implement the NBSIR 75-950 radiant panel test (already adopted in the USA as ASTM E 648) for testing the fire performance of floor coverings. This method is under discussion in the Netherlands, Austria, Switzerland and Australia.

Many ISO tests have already been introduced worldwide including the ISO 1182 combustibility/non-combustibility test. Others will be adopted once the relevant work of ISO/TC 92 on ignitability, flame spread, heat release, smoke development and toxicity of fire gases has been completed. The Nordic countries for example intend to adopt all the tests at some stage. A few countries wish to incorporate certain test methods in their present draft standards (e.g. Italy – the ignitability test and Spain – the spread of flame test) or have expressed great interest in them (the Netherlands and Hungary are interested in the ISO smoke box, Japan in the ignitability test); Italy is interested in introducing the NBS smoke box.

The ISO methods are particularly important for those countries which are currently developing their regulations and associated test methods, as in Latin America, Africa and Asia.

References for 8.2.1

[1]   *H. L. Malhotra:* International and European Activities on Reaction to Fire Tests. Eurogypsum Seminar, Turin 21. 9. 1978.
[2]   *H. Bub, N. Schmidt-Ludowieg:* Internationale Harmonisierung im Bauwesen. Mitteilungen IfBt 9 (1978) 3, p. 65.
[3]   Etudes et Recherches sur la Réaction au Feu. Syndicat Professionnel des Producteurs de Matières Plastiques (SPMP), Paris, July 1979.
[4]   *W. Becker:* Kunststoffe 69 (1979) 9, p. 549.
[5]   *H. Bub:* DIN-Mitt. 58 (1979) 11, p. 669.
[6]   *H. L. Malhotra:* Fire and Materials 4 (1980) 4, p. 177.
[7]   *K. Kovács:* Normalization and Harmonization in the Socialist Countries of Eastern Europe. CIB-Symposium "Fire Safety in Buildings: Needs and Criteria". Amsterdam 2/3. 6. 1977, CIB Proceedings, Publication 48, p. 200.
[8]   *G. A. Atkinson:* Building Law in Western Europe. Building Research Station Current Paper CP 6/71, Feb. 1971.
[9]   *E. J. Cibula:* The Structure of Building Control- an International Comparison. Building Research Station Current Paper CP 28/71, Oct. 1971.
[10] *C. R. Honey:* International Comparison of Building Regulations. Building Research Station Current Paper CP 37/70, Nov. 1970.
[11] *E. J. Cibula:* Product Approvals for Building: an International Review. Building Research Station Current Paper CP 15/74, Feb. 1974.
[12] Current and draft Spanish Standards.
      Based on ISO (see Section 8.2.18):
      – UNE 23-102-81. Dec. 1981. Ensayos de reacción al fuego. Determinación de la no combustibilidad de los materiales de construcción (corresponds to ISO 1182 Non-combustibility Test).
      – UNE 23-103-78. Nov. 1978. Determinación del calor de combustión de los materiales de construcción mediante la bomba calorimétrica (corresponds to ISO 1716 Calorimeter Method).
      – PNE 23-701. Jan. 1980. Ensayos de reacción al fuego. Inflamabilidad de los materiales de construcción (this draft standard corresponds to ISO/DP 5657 Ignitability Test).
      – PNE 23-702. Apr. 1980. Ensayos de reacción al fuego. Propagación de llama de los materiales de construcción (this draft standard corresponds to ISO/DP 5658 Spread of Flame Test).

The following draft standards are based on French Standards NF P 92-501 to 92-507) (see Section 8.2.4).
- UNE 23-721-81. Dec. 1981. Ensayo por radiación . . . (corresponds to NF P 92-501 Epiradiateur Test).
- UNE 23-722-81. Nov. 1981. Ensayo a la llama de alcohol . . . (corresponds to NF P 92-502 Alcohol Flame Test).
- UNE 23-723-81. Dec. 1981. Ensayo del quemador eléctrico . . . (corresponds to NF P 92-503 Electrical Burner Test).
- UNE 23-724-81. Dec. 1981. Ensayo de velocidad de propagación de la llama . . . (corresponds to NF P 92-504 Rate of Spread of Flame Test).
- UNE 23-725-81. Dec. 1981. Ensayo de goteo . . . (corresponds to NF P 92-505 Dripping Test).
- UNE 23-726-81. Dec. 1981. Ensayo en el panel radiante . . . (corresponds to NF P 92-506 Radiant Panel Test for Floor Coverings).
- UNE 23-727-81. Dec. 1981. Clasificación de los materiales utilizados en la construcción (corresponds to classification of building materials according to NF P 92-507).

8.2.2 Federal Republic of Germany

Statutory regulations

The regulations relating to building inspection in the Federal Republic of Germany are derived from the Musterbauordnung or MBO (Model Building Code) which forms the basis of all the Landesbauordnungen (LBO) (State Building Codes). The building inspectorate is responsible for averting hazards which threaten the life, health and property of the individual. It is backed by a comprehensive range of legislation, directives and standards (Table 8.2) [1−4].

Table 8.2   Building inspection regulations and structural fire protection provisions

Laws	"Länder" building codes	
Statutory orders	1. Implementing order Furnace order Garage order Restaurant building order* Business premises order Quality control order Industrial premises order* Hospital building order Test mark order Places of assembly order	
Administrative regulations	Guidelines for the use of combustible building materials in buildings	
Recognised practice in building	DIN 4102 DIN 18081 ff. DIN 18090 ff. DIN 18160 TVR Gas VDE 0100	– Fire performance of building materials and components – Fire barriers** – Lift doors** – Furnaces** – Power installations
Building inspection provisions (not introduced)	DIN 18230 DIN 18231 DIN 18232 DIN 18238	– Structural fire protection in industrial premises* – Structural fire protection: total structures*** – Structural fire protection: smoke and heat control installations* – Structural fire protection for nuclear plants***

*   Draft
**   Revised
*** Planned

Structural fire precautions are covered in the state building regulations in line with MBO § 19 as follows:

- Structural installations are to be laid out, erected and maintained in such a way that the incidence and spreading of fire are prevented and that in the event of a fire, effective measures exist for extinguishing it and rescuing humans and animals.
- Building materials which are highly flammable even after processing and installation must not be used in the erection and installation of structures.

The fire performance requirements for building materials and components are laid down in further sections of the state building regulations, associated ordinances and additional statutory orders and administrative directives. Amongst the administrative directives, those concerning the use of combustible materials in buildings are particularly important since they give precise details of permitted use and fire performance requirements. These guidelines were recommended to the "Länder" as a model directive for building inspection in May 1978 and have since been introduced by decree by several Länder. This directive will certainly be altered as the Model Building Code and DIN 4102 Part 1 are revised.

The arrangement and contents of the directives for the use of combustible building materials in buildings are given in Table 8.3.

Table 8.3 Sections and contents of the directives for the use of combustible building materials in buildings

Section	Contents
1. Scope	Residential buildings
2. Terminology and comments	DIN 4102, marking, burning drops, insulating layers and linings
3. General fire performance requirements for building materials	Highly flammable building materials, joints
4. Non-load bearing external walls	Fire resistance classes W 30 to W 90
5. Linings and insulating layers for walls	Linings for internal and external walls
6. Insulating layers and linings for ceilings	Insulating materials under screed
7. Roofing	Insulating materials, skylights, dome lights
8. Escape routes	Openings, linings
9. Pipes, service ducts and channels	Sleeving through walls and ceilings

Classification and testing of the fire performance of building materials

Compliance with building inspection regulations can be substantiated with the aid of the standards generally recognised as standard building practice.

The DIN 4102 Standard – Fire performance of building materials and components – defines in tangible terms the terminology of fire protection (e.g. combustible, non-combustible) employed in the rules and regulations covering building inspection and fire protection. The latest version of this standard was issued by the Committee for Uniform Technical Building Regulations (ETB) of the Building Standards Committee (NA Bau) at the German Standards Institute (DIN) in September 1977 and March and May 1981. The original version dates back to 1934.

DIN 4102 is divided into 8 parts (Table 8.4). Parts 2 to 3 and 5 to 7 were issued in September 1977 [5−6] and have since been adopted by all the federal states [7−9]. Parts 1 and 4 were issued in May and March 1981 respectively while Part 8 is still only available as a draft. Further details on this topic are given in [3, 10−14].

Table 8.4   DIN 4102

DIN 4102 –	Fire performance of building materials and components
	Part 1 Building materials
	Part 2 Building components
	Part 3 Fire walls and non-structural exterior walls.
	Part 4 Grouping and use of classified building materials, building components and special building elements
	Part 5 Fire shutters, shutters in lift wells and fire resistant glazing
	Part 6 Ventilation ducts
	Part 7 Roofing
	Part 8 Small scale test furnace (draft)

Table 8.5   DIN 4102 Part 1 classification and test methods for building materials

Building material class	Building inspection designation	Test method
A	non-combustible	
A1* A2		− furnace test 750 °C − 'Brandschacht − smoke density to ASTM D 2843-70 or DIN E 53436/37 − toxicity to DIN E 53436 − calorific potential to DIN 51900 Part 2 and heat release to DIN 4102 Part 8 (draft) or furnace test 750 °C
B	combustible	
B1**	low flammability	− Brandschacht and small burner test − special case of floor coverings, radiant panel test (NBSIR 75-950) and small burner test (DIN 54332)
B2	moderately flammable	− small burner test − special case of floor coverings (DIN 54332)
B3	highly flammable	− no tests

*   Class A2 requirements must also be satisfied.
** Class B2 requirements must also be satisfied.

The following section deals only with the fire performance of building materials (DIN 4102 Part 1); building components lie outside the scope of this book.

The list and application of classified building materials is contained in DIN 4102 Part 4 [6]. DIN standards are issued by the Deutsche Institut für Normung (DIN), Burggrafenstr. 4−10, Postfach 1107, D-1000 Berlin 30.

DIN 4102 Part 1 − Building materials

Building materials may be divided into various classes using this standard and the fire tests described therein. These classes and the prescribed test methods are summarised in Table 8.5.

Building materials can be classified in classes A (non-combustible) or B (combustible). Due to their organic structures, plastics usually only achieve class B. In certain cases, for example as composites with inorganic materials, they achieve class A.

The test methods for non-combustible and combustible building materials are described in DIN 4102 Part 1, sections 5 and 6. Additional requirements for building materials subject to mandatory test marking are laid down in the test principles for non-combustible (class A) or low flammability (class B1) building materials as per DIN 4102 Part 1 − July 1978 version [15−16].

Non-combustible building materials

Class A1 building materials

Non-combustible building materials satisfy the prerequisites for inclusion in class A1 if they pass the 750 °C furnace test and fulfil the additional requirements of class A2. At present, the Institut für Bautechnik (IfBt) (Institute for Building Technology) does not require a test mark in the case of building materials with an organic content of less than 1%; the official tests for class A1 suffice. Test marks are mandatory for materials with an organic content above 1%.

A diagram and specifications for the furnace test are given in Fig. 8.1 and Table 8.6 respectively.

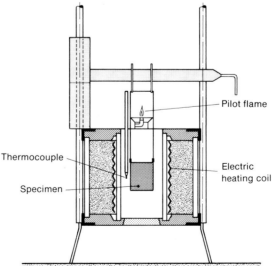

Fig. 8.1 Electric furnace

Table 8.6   Test specifications for class A1 electrically heated furnace

Specimens	5 specimens 40 mm × 40 mm × 50 mm
Specimen position	vertical
Ignition source	electric furnace: heated to 750 °C
	pilot flame: height 20 mm
Test duration	15 to 30 min
Conclusions	passed if none of the 5 samples give rise to
	– flaming
	– a temperature rise of more than 50 °C in the furnace

Flaming is considered to have occurred if flames are observed in the furnace or if the sample glows or if the enlarged pilot flame exceeds a height of 45 mm or fills the opening in the furnace lid.

Class A2 building materials

In order to achieve class A2, building materials must satisfy the following:

– Brandschacht test
– smoke density test
– toxicity test
– calorific potential and heat development test or the furnace test.

A diagram and specifications for the Brandschacht test are given in Fig. 8.2 (see under combustible building materials below) and Table 8.7 respectively.

Table 8.7   Test specifications for class A2 Brandschacht

Specimens	4 specimens 190 mm × 1000 mm × original thickness
	(max. 80 mm)
Specimen position	vertical, specimens at right angles to one another
Ignition source	ring burner
Test duration	10 min
Conclusions	passed if
	– the mean residual length is at least 350 mm; no specimen less than 200 mm
	– mean smoke gas temperature does not exceed 125 °C
	– the back of any sample does not flame
	– no other reservations exist

The determination of smoke density and toxicity of fire gases is described in the principles of testing non-combustible (class A) building materials subject to mandatory test markings according to DIN 4102 Part 1 [15].

Measurement of smoke density is based on ASTM D 2843-70 (XP2 apparatus) or on DIN E 53436/37. The equipment and test specifications are described in Section 9.2.2.1.

The determination of the toxicity of thermal decomposition products is carried out according to DIN 53436 Parts 1 to 3. Diagrams and test specifications are given in Section 9.3.

The calorific potential H_u is determined according to DIN 51900 Part 2 using an isothermal bomb calorimeter. In order to satisfy the test, the calorific value H_u must not exceed 4,200 kJ/kg.

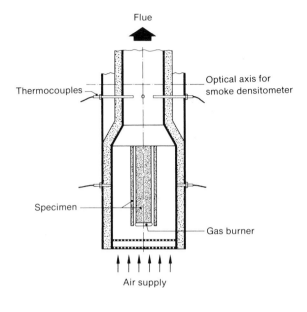

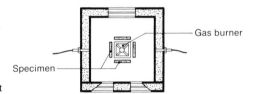

Fig. 8.2 Brandschacht

Heat release is measured on a small scale test rig to DIN 4102 Part 8 (draft). The test is passed if the heat liberated determined from the calorific value H_u and the weight per unit area before and after the test does not exceed 16,800 kJ/kg.

Tests for calorific potential and heat release can be dispensed with if the furnace test (Fig. 8.1) is carried out under the conditions for A2 rather than A1 materials (Table 8.6) and is passed. A 15 min test suffices and flaming for a total of 20 s is allowed.

Combustible building materials

Class B1 building materials

Combustible building materials are placed in class B1 if they pass the Brandschacht test and satisfy class B2 requirements.

A diagram of the Brandschacht equipment is shown in Fig. 8.2 and the test specifications are listed in Table 8.8.

Fire performance testing of floor coverings is a special case [16]. Classification in class B1 is based not on successful completion of the Brandschacht test but of the flooring radiant panel test (NBSIR 75-950), and the small burner test (DIN 54332). Further evidence that

Table 8.8   Class B1 Brandschacht test specifications

Specimens	4 specimens 190 mm × 1000 mm × original thickness (max. 80 mm)
Specimen position	vertical, samples at right angles to one another
Ignition source	ring burner
Test duration	10 min
Conclusions	passed if
	– mean value of residual length is at least 150 mm; residual length must not be 0 mm for any specimen
	– mean smoke gas temperature should not exceed 200 °C
	– no other reservations exist

class B2 requirements are satisfied is unnecessary. The requirements, testing and evaluation of floor coverings are described in [16]. The flooring radiant panel test is illustrated in Fig. 8.3 while the test specifications are summarised in Table 8.9.

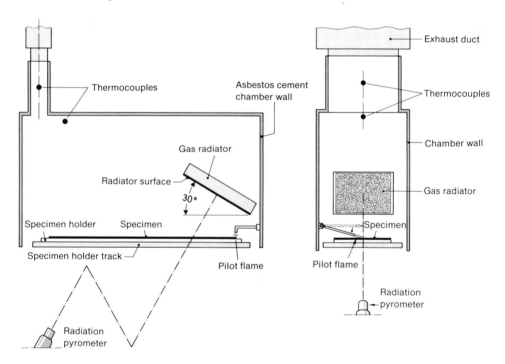

Fig. 8.3   NBSIR 75-950 Flooring radiant panel
left: Longitudinal section, *right:* Cross section

The DIN 54332 small burner test [17] corresponds in principle to the apparatus for testing class B2 building materials, though without the basket and filter paper for testing burning drops. A diagram of the test equipment is shown in Fig. 8.4. The test specifications are listed in Table 8.10; the flame is applied uniformly for 30 s in contrast to DIN 54332.

Table 8.9   Flooring radiant panel test specifications

Specimens	3 specimens 250 mm × 1050 mm × usual thickness
Specimen position	horizontal
Ignition source	– gas heated radiator 305 mm × 457 mm. Operating temperature up to 815 °C, inclined at 30° to the horizontal; lower edge 140 mm above the specimen; radiation on specimen 1.0 to 0.1 W/cm²
	– swivelling propane pilot flame, inner blue flame cone 13 mm long. Flame impinges perpendicularly to the longitudinal axis on the middle of the narrow edge on the radiant panel side; ignition flame can be pivoted up parallel to the specimen at a height of 50 mm
Duration of test	10 min of flaming and irradiation; if ignition does not occur, swing flame up and irradiate for additional 10 min; if ignition occurs, continue till flame extinguishes, up to a maximum of 30 min
Conclusions	passed if the average radiation flux is at least 0.45 W/cm²

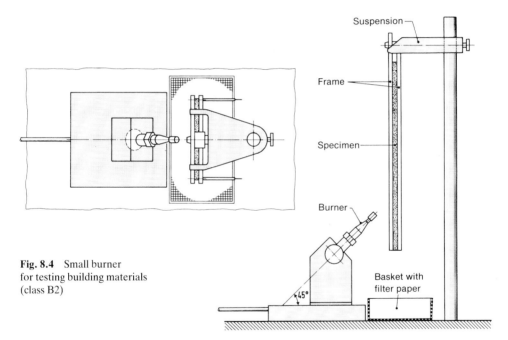

Fig. 8.4   Small burner
for testing building materials
(class B2)

Table 8.10   Specifications for the small burner test

Specimens	5 samples 340 mm × 104 mm, reference marks 40 mm from lower edge of sample, cotton thread drawn through sample reaching 250 mm above the ignition point
Specimen position	vertical
Ignition source	small burner, inclined at 45°, flame height 20 mm
Duration of test	30 s
Conclusions	test passed if
	– the cotton thread has not burnt through in any of the 5 samples
	– the after burn time after removal of the ignition flame <5 s

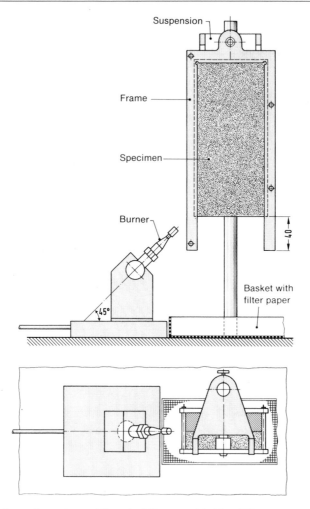

Fig. 8.5   Set up for testing multilayer building materials (class B2)

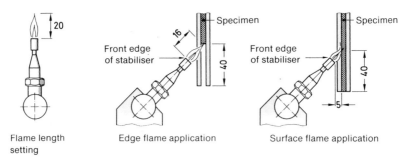

Fig. 8.6   Various burner settings
left: Flame length setting, *centre:* Edge flame application, *right:* Surface flame application

Class B2 building materials

Building materials achieve class B2 if they satisfy the test requirements given in Table 8.11. Diagrams of the test rigs are shown in Figs. 8.4 to 8.6.

Table 8.11 Test specifications for class B2 building materials

Specimens	edge application of flame:	5 specimens 90 mm × 190 mm, reference mark 150 mm from lower edge
	surface application of flame:	5 specimens 90 mm × 230 mm, reference marks 40 mm and 190 mm from lower edge
Specimen position	vertical	
Ignition source	small burner, inclined at 45°, flame height 20 mm	
Test duration	15 s	
Conclusions	passed if the tip of the flame does not reach the reference marks within 20 s on any sample for – edge application of flame or, if failure is expected with this test, then for – surface application of flame	
Additional test	if the filter paper under the sample ignites within 20 s after flaming, the material is judged to burn with flaming droplets	

These specifications are contained in the revised version of DIN 4102 Part 1 published in May 1981 and apply to single and multilayer building materials. For the latter, the flame impinges on the least favourable point on the front edge of the specimen as shown in Fig. 8.5.

Textile floor coverings can be classified in class B2 if they meet at least the requirements of burning class T-b to DIN 66081.

Class B3 building materials

Combustible building materials which cannot be classified in classes B1 or B2 are placed in class B3.

Official approval

In the Federal Republic of Germany, fire performance and secondary fire effects of building materials are tested by the following recognised institutions (as at 1981):

– Bundesanstalt für Materialprüfung (BAM)
  Unter den Eichen 87
  D-1000 Berlin 45 (Dahlem)

– Staatliches Materialprüfungsamt*
  Nordrhein-Westfalen
  Marsbruchstraße 186
  D-4600 Dortmund 41 (Aplerbeck)

- Institut für Holzforschung*
  Universität München
  Winzererstraße 45
  D-8000 Munich 40

- Forschungs- und Materialprüfungsanstalt für das Bauwesen
  Baden-Württemberg
  – Otto-Graf-Institut –
  Pfaffenwaldring 4
  D-7000 Stuttgart 80 (Vaihingen)

- Institut für Baustoffkunde und Materialprüfwesen der Technischen Universität Hannover
  – Amtliche Materialprüfstelle –
  Nienburger Straße 3
  D-3000 Hannover 1

For toxicity:

- Rheinisch-Westfälische Technische Hochschule Aachen
  Medizinische Fakultät Abt. Hygiene
  Lochner Straße 4–20
  D-5100 Aachen

For smoke:
- those institutions marked*

For testing class B2 building materials only:

- Staatliche Materialprüfungsanstalt an der TH Darmstadt
  Grafenstr. 2
  D-6100 Darmstadt

- Forschungsinstitut für Wärmeschutz e. V. München
  Lochhamer Schlag 4
  D-8032 Gräfelfing

For testing class B2 floor coverings only:

- Deutsches Teppich-Forschungsinstitut e. V.
  Germanusstr. 5
  D-5100 Aachen

Proof of compliance with established building regulations suffices for most materials utilised in the building industry. Special proof of usability is required for certain materials and can be obtained as follows:

- general building inspection approval
- test mark
- permission for use in individual cases.

The most common proof of usability is the test mark. Regulations exist in all parts of the Federal Republic laying down which building materials must be test marked within the framework of fire protection.

These are:

– building materials which must be non-combustible but have combustible components,
– building materials and textiles which must be of low flammability,
– fire retardants for building materials and textiles which must be of low flammability.

DIN 4102 and the "Principles for testing non-combustible (class A) and low flammability (class B1) building materials subject to mandatory test marking" act as guidelines for granting test marks [15, 16].

The test principles state the number of specimens for fire testing (first test, ageing tests, reserve samples) and describe the determination of smoke density and of toxicity of thermal decomposition products of non-combustible building materials. The regulations for composites are also given. In the case of low flammability building materials, special regulations are listed for:

– textiles,
– fire retardants for wood and wooden materials,
– fire retardants for cellulose fibre textiles,
– composites,
– adhesives and bonded composites (especially for rigid foam polystyrene panels),
– facade claddings,
– pipes,
– floor coverings.

The test principles also contain a short section on burning drops. Building materials are considered to give rise to burning drops if during at least two tests for class B1, drops or parts of the specimen continue to burn for 20 s or longer on the sieve beneath the burner or if during the class B2 test burning drops are detected. Burning drops are not otherwise evaluated in building inspection techniques.

Finally, the test principles give particulars on extending a test certificate, on reserve specimens and monitoring.

Issuing of test marks

All federal states have delegated the competence for granting test marks to the Institut für Bautechnik (IfBt – Building Technology Institute) in Berlin.

The route towards granting a test mark comprises several steps. An application for a test mark and a test certificate should be addressed to the IfBt and, in order to save time, a recognised test institute should be appointed to carry out the necessary tests.

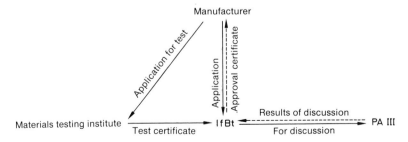

Fig. 8.7 Approval scheme

The results of the fire tests are transmitted to the applicant and the IfBt by the test institute. A draft test certificate based on these is deliberated in the Sachverständigenausschuß (PA III) (Expert Committee for Fire Performance of Building Materials) appointed by the IfBt. If the conclusion is positive the IfBt issues a test certificate and grants a test mark.

A simplified scheme for obtaining a test certificate is shown in Fig. 8.7 [18].

The test decisions and corresponding test marks are published regularly in the "Mitteilungen" (communications) of the IfBt and later in the "Verzeichnis der Prüfzeichen" [19]. The test mark must appear on the object or its packaging. All test marks start with the letters PA followed by the Roman number III and further Arabic numbers, the first of which represent:

1 – fire retardants for textiles
2 – low flammability building material
3 – fire retardants for building materials
4 – non-combustible building material
5 – special substantiation procedures
6 – floor coverings.

The remaining figures are a specific reference number [19].

Approval for building materials is valid for an initial period of 2 years. During this time, ageing tests are carried out. If the results are positive, the validity is extended for a total of 5 years and then for further periods of 5 years on application. When testing building materials, a distinction is made between those which will definitely be exposed to weathering and those which might be so exposed.

Inspection

Proof that a building material is suitable for use is provided by the test mark. However the material cannot be used until its manufacture has been inspected. An approach must be made to one of the recognised test institutions to arrange an inspection agreement. Quality assurance associations exist for various classes of building materials, – e.g. for rigid foams the "Güteschutzgemeinschaft Hartschaum". Members of such organisations can apply for an inspection mark. A precondition for this to be granted or for an agreement is a full scale inspection.

The initial examination for obtaining a test certificate can also count as the first inspection test if sampling is carried out by the materials testing institute or quality assurance organisation and the manufacturing plant has been inspected. A positive outcome leads to the IfBt granting approval (in the case of an inspection agreement) or a quality assurance certificate (in the case of an inspection mark). This makes the relevant agreement valid for building inspection purposes.

Actual inspection is made up of quality control and official monitoring

- Quality control. The type and extent of quality control is laid down in the inspection agreement. The results of quality control must be recorded, evaluated and retained for at least 5 years.
- Official monitoring. This is carried out by a materials testing institute or quality assurance organisation. It comprises:
  Checks on quality control.
  Checks on marking the material in accordance with the test certificate.
  Sampling and testing at the test institute.

Checks are made at least twice a year. Reports on the results of the inspections are prepared which, together with the report on the result of the ageing test, form the basis for renewal of the test certificate. This topic has been discussed in detail by *Hertel* [20].

Marking

The marking of building materials with mandatory test marks (classes A and B1) is pre-scribed by the building inspectorate. The PA III mark together with the marking "low flammability according to DIN 4102 (class B1)" ("schwerentflammbar nach DIN 4102 (Klasse B1)") are the best known.

The marking of all building materials which should be tested by DIN 4102 Part 1 is clearly required by the standard. Only wood and class A1 building materials listed in DIN 4102 Part 4 are exempt. This applies not only to building materials subject to mandatory marking but also to combustible materials of classes B2 and especially B3 which are marked "DIN 4102−B3 leichtentflammbar" (highly flammable).

The required markings are reproduced in Table 8.12.

Table 8.12   Marking of building materials according to DIN 4102 Part 1.

Building Materials Class	Evidence of test	Marking	Remarks
A1	no test	none	standardised building materials*
	test certificate	DIN 4102-A1	building materials without organic content
	test certificate	DIN 4102-A1 or	building materials organic content <1%
	test mark	DIN 4102-A1 as well as PA III − 4. . . .	
A2	test mark	DIN 4102-A2 as well as PA III − 4. . . .	building materials organic content >1%
B1	no test	DIN 4102-B1	standardised building materials*
	test mark	DIN 4102-B1 as well as PA III − 2. . . .**	
B2	no test	none	wood $\geq$ 400 kg/m^3; thickness $\geq$ 2 mm
	no test	DIN 4102-B2	standardised building materials*
	test certificate	DIN 4102-B2	
B3	no test	DIN 4102-B3 highly flammable	

*   to DIN 4102 Part 4
** Numbers 1, 3, 5, 6 may be used – for explanation see "Official approval".

Future developments

The Federal German Model Building Code is being fundamentally revised and the new version is almost complete. As a result, changes have also been made to the fire performance requirements of building materials and components:

- DIN 4102 Part 1 was reissued in May 1981 with some revised passages; a new feature is the differentiation between single and multilayer materials in the moderate-flammability test (class B2).
- DIN 4102 Part 4 (grouping and use of classified building materials, components and special elements) was reissued in March 1981.

Two further standards will be added to DIN 4102, covering testing of cable sleeves (fire stops) (Part 9) and pipe sleeves (Part 11).

The adoption of the "Test principles for class A and B1 building materials requiring test marks" as inspection guidelines is under consideration.

A uniform inspection mark has been introduced for building materials and components subject to inspection. In North Rhine Westphalia, this was introduced by decree.

Parts 1 and 2 of the completely revised standard DIN 53436 covering the toxicological testing of thermal decomposition products of materials appeared during 1981. Part 3 is available as a draft standard (see Section 9.3).

References for 8.2.2

[1] W. Becker, H. Lange: Brandverhalten von Baustoffen und Bauteilen, in Hj. Saechtling (Ed.) Bauen mit Kunststoffen. Carl Hanser Verlag, München, 1973.
[2] H. Bub: Brandverhalten von Baustoffen und Bauteilen aus Kunststoffen. Styropor-Report 30, May 1975.
[3] A. Klose: Boden-Wand-Decke (1979) 2, p. 61.
[4] H. Gallep: Die bauaufsichtliche Behandlung von Kunststoff-Membranen. Symposium Beschichtete Chemiefasergewebe, 7/8. 3. 1979, Aachen.
[5] K.-D. Wüstermann: Die Brandschutz-Norm DIN 4102. DIN-Mitt. 56 (1977) 10, p. 592 and p. 597.
[6] DIN 4102 Parts 2–3 and 5–7 (September 1977). DIN 4102 Part 1 (May 1981) and Part 4 (March 1981).
[7] H. Hertel: Mitt. IfBt 9 (1978) 2, p. 36.
[8] Model introductory decree DIN 4102; Mitt. IfBt 9 (1978) 2, p. 37.
[9] Introductory decrees DIN 4102 Parts 1–3 and 5–7.
      Baden-Württemberg: Gemeinsames Amtsblatt Nr. 29 of 18. 9. 1978, pp. 777/781.
      Bayern: Ministerialamtsblatt No. 5 of 17. 2. 1978, pp. 133/134.
      Berlin: Amtsblatt No. 29 of 18. 5. 1978, p. 661/662.
      Bremen: Amtsblatt No. 76, of 14. 12. 1978, pp. 581/632.
      Hamburg: Amtlicher Anzeiger No. 29 of 9. 2. 1978, pp. 193/195.
      Hessen: Staatsanzeiger No. 6 of 6. 2. 1978, pp. 291/293.
      Niedersachsen: Ministerialblatt No. 46 of 12. 10. 1978, pp. 1797/1798.
      Nordrhein-Westfalen: Ministerialblatt No. 10 of 3. 2. 1978, pp. 104/106.
      Rheinland-Pfalz: Ministerialblatt No. 6 of 14. 4. 1978, pp. 147/149.
      Saarland: Gemeinsames Ministerialblatt No 8 of 10. 4. 1978, pp. 229/231.
      Schleswig-Holstein: Amtsblatt No. 25 of 19. 6. 1978, pp. 329.

[10]   *W. Becker:* Kunststoffe im Bau 14 (1979) 2, pp. 68.

[11]   Normen, Vorschriften und Richtlinien für den Brand- und Wärmeschutz bei der Anwendung von Schaumkunststoffen und Dichtungsbahnen im Dachbereich. Bauen mit Kunststoffen 22 (1979) 2/3, p. 3.

[12]   *A. Klose:* Brandsicherheit baulicher Anlagen. Vol. 1. Werner-Verlag GmbH, Düsseldorf, 1978.

[13]   Prüfung von Baustoffen nach DIN 4102. Review issued by Gesamtverband Kunststoffverarbeitende Industrie (GKV), August 1979.

[14]   Zum Thema Brandschutz: Kunststoffe am Bau. Issued by Verband Kunststofferzeugende Industrie e. V. (VKE), Frankfurt, 1980.

[15]   Prüfgrundsätze für prüfzeichenpflichtige nichtbrennbare (Klasse A) Baustoffe nach DIN 4102 Teil 1 – Version July 1978. Mitt. IfBt 9 (1978) 5, pp. 156/159.

[16]   Prüfgrundsätze für prüfzeichenpflichtige schwerentflammbare (Klasse B1) Baustoffe nach DIN 4102 Teil 1 – Version July 1978. Mitt. IfBt 9 (1978) 5, pp. 150/155.

[17]   DIN 54332. Bestimmung des Brennverhaltens von textilen Fußbodenbelägen. February 1975.

[18]   *P. Jagfeld:* Das Stuckgewerbe (1976) 4, p. 27.

[19]   Verzeichnis der Prüfzeichen für nichtbrennbare Baustoffe, schwerentflammbare Baustoffe und Textilien, Feuerschutzmittel für Baustoffe und Textilien. Schriften des Instituts für Bautechnik (IfBt), Reihe A. Erich Schmidt Verlag, Berlin.

[20]   *H. Hertel:* WKSB, Neue Folge 23 (1978) 7, p. 10.

8.2.3 Benelux

Statutory regulations

Belgium

The Belgian building codes have few statutory regulations with technical content. The most important statutes are the "Code Civil", the communal "Règlements sur les Bâtisses" (building regulations) and the "Loi de l'Aménagement du Territoire et de l'Urbanisme" (urban building law) [1].

Belgian fire protection regulations apply only to high rise buildings (>25 m) and are described in Standard NBN 713-010 (1971) "Protection contre l'incendie dans les bâtiments – Bâtiments élevés" (Fire protection in buildings, high buildings) [2]. This standard is being revised and will be replaced by three standards already available in draft form (as at 1980).

- NBN S 21-201 Fire protection in buildings – high buildings – terminology [3].
- NBN S 21-202 Fire protection in buildings – high buildings – general conditions [4].
- NBN S 21-203 Fire protection in buildings – high buildings – regulations relating to fire performance of building materials [5].

Other standards relevant to fire protection in buildings of medium height are at the draft stage [6, 7]. In addition, work is being carried out on standards relating to fire protection in school buildings [8] and in high rise buildings with heating and ventilation equipment [9]. Finally, regulations governing fire protection in low (less than 3 storeys) buildings are planned as standards. For completeness it is pointed out here that the fire resistance of building components conforming to NBN 713-020 [10] is determined according to ISO/R 834. These standards are issued by the Institut Belge de Normalisation, Avenue de la Brabançonne 29, B-1040 Brussels.

Netherlands

The Dutch building regulations are based on two laws: the "Woningwet" (housing law) which empowers all local authorities to set up their own building code and the "Wet op de ruimtelijke ordening" (area planning law) which obliges local authorities to draw up town development plans. The "Vereniging van Nederlandse Gemeenten" (Association of Dutch Local Authorities) has drawn up a "Model Bouw-Verordening" (Model Building Code) which can be adopted by the autonomous local authorities with the aim of unifying the communal building regulations.

Technical regulations for subsidised housing (approx. 75% of all housing construction) have been decreed by the Ministry of Housing and Area Planning. These override the communal regulations and are thus of particular importance.

The technical regulations of the building codes are supplemented by sets of rules such as the NEN-Standards (Nederlandse Norm) and the KOMO guidelines (Stichting voor Onderzoek, beoordeling en keuring van materialen en constructies = Foundation for investigating, assessing and testing building materials and components) [1]. A series of NEN-standards governs fire protection in buildings in general (NEN 3891) [11] and in specific types of building such as houses for single family occupation (NEN 3892) [12], high rise buildings (NEN 3893) [13], hotels (NEN 3894) [14] and office buildings (NEN 3895) [15]. The above standards are issued by the Nederlands Normalisatie-Instituut, Polakweg 5, NL-2280 HV Rijswijk ZH.

Luxembourg

Due to its history and geographic situation, Luxembourg has close ties with its neighbours, Belgium, Germany and France. Luxembourg has entered into a monetary association and economic union with Belgium. The building code exhibits strong similarities to that of Germany. Town planning and building regulations in Luxembourg are, as in the Netherlands, the responsibility of local authorities. The local authorities enact communal regulations such as the "Règlement sur les Bâtisses" (Building code) of the "Ville de Luxembourg" [1].

Classification and testing of the fire performance of building materials

Belgium

Classification and testing of the fire performance of building materials is described in NBN 713-010 (1971) [2]. Standard NBN S 21-201 [3] which will replace it differs in some aspects.

The fire performance of a building material is defined as "the totality of the properties of a building material with regard to the initiation and development of a fire".

A material is considered to be non-combustible "if during the course of a standardised test, in which it is subjected to prescribed heating, no external indication of a recognisable development of heat is manifested". Determination of non-combustibility is carried out in accordance with recommendation ISO/R 1182-1970 [16]. A diagram of the non-combustibility furnace and the test specifications are given in Section 8.2.18.2.

If the material fails the ISO/R 1182 test, its combustibility is then investigated. Flammability according to the French decrees of 9. 12. 1957 and 10. 7. 1965 and rate of flame spread to "British Standard 476: 1953 Part 1, Section 2" are used as criteria for determining combustibility and as a basis for classification. According to draft NBN S 21-201, the French (decree of 4. 6. 1973) and British (BS 476: Part 7: 1971) test regulations and classifications will be introduced in the new versions. The previous French test and classification regulations will remain valid for a transition period of 5 years after NBN S 21-201 comes into force.

According to the French decrees, the old system classified building materials into four categories: highly, moderately, slightly and non-flammable. In the later version, the classes are M.0 to M.5 (see Section 8.2.4).

According to both the old and new versions of BS 476, building materials are classified by their rate of surface spread of flame into four classes, viz: very slow (Class 1), slow (Class 2), moderate (Class 3) and rapid (Class 4) (see Section 8.2.5).

Fire performance is determined by the French Epiradiateur test. Diagrams of the test apparatus, test specifications, calculation of the various indices and classification of building materials are given in Section 8.2.4.

Flame spread is determined by the British "Surface Spread of Flame Test" to BS 476 described in Part 1 (1953) (old version) and in Part 7 (1971) (new version). A diagram of the apparatus, test specifications and classification of building materials according to test performance are given in Section 8.2.5.

Netherlands

Test methods

The classification and testing of the fire performance of building materials are described in two standards. The determination of non-combustibility of building materials is described in NEN 3881 (Dec. 1975) [17] and corresponds in principle to ISO/DIS 1182 (August 1973 edition) [16]. A diagram of the non-combustibility furnace and test specifications are given in Section 8.2.18.2.

Determination of the combustibility of building materials is laid down in NEN 3883 (Dec. 1975) [18]. The "bijdrage tot brandvoortplanting" (contribution to fire propagation) by "vlamuitbreiding" (flame spread) and the "bijdrage tot vlamoverslag" (contribution to flash-over) are characterised here. In addition, the "mate van rookontwikkeling bij brand" (level of smoke development during a fire) of the building material is determined.

Testing of flame spread is based on the British surface spread of flame test to BS 476: Part 7 (1971). A diagram of the test apparatus is given in Fig. 8.17 in Section 8.2.5. The test specifications differ slightly and are shown in Table 8.13.

Table 8.13   Test specifications for vlamuitbreiding (flame spread)

Specimens	10 samples 1000 mm × 300 mm × max. 100 mm
Specimen position	vertical; long side (1000 mm) at approx. 90° to radiator surface
Ignition sources	– natural gas fired radiant panel: surface temperature approx. 900 °C
	– natural gas pilot flame (flame height 180 mm) below the test specimen on the same side as the radiant panel
Test duration	10 min
Conclusion	classification in classes 1 to 5, depending on the test results

The test involves subjecting the specimen to the temperature of the radiant panel and the effect of the pilot flame. In contrast to BS 476: Part 7 the pilot flame burns throughout the test (only 1 min in the British test). Considerable differences in classification can thus occur with certain building materials. The maximum spread of the flame front in the middle of the specimen is noted at 1.5 and 10 minutes.

Table 8.14   Test specifications for vlamoverslag (flash-over)

Specimens	10 × 2 specimens 295 mm × 295 mm
Specimen position	2 specimens vertical and parallel to each other, separated by 160 mm
Ignition sources	– 12 electric filaments with variable output (190 to 2250 W), distance from test specimens 80 mm
	– pipe burner (d = 10 mm) with 9 openings at intervals of 30 mm, flame length 20 mm, gas mixture 70 % H_2 and 30 % natural gas ≙ 500 W, distance from first test specimen: 25 mm
Test duration	until flash-over occurs
Conclusions	classification in classes 1 to 4 depending on the energy supply to the filament required for flash-over at exactly 15 or 5 min

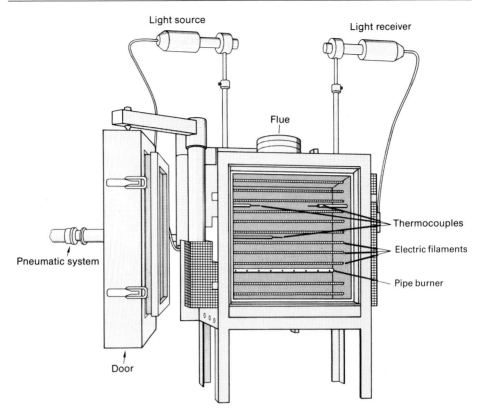

Fig. 8.8   Apparatus for testing flash-over and smoke development

The contribution to flash-over is determined with the apparatus shown in Fig. 8.8. The test specifications are presented in Table 8.14. One of the two test specimens in the apparatus is flamed by the 9 flames of the pipe burner. The filaments, which are located exactly midway between the specimens are run initially at 1500 W. The temperature is continuously monitored by thermocouples in the apparatus connected to a chart recorder. The test is continued until flash-over. The second specimen (i.e. the one to which the burner is not applied) is observed through a slit and flash-over is considered to have occurred if this specimen burns for longer than 5 s. The increase in temperature due to flash-over registered by the recorder is noted. The flash-over time is determined, i.e. the time measured between switching on the filament and the occurrence of flash-over. At least three tests are carried out running the filaments at outputs varying from 190 W to 2250 W. The power necessary to cause flash-over at exactly 5 or 15 minutes is determined by inter- or extrapolation. The values obtained form the basis for classifying materials in classes 1 to 4.

The flash-over test apparatus is also equipped to measure smoke development. Exact details, diagrams and test specifications are given in Section 9.2.2.2.

Two further standards are concerned with fire precautions in the building industry. These are NEN 3882 (Dec. 1975) "Determination of fire hazard for roofing affected by spreading fire" [19] and NEN 3884 (Feb. 1978) "Determination of fire resistance of building components" [20].

Classification

The "bijdrage tot brandvoortplanting" (contribution to fire propagation) consists of "vlam-uitbreiding" (flame spread) and the "bijdrage tot vlamoverslag" (contribution to flash-over) expressed as the classification achieved by the material. If the two test methods result in different classifications, the least favourable classification is taken as the basis for the contribution to propagation of fire.

Table 8.15   Division of flame spread into classes

Flame spread [mm]				Flame spread class
during the first 1½ min		during 10 min		
class limit	max. permitted upper deviation for 1 sample	class limit	max. permitted upper deviation for 1 sample	
175	25	175	25	1
250	50	550	50	2
350	50	750	100	3
500	50	if not in classes 1 to 3		4
if not in classes 1 to 4				5

Table 8.16   Division of flash-over intensity into classes

E_{15}	E_5	Flash-over intensity class
$\geqq 1500\,W$	$\geqq 1875\,W$	1
	$<1875\,W$	2
$< 1500\,W$	$\geqq 1125\,W$	
$\geqq 750\,W$	$<1125\,W$	3
$< 750\,W$	$\geqq 565\,W$	
$\geqq 190\,W$	$< 565\,W$	4
$< 190\,W$	–	

Flame spread is divided into five classes as shown in Table 8.15. Division of flash-over intensity is divided into 4 classes as shown in Table 8.16. The determining factors are

– the electrical power (E_{15}) necessary to cause flash-over in 15 minutes,
– the electrical power (E_5) necessary to cause flash-over in 5 minutes.

Building materials which fall into class 4 in the above scheme are designated as "gemakkelijk ontvlambaar" (highly flammable); those which fall into the other classes as "niet gemakkelijk ontvlambaar" (not highly flammable).

If a building material falls into different classes as a result of the flame spread and flash-over tests the least favourable is taken for its classification for contribution to fire propagation. The contribution to fire propagation is divided into 5 classes as shown in Table 8.17.

Table 8.17   Classification of contribution of building materials to fire propagation

Class	Contribution to fire propagation
1	very weak
2	weak
3	moderate
4	strong, satisfies the basic requirements defined in NEN 3891
5	strong, does not satisfy the basic requirements defined in NEN 3891

The basic requirements are defined in NEN 3891 as meaning that "the assembled element should not be so constructed that it generates smoke or catches completely alight soon after an outbreak of fire". The term "catches completely alight" signifies that the fire propagation contribution of the surface of the finished component must not fall into class 5 according to NEN 3883. Classification of building materials according to their contribution to smoke development is described in Section 9.2.2.2.

Luxembourg

No building inspection regulations relevant to fire protection exist in Luxembourg. As a result there are no institutes testing the fire performance of building materials. In practice, the building regulations of neighbouring countries are adhered to. Public contracts are executed by foreign building contractors, resulting in the application of the building regulations valid in the contractors' own country. The contractors are required to provide test reports from the relevant country on the fire performance of their building materials. This meets the requirements of the authorities.

Official approval

Belgium

The tests described above must be carried out to classify the fire performance of building materials and to obtain official recognition. The fire performance of building materials is tested in Belgium by the following institutes:

- Laboratorium voor Aanwending der Brandstoffen en Warmte-overdracht
  Ottergemseteenweg, 711
  B-9000 Gent

- Centre d'étude des matériaux plastiques
  Université de Liège
  Quai Banning 6
  B-4000 Liège

The test results and classification achieved are recorded in a test report, which meets the requirements of the authorities. Marking and inspection are not carried out.

Netherlands

The tests described above and the resultant classifications provide the basis for official approval. In the Netherlands, fire performance testing of building materials is carried out by a single test institute:

- Centrum voor brandveiligheid
  Instituut TNO voor bouwmaterialen en bouwconstructies
  Lange Kleiweg 5
  NL-2288 GH Rijswijk ZH or
  Postbus 49
  NL-2600 AA Delft

The test results and classification achieved are recorded in a test report issued by the TNO. This document substantiates the fire performance of the building material for officials and the fire brigade. Marking and inspection are not carried out. Foam polystyrene is, however, an exception and is subject to inspection and marking through KOMO as a result of NEN 7043 [21]. As with other materials the fire performance is tested to NEN 3883.

Future developments

Standard NBN 713-010 will be superseded in Belgium by NBN S 21-201 to NBN S 21-205. Testing will then be carried out in the "Epiradiateur" to the French NF P 92-501 standard. The so-called Herpol-Chamber test which was planned at one time as NBN 713-030 has been finally withdrawn. NBN 713-020 covering the fire resistance of building components is also being revised.

Neither a special test for the fire performance of floorings nor other activities regarding smoke development and toxicity of fire gases are planned at present. Rather, developments are awaited in ISO/TC 92 (see Section 8.2.18).

In the Netherlands, there are no new initiatives regarding the fire performance of building materials. However a method for testing the fire performance of floor coverings is in preparation. As far as secondary fire effects are concerned, the introduction of the ISO smoke chamber as a national standard is under consideration (see Section 9.2.3.2).

References for 8.2.3

[1] *H. Braun:* Bauvorschriften in sechs EWG-Ländern. Part 2: Nationale Systeme der Bauvorschriften. D. Niederlande. E. Belgien. F. Luxemburg. Baurecht-Technische Vorschriften-Institutionen, Ifo: Studien zur Bauwirtschaft 1, Ifo-Institut für Wirtschaftsforschung e. V., Munich, Feb. 1973.

[2] NBN 713-010 (1971) Protection contre l'incendie dans les bâtiments – Bâtiments élevés – Conditions générales.

[3] NBN S 21-201 Protection contre l'incendie dans les bâtiments – Bâtiments éléves – Terminologie (Draft).

[4] NBN S 21-202 Protection contre l'incendie dans les bâtiments – Bâtiments élevés – Conditions générales (Draft).

[5] NBN S 21-203 Protection contre l'incendie dans les bâtiments – Bâtiments élevés – Prescriptions relatives à la réaction au feu des matériaux (Draft).

[6] NBN S 21-204 Protection contre l'incendie dans les bâtiments – Bâtiments moyens – Conditions générales (Draft).

[7] NBN S 21-205 Protection contre l'incendie dans les bâtiments – Bâtiments moyens – Prescriptions relatives à la réaction au feu des matériaux (Draft).

[8] NBN S 21-206 Protection contre l'incendie dans les bâtiments – Bâtiments scolaires, internats et homes pour étudiants (Draft).

[9] NBN S 21-207 Protection contre l'incendie dans les bâtiments – Bâtiments élevés – Equipements thermiques et aérauliques (Draft).

[10] NBN 713-020 (1968) Protection contre l'incendie – Comportement au feu des matériaux et éléments de construction – Résistance au feu des éléments de construction.

[11] NEN 3891 (Dec. 1971) Richtlijnen brandbeveiliging van gebouwen. Deel 1. Algemeen gedeelte.

[12] NEN 3892 (Nov. 1975) Brandbeveiliging van gebouwen. Eengezinshuizen lage woongebouwen.

[13] NEN 3893 (Nov. 1975) Brandbeveiliging van gebouwen. Hoge woongebouwen.

[14] Ontwerp NEN 3894 (Nov. 1978) Brandbeveiliging van gebouwen. Logiesgebouwen (Draft).

[15] Ontwerp NEN 3895 Brandbeveiliging van gebouwen. Kantoorgebouwen (Draft).

[16] ISO/R 1182 – 1970 Building materials – Non-combustibility test, see also ISO/DIS 1182 Aug. 1973 as basis for NEN 3881.

[17] NEN 3881 (Dec. 1975) Bepaling van de onbrandbaarheid van bouwmaterialien.

[18] NEN 3883 (Dec. 1975) Bepaling van de bijdrage tot de brandvoortplanting van bouwmaterialen en hun rookontwikkeling bij brand.

[19] NEN 3882 (Dec. 1975) Bepaling van het brandgevaarlijk zijn van daken uitsluitend onder inwerking van vliegvuur.

[20] NEN 3884 (Feb. 1978) Bepaling van de brandwerendheid van bouwdelen.

[21] NEN 7043 (May 1977). Platen van hard polystyreenschuim voor thermische isolatie.

8.2.4 France

Statutory regulations

French building regulations for the public building sector differ greatly from those for the private sector. While extensive building regulations apply in the former, those for the private sector are limited to general requirements or overall aims [1, 2]. This explains why French fire regulations relate mainly to high rise buildings and buildings open to the public. The regulations are contained in brochures entitled "Sécurité contre l'Incendie" (Fire Safety) [3] as follows:

– Regulations for buildings open to the public (établissements recevant du public = E.R.P.) laid down in sections R.123-1 to R.123-55 of the building and housing code (code de la construction et de l'habitation [3] Vol. I, p. 3 ff). The implementation of these safety regulations is covered in ministerial circulars no 73-552 of 22. 11. 1973 and no 75-134 of 12. 3. 1975 ([3] Vol. I, p. 513 and p. 517).
– Regulations for high rise buildings (immeubles de grande hauteur = I.G.H.) contained in sections R.122-1 to 122-29 and R.152-1 to 152-3 of the building and housing code ([3], Vol. II, p. 123 ff) and in the decree (Arrêté) of 18. 10. 1977 concerning the construction of high rise buildings and anti-fire and anti-panic measures ([3], Vol. II, p. 133 ff).
– The decree of 10. 9. 1970 ([3], Vol. II, p. 233 ff) and ministerial circular no 73-178 of 5. 10. 1973 ([3], Vol. II, p. 251 ff) concerning fire protection of residential buildings.

Classification and testing of the fire performance of plastics

The classification of building materials and components with regard to fire hazard is laid down in sections R. 121-1 to 121-13 of the building and housing code ([3], Vol. II, p. 13).

The terms "réaction au feu" (reaction to fire or fire performance) and "résistance au feu" (fire resistance) are defined in Article 2. The French view "réaction au feu" as including the supply to the fire and fire development, while the "résistance au feu" is defined as "the time during which the building components can fulfil their intended function in spite of the effects of fire".

The classification characteristics laid down in article 3 for the "réaction au feu" are "the heat evolved during combustion and the presence or absence of combustible gases. The classification should thus specify the non-combustible or combustible nature of the building material and in the latter case its degree of combustibility".

The methods used to determine fire performance are described in the "Arrêté" of 4. 3. 1973 ([3], Vol. II, p. 17) modified on 19. 12. 1975. These methods are also the subject of a series of standards issued by the Association Française de Normalisation (AFNOR) in October 1975, namely NF P 92-501 to 92-507 [4] which correspond to the regulations of the Arrêté but are expressed in a more easily understood form. These standards are issued by AFNOR, Tour Europe, Cedex 7, F-92080 Paris la Défense.

The fire performance of building materials is divided into six classes as shown in Table 8.18.

Only the abstract symbols M.0 to M.5 are now used to characterise the results of fire tests. Terms such as non-flammable, etc. used previously were frequently regarded as properties of the material and often led to incorrect interpretation.

Building materials are divided into two groups for test purposes:

– flexible materials up to 5 mm thick,
– flexible materials more than 5 mm thick and rigid materials of any thickness.

Table 8.18   Classification of the fire performance of building materials

M.0	incombustible	(non-combustible)
M.1	non inflammable	(non-flammable)
M.2	difficilement inflammable	(low flammability)
M.3	moyennement inflammable	(moderately flammable)
M.4	facilement inflammable	(high flammability)
M.5	très facilement inflammable	(extremely flammable)

A primary test is carried out in both cases to ascertain whether the material can be classified in categories M.1 to M.3. Complementary tests are carried out for classification in classes M.4 and M.5 or, in certain cases, to confirm classification in classes M.1 to M.3. If there are doubts as to which group the material belongs, both types of test are carried out and the least favourable result evaluated.

Where possible, materials are tested as used in buildings. For example, wall coverings are stuck on asbestos-cement panels and tested as rigid materials.

Regulations covering the testing, classification and use of electrical conductors and cables also exist in the building sector ([3], Vol. II, p. 17, p. 79 and p. 111).

The radiators used as ignition sources in the following tests are calibrated in accordance with NF P 92-508 (electrical burner test to NF P 92-503) and NF P 92-509 (epiradiateur test to NF P 92-501) and drip test to NF P 92-505 [5].

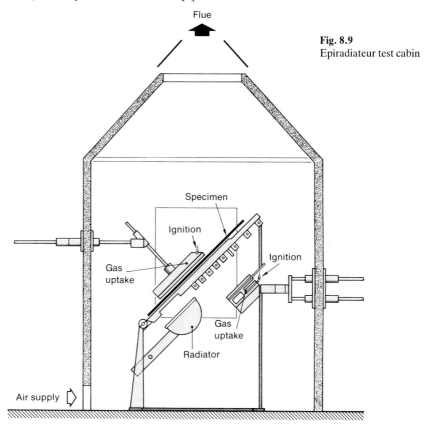

Flue

Fig. 8.9
Epiradiateur test cabin

Specimen

Ignition

Ignition

Gas
uptake

Gas
uptake

Radiator

Air supply

NF P 92-501. Epiradiateur test

The epiradiateur test is the primary method of determining the fire performance of rigid samples of any thickness and of flexible samples more than 5 mm thick. The apparatus is illustrated in Fig. 8.9 and the test specifications are summarised in Table 8.19.

Table 8.19   Epiradiateur test specifications

Specimens	4 specimens 300 mm × 400 mm
Specimen position	inclined at 45°
Ignition sources	– electric radiator (inclined at 45°) 500 W, radiation falling on specimen (distance from radiator: 30 mm): 3 W/cm²
	– 2 butane pilot flames for igniting the combustible decomposition gases above and below the specimen
Test duration	20 min
Conclusion	classification according to flammability in classes M.1 to M.3 or >M.3, M.1 achieved if specimen burns ≦ 5 s

During the test the following must be recorded:

– the time elapsed until flaming first occurs for longer than 5 s on both sides of the specimen,
– the maximum flame height every 30 s,
– the mean temperature of the thermocouples recorded continuously by chart recorder or every 15 s manually,
– further primary and secondary fire effects such as smoke generation, burning droplets, after-flaming, glowing etc.

Four indices, calculated from the above data, serve as a basis for classification in classes M.1 to M.3.

– *Flammability index i:*
$$i = \frac{1000}{15\,t_1} + \frac{1000}{15\,t_2}$$

t_1 and t_2 are the time intervals in s until the front and back of the specimen flame.

– *Spread index s:*
$$s = \frac{\Sigma \text{ flame lengths}}{140}$$

the sum of maximum flame length in cm measured every 30 s is divided by 140.

– *Index of maximum flame length h:* $h = \dfrac{\text{max. flame length}}{20}$

the maximum flame length determined during the test is divided by 20.

– *Combustibility index c:*
$$c = \frac{S'}{120}$$

S' is the "algebraic surface", i.e. the product of the time in min and temperature rise in K, due to the combustion of the test specimen.

NF P 92-502. Alcohol flame test

The alcohol flame test (essai à la flamme d'alcool) used to be the principal method of determining the combustibility of flexible materials. It is not very suitable for many newer materials including synthetic textiles and is thus rarely used. It will be made obsolete at the next revision of the decrees and will be replaced by the electric burner test (see below).

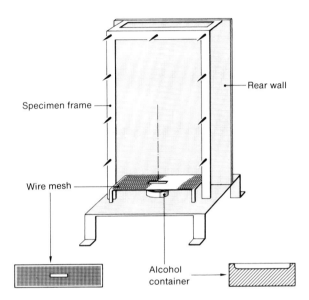

Fig. 8.10   Alcohol flame test rig

For completeness the alcohol flame test apparatus is illustrated in Fig. 8.10 and the test specifications are given in Table 8.20.

Table 8.20   Alcohol flame test specifications

Specimens	4 specimens 300 mm × 240 mm
Specimen position	stretched vertically over specimen flame
Ignition source	alcohol flame (96% ethyl alcohol)
Test duration	3 min
Conclusion	Classification according to flammability in classes M.1 to M.3 or >M.3

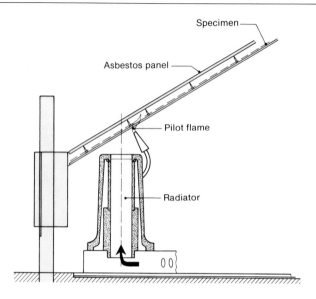

Fig. 8.11   Electrical burner

NF P 92-503. Electrical burner test

The electrical burner test (essai au brûleur électrique) is now used de facto as the primary method for determining the fire performance of flexible materials. A diagram and test specifications are given in Fig. 8.11 and Table 8.21, respectively.

Table 8.21   Electrical burner test specifications

Specimens	4 specimens 600 mm × 180 mm
Specimen position	inclined at 30° to horizontal
Ignition sources	– 500 W electric radiator, 30 mm from specimen
	– butane gas pilot flame (20 mm wide × 30 mm high)
Test duration	5 min
Conclusion	classification according to flammability in classes M.1 to M.3 or >M.3
	M.1 is achieved if combustion lasts less than 5 s

The following must be noted during the test which lasts until the specimen extinguishes completely:

– instant and duration of flaming,
– burning drippings,
– appearance of the damaged specimen,
– effect of complete or partial spread of flame, afterglow,

– extent of smoke development,
– other observations.

After the test the maximum damaged length and width of the four specimens is determined and the arithmetic mean of each calculated.

NF P 92-504. Rate of spread of flame test

The rate of spread of flame test (essai de vitesse de propagation de la flamme) serves as a complementary test to the primary tests and enables the criteria which cannot be determined by the latter to be established.

This test is used to determine the contribution to flame spread to enable a classification in categories M.1 to M.5 to be made if a material melts rapidly without burning in the vicinity of the radiator in the primary test (for flexible materials $\leqq 20$ s) and if a material does not achieve classes M.1 to M.3.

The apparatus is illustrated in Fig. 8.12 and the test specifications are summarised in Table 8.22.

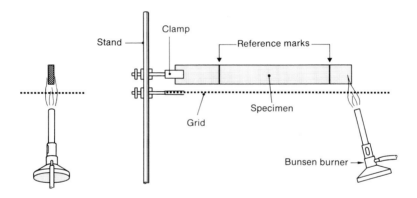

Fig. 8.12 Determination of spread of flame rate
left: Front view, *right:* Side view

Table 8.22 Rate of spread of flame test specifications

Specimens	3 specimens 400 mm × 35 mm reference marks at 50 mm and 300 mm parallel to the free (35 mm high) end of the specimen
Specimen position	long side (400 mm) horizontal, short side (35 mm) vertical
Ignition source	town gas Bunsen burner (25 mm flame)
Test duration	the flame is applied to the free end of the specimen for 30 s, if no ignition, five further attempts at ignition are made, if specimen ignites, measure time from first reference mark
Conclusion	classification in classes M.1 to M.5 depending on course of test

The test is carried out by applying the Bunsen flame to the bottom of the free end of the specimen for 30 s. If flaming does not occur, five further attempts to ignite the specimen are made. If the specimen continues to burn after removal of the ignition source but the first reference mark is not reached, the burning time is noted. Otherwise the time taken for the flame front to travel between the first and second reference marks is noted. However, if the flame extinguishes between the two marks, the distance between the reference mark and the limit of the flame front is measured.

The rate of spread of flame, v, is computed from $v = \frac{250}{t}$ where t is the time in s required to reach the second reference mark. Note should also be made of whether the material burns continuously, melts or drips during application of the flame, the level of smoke development and other observations.

NF P 92-505. Dripping test

The dripping test (essai de goutte) is a further complementary test to determine burning drops, a phenomenon which cannot be clearly assessed in the primary tests. It is carried out if, during the relevant primary test, non-burning drops are observed or if the material withdraws very rapidly or without burning (flexible materials $\leqq$ 20 s) from the vicinity of the radiator. The material is classified in classes M.1 to M.4 depending on test performance. A diagram of the test rig and the test specifications are presented in Fig. 8.13 and Table 8.23, respectively.

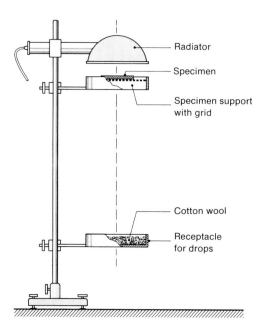

Fig. 8.13 Test rig for burning drops

If the geometry of the specimen alters during the test, the distance of the radiator from the specimen must be readjusted to 30 mm. If the specimen ignites during the first 5 min, the radiator is removed 3 s after ignition; irradiation is continued as soon as the specimen

Table 8.23   Dripping test specifications

Specimens	4 specimens 70 mm × 70 mm
Specimen position	horizontal on a grid
Ignition source	horizontal 500 W electric radiator, radiation intensity on specimen (30 mm from radiator) 3 W/cm²
Receptacle for catching droplets	contains cotton wool and is located 300 mm below the grid
Test duration	max. 10 min
Conclusion	if cotton wool ignites, material is classified in class M.4

extinguishes. During the second 5 min, irradiation is maintained throughout regardless of whether the specimen burns.

Note is made of any dripping and whether the cotton wool ignites. Ignition of the specimen is noted if it is longer than 5 s.

NF P 92-506. Radiant panel test for floor coverings

The radiant panel test (essai au panneau radiant) is a complementary test used exclusively for determining the fire performance of floor coverings if the material does not achieve class M.1 or M.2 in the primary test. The apparatus is illustrated in Fig. 8.14 and the test specifications are summarised in Table 8.24.

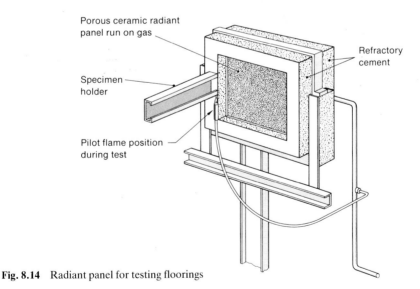

Porous ceramic radiant panel run on gas

Refractory cement

Specimen holder

Pilot flame position during test

Fig. 8.14   Radiant panel for testing floorings

The specimen is subjected to the temperature of the radiant panel (850 °C) and the effects of the pilot flame until it ignites or for a maximum of 60 s. If the specimen extinguishes, the procedure is repeated for 10 s at 2, 3, 4, 6 and 8 min. The distances travelled by the flame front at 1 min and at the end of the test are noted. The arithmetic mean is computed from the results of three tests.

Table 8.24   Radiant panel test specifications for floorings

Specimens	3 specimens 400 mm × 95 mm × max. 55 mm
Specimen position	vertical, long side (400 mm) at 90° to radiator surface
Ignition sources	– radiant panel 305 mm × 305 mm run on propane, surface tempera- ture 850 °C
	– propane pilot flame (flame height 40 mm) below the specimen on the same side as the radiator
Test duration	10 min
Conclusion	classification in classes M.3 to M.5 depending on test performance

This method corresponds in principle to the small scale surface spread of flame test described in the British BS 476: Part 7 (see Section 8.2.5).

Determination of calorific potential to NF M 03-005

The calorific potential (pouvoir calorifique) [6] is determined in order to provide proof that a building material is non-combustible (incombustible = M.0). Classification M.0 applies if the upper calorific potential does not exceed 2500 kJ/kg. Most class M.0 building materials are inorganic and usually contain organic components only as binders. Such materials are classified in class M.1 without testing although the organic component is found mainly on the surface and brief ignition of more than 5 s can occur.

The test apparatus consists of a bomb calorimeter in which the powdered material is placed. At least three determinations are made and the arithmetic mean computed.

This test method is basically similar to the ISO 1716 high pressure bomb calorimeter method (see [13] in references for Section 8.2.18).

Classification of building materials to NF P 92-507

The only primary test used for flexible materials ≦ 5 mm thick is the electrical burner test (NF P 92-503). The superseded alcohol flame test (NF P 92-502) is therefore not discussed here.

Class M.0 "incombustible" (non-combustible)

Materials are placed in class M.0 if the requirements for M.1 are satisfied and the upper calorific potential, determined by NF M 03-005, does not exceed 2500 kJ/kg. This applies to flexible as well as rigid materials.

Classification of flexible materials ≦ 5 mm thick

Classification in classes M.1 to M.3 is carried out with the electrical burner test (NF P 92-503). The classification criteria are shown in Table 8.25.

Table 8.25   Criteria for classifying materials in classes M.1 to M.3 by the NF P 92-503 test

Classification		M.1	M.2	M.3	>M.3
duration of combustion	[s]	≦ 5	>5	>5	>5
damaged length	[mm]	–	<350	<600	600
width	[mm]	–	–	<90	>90

If classification in M.1, M.2 or M.3 is not achieved in the primary test, the rate of flame spread test (NF P 92-504) must be carried out. If the rate of flame spread $\leqq$ 2 mm/s the material is classified in class M.4, otherwise it is considered as class M.5.

Classifications M.1 to M.3 can be subject to doubt in two cases: if droplets are formed or if the test specimen melts prematurely ($\leqq$ 20 s) in the vicinity of the radiator before igniting.

Dripping

If burning droplets occur during the primary test, the material is placed in class M.4 regardless of the test results.

If non-burning droplets are formed, the NF P 92-505 dripping test must be carried out. If the cotton wool is ignited by the droplets, the material is classified in class M.4. If ignition does not occur the classification achieved in the primary test is retained.

Premature melting ($\leqq$ 20 s)

If premature melting ($\leqq$ 20 s) occurs without the test specimen igniting, the dripping test (NF P 92-505 – classification criteria as above) and the rate of spread of flame test (NF P 92-504) must be carried out as complementary tests. If in the rate of flame spread test the flame is immediately extinguished when the burner is removed, the classification achieved in the primary test is retained. If the test specimen does not burn as far as the second reference mark, it is classified in class M.3. If the second reference mark is exceeded, the material is classified in M.4 for a rate of $\leqq$ 2 mm/s and in M.5 for a rate of >2 mm/s.

Classification of rigid materials of any thickness and flexible materials >5 mm thick

Classification in classes M.1 to M.3 is carried out with the epiradiateur test (NF P 92-501). The classification criteria are given in Table 8.26.

Table 8.26 Classification criteria for classes M.1 to M.3 according to the NF P 92-501 test

Classification		M.1	M.2 a* or b		M.3 a or b		>M.3
Indices for							
flammability	$\overline{i}$	0	to choice	<1	to choice	<2	
flame spread	$\overline{s}$	0	<0.2	<1	<1	<5	>5
max. flame length	$\overline{h}$	0	<1	<1	<1.5	<2.5	>2.5
combustibility	$\overline{c}$	<1	<1	<1	<1	<2.5	>2.5

* a or b may be chosen

If classes M.1, M.2 or M.3 are not achieved in the primary test, the rate of flame spread is determined to NF P 92-504 to ascertain whether the material can be classified in class M.4 (rate of flame spread $\leqq$ 2 mm/s) or M.5 (>2 mm/s).

Two complementary tests exist for materials which melt without igniting in the vicinity of the radiant panel. These are the dripping test to NF P 92-505 and the rate of flame spread test to NF P 92-504.

If burning droplets do not occur in the dripping test, classification M.1 to M.3 is retained. If burning droplets occur, the material is classified in class M.4. If the flame extinguishes immediately the burner is removed in the rate of spread of flame test, M.1 is retained, otherwise the material is classified in class M.3 (test specimen does not burn as far as the second reference mark) or M.4 (rate of spread of flame $\leqq$ 2 mm/s) or M.5 (>2 mm/s).

The NF P 92-506 radiant panel test is intended to classify floor coverings in classes M.3 to M.5 if they do not achieve M.1 or M.2 classification in the epiradiateur test. M.3 is achieved if the mean maximum distance travelled by the flame front $\leqq$ 300 mm. Materials are classified in class M.4 if the flame front has advanced $\leqq$ 100 mm after 1 min and has travelled more than 300 mm at the end of the test. Class M.5 is achieved if the flame front has advanced more than 100 mm and 300 mm at 1 min and at the end of the test, respectively.

Official approval

The tests described above must be carried out in order to classify building materials and obtain official approval. Four test institutes in France are licensed by the decree of 5. 2. 1959 ([3], Vol. II, p. 77) to test the fire performance of building materials (réaction au feu des matériaux de construction):

- Centre scientifique et technique du bâtiment (C.S.T.B.)
  Laboratoire du feu. Station de recherche
  84, avenue Jean-Jaurès – Champs-sur-Marne
  F-77428 Marne la Vallée Cédex 2
- Laboratoire central de la préfecture de police (L.C.P.P.)
  39 bis, rue de Dantzig
  F-75015 Paris
- Laboratoire national d'essais (L.N.E.)
  1, rue Gaston-Boissier
  F-75015 Paris
- Société nationale des poudres et explosifs (S.N.P.E.)
  Centre de recherches du Bouchet
  B.P. 2
  F-91710 Vert-le-Petit

Materials should be submitted directly to one of the above addresses. Following the tests, the laboratory issues so-called procès-verbaux (test protocols) describing the test performance and resultant classification. The "demande d'homologation de classement" (application for official approval) enclosed with the procès-verbal should be sent to the Ministry of the Interior, Dept of Civil Safety at the address below.

Ministère de l'Intérieur
Direction de la sécurité civile (D.S.C.)
1, Place Beauvau
F-75800 Paris Cédex

In practice the "homologation" is used only for publication in the Journal Officiel as official recognition comes into force de facto with the issue of the procès-verbal by the test institute.

In cases of dispute, a committee of experts, the comité d'étude et de classification des matériaux et éléments de construction par rapport au danger d'incendie (C.E.C.M.I.) (committee for the study and classification of building materials and components with regard to fire hazard) can order further fire tests, not laid down in the regulations, to be carried out.

The use of synthetic materials

The problem of secondary fire effects and, in particular, of fire gases has achieved prominence due to various spectacular fire incidents. One result has been pressure by the Paris fire brigade on the Ministry of the Interior which has led to official controls on the use of synthetic materials in buildings open to the public.

The regulations governing the use of such materials laid down in the Arrêté of 4. 11. 1975 ([3], Vol. II, p. 101) and its revision of 1. 12. 1976 (Journal Officiel no 7 N.C. of 20. 1. 1977) specify that the total amounts of nitrogen (N) and chlorine (Cl) contained in synthetic materials which can be liberated as HCN or HCl must not exceed 5 g and 25 g respectively per m^3 of enclosed space.

Plastics, man-made fibres and textiles, elastomers, paints, varnishes and adhesives are considered as synthetic materials. Materials which achieve classes M.0 and M.1 are not taken into account. Certain materials, such as foams, and special applications are rated with other fire risk factors as shown in Table 8.27.

Table 8.27   Special provisions concerning chlorine and nitrogen levels

Building material classification	Application		
	Ceiling	Floor	Miscellaneous
M.0 or M.1	0	0	0
M.2 or M.3 Density ≥ 0.02 g/cm^3	$\dfrac{4 \cdot bP*}{3}$	0	bP
< 0.02 g/cm^3	$\dfrac{16 \cdot bP}{9}$	0	$\dfrac{4 \cdot bP}{3}$
M.4 or M.5 Density ≥ 0.02 g/cm^3	–	$\dfrac{bP}{5}$	bP
< 0.02 g/cm^3	–	–	$\dfrac{4 \cdot bP}{3}$

*P = weight in kg of the nitrogen- or chlorine-containing product
 b = nitrogen or chlorine content in % by weight

Future developments

No major changes are foreseen in the fire performance regulations and testing of building materials in France. In the medium term, a reduction in the classifications M.0 to M.5 is under consideration.

The procedures in the NF P 92-501 to 92-506 test methods will be precisely defined and published as an "arrêté" in the Journal Officiel.

No change in the Cl/N provisions is planned.

Attempts are being made to introduce marking and inspection of building materials, on a purely voluntary basis. Building materials are classified on the basis of a fire test carried out by the materials testing institutes on a reference sample. Reserve samples are used, not for ageing tests, but for subsequent identification of the material. Since no obligatory marking exists, such identification is not legally relevant.

The Association Française de Normalisation (AFNOR) has been appointed by the Ministry of the Interior to establish regulations covering certification and inspection of the fire performance of building materials. Conformation with these regulations will be guaranteed by a quality mark or "marque NF". Products carrying a "marque NF" will be subject to quality control carried out by quality assurance associations. Fire tests, factory inspection and regular sampling will be involved [7].

A standard for determining the smoke density of fire gases was published in October 1976 within the framework of AFNOR. According to this unofficial experimental standard, the smoke density is determined with the aid of the NBS smoke chamber [8] (see Section 9.2.2.1).

References for 8.2.4

[1]   *H. Bub:* Bauordnungen im europäischen Raum und Entwicklungen in der Bundesrepublik. Arbeitstagung der Bundesvereinigung der Prüfingenieure für Baustatik, Sept. 1978, Lübeck-Travemünde.

[2]   *H. Braun:* Vorschriften in sechs EWG-Ländern; Part 2: Nationale Systeme der Bauvorschriften. 3. Frankreich. Baurecht-Technische Vorschriften-Institutionen, in Ifo: Studien zur Bauwirtschaft 1, Ifo-Institut für Wirtschaftsforschung e. V., Munich, Feb. 1973.

[3]   Journal Officiel de la République Française. Sécurité contre l'Incendie; 2 volumes.
      Broschure N° 1011-I, Tome I: Etablissements recevant du public.
      Broschure N° 1011-II, Tome II: Législation et réglementation générales. Immeubles de grande hauteur. Bâtiments d'habitation. Etablissements industriels et commerciaux. Divers.
      Edition giving situation at 15. 8. 1979. Journaux Officiels, 26, rue Desaix, 75732 Paris CEDEX 15.
      (These brochures are kept up to date by supplements available from the Journaux Officiels. A supplement concerning buildings open to the public appeared in the Journal Officiel on 14th August 1980, pp. 7363–7416.)

[4]   Bâtiment. Essais de réaction au feu des matériaux. Normes NF P 92-501 to P 92-507, October 1975. Association Française de Normalisation (AFNOR), Tour Europe, CEDEX 7, 92080 Paris la Défense.
      NF P 92-501: Essai par rayonnement applicable aux matériaux rigides ou rendus tels (matériaux de revêtement) de toute épaisseur et aux matériaux souples d'épaisseur supérieure à 5 mm.
      NF 92-502: Essai à la flamme d'alcool applicable aux matériaux souples d'une épaisseur inférieure ou égale à 5 mm.
      NF P 92-503: Essai au brûleur électrique applicable aux matériaux souples d'une épaisseur inférieure ou égale à 5 mm (essai complémentaire).
      NF P 92-504: Essai de vitesse de propagation de la flamme applicable aux matériaux non destinés à être placés sur un subjectile (essai complémentaire).
      NF P 92-505: Essai de goutte, au radiateur, applicable aux matériaux fusibles (essai complémentaire).
      NF P 92-506: Essai au panneau radiant pour revêtements de sol (essai complémentaire).
      NF P 92-507: Classement des matériaux utilisés dans la construction.

[5]   NF P 92-508: Essai au brûleur électrique. Méthode de réglage de l'appareil. September 1978.
      NF P 92-509: Réglage du radiateur. September 1978.

[6]   NF M 03-005: Combustibles solides. Détermination du pouvoir calorifique supérieur d'un combustible solide. October 1967.

[7]   *A. Thiard:* Marquage et contrôle des matérieux de bâtiment quant à leur réaction au feu from G.P.C.P. les plastiques et le feu-Journées d'Etude, 24–26. 11. 1976, p. 171, Compagnie Française d'Editions, Paris, 1978.

[8]   Norme expérimentale X 10-702: Essai de mesure de la densité optique spécifique de la fumée. October 1976.

8.2.5 Great Britain and Northern Ireland

Statutory regulations

The following building regulations and bylaws apply in the various parts of the United Kingdom:

– England and Wales: The Building Regulations 1976 – also valid in the outer London area [1].
– Inner London area: The Building Bylaws of the Greater London Council 1972 [2].
– Scotland: The Building Standards (Scotland) Regulations 1971–1979 [3].
– Northern Ireland: The Building Regulations 1977 [4].

The use and fire performance requirements of building materials and components are specified in the various building regulations, e.g. under "Structural Fire Precautions" – in Part E for England, Wales and Part D for Scotland. The regulations for England, Wales and Northern Ireland are identical. Those for Scotland differ in minor aspects only. All the regulations are based on the same test methods specified in British Standards. The requirements of the Greater London Council have a different basis and are expressed in terms of acceptable materials and components with test results given as an alternative where appropriate.

The individual building regulations are being increasingly brought into line with those of England and Wales with the aim of achieving a uniform system throughout the United Kingdom.

Classification and testing of the fire performance of building materials

Compliance with the fire performance requirements of building materials and components laid down in the building regulations must be demonstrated with certain tests. The methods are described in British Standards BS 476: Parts 3 to 8 and, for certain special cases, in BS 2782: Method 102 C and Methods 508 A, C and D. These standards are issued by the British Standards Institution, 2 Park Street, London W1A 2BS.

BS 476 "Fire Tests on Building Materials and Structures" consists of [5]:

– Part 3: External Fire Exposure Roof Test
– Part 4: Non-Combustibility Test for Materials
– Part 5: Method of Test for Ignitability
– Part 6: Fire Propagation Test for Materials
– Part 7: Surface Spread of Flame Test for Materials
– Part 8: Test Methods and Criteria for the Fire Resistance of Elements of Building Construction.

The whole of BS 476 is in the course of revision and a new edition of Part 5 was issued in 1979.

BS 476: Part 3 and 8 describe the testing of roofs and elements of building construction and are not covered in this book.

Building materials are classified in various classes of combustibility listed in the Building Regulations with the aid of test methods described in BS 476: Parts 6 and 7. Separation into non-combustible and combustible materials is carried out according to BS 476: Part 4. Combustible building materials are graded in classes 0 to 4 with increasing fire hazard. Testing for classification in class 0 is carried out according to Part 6 while classes 1 to 4 are classified in accordance with BS 476: Part 7. The performance of certain plastics which cannot be tested by BS 476: Parts 3, 6 and 7 is investigated with the tests in BS 2782 methods 102 C and 508 A, C and D.

Part E "Safety in Fire" of the Building Regulations for England and Wales is subdivided into 23 sections [1]. The use of combustible building materials is specified in Sections E 6 (suspended ceilings), E 7 (external walls), E 15 (internal walls and ceilings) and E 16 (exceptions for the use of certain plastics materials).

No regulations exist at present for testing combustible floor coverings and for determining smoke evolution or toxicity of fire gases.

Malhotra reviews the Building Regulations and test methods for determining and classifying the fire performance of building materials [6].

BS 476: Part 4. Non-combustibility test

The non-combustibility of building materials is tested to BS 476: Part 4 (1970 version). A revision of this standard is in preparation [7] but its incorporation in building regulations will probably be lengthy since changes in terminology such as "combustibility" must be taken into account. BS 476: Part 4 is substantially similar to ISO 1182. A diagram of the non-combustibility furnace is shown and test specifications are discussed in Section 8.2.18.2.

BS 476: Part 5. Ignitability test

The ignitability of building materials is determined by BS 476: Part 5, 1979. A diagram and test specifications are reproduced in Fig. 8.15 and Table 8.28, respectively.

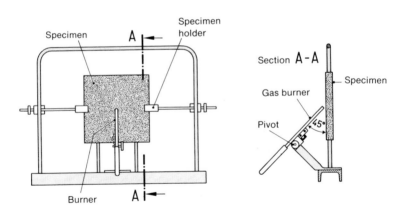

Fig. 8.15   Ignitability test apparatus

The test is carried out by exposing the test specimen to a 10 mm long gas flame for 10 s. A note is made of the extent of flaming during the application of the pilot flame and for 10 s immediately thereafter.

This method was previously required as an additional test to BS 476: Part 6 but is not specifically mentioned in the Building Regulations. Experience has shown that it is not particularly successful at predicting performance and it is therefore seldom used for classifying building materials.

Table 8.28   Ignitability test specifications

Specimens	3 specimens 225 mm × 225 mm
Specimen position	vertical
Ignition source	small burner inclined at 45°, flame length 10 mm; tip of burner sited 3 mm from the central point of the face of the specimen
Test duration	10 s
Conclusions	– classification P if none of the specimens flame for more than 10 s after removal of the flame and burning of the specimen does not extend to an edge – classification X if the requirements for P are not met

BS 476: Part 6. Fire propagation test

This method for testing fire propagation is in fact a determination of heat release. A diagram of the equipment and test specifications are reproduced in Fig. 8.16 and Table 8.29, respectively.

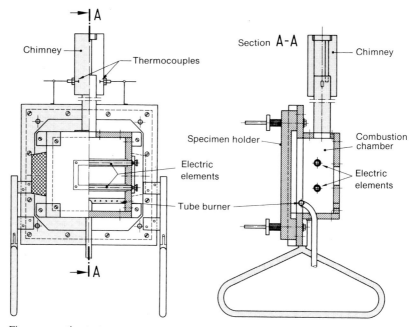

Fig. 8.16   Fire propagation test apparatus

Fire propagation is determined by exposing the specimen to the 14 jets of a gas pipe burner at a distance of 3 mm. The heat evolved is 530 J/s. The two electric elements with a total output of 1800 W are switched on after 2 min 45 s. Their output is reduced to 1500 W after 5 minutes and maintained constant until the end of the test (20 min).

The difference between ambient temperature and that in the chimney is recorded continuously using thermocouples and compared with a calibration curve. The two curves are

Table 8.29   Fire propagation test specifications

Specimens	3 specimens 228 mm × 228 mm × max. 50 mm
Specimen position	vertical
Ignition sources	– two 1000 W electric elements with variable output (1800 W after 2 min 45 s and 1500 W after 5 min); distance from specimen: 45 mm – gas pipe burners (internal diameter 9 mm) with 14 holes (internal diameter 1.5 mm) at 12.5 mm centres, distance from specimen 3 mm, flame applied 25 mm above the bottom of the exposed face of the specimen
Test duration	20 min
Conclusion	class 0 achieved if indices $i_1 \leqq 6$ and $I \leqq 12$ (for explanation, see below)

evaluated by establishing the temperatures from the calibration curve and test curve at 30 s intervals from the start of the test to 3 min, at 1 min intervals from 4 to 10 min and at 2 min intervals from 12 to 20 min.

The individual indices are calculated as follows from these values:

$$i_1 = \sum_{1/2}^{3} \frac{\Theta_m - \Theta_c}{10\,t} \quad ; \quad i_2 = \sum_{4}^{10} \frac{\Theta_m - \Theta_c}{10\,t} \quad \text{and} \quad i_3 = \sum_{12}^{20} \frac{\Theta_m - \Theta_c}{10\,t}$$

The total index I is $I = i_1 + i_2 + i_3$

where i_1, i_2 and i_3 are subindices

t = time in minutes from the origin at which the reading is taken
Θ_m = temperature in °C of the test curve at time t
Θ_c = temperature in °C of the calibration curve at time t.

The fire propagation test serves mainly to investigate whether materials which have achieved class 1 according to BS 476: Part 7 conform to class 0. The conditions of class 0 are met if subindex $i_1 \leqq 6$ and the total index $I \leqq 12$. Class 0 makes increased demands on the fire performance of class 1 building products and differentiates between them as regards fire hazard. The method is also used to examine the suitability of building materials for certain applications. For example, external claddings for houses higher than 15 m must have a total index $I \leqq 20$.

BS 476: Part 7. Surface spread of flame test

The surface spread of flame is determined with the apparatus shown in Fig. 8.17. The test specifications are summarised in Table 8.30.

The specimen is exposed to the radiant panel and, in addition, the pilot flame is applied during the first minute of the test. The time required for the flame front to reach reference marks on the specimen is noted.

The materials are classified according to test performance as shown in Table 8.31. Only classes 1 and 3 are considered in the building regulations. Class 4 materials are high risk and their use is not permitted.

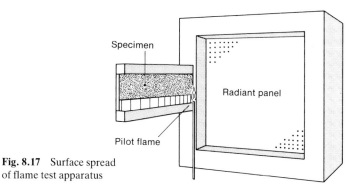

Fig. 8.17 Surface spread
of flame test apparatus

Table 8.30 Surface spread of flame test specifications

Specimens	6 specimens 900 mm × 230 mm × max. 50 mm
Specimen position	vertical, longitudinal axis (900 mm), perpendicular to the radiant panel
Ignition sources	– gas fired radiant panel, radiation intensity 75 mm from radiant panel surface: 37 kW/m²
	– gas pilot flame (height: 75 to 100 mm) below the specimen on the same side as the radiant panel
Test duration	10 min
Conclusion	classification in classes 1 to 4 depending on test performance

Table 8.31 Spread of flame classification

Classi-fication	Flame spread at 1.5 min		Final flame spread	
	Limit [mm]	Tolerance for one specimen [mm]	Limit [mm]	Tolerance for one specimen [mm]
Class 1	165	25	165	25
Class 2	215	25	455	45
Class 3	265	25	710	75
Class 4	Exceeding class 3 limits			

The "small scale spread of flame test", also described in BS 476: Part 7 is neither mandatory nor does it correlate with the actual spread of flame test and is therefore not discussed here. However, it forms the basis of the French test for fire performance of floor coverings to NF P 92-506 (see Fig. 8.14).

BS 2782. Test methods for plastics

It is usual to test building materials in general and not specific groups for fire performance. The English regulations, however, make an exception of plastics due to the realisation that some thermoplastics cannot be tested by the surface spread of flame method as they fall out

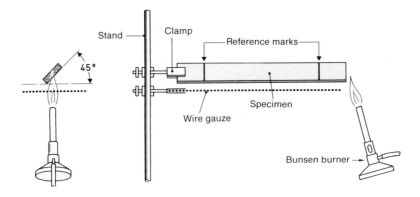

Fig. 8.18   Rate of burning apparatus
left: Front view, *right:* Side view

of the specimen holder. As a result section E 16 "Exceptions permitting the use of certain plastics materials" was incorporated in the Building Regulations for England and Wales. Materials such as plastic ceiling tiles and sheeting must pass the fire performance tests of BS 2782. The use of such materials is, however, subject to restrictions on size, thickness and separation from each other.

The procedures specified in the Building Regulations for testing plastics are BS 2782 Methods 102 C, 508 A, 508 C and 508 D [8]. Method 102 C to BS 2782: Part 1 is used for determining the softening point of thermoplastics and does not constitute a fire test. Plastics with a softening point lower than 120 °C cannot be classified in class 0 although there are exceptions (Section E 15 in [1]).

Method 508 A. Rate of burning

The rate of burning is determined by BS 2782: Part 5, Method 508 A using the apparatus illustrated in Fig. 8.18. The test specifications are summarised in Table 8.32.

Table 8.32   Rate of burning test specifications

Specimens	3 specimens 150 mm × 13 mm × 1.5 mm, reference lines at 25 mm and 125 mm parallel to the free end of the specimen
Specimen position	longitudinal axis (150 mm) horizontal, short edge (13 mm) inclined at 45° to horizontal
Ignition source	alcohol or Bunsen burner (flame length 13 mm to 19 mm)
Test duration	flame applied to free end of specimen for 10 s, specimen monitored until flame extinguishes
Conclusions	Building Regulations satisfied if – rate of burning $\leq$ 50 mm/min (for all plastics) – burnt length $\leq$ 25 mm and residual flaming $\leq$ 5 s (rigid PVC panels)

A non-luminous alcohol or Bunsen flame is applied for 10 s to the free end of the specimen. The times at which the first and second reference lines are reached by the flame front are noted and the rate of burning computed in mm/min. If the flame does not reach the first line, the duration of residual flaming or afterglow is measured.

Method 508 C. Flammability of thin PVC sheeting

The flammability of plasticised PVC sheeting is determined by BS 2782: Part 5, Method 508 C using the apparatus shown in Fig. 8.19. Test specifications are given in Table 8.33.

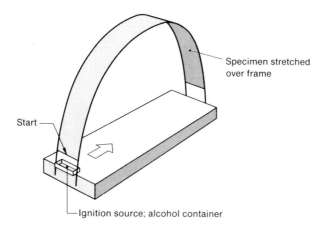

Specimen stretched over frame

Start

Ignition source; alcohol container

Fig. 8.19   Apparatus for determining the combustibility of plasticised PVC sheeting

Table 8.33   Specifications for testing the flammability of thin PVC sheeting

Specimens	6 specimens 550 mm × 35 mm
Specimen position	stretched over 2 parallel semi-circular (r = 178 mm)
	frames 25 mm apart
Ignition source	alcohol flame (absolute ethanol)
Test duration	until alcohol flame or specimen extinguish
Conclusions	complies with Building Regulations if extent of burning ≦ 75 mm for plasticised PVC sheeting less than 1 mm thick

The specimen is stretched over both frames so that one end lines up with the starting mark. 0.1 ml of absolute alcohol are poured into a copper container located beneath the start mark and ignited. After the flame extinguishes the extent of burning from the start mark is noted.

Method 508 D. Alcohol cup test

The alcohol cup test to BS 2782: Part 5, Method 508 D is suitable for testing the flammability of bulky plastics materials. The principle is illustrated in Fig. 8.20 and the test specifications are summarised in Table 8.34.

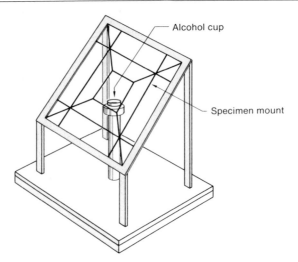

Fig. 8.20   Alcohol cup test apparatus for determining flammability

Table 8.34   Alcohol cup test specifications

Specimens	3 specimens 150 mm × 150 mm
Specimen position	inclined at 45° to horizontal
Ignition source	alcohol flame (cup with 0.3 ml absolute ethanol) 25 mm away from specimen
Test duration	until alcohol flame or specimen extinguish
Conclusions	Building Regulations satisfied if afterflame time ≤ 5 s, charred surface $\leq 20\%$ and no burning droplets

The alcohol cup is first warmed by burning 0.3 ml absolute alcohol. It is refilled within 2.5 min and the test specimen is exposed to the alcohol flame which burns for approximately 45 s. After the alcohol flame extinguishes, afterflame time and afterglow time of the specimen are recorded. Note is also made of the occurrence or otherwise of flaming droplets and how great the charred area of the specimen is.

Further methods for testing plastics

Other methods besides the BS 2782 flammability tests described above exist although these are not mandatory for the building sector. For completeness, they are mentioned here. The tests are BS 2782: Part 5, Method 508 B (Flammability of an extruded PVC compound) and 508 E (Glow bar test for thermosets) [8]. Methods 141 A to 141 D, which use the oxygen index to characterise the thermal properties of plastics, were incorporated in BS 2782: Part 1 [9] in 1978.

All the test procedures for plastics mentioned here are laboratory scale flammability tests used mainly for quality control by manufacturers. They are also frequently used by local authorities in purchasing specifications.

The flammability tests in specification standards for plastics are often based on BS 2782: Methods 508 A to 508 E (e.g. 508 A in BS 1524, BS 3932, BS 4584; 508 C in BS 5550 and 508 D in BS 4790).

Official approval

The tests described above must be carried out in order to classify the fire performance and to obtain official approval of building materials. In principle the fire performance of building materials can be assessed by any test laboratory in the UK if the test methods laid down in the Building Regulations are used. There are therefore no state or officially recognised test institutes. However, due to the onerous test procedures, there are relatively few organisations carrying out such tests. In general, the tests are carried out by Institutes which have been granted a Certificate of Competence by the Department of the Environment (DOE). The Fire Research Station (FRS) run by the Building Research Establishment (BRE) on behalf of the DOE is one of the largest of its kind in Europe. Fire tests of building materials have not been carried out for some years at the FRS. They are now carried out by FIRTO (address given below which is also the FRS address) located on the same site. The principal test laboratories are listed below (those with a DOE certificate are marked "DOE").

– Fire Insurers' Research & Testing Organisation (FIRTO) "DOE"
  Melrose Avenue
  Borehamwood
  Hertfordshire WD6 2BL

  Tests: BS 476, Parts 3 to 8
      BS 2782, 508 A to 508 D

– Minton, Treharne & Davies Ltd.
  Merton House
  Bute Crescent
  Cardiff CF1 6NB

  Tests: BS 476, Parts 4 to 7

– Thorn Lighting Ltd. "DOE"
  Great Cambridge Road
  Enfield
  Middlesex EN1 1UL

  Tests: BS 2782, 102 C, 508 A to 508 D

– Warrington Research Centre "DOE"
  Holmesfield Road
  Warrington WA1 2DS

  Tests: BS 476, Parts 3 to 8
      BS 2782, 102 C, 508 A to 508 D

– Yarsley Testing Laboratories "DOE"
  The Street
  Ashtead
  Surrey K21 2AB

  Tests: BS 476, Parts 3 to 8.

After the test, the laboratory issues a report giving the test results and, where required, the classification of the building material. This document provides sufficient confirmation of the fire performance of the building materials. Building materials are not marked or inspected.

Future developments

All parts (from 3 to 8) of BS 476 are being revised but it will be some years before revision is complete. The adoption of this new version in building inspection is a long way off since new experience and terminology must be taken into account in the Building Regulations. BS 476: Parts 3 (1958) and 5 (1968) are still officially in force although revisions of both have appeared (Part 3 in 1975, Part 5 in 1979).

As far as secondary fire effects such as smoke development and toxicity of fire gases are concerned ISO developments are awaited and these will be adopted as national tests.

References for 8.2.5

[1] The Building Regulations 1976. London HMSO, 1976.
[2] London Building (Constructional) Bylaws. Greater London Council, London, 1972.
[3] The Building Standards (Scotland) Regulations 1971–1979, London HMSO.
[4] The Building Regulations (Northern Ireland). Belfast HMSO, 1977.
[5] BS 476. Fire Tests on Building Materials and Structures.
      – Part 3: 1975. External Fire Exposure Roof Test (the Building Regulations tests are still based on the 1958 version).
      – Part 4: 1970. Non-Combustibility Test for Materials.
      – Part 5: 1979. Method of Test for Ignitability.
      – Part 6: 1968. Fire Propagation Test for Materials.
      – Part 7: 1971. Surface Spread of Flame Test for Materials.
      – Part 8: 1972. Test Methods and Criteria for the Fire Resistance of Elements of Building Construction.
[6] H. L. Malhotra: Use of Reaction to Fire Tests in the United Kingdom. Eurogypsum-Conference Turin, 21. 9. 1978.
[7] Revision of BS 476 Fire Tests for Building Materials and Structures. Part 4. Combustibility Test. Document 79/14300, October 1979.
[8] BS 2782. Methods of Testing Plastics. Part 5. Miscellaneous Methods. Methods 508 A to 508 E. Flammability. 1970.
      AMD 1524. Amendment Slip No. 3, 17. July 1974.
      – Method 508 A. Rate of Burning (Laboratory Method).
      – Method 508 B. Flammability of a Specimen 230 mm × 25 mm × 1.3 mm of Polyvinyl Chloride Extrusion Compound (Laboratory Method).
      – Method 508 C. Flammability of a Specimen 550 mm × 35 mm of thin Polyvinyl Chloride Sheeting (Laboratory Method).
      – Method 508 D. Flammability of a Specimen 150 mm Square, not Exceeding 50 mm in Thickness, of a Plastics Material (Alcohol Cup Test) (Laboratory Method).
      – Method 508 E. Incandescence Resistance of a Specimen 10 mm × 4 mm × Approximately 100 mm of Rigid Thermosetting Plastics (Laboratory Method).
[9] BS 2782: Part 1: Methods 141 A to 141 D: 1978.
      Plastics. Part 1. Thermal Properties.
      – Method 141 A. Oxygen Index of Combustion of a Rigid Bar of 10 mm × 4 mm Nominal Cross Section.
      – Method 141 B. Oxygen Index of Combustion of a Rigid Bar of 6.5 mm × 3 mm Nominal Cross Section.
      – Method 141 C. Oxygen Index of Combustion of a Bar 10 mm Wide Cut from Rigid Sheet 1.2 mm to 6.5 mm Thick.
      – Method 141 D. Oxygen Index of Combustion of a Rigid Bar of 6.5 mm × 3 mm Nominal Cross Section of Electric Cable Insulation or Sheeting Material.

8.2.6 Italy

Statutory regulations

Numerous building laws and regulations exist in Italy. The state building law (Legge Urbanistica) was enacted in 1942, brought up to date in 1967 by further legislation (Legge Ponte) and has since been superseded by a mass of laws and general decrees covering various subjects such as town planning, finance, energy etc. Local authorities are empowered to pass local building regulations based on these laws [1].

The following preventative fire protection regulations apply to public and high rise buildings:

- Circolare No 91 (14. 9. 1961) of the Ministry of the Interior, covering fire safety standards for buildings with a steel structure.
- Circolare No 37 (29. 6. 1973) of the Consiglio Nazionale delle Ricerche (CNR) (National Research Institute) in which new principles are suggested for a standard concerning fire protection in buildings with a steel structure (Both "circulars" apply only to the fire resistance of building components).
- Circolare No 12 (17. 5. 1980) of the Ministry of the Interior relating to fire performance of building materials describes methods for determining the fire performance and classification of building materials and is discussed in detail in the following section.

Testing and classifying the fire performance of building materials according to Circolare No 12

Circolare No 12 contains test procedures enabling the fire performance of building materials to be determined and classified. These test methods have been adopted by the Italian Standards Organisation, UNI (Ente Nazionale Italiano di Unificazione) and other organisations, such as Uniplast, Unitex, etc.

The methods contained in Circolare No 12 are the non-combustibility test for building materials based on ISO/DIS 1182.2, the CSE* RF** 1/75/A (edge application of flame) and CSE RF 2/75/A (surface flame application) small burner ignitability tests for combustible materials and the CSE RF 3/77 test for the contribution of a material to spread of flame. According to Italian opinion, these procedures define the characteristic parameters determining the fire hazard of building materials in the early and advanced stages of an initiating fire. The results of these tests enable building materials to be classified in various fire classes which are also specified in Circolare No 12.

Further standards for assessing the fire resistance of building components (UNI 7678, 1978) and for determining the calorific potential of building materials (UNI 7557, 1976) exist but are not dealt with in this book.

Standards and draft standards are issued by the Ente Nazionale Italiano di Unificazione (UNI), Piazza Armando Diaz 2, I-20123 Milano.

Testing non-combustibility according to ISO/DIS 1182.2

The non-combustibility of building materials is tested in accordance with Circolare No 12 to ISO/DIS 1182.2. A diagram of the non-combustibility furnace and test specifications are given in Section 8.2.18.2.

---

* CSE = Centro Studi ed Esperienze (Research Centre of the Ministry of the Interior).
** RF = Reazione al fuoco (Reaction to Fire).

CSE RF 1/75/A. Small burner test (edge application of flame)

Method CSE RF 1/75/A [2] is used to determine afterflame time, afterglow and the extent of damage of materials such as curtains and awnings which may be subjected to the effects of a flame from both sides. The method is based on the DIN 53 906 small burner test. The test rig is basically similar to the small burner used in DIN 4102 Part 1 for testing moderate flammability (building material class B2) (see Section 8.2.2, Fig. 8.4). The test specifications are summarised in Table 8.35:

Table 8.35   CSE RF 1/75/A small burner test specifications

Specimens	340 mm × 104 mm, 2 series of 10 specimens (5 in the direction of warp and 5 in the direction of weft)
Specimen position	vertical
Ignition source	small propane gas burner inclined at 45°, flame length 40 mm, edge application of flame
Test duration	12 s
Conclusion	depending on test performance classification into various categories taking into consideration afterflame time, afterglow, extent of damage and flaming droplets

The flame is applied to the specimen for 12 s. The afterflame time, afterglow time, extent of damage and flaming droplets are observed and recorded. The four parameters above are divided into three grades as shown in Table 8.36.

Table 8.36   Grading of building materials to CSE RF 1/75/A

Grade	Afterflame time [s]	Afterglow time [s]	Extent of damage [mm]	Time for drippings to extinguish [s]
1	≤ 5	≤ 10	≤ 150	non burning
2	$> 5 - \leq 60$	$> 10 - \leq 60$	$> 150 - \leq 200$	≤ 3
3	> 60	> 60	> 200	> 3

Table 8.37   Determination of building material categories

Parameter	Weighting factor
Afterflame time	2
Afterglow time	1
Extent of damage	2
Dripping	1
Category	Weighted sum of grades (grade × weighting)
I	6– 8
II	9–12
III	13–15
IV	16–18

In order to establish the category which serves as the basis for classifying the building material, the grades of the four parameters are multiplied with weighting factors (Table 8.37). Materials which are consumed in under 5 s are placed in the worst category, i.e. IV; if they burn for more than 10 min they are classified in grade 3 for extent of damage.

CSE RF 2/75/A. Small burner test (surface application of flame)

Method CSE RF 2/75/A [3] is used to determine afterflame time, afterglow, extent of damage and hence fire performance of linings and materials for floors, walls and ceilings by surface application of flame from one side.

This fire test closely resembles DIN 54 332 and thus the DIN 4102 Part 1 test for moderate flammability (class B2 building materials). The test apparatus is illustrated in Section 8.2.2, Fig. 8.4. The Italian version, however, does not include a basket with a filter paper to test for burning droplets. The test specifications are summarised in Table 8.38.

Table 8.38   CSE 2/75/A small burner test specifications

Specimens	340 mm × 104 mm × 3 to 5 mm thick
	2 series of 10 specimens (5 in the direction of warp and 5 in the direction of weft)
Specimen position	vertical, cotton thread 290 mm above lower edge of specimen
Ignition source	small propane burner, inclined at 45°, flame height 20 mm (flame applied to surface of specimen 40 mm above lower edge)
Test duration	30 s
Conclusion	depending on test performance, classification into various categories taking into account afterflame and afterglow times, extent of damage and flaming droplets

The flame is applied to the specimen for 30 s. The four parameters, afterflame time, afterglow time, extent of damage and flaming droplets are observed and recorded. These parameters are divided into three grades. The evaluation criteria are identical to those in Table 8.36 except for extent of damage which is placed in grade 3 if $\geqq 200$ mm and/or the cotton thread burns through.

The procedure for establishing the building material category is the same as that given for CSE RF 1/75/A in Table 8.37. Similarly, materials which burn for less than 5 s are placed in category IV and those which burn for longer than 10 min are placed in grade 3 as regards extent of damage.

CSE RF 3/77. Spread of flame test

The CSE RF 3/77 spread of flame test for building materials is carried out with a small flame and a radiant panel. The intensity of this ignition source system corresponds to the advanced phase in the initiating fire. By varying the position of the specimen, materials and finished components can be tested under conditions simulating use in floors, walls and ceilings.

This test method is based on and is practically identical with ISO/TC 92 draft proposal DP 5658 (Spread of flame). A diagram of the spread of flame test apparatus and the test specifications are given in Section 8.2.18.2.

The specimen is exposed to the radiant panel and pilot flame. Note is made of whether the specimen self-ignites and of the rate of spread of flame, extent of damage, afterglow and of flaming droplets. The four parameters are each divided into three grades (Table 8.39).

Table 8.39   Grading of building materials according to CSE R 3/77*

Grade	Rate of spread of flame [mm/min]	Extent of damage, maximum length [mm]	Afterglow time [s]	Time for drippings to extinguish [s]
1	not measurable	≦300	≦180	non-burning
2	≦30	≧350 – ≦600	>180 – ≦360	≦3
3	>30	≧650	>360	>3

The building material category on which classification is based is arrived at by multiplying the above grades with weighting factors which, in the case of flaming droplets, distinguish between floor, wall and ceiling use (Table 8.40).

Table 8.40   Determination of building material categories

Parameter	Weighting		
Rate of spread of flame	2		
Extent of damage	2		
Afterglow	1		
Dripping: floor	0		
wall	1		
ceiling	2		
Category	Weighted sum of grades (grade × weighting)		
	Floor	Wall	Ceiling
I	5– 7	6– 8	7– 9
II	8–10	9–12	10–13
III	11–13	13–15	14–17
IV	14–15	16–18	18–21

If a material burns for longer than 60 min, it is placed in extent of damage grade 3. If the rate of flame spread ≧ 200 mm/min and the extent of damage ≧ 650 mm the material is classified in the worst category, i.e. IV.

Classification

The categories obtained from the tests laid down in Circolare No 12 form the basis for classifying building materials as shown in Table 8.41.

---

* these figures are quoted directly from the Italian standard

Table 8.41 Classification of building materials according to ISO/DIS 1182.2, CSE RF 1/75/A, 2/75/A and 3/77

Test method	Conditions	Class
ISO/DIS 1182.2	as described in Section 8.2.18.2	0
method CSE RF 1/75/A or 2/75/A 3/77	compliance with categories to choice I I	1
1/75/A or 2/75/A 3/77	II I I II	2
1/75/A or 2/75/A 3/77	III II I III II II III III I II	3
1/75/A or 2/75/A 3/77	IV III III IV II IV I III IV III II IV I IV	4
1/75/A or 2/75/A 3/77	IV IV	5

Building materials are classified by testing according to ISO/DIS 1182.2, CSE RF 1/75/A, 2/75/A or 3/77. Two, five and seven equivalent combinations of the categories obtained are available for classification in classes 2, 3 and 4, respectively. Fire hazard increases from class 0 (lowest hazard) to class 5 (highest hazard).

Official approval

The tests for determining fire performance of building materials required as a result of the introduction of Circolare No 12 can be carried out by three state test institutes and five industrial laboratories.

State test institutes

– Ministro dell'Interno
  Direzione Generale della Protezione Civile
  Centro Studi ed Esperienze dei Vigili del Fuoco
  Capannelle-Roma

This fire laboratory (CSE), attached to the Ministry of the Interior, is the only officially approved one at the present time.

– Consiglio Nazionale delle Ricerche
  ICITE
  Via Lombardia-Frazione Sesto Ulteriano
  I-20098 S. Giuliano Milanese (MI)
– Consiglio Nazionale delle Ricerche
  Instituto del legno
  S. Michele all'Adige (TN)

Industrial laboratories

– ANIC
  Centro Tecnologico Materie Plastiche
  Via Jannozzi
  I-20097 S. Donato Milanese (MI)
– Montedison
  Divisione Petrolchimica
  Laboratorio Applicazioni Tecnologie
  Viale Lombardia 20
  I-20021 Bollate (MI)
– Rossifloor
  I-36035 Marano Vicentino (VC)
– Snia Viscosa
  Centro Sperimentale "F. Marinotti"
  Cesano Maderno (MI)
– STL
  Via Barozzo
  I-22075 Lurate Caccivio (CO)

As a result of the introduction of Circolare No 12 in May 1980 a commission of the Ministry of the Interior supported by industry, underwriters and other interested parties is drawing up a programme to clarify various aspects of preventative fire protection. Main points of this programme include definition of the area of application of Circolare No 12, the resultant transition arrangements, establishing a list of officially licensed fire testing laboratories and matching the classifications laid down in Circolare No 12 with actual uses of building materials.

Due to these continuing activities, no fire protection regulations regarding test procedures and inspection of building materials have been agreed or introduced in Italy.

Future developments

Further long term programmes are envisaged in addition to the continuing activities mentioned above. These will cover the testing of smoke development of fire gases. The work of ISO (ISO smoke box, see Section 9.2.3.2) and of I-ILDA (improvement of the NBS smoke chamber, see Section 9.2.3.1) is being followed closely. The NBS smoke chamber, particularly, is under discussion and its suitability will be investigated in greater detail. The establishment of tests for furniture and furnishings is also of major interest. Here too, international activities (particularly in Great Britain and ISO) are being closely monitored.

References for 8.2.6

[1] *H. Braun:* Bauvorschriften in sechs EWG-Ländern. Part 2: Nationale Systeme der Bauvorschriften. C. Italien. Baurecht-Technische Vorschriften-Institutionen, Ifo: Studien zur Bauwirtschaft 1; Ifo-Institut für Wirtschaftsforschung e. V., Munich, Feb. 1973.
[2] Metodo di prova CSE RF 1/75/A. Reazione al fuoco dei materiali sospesi e suscettibili di essere investiti da una piccola fiamma su entrambe le facce.
[3] Metodo di prova CSE RF 2/75/A. Reazione al fuoco dei materiali che possono essere investiti da una piccola fiamma su una sola faccia.
[4] Metodo di prova CSE RF 3/77. Reazione al fuoco dei materiali sottoposti all'azione di una fiamma d'innesco in presenza di calore radiante.

8.2.7 Austria

Statutory regulations

Structural fire protection in the nine Austrian provinces and certain towns such as Innsbruck and Linz is governed by various building department regulations. These building codes are based principally on that in force in Vienna contained in legislation originally passed in 1883 following the Ring Theatre fire and which has existed as a separate, frequently revised, building code for Vienna since 1930 [1]. Due to its complexity the Viennese building code has been discussed by various authors including *Newald* [2].

Efforts are being made to unify the various Austrian building codes by incorporating existing urban regulations in the relevant provincial building codes. A model building code was issued in 1961 with the intention of achieving further unification of the provincial codes. In practice the Viennese building code still has a certain pilot function for most provincial regulations.

Regulations relating to structural fire protection are scattered throughout the building codes. The fire performance requirements of building materials and components are laid down in these regulations and depend on the type of building (single family dwelling, industrial buildings, public and high rise buildings) and application (internal or external walls, ceilings and floors).

Classification and testing of the fire performance of building materials

Classification and testing of the fire performance of building materials are described in ÖNORM B 3800. This standard is arranged in four parts, Part 1 of which deals with fire performance of building materials while Parts 2 to 4 cover fire performance of building components. The section on fire retardants and fire protective coatings originally intended as Part 5 will probably be issued as a separate standard, ÖNORM B 3805, with the title "Flame retardants for wood".

ÖNORM B 3800. Fire performance of building materials and components

Part 1 Building materials: terminology, requirements, tests
            (provisional standard Nov. 1979).
Part 2 Building components: terminology, requirements, tests (Jan. 1972).
Part 3 Special building components: terminology, requirements, tests (Dec. 1973).
Part 4 Building components: arrangement into fire resistance classes (July 1977).

Parts 2 to 4 are not dealt with in this book since they are devoted exclusively to building components.

All Austrian standards are issued by the Österreichisches Normungsinstitut, Leopoldsgasse 4, A-1021 Wien 2.

ÖNORM B 3800 Part 1 was issued as a provisional standard in November 1979. The final standard will be published when the non-combustibility test for class A building materials based on ISO 1182 has been finalised. Fire performance as defined in ÖNORM B 3800 Part 1 includes characteristics such as combustibility, smoke generation and droplet formation.

Classification

According to ÖNORM B 3800 Part 1, combustibility, smoke generation and droplet formation during the burning of building materials are divided as shown in Table 8.42.

Table 8.42 Classification of the fire performance of building materials according to ÖNORM B 3800 Part 1

Class of building material	Designation
1. Combustibility Combustibility class A B B1 B2 B3	 non-combustible combustible low combustibility moderately combustible highly combustible
2. Smoke generation during burning Smoke generation class Q1 Q2 Q3	 low smoke generation moderate smoke generation strong smoke generation
3. Formation of drops during burning Drop formation class Tr1 Tr2 Tr3	 non-dripping dripping flaming drops

Test procedures

Combustibility, smoke generation and drop formation are measured by various methods which enable building materials to be classified in various classes as shown in Table 8.42.

Smoke generation and drop formation are determined only by ancillary tests if observations during the combustibility tests indicate that this is necessary. However, these tests can be required in individual cases for legal and practical reasons.

Although the formation of toxic gases in fire incidents is considered to be of major importance, standard tests or evaluation criteria are yet to be established. Consequently no binding requirements relating to toxicity exist.

A non-combustibility test for building materials based on ISO 1182 will shortly be introduced [3]. However, the procedures will be simplified and the classification criteria will be modified from those of the ISO method (for further details see Section 8.2.18.2). At present, a building material is considered to be non-combustible if it cannot be made to burn or to ash in air at 750 °C; furthermore, there should be no or only slight smoke development (smoke generation class Q1). Inorganic materials such as sand, earthenware, plaster, asbestos and steel, etc. are considered to be non-combustible without any special proof (see ÖNORM B 3800 Part 1, Section 4.1.1).

Combustibility class B1: low combustibility according to the Schlyter test.

The Schlyter test must generally be used to provide evidence that building materials are of low combustibility; however a few building materials such as certain wood products, plaster board and special grades of plastics (see ÖNORM B 3800 Part 1, Section 4.1.2.1) are considered to meet this description without proof. The Schlyter test is derived from the Nordtest NT Fire 002 Ignitability test (see Section 8.2.9). The test equipment is illustrated in Fig. 8.21 and the test specifications are summarised in Table 8.43.

Table 8.43 Schlyter test specifications

Specimens	3 × 2 specimens 800 mm × 300 mm
Specimen position	2 vertical specimens parallel to and at a distance of 50 mm from each other, 1 specimen displaced 50 mm downwards
Ignition source	row of 6 gas jets at 30 mm intervals, flames impinge on lower specimen at an angle of 30° to horizontal, distance of jets from flamed specimen: 40 mm, flame length in vertical position: 120 mm, gas supply: 3.5 parts N_2 to 1 part propane $\triangleq$ 21 MJ/m^3
Test duration	15 min
Conclusions	combustibility class B1 achieved if – specimen which is not flamed does not ignite – after removal of ignition source, flamed specimen continues to burn $\leqq$ 1 min and to glow $\leqq$ 5 min – unburnt length of flamed specimen $\leqq$ 40 cm

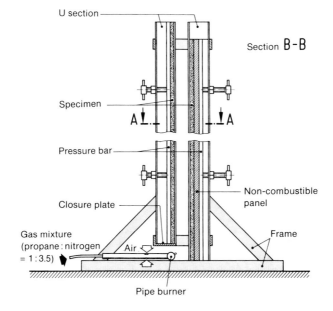

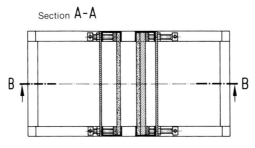

Fig. 8.21 Schlyter test apparatus
top: Side view, *bottom:* Plan

Combustibility class B2: moderately combustible according to the small burner test

Various building materials such as certain wood products and plastics listed in ÖNORM B 3800 Part 1, Section 4.1.2.2 are considered to be moderately combustible without testing. All other materials are required to pass the so-called small burner test which is practically identical to the Federal German test for class B2 building materials. The equipment and test specifications are almost the same as those given in Section 8.2.2.

Ten samples are tested, 5 by the edge flaming and 5 by the surface flaming method. The test is considered to have been passed if, with all 10 specimens the flame tip has not reached the reference mark within 20 s of application of the flame.

Combustibility class B3: highly combustible

Building materials are considered to be highly combustible if they cannot be classified in classes A, B1 or B2. In particular, paper, wood wool, straw as well as other materials listed in ÖNORM B 3800 Part 1, Section 4.1.2.3 are considered to be highly combustible.

Smoke generation

Building materials are classified in three smoke generation categories as shown in Table 8.42. The tests, apparatus and criteria are given in Section 9.2.2.1.

Drop formation

Drop formation during burning of building materials is classified as shown in Table 8.42. The small burner test for combustibility class B2 (for diagram of test apparatus see Section 8.2.2, Fig. 8.4) is used with a basket containing a filter paper placed under the test rig.

The criteria for the various drop formation classes are shown in Table 8.44.

Table 8.44   Criteria for drop formation class

Dripping $\leqq$ 20 s after start of flaming	Drop formation class
No dripping Filter paper not ignited Filter paper ignited	Tr1 non dripping Tr2 dripping Tr3 flaming drops

Table 8.45   Waste-paper basket test specifications

Specimen Specimen position Ignition source Test duration Conclusions	2.50 m × 2.00 m angled at 45° to the horizontal waste-paper basket: open wire frame 30 cm × 30 cm × 20 cm filled with 600 g pine wood wool is ignited, the test is carried out at 4 positions on the test specimen until the flame extinguishes classification in classes B1 or B2 as per following characteristics:		
		B1	B2

	− charred, burnt or otherwise destroyed
	  area
	− destruction from the upper edge of the
	  basket
	− self extinguishing
		$\leqq$ 0.15 m^2
		
		$\leqq$ 25 cm
		$\leqq$ 10 min
			$\leqq$ 0.25 m^2
			
			$\leqq$ 40 cm
			$\leqq$ 20 min

Certain materials listed in Section 6.1.1 of ÖNORM B 3800 Part 1 are considered to be non-dripping without special proof.

Floor coverings

At present the fire performance of floor coverings has to satisfy certain requirements only in Vienna where the building department has issued a directive for classifying floor coverings in combustibility classes B1 and B2. Classification in class B1 low combustibility, can be carried out by the Schlyter test and in class B2 moderately combustible by the small burner test as described in ÖNORM B 3800 Part 1. Classification in classes B1 or B2 can, however, also be made with the waste-paper basket test (ÖNORM B 3800 Part 3, Section 4.2 which is actually intended for roofing) on a flat surface inclined at 45°. Details on the use of floor, wall and ceiling coverings are given in [4]. The specifications for the waste-paper basket test are summarised in Table 8.45.

Official approval

The classification of the fire performance of building materials and official approval is carried out with the aid of the above tests performed by the state owned or state authorised test institutes listed below:

– State test institutes for the fire testing of building materials and components:

1. Magistratsabteilung 39 (MA 39) der Stadt Wien
   Prüf- und Versuchsanstalt der Stadt Wien
   Rinnböckstr. 15
   A-1110 Wien

2. Brandverhütungsstelle für Oberösterreich
   Petzoldstr. 45/47
   A-4020 Linz

– State recognised test institutes for the fire testing of specific products:

3. Österreichisches Kunststoffinstitut
   Arsenal, Objekt 213
   A-1030 Wien

4. Versuchsanstalt für Kunststofftechnik am Technologischen Gewerbemuseum
   Wexstr. 19−23
   A-1200 Wien

5. Österreichisches Textilforschungsinstitut
   Spengergasse 20
   A-1050 Wien

6. Gebäudeverwaltung der Österreichischen Bundestheater
   Goethegasse 1
   A-1010 Wien

After the fire test, the institute provides a test certificate giving the test results and the classification of the building material. This document forms the basis for obtaining approval from the building authorities in the various Austrian provinces. Approval of some building materials remains valid only for a limited period.

Marking and inspection of building materials does not take place except where material standards for certain building materials require goods to be marked "ÖNORM . . . geprüft"

(Austrian standard . . . tested). This is usually coupled with independent inspection. A list of products which have the right to carry the test mark is given in a register published by the Austrian Standards Institute [5].

Draft ÖNORM B 3500 polystyrene foams for building [6], is quoted as an example. Combustibility is tested according to ÖNORM B 3800 Part 1 and is monitored together with other material properties by a state licensed test institute under an inspection agreement.

Future developments

Various activities are taking place in the field of standardisation. Revision of ÖNORM B 3800 Parts 2 to 4 has started. Part 5 will probably be published as ÖNORM B 3805.

ÖNORM B 3810 determination of the fire performance of floor coverings by the radiant panel method is in preparation. This is a variation of the American flooring radiant panel test (NBSIR 75-950), which has generated much international interest and has already been introduced in several countries (e.g. Federal Republic of Germany).

The fire performance of decorative materials, furniture and wall coverings is also being investigated. The first is the subject of a research contract intended to establish the basic principles for a standard.

It is hoped to introduce a method for determining toxicity based on reproducible practical tests. Foreign and domestic developments are awaited and there is no activity on this front at present.

References for 8.2.7

[1] Bauordnung für Wien. Version valid from 14. 11. 1976 (Bauordnungsnovelle 1976). 2nd ed. Prugg Verlag, Vienna, 1977.
[2] *P. Newald:* Bauordnung für Wien. Author's edition, Vienna, 1976.
[3] ÖNORM B 3800 Teil 1, Beiblatt 1, Draft July 1980. Brandverhalten von Baustoffen und Bauteilen. Baustoffe: Prüfung der Nichtbrennbarkeit.
[4] Bundesländerausschuß für die Beurteilung neuer Baustoffe und Bauweisen (Bauarten). Technische Richtlinien für die Verwendung von Boden-, Wand- und Deckenbelägen. June 1979. Verbindungsstelle der Bundesländer beim Amt der Niederösterreichischen Landesregierung A-1014 Vienna, Schenkenstrasse 4.
[5] Österreichisches Normungsinstitut. Register ÖNORM . . . geprüft. State at: 1. 11. 1979. ON-V 95. Published by Österreichisches Normungsinstitut, Leopoldsgasse 4, Postfach 130, A-1021 Vienna.
[6] ÖNORM B 3500, Draft Feb. 1980. Polystyrolschaumstoff für das Bauwesen. Partikelschaumstoff. Eigenschaften, Anforderungen, Prüfungen.

8.2.8 Switzerland

Statutory regulations

Safety in Switzerland is regulated by federal law which delegates responsibility for implementation to the cantons.

Each of the 26 cantons has its own fire regulations and codes based largely on the directive of the Association of Cantonal Fire Insurances (VKF)[1]. While some cantons have incorporated this directive in its entirety in legislation, others have adopted only certain parts. The regulations of the Canton of Zurich are a typical example of the latter situation [1].

The fire regulations directive covers fire safety and has also been adopted and issued as a recommendation by organisations such as the Swiss Engineers and Architects Association (SIA)[2]. It has also been introduced as a standard by the Swiss Standards Association (SNV)[3]. The following recommendations exist at present [2]:

- S.I.A. Recommendation 183 (1974) = SNV 520183
  Structural fire protection:
  General provisions.
  Evaluation of fire hazard and suitable safety measures.
  Technical installations.
  Special structures and establishments.
- S.I.A. Supplement 183/1 (1975)
  Underground garages.
- S.I.A. Supplement 183/2 (1976) = SNV 520183/2
  Use of combustible building materials in buildings.
  Testing of building materials and components.
- S.I.A. Supplement 183/3 (1977) = SNV 520183/3
  Signposting of escape routes and exits.
  Emergency lighting.

The VKF first considered the fire performance of building materials in 1962 in the fire protection guidelines for the use of combustible building materials. The guidelines underwent several revisions and led in 1976 to the new edition mentioned above titled "Use of combustible building materials in buildings". This version was produced by the Technical Commission of the VKF in cooperation with the Swiss plastics industry, the SIA fire protection commission, the Federal Materials Testing and Research Institute (EMPA)[4] and the Fire Prevention Service for Industry and Commerce.

Fire protection and the regulations covering the use and testing of combustible building materials are the subject of several reviews [3—5].

Classifying and testing the fire performance of building materials

The regulations relating to the use, classification and testing of the fire performance of combustible building materials are specified in the directive and in SIA 183/2 "Use of combustible building materials in buildings" and "Testing of building materials and components" [2].

[1]) Vereinigung kantonaler Feuerversicherungen
[2]) Schweizerischer Ingenieur- und Architekten-Verein
[3]) Schweizerische Normenvereinigung
[4]) Eidgenössische Materialprüfungs- und Versuchsanstalt

Use of combustible building materials in buildings

In the first part of "Use of combustible building materials in buildings", the fire protection characteristics of materials are assessed in terms of combustibility, smoke generation and toxic and corrosive decomposition products. The combustibility of a material in the sense of this assessment is determined by its ignitability and burning rate demonstrated by testing. The classification of building materials is made with the aid of the following combustibility grades:

I   extremely easily ignited and extremely rapidly burning (not permitted as a building material)
II   easily ignited and rapidly burning (not permitted as a building material)
III   highly combustible
IV   moderately combustible
V   low combustibility
VI   non-combustible

Materials which are classified as being of low combustibility (combustibility grade V) can in fact perform less well in certain applications. In such cases an additional determination of the combustibility grade must be made at a higher temperature (200 °C).

The smoke characteristics of building materials are classified in smoke grades 1 (strong), 2 (medium) and 3 (weak). Further details are given in Section 9.2.2.1. Building materials which give rise not only to carbon monoxide in a fire but also to toxic, corrosive or strongly irritating, panic-causing fire gases are registered in the Directory of Materials and Goods (Verzeichnis der Stoffe und Waren, BVD-Blatt SW/2/2205-6) [6] and marked with the symbols Tx or Co. No regulations or methods for testing these secondary fire effects exist at present.

The combustibility and smoke grades determined from the test results are contained in the Brandkennziffer (fire code number). In addition, the corrosive and toxic properties can be indicated with Co and Tx, respectively. Thus code number IV.2 (Co) defines a moderately combustible building material which gives rise to moderate smoke levels and liberates corrosive gases or vapours. If the combustibility is determined at higher surrounding temperatures, this must also be indicated e.g. V (200 °C). 2.

The permitted use of combustible building materials is defined by minimum combustibility and smoke emission requirements expressed by the fire code number. These minimum requirements depend on the type of building, its usage and number of storeys and also on the application of the building material (see S.I.A. 183/2, Table for Section 5, conditions of certification, permitted combustibility and smoke grades). Buildings are divided into 8 groups with increasing hazard (flats with differing number of storeys, public and high rise buildings etc.). The applications listed for combustible building materials are external and internal walls, wall linings, ceilings, floor coverings, roofing and technical installations.

The minimum requirements do not permit the use of building materials of combustibility grades I and II. Class III materials are allowed in certain cases, otherwise they must be provided with a fire resistant covering. Class V building materials are required, in certain cases, to retain their low combustibility in ambient temperatures of up to 200 °C (see also *Hoffmann* in [5], p. 5).

Testing of building materials and components

The methods for determining the combustibility and smoke grades of building materials are described in Part 2 of S.I.A. 183/2 ([2], p. 11 to 18, see also *Camani* in [5], p. 11).

Determination of combustibility grade

This method is based on the small burner test utilised in the Federal Republic of Germany for determining moderate flammability (B2 according to DIN 4102 Part 1) but is extensively automated. Both compact materials and foams can be tested. The apparatus is illustrated in Fig. 8.22 and the test specifications are given in Table 8.46.

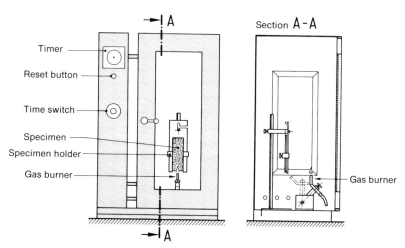

Fig. 8.22 Combustibility test apparatus
left: Front view, *right:* Side view

Table 8.46 Combustibility test specifications

Specimens	12 specimens – compact materials: 160 mm × 60 mm × 4 mm – foams: 160 mm × 60 mm × 6 mm
Specimen position	vertical
Ignition source	moveable butane or propane burner, flame tip temperature: approx. 900 °C, flame length: 20 mm, inclined at 45° to horizontal – edge flame application: flame impinges on specimen at centre of lower front edge – surface flame application: flame impinges on specimen 25 mm above centre of lower edge
Test duration	ignition time: edge flame application: 15 s surface flame application: 45 s until the flame reaches the upper part of the specimen holder or extinguishes
Conclusion	classification in combustibility classes II to IV depending on test performance

A defined ignition flame is applied to the edge of the specimen. The time elapsed from first applying the flame until its tip reaches a certain height or the specimen extinguishes is noted. If six tests on a grade III to V material do not enable classification to be made, an ancillary test with surface flame application is performed.

Approval regulations sometimes specify a test at 200 °C for low combustibility materials (combustibility grade V). A suitable test procedure is under development (see also *Lindenmann* and *Hoffmann* in [5], p. 17).

Table 8.47 shows how building materials are classified according to performance in the basic test (edge application of flame) and ancillary test (surface application of flame).

Table 8.47   Classification of building materials by edge and surface application of flame

Test result	Classification	
Basic test (edge flame application)		
Specimen ignites and is rapidly consumed, time ≦5 s	II	easily ignited, burns rapidly
Specimen ignites and is consumed, time ≦20 s	III	highly combustible
Specimen ignites and continues to burn, burn time >20 s	IV	moderately combustible
Specimen ignites and extinguishes before height of flame reaches 150 mm, burn time ≦20 s	V	low combustibility
Specimen does not ignite or char or ash	VI	non-combustible
	VI q	quasi-non-combustible
Ancillary test (surface flame application)		
Specimen ignites and is consumed, time ≦40 s	III	highly combustible
Specimen ignites and continues to burn, time >40 s, burn time >50 s	IV	moderately combustible
Specimen ignites and continues to burn, after ignition time has elapsed (45 s), specimen extinguishes ≦5 s, burn time ≦50 s	V	low combustibility

The procedure for testing combustibility is not suitable for demonstrating non-combustibility and quasi-non-combustibility (classes VI and VI q). No Swiss method has, in fact, been developed for this and the Federal German DIN 4102 Part 1 non-combustibility 750 °C furnace test is used.

Building materials are classified in class VI (non-combustible) if they satisfy the criteria for class A1 described in DIN 4102 (electrical furnace test). Class VI q (quasi non-combustible) is achieved if the material passes the A1 furnace test or the calorific potential test required for class A2.

Testing the upper surface of floor coverings

Floor coverings must achieve a fire code number of at least IV.2. The burning characteristics of the upper layer of composite floor coverings must also be determined by SNV 198897 "Determination of the burning behaviour of textile floor and wall coverings" [7] based on DIN 54332. The test apparatus resembles that of the German small burner test and is shown in Fig. 8.4 in Section 8.2.2. The test specifications are summarised in Table 8.48. Materials are classified in combustibility classes on the basis of test performance as shown in Table 8.49.

Table 8.48   Test specifications for the burning behaviour of floor coverings

Specimens	5 specimens 290 mm × 105 mm
Specimen position	vertical on non-combustible substrate
Ignition source	small burner, inclined at 45° to horizontal, flame length: 20 mm, flame impinges on specimen 40 mm above the lower edge, distance of burner from specimen: 5 mm
Test duration	ignition time 30 s, test terminated if cotton thread fixed parallel to upper edge of specimen burns through or flame extinguishes
Conclusion	classification in combustibility classes III to V (see below) depending on test performance

Table 8.49   Classification of floor coverings

Test result	Classification
Specimen ignites, flame tip reaches a height of 250 mm (cotton thread) after >35 s − ≦60 s	III highly combustible
Specimen ignites and extinguishes before the flame tip reaches a height of 250 mm (cotton thread) or reaches it after >60 s, burn time >35 s	IV moderately combustible
Specimen ignites and extinguishes before flame tip reaches a height of 250 mm (cotton thread), burn time ≦35 s	V low combustibility

Determination of smoke grade

Building materials are classified in three smoke grades: 1 "strong", 2 "moderate" and 3 "weak". The test procedure, a diagram of the test apparatus (based on the American XP2 chamber), test specifications and classifications are given in Section 9.2.2.1.

Official approval

Building materials are classified and officially approved on the basis of the tests described above. Fire testing is carried out by the following official Swiss test institutes:

– for combustibility and smoke:

Eidgenössische Materialprüfungs- und Versuchsanstalt (EMPA)
Abt. Bauphysik
CH-8600 Dübendorf

Brand-Verhütungs-Dienst für Industrie und Gewerbe (BVD)
Nüschelerstr. 45
CH-8001 Zürich

– for burning behaviour of floor coverings according to SNV 198897:

Eidgenössische Materialprüfungs- und Versuchsanstalt (EMPA)
CH-9001 St. Gallen

Following the fire tests, a test certificate giving the fire code number is issued. Application for approval must then be made to the Test Committee of the Association of Cantonal Fire Insurers (VKF):

Prüfausschuß für Baustoffe und Bauteile
c/o Vereinigung Kantonaler Feuerversicherungen
Bundesgasse 20
CH-3011 Bern

The test committee is composed of representatives of the VKF, the Fire Prevention Service for Industry and Commerce (BVD)*, the Zurich Property Insurance (GVZ)**, and the Federal Materials Testing Institute (EMPA).

If approval is granted, a so-called technical memo (Technische Auskunft) of the Cantonal fire authorities recommends official certification for use in accordance with the fire regulations directive and this is then generally granted by the authorities. Marking and inspection of the product are not required at present.

The approved product is listed in a directory which is brought up to date annually. The directory appears in two publications [8, 9]:

– Brandschutzregister / Verzeichnis der Technischen Auskünfte
– Produkte-/Lieferantennachweis. Baulicher Brandschutz.

Future developments

New methods for investigating the fire performance of floor coverings are under consideration since the present SNV 198897 test does not always differentiate sufficiently between materials. The American flooring radiant panel test (NBSIR 75-950), already introduced in several countries (e.g. Federal Republic of Germany) is a front runner.

The method for testing the combustibility grade at elevated temperature (200 °C) will be published as a supplement to fire regulations. At present the BVD and EMPA are developing a method for testing the fire performance of external insulation on façades. The test rig consists of a façade test wall and a mobile propane burner system and will enable full scale tests to be carried out under actual conditions of use.

* Brandverhütungsdienst für Industrie und Gewerbe
** Gebäudeversicherung Zürich

References for 8.2.8

[1] Canton Zürich. Verordnung über den baulichen Brandschutz. 27. 6. 1979. Parts I to IV: Allgemeine Bestimmungen; Anforderungen an Bauten und Anlagen; Verfahren; Inkrafttreten.

[2] S.I.A. Recommendation 183, 1974 edition (SNV 520183)
Baulicher Brandschutz; also Supplement 183/1 "Tiefgaragen" (1975). S.I.A. Supplement 183/2 to Recommendation 183, 2nd edition 1976, 1974 edition (SNV 520183/2). Verwendung brennbarer Baustoffe in Gebäuden. Prüfung von Baustoffen und Bauelementen. S.I.A. 183/3, 1977 edition (SNV 520183/3). Markierung von Fluchtwegen und Ausgängen. Notbeleuchtung. Supplement to S.I.A. Recommendation 183 (1974).
Reprint from the Wegleitung für Feuerpolizeivorschriften of the Vereinigung kantonaler Feuerversicherungen, Bundesgasse 20, CH-3011 Bern. Published by the Schweizerischer Ingenieur- und Architektenverein, Zürich.

[3] *R. Hoffmann:* Kunststoffe-Plastics 21 (1974) 8, p. 13.

[4] *H. Grünig:* Kunststoffe-Plastics 22 (1975) 2, p. 21.

[5] Kunststoffe und Brandverhalten. Comments on the "Brandschutztechnische Richtlinien". Annual 1976. BAG Brunner Verlag AG, Zürich. This brochure contains contributions by:
– *R. Hoffmann:* Verwendung brennbarer Baustoffe in Gebäuden. p. 5
– *A. Camani:* Die neuen Methoden zur Bestimmung der Brandkennziffer brennbarer Baustoffe. p. 11.
– *G. Stamm:* Kurzbeschreibung der Prüfung des Brennverhaltens textiler Bodenbeläge gemäß SNV-Prüfnorm Nr. 198897/1974. p. 16.
– *W. A. Lindenmann, R. Hoffmann:* Bestimmung der Brennbarkeit fester Stoffe bei erhöhter Umgebungstemperatur. p. 17.
– *A. Camani:* Richtwerte über Brandkennziffern der wichtigsten brennbaren Baustoffe. p. 20.

[6] Brandschutztechnische Klassierung der Stoffe und Waren BVD-Blatt SW/2/2205 and Alphabetisches Verzeichnis der Stoffe und Waren BVD-Blatt SW/2/2206. Published by Brand-Verhütungs-Dienst für Industrie und Gewerbe (BVD), Zürich.

[7] SNV 198897-1974. Textilien: Bestimmung des Brennverhaltens textiler Boden- und Wandbeläge. Published by Schweizerische Normen-Vereinigung (SNV), Zürich.

[8] Brandschutzregister/Verzeichnis der Technischen Auskünfte 1980 (available from: Vereinigung Kantonaler Feuerversicherungen, Bundesgasse 20, CH-3011 Bern).

[9] BVD Produkte-/Lieferantennachweis 1980. Baulicher Brandschutz. Baustoffe, Bauteile, Brandschutzabschlüsse, Feuerschutzmittel (available from: Brand-Verhütungs-Dienst für Industrie und Gewerbe, Nüschelerstr. 45, CH-8001 Zürich).

8.2.9 Nordic countries

Statutory regulations

The Nordic countries, Denmark, Finland, Iceland, Norway and Sweden, cooperate within the framework of the Nordic Council whose aims include harmonisation of national laws. Thus the "Nordiska Kommitten för byggbestämmelser" (NKB) (Nordic committee for building regulations) has the task of harmonising the Nordic building regulations including those relating to fire protection. It issues recommendations which can be incorporated voluntarily in the national regulations. The relevant national building regulations are:

- Denmark: Bygningsreglement 1977 [1],
- Finland: Suomen Rakentamismääräyskokoelma [2],
- Iceland: Byggingarreglugerd 1979 [3] and
            Reglugerd um brunavarnir og brunamál [4],
- Norway: Bygningslov av 18. juni 1965 and Byggeforskrifter av 1. august 1969 [5],
- Sweden: Svensk Byggnorm 1975 [6].

Guidelines for the classification of building materials and components were issued in 1977 by the NKB as "Coordinated Nordic fire technical classes" [7]. These guidelines are the result of efforts to harmonise technical fire requirements in the following areas:

- fire classification [7],
- fire precautions,
- escape routes,
- stability to fire,
- limitation of spread of fire and smoke,
- fire fighting and rescue measures.

Many of these guidelines, based on the Nordtest test methods introduced in 1976 for all Nordic countries, will be incorporated in national building regulations. The structure of the building regulations in the Nordic countries is summarised below.

Denmark

The building act passed in 1960 and since frequently amended [8, 9] is valid throughout the country. Copenhagen has its own building code [10]. The building regulations are laid down in the "Bygningsreglement" of 1977 [1] and are issued by the Danish Ministry of Housing. "Brandforhold" (fire performance) is covered in Section 6 while terminology is dealt with in Appendix 3.

Finland

The Ministry of the Interior passed Building Act no. 370 of 16. 8. 1958 and Building Decree no. 266 of 26. 6. 1959.
    The building regulations are divided into parts A to F:

A. General.
B. Stability of structures.
C. Insulation.
D. Installations for heating, water and ventilation.
E. Structural fire protection.
F. General building designs.

Part E which contains the Finnish regulations for fire precautions is made up of several subsections.

E 1: Structural fire precautions. Regulations, 1976.
E 2: Fire precautions in industrial and warehouse buildings. Recommendations, 1976.
E 3: Small chimneys. Recommendations, 1976.
E 4: Fire precautions in garages. Recommendations, 1977.
E 5: Fire resistance of structural and enclosing elements. Recommendations, 1977.
E 6: Doors and shutters. Recommendations, 1978.

The regulations are mandatory while the recommendations indicate solutions acceptable to the building authorities. Other solutions are acceptable in special cases.

Iceland

Fire precautions are covered by the "Byggingarreglugerd" (building regulations) [3] and in the "Reglugerd um brunavarnir og brunamál" (fire precaution regulations) [4].

Norway

The Norwegian building regulations are based on the building code of 18 June 1965. Fire precautions are dealt with in Chapter 55 of the building regulations (Byggeforskrifter) of 1 August 1969. The use of combustible linings and insulating material is regulated in Circular H-17/73 of 2 April 1973, a provisional regulation [5].

Sweden

The Svensk Byggnorm (SBN) (Swedish Building Code) of 1977 issued by the Statens Planverk (SPV) (State Planning Authority) contains important approval regulations for fire protection [11] and classification of fire performance [12].

Classification and testing of the fire performance of building materials

In order to comply with fire performance requirements in the building regulations, building materials and components must satisfy certain tests for classification.

NKB classification and Nordtest methods

The classification of building materials and relevant tests are laid down in the NKB "Coordinated Nordic fire technical classes" [7]. The actual fire tests are described in Nordtest methods NT Fire 001 to 009 [13]:

– NT Fire 001. Building materials. Non-combustibility test (identical to ISO/DIS 1182).
– NT Fire 002. Materials – coverings and linings: Ignitability.
– NT Fire 003. Coverings: Resistance to fire.
– NT Fire 004. Surfaces: Tendency to fire spread and smoke development.
– NT Fire 005. Fire resistance tests on elements of building construction (identical to ISO 834).
– NT Fire 006. Roof coverings: Resistibility to spreading fire.
– NT Fire 007. Floorings: Resistibility to spreading fire and smoke development.
– NT Fire 008. Door and shutter assemblies: Fire resistance (identical to ISO 3008).
– NT Fire 009. Glazed elements: Fire resistance (identical to ISO 3009).

The NKB classification of building materials and components [7] is shown in Table 8.50 (elements of building construction as defined in NT Fire 005 are not included).

Table 8.50   NKB classification of materials

Material	Classification according to Nordtest	Test method NT Fire
Building materials	non-combustible combustible	} 001
Fire resistance of wall and ceiling linings	K 1 K 2	} 003

Surface finishes	interior In 1
	          In 2
	          In 3
	exterior Ut 1
	          Ut 2
		002
		and
		004

Roofing	Ta 1 Ta 2	} 006
Floor coverings	G	007

The procedures for testing the fire performance of building materials are described below. This book does not cover the following methods: NT Fire 003. Coverings: Resistance to fire; NT Fire 005. Fire resistance tests on elements of building construction; NT Fire 008. Door and shutter assemblies: Fire resistance and NT Fire 009. Glazed elements: Fire resistance.

Nordtest NT Fire 001. Non-combustibility test

The combustibility or non-combustibility of building materials is assessed by Nordtest NT Fire 001 which is identical to ISO/DIS 1182. An illustration of the non-combustibility furnace and test specifications are thus given in Section 8.2.18.2.

Nordtest NT Fire 002. Ignitability test

The ignitability of building materials, and in particular of coverings and linings, is tested to Nordtest NT Fire 002 also known as the Schlyter test. The apparatus is illustrated in Fig. 8.23 and the test specifications are summarised in Table 8.51.

Table 8.51   Schlyter test specifications

Specimens	3 × 2 specimens 800 mm × 300 mm
Specimen position	2 specimens vertical at intervals of 50 mm parallel to each other, 1 specimen displaced 125 mm upwards with lower edge shielded by a 25 mm × 25 mm × 3 mm angle iron
Ignition source	Teclu propane burner 25 mm below the shielded edge of the upper specimen. Burner at right angles to and 60 mm away from the lower specimen
Test duration	flame applied to both specimens until they burn on their own. If they do not ignite test is terminated after 30 min
Conclusion	classification in the various NKB or national classes depending on test performance

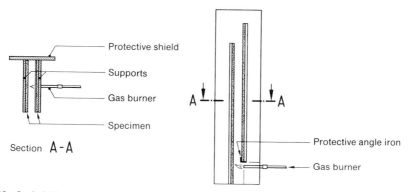

Fig. 8.23   Ignitability apparatus for linings and coverings

The specimens are flamed until both burn on their own. The time up to ignition of each of the two test specimens is noted. The average ignition time calculated from at least 3 runs forms the basis of classification as follows:
- Classes In 1 and Ut 1 achieved if the specimen not exposed to the gas flame does not ignite in the first 15 min in any of the 3 tests.
- Classes In 2, In 3 and Ut 2 achieved if the specimen not exposed to the gas flame does not ignite in the first 5 min in any of the 3 tests.

The final classification is made with the additional help of the NT Fire 004 test (see below).

NT Fire 004. Fire spread and smoke development test

The tendency of wall and ceiling surfaces to fire spread and smoke development is tested by Nordtest NT Fire 004. A diagram of the apparatus and the test specifications are given in Fig. 8.24 and Table 8.52, respectively.

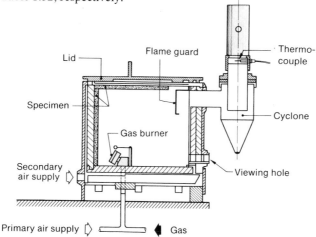

Fig. 8.24   Apparatus for determining fire spread and smoke development

Table 8.52   Specifications for the fire spread and smoke development test

Specimens	3 × 4 specimens 225 mm × 225 mm × 11 mm
Specimen position	4 specimens fixed to the rear wall, side walls and top of the fire chamber
Ignition source	ring propane burner, 45 mm diameter, angled at 45°
Test duration	max. 10 min
Conclusion	classification in the various NKB or national classes depending on test performance

The burner is lit with a heated filament and the test carried out for a maximum of 10 min. The NKB regulations allow earlier termination if the smoke gas temperatures exceed the permitted limits (see Fig. 8.25) by a certain amount or if the smoke density exceeds certain tolerances.

The test apparatus is equipped with a device to measure smoke intensity. Exact details, a diagram and test specifications are given in Section 9.2.2.2. The experimental smoke gas temperature curves enable materials to be classified in classes In 1 to 3, Ut 1 and Ut 2.

Table 8.53   Definition of NKB fire classes for surface finishes

Surface finish	Class	Tendency to spread flame	Smoke development
Interior	In 1	none	none
	In 2	low	moderate
	In 3	moderate	moderate
Exterior	Ut 1	none	n/a
	Ut 2	moderate	n/a

Table 8.54   NKB classification of surface finishes

Test method	Criterion	Condition	Class In 1	In 2	In 3	Ut 1	Ut 2
NT Fire 002	Ignitability Flash-over	unflamed specimen does not ignite within [min]	15	5	5	15	5
NT Fire 004	Smoke gas temperature	limiting curves not exceeded (see Fig. 8.25)	1	2	3	1	3
	Smoke density	absorption (in %) not greater than: a) mean value of 3 runs	10	30	30	n/a	n/a
		b) individual values	50	95	95	n/a	n/a

Materials are classified as follows:

Classes In 1 and Ut 1 if limiting curve *1* (Fig. 8.25)
Class In 2 if limiting curve *2*
Classes In 3 and Ut 2 if limiting curve *3*

in all three tests is not exceeded by the measured temperature curve for more than 30 s and the area between the measured temperature curve and the limiting curve does not exceed 15 (°C · min).

The complete NKB classification of surface finishes is made on the basis of NT Fire 002 and NT Fire 004. Ignitability, flame spread and smoke development are all taken into account. The individual classes are defined as in Table 8.53. Materials are classified in the various fire classes as shown in Table 8.54.

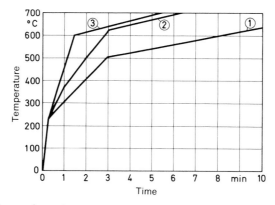

Fig. 8.25 NKB limiting smoke gas temperature curves

NT Fire 006. Test for resistibility to spreading fire for roof coverings

The resistance of roof coverings to flying brands is tested by Nordtest NT Fire 006. The apparatus is shown in Figs. 8.26 and 8.27 while the test specifications are given in Table 8.55.

Table 8.55 Specifications for testing the resistibility of roof coverings to spreading fire

Specimens	3 × 1 specimen 1000 mm × 400 mm
Specimen position	inclined at 30° to horizontal between two air ducts, upper duct with suction fan, lower duct with blower
Ignition source	wood crib 100 mm × 100 mm consisting of 8 pieces of pinewood 10 mm × 10 mm × 100 mm, set alight by a defined gas pilot burner and placed on test specimen 100 mm from lower edge
Test duration	until flames and glow die out
Conclusion	classification in the NKB or national classes

A flame is applied for 30 s to the wood crib by the separate pilot burner shown in Fig. 8.27. The burning crib is then placed on the specimen. After 15 s the blower and suction fans are switched on giving an air flow of 2 m/s or 4 m/s. A note is made of the time elapsed until a) the specimen ignites, b) the flames and glow die out. The extent of damage to both the roof covering and substrate is measured.

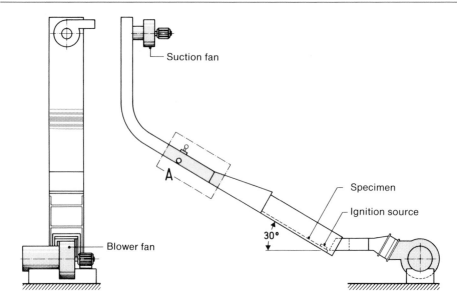

Fig. 8.26   Apparatus for determining the resistibility of roof coverings to spreading fire

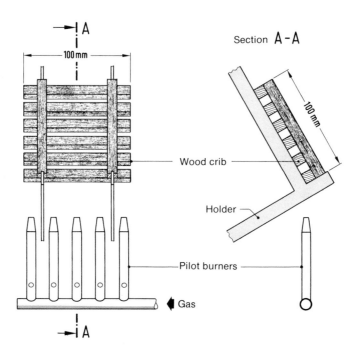

Fig. 8.27   Ignition device for wood crib

Table 8.56 National equivalents to Nordtest NT Fire methods

Test	Nordtest NT Fire	Denmark DS	Finland SFS	Norway NS	Sweden SIS
Building materials. Non-combustibility test	001	1056	4400	[1]	–
Materials – coverings and linings: Ignitability	002	1058.1	4190	3901	024821
Coverings: Resistance to fire	003	1060.1	4191	3902	024822
Surfaces: Tendency to fire spread and smoke development	004	1058.2	4192	3903	024823
Fire-resistance tests on elements of building construction	005	1051.1	4193	3904	024820
Roof coverings: Resistibility to spreading fire	006	1059.1	4194	3905	024824
Floorings: Resistibility to spreading fire and smoke development	007	1059.2	4195	3906	024825

[1] IMCO Resolution A. 270

According to the NKB, classification is necessary in order to ascertain whether roof coverings are capable of protecting the underlying material against spreading fire and in preventing flame spread on the roof covering or substructure if ignition does occur.

– Materials qualify for class Ta 1 if flame spread does not occur along the roof covering or the underlying material in any of the three tests. Charring of the latter must not extend over more than 100 cm².
– Class Ta 2 is achieved if flame does not spread more then 55 cm or 30 cm from the centre of the ignition source for the roof covering or underlying material respectively in any of the three tests.

NT Fire 007. Test for resistibility of floor coverings to spreading fire and smoke development

The ability of floor coverings to resist fire spread and smoke development is tested by Nordtest method NT Fire 007. The same apparatus and test specifications apply as for testing roof coverings (see Figs. 8.26 and 8.27 and Table 8.55, respectively).

Asymmetrically woven floor coverings must be tested both warp and weftwise. The actual test is identical to that for roof coverings although only a single flow rate of 2 m/s is used and smoke density is also measured (for details see Section 9.2.2.2).

According to NKB, floor coverings qualify for class G if in three tests (in the case of asymmetrical textiles two tests must be carried out in both weft and warp directions):

– the flame does not spread more than 55 cm from the centre of the ignition source,
– if the smoke density of the combustion gases (max. absorption ≙ 100) does not exceed 30 during the first five minutes of the test and 10 subsequently.

Equivalents of the Nordtest methods in the individual Nordic countries

The Nordtest methods for fire precautions described above have been incorporated without modification in the individual national standards. Nevertheless, the national building regulations also contain their own additional standards, details of which are given in the sections on the individual countries. The national standards equivalent to the Nordtest methods are listed in Table 8.56. No Nordic country has adopted all the NKB classifications for building materials and components based on Nordtest methods although efforts are being made in this direction, for example, in Norway.

Denmark

In Denmark the fire performance of building materials and components is classified in accordance with Appendix 3 of the Bygningreglement 1977 [1]. The classification is summarised in Table 8.57.

Nationally adopted Nordtest methods

All the test methods used in Denmark for determining fire parameters are identical to Nordtest methods NT Fire 001 to 007 with the exception of DS 1058.3 which is described below. The corresponding DS standards are given in Table 8.57.

Non-combustibility of building materials is tested according to DS 1056 and corresponds to NT Fire 001. Classification conforms to DS 1057. These standards are identical to ISO/DIS 1182, details of which are given in Section 8.2.18.2.

Table 8.57 Danish Building Regulations fire protection classification

Material	Classification	Test method DS	≙ NT Fire
Building materials	non-combustible combustible	1056	001
Building materials	*class A* not easily ignitable	1058.1 or 1058.3 and	002 –
	low fire spread low smoke development	1058.2	004
	class B not easily ignitable	1058.3 and	–
	moderate fire spread moderate smoke development	1058.2	004
Linings	*class 1* (building materials class A must also be satisfied)	1060.1	003
	class 2 (building materials class B must also be satisfied)	1060.1	003
Floor coverings	moderate fire spread moderate smoke development	1059.2	007
Roof coverings	moderate fire spread	1059.1	006

The ignitability of linings and coatings is tested according to DS 1058.1 (≙ NT Fire 002). A diagram of the apparatus and test specifications are given in Fig. 8.23 and Table 8.51, respectively.

The tendency of surfaces to spread fire and develop smoke is tested according to DS 1058.2 which is identical to NT Fire 004 (for diagram and test specifications see Fig. 8.24 and Table 8.52 respectively).

Test methods DS 1058.1, DS 1058.2 and DS 1058.3 provide the basis for the classification of building materials in classes A and B which is explained below together with a description of DS 1058.3.

Testing of the fire resistance of linings which is the subject of DS 1060.1 (identical to NT Fire 003), is not covered in this book. Linings are classified in class 1 if they meet the requirements of class A building materials and prevent the underlying combustible material igniting for at least 10 min when applying a flame to one or both sides.

The fire performance and smoke development of floor coverings is tested to DS 1059.2 or NT Fire 007. The test equipment is illustrated in Fig. 8.26 and the test specifications are given in Table 8.55 (for smoke development see Section 9.2.2.2). According to the Danish building regulations [14] a floor covering is considered to spread fire moderately and develop smoke moderately if it satisfies the following conditions in three tests:

– the damaged area of the floor covering does not extend more than 550 mm from the centre of the ignition source,

– the damaged area of the substrate does not extend more than 300 mm from the centre of the ignition source,
– the smoke density must not exceed 30% during the first 5 min and 10% during the remainder of the test (100% corresponds to total obscuration).

Fire spread on roof coverings is tested to DS 1059.1 which is equivalent to NT Fire 006. The apparatus is shown in Fig. 8.26 while the test specifications are summarised in Table 8.55. Roof coverings are considered to spread fire moderately according to [14] if the damage to the roof covering and substrate does not extend more than 550 mm and 300 mm, respectively from the centre of the ignition source. Three tests each must be carried out at air flows of 2 m/s and 4 m/s.

DS 1058.3. Ignition temperature and flame spread test

The DS 1058.3 ignition temperature and flame spread test [15] is carried out only in Denmark and does not form part of the Nordtest methods. The apparatus is shown in Fig. 8.28 and the test specifications are summarised in Table 8.58.

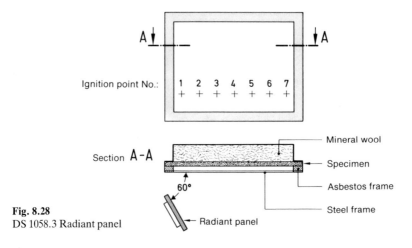

Fig. 8.28
DS 1058.3 Radiant panel

Table 8.58   DS 1058.3 ignition temperature and surface spread of flame test specifications

Specimens	2 × 4 specimens 800 mm × 600 mm
Specimen position	vertical in steel frames, irradiated surface 700 mm × 500 mm, 7 "ignition points" on sample 100 mm above lower edge of frame at intervals of 100 mm
Ignition sources	– propane radiant panel consisting of 3 radiators 185 mm × 140 mm arranged above one another, operating temperature 920 °C, vertical surface of radiant panel angled at 60° to test specimen – small propane burner 76 mm away from and perpendicular to test specimen applies flame to each of 7 "ignition points" for 15 s
Test duration	varies according to type of test (see below)
Conclusion	classification in building material classes A or B depending on ignition temperature and surface spread of flame

The specimen may be tested with or without preheating. In both cases two specimens are used. In the latter case, the specimens are exposed to the radiator and a flame is applied simultaneously for 15 s by the small burner to each of the seven ignition points on the specimen. These points are located at increasing distances (from 1 to 7) from the radiator surface. The radiation intensities at each point are assumed to be those given in Table 8.59.

Table 8.59 Assumed radiation intensities at each ignition point

Ignition point no.	Assumed radiation intensity [kW/m^2]
7	1.2
6	1.3
5	1.9
4	2.8
3	4.3
2	6.3
1	8.6

The ignition tests are carried out starting at point 7. When testing the first specimen, any flames are extinguished immediately the pilot flame is removed. If any flames occur with the second specimen, they are extinguished 30 s after the pilot flame is removed.

The former procedure involves preheating both specimens by exposing them to the radiator for 17.5 min. The ignition tests are then carried out in exactly the same manner as in the test without preheating.

After the tests the burnt areas on the specimen are measured and their growth at 30 s computed by subtracting the values obtained for specimen 2 from those obtained for specimen 1.

The following parameters can be calculated by interpolation using the given values of radiation intensity:

– the ignition temperature as a function of radiation intensity corresponding to a burnt area 100 × 100 mm^2 on the first specimen,
– the surface spread of flame as a function of radiation intensity corresponding to an increase in burnt surface of 100 × 100 mm^2 in 30 s, i.e. approximately the difference in burnt surfaces on specimens 1 and 2.

Standard DS 1058.3 or DS 1058.1 (≙ NT Fire 002) is used to test materials for low ignitability while DS 1058.2 (≙ NT Fire 004) is used to establish low flame spread and low smoke development for classification in class A.

In order to achieve class B, building materials must not be easily ignitable according to DS 1058.3 and make only moderate contributions to fire spread and smoke development according to DS 1058.2.

Materials achieve class A under the following conditions:

1. The material must be shown to be difficult to ignite in three tests according to DS 1058.1, i.e.

– the test specimen which is not flamed does not ignite within 15 min,
– the flamed specimen ceases to burn (if it burns at all) within 1 min of removal of the ignition source,

– any afterglow of the specimens ceases within 3 min of removal of the ignition source.

The gas flame must be withdrawn if both specimens catch fire or if the test has lasted 30 min. Materials are also considered to be difficult to ignite if the burnt area in two tests according to DS 1058.3 (with or without preheating) $\leqq 40 \times 100$ mm^2.

2. A building material has low fire spread if the experimental mean smoke gas tempera-ture curve during a test of 10 min duration to DS 1058.2 does not exceed the prescribed limiting curve 1 of Fig. 8.29 by more than 30 s. Furthermore, the area enclosed by the mean smoke gas temperature curve and the limiting curve must not exceed 15 (°C · min).

3. A material develops smoke weakly if, in three 10 min tests to DS 1058.2, the mean smoke density does not exceed a scale interval of 10% where the scale interval gives the absorption in % of total absorption.

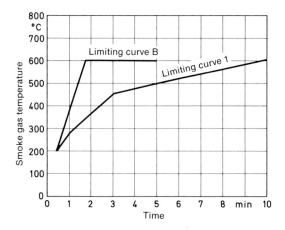

Fig. 8.29   Limiting smoke gas temperature curves for DS 1058.2 test

Class B is achieved under the following conditions:

1. The material must be classified as not easily ignitable according to DS 1058.3. This is the case if in two tests the burnt area or area differences $\geqq 100 \times 100$ mm^2 occur for ignition points 7, 6 and 5 either with or without preheating.

2. The material makes a moderate contribution to fire spread if according to DS 1058.2 the mean smoke gas temperature curve does not exceed the limiting curve B shown in Fig. 8.29 after 5 min.

3. The material makes a moderate contribution to smoke development, i.e. the area under the mean smoke density curve after 5 min by DS 1058.2 does not exceed 250 (min · %).

Finland

In Finland building materials are classified according to Part E 1 "Structural Fire Precautions" of the Finnish Building Regulations. The classification is summarised in Table 8.60.

Table 8.60   Finnish Building Regulations fire protection classification

Material	Classification	Test method SFS	≙ NT Fire
Building materials	non-combustible combustible	4400	001
Surface coatings	low flammability (class 1) slowly flammable (class 2)	4190	002
	does not spread fire (class I) spreads fire slowly (class II)	4192	004
Linings Roof coverings	flame protecting non-flammable and protects substrate from igniting (class K1) flammable but does not spread fire and partially protects substrate from igniting (class K2) Other (class K3)	4191 4194	003 006
Floor coverings		4195	007

All the tests used in Finland for determining fire protection parameters are identical with Nordtest methods NT Fire 001 to 007. The corresponding SFS Standards are listed in Table 8.60.

Building materials are tested for non-combustibility by SFS 4400 which is equivalent to NT Fire 001 and to ISO/DIS 1182, full details of which are given in Section 8.2.18.2.

Surface coatings which are of low flammability (class 1) or slowly flammable (class 2) are tested by SFS 4190 (≙ NT Fire 002). A diagram and test specifications are given in Fig. 8.23 and Table 8.51, respectively.

SFS 4192 (≙ NT Fire 004) is used to test whether surface coatings do not spread fire (class I) or spread fire slowly (class II). A diagram and test specifications are shown in Fig. 8.24 and Table 8.52, respectively.

The fire resistance of linings (classification: flame protecting) is determined by SFS 4191 (≙ NT Fire 003) and is not dealt with in this book.

The fire performance of roof coverings is tested by SFS 4194 (≙ NT Fire 006). The test rig is illustrated in Fig. 8.26 and Table 8.55 summarises the test specifications. Materials are classified in classes K1 "non flammable, protects substrate from igniting", K2 "flammable but does not spread fire and partially protects substrate from igniting" or K3 if the conditions of classes K1 and K2 are not met.

The fire performance of floor coverings is tested to SFS 4195 (≙ NT Fire 007). The apparatus in shown in Fig. 8.26 and test specifications are given in Table 8.55.

No official fire test standards exist in Finland apart from the above Nordtest/SFS methods.

Iceland

In principle testing of the fire performance of building materials and components conforms to Nordtest methods NT Fire 001 to 007. At present there is no fire test laboratory in Iceland and reference is usually made to the results of Nordtest laboratories or, if necessary, additional tests are carried out at the official Danish fire test laboratory.

The classification of the fire performance of building materials and components is based on the NKB or Danish version. Attempts are being made however to coordinate the classification in [3].

Norway

The Norwegian classification of the fire performance of building materials and components is similar to those in Sweden and Denmark and is summarised in Table 8.61.

Table 8.61   Norwegian Building Regulations fire protection classification

Material	Classification	Test method NS	$\triangleq$ NT Fire
Building materials	non-combustible	IMCO Resolution	
	combustible	A.270	
Coverings and	low flammability	3901	002
linings	(in certain cases ASTM D 2863)		(013)
Coverings	fire retardant (class A 10)	3902	003
	non-combustible (class A 20)	and	
	practically non-combustible (class A 30)	3903	004
Surface finishes	class 1	3903	004
Roof coverings		3905	006
Floor coverings		3906	007

Nationally adopted Nordtest methods

The methods used in Norway to determine the fire performance of building materials and components are identical to Nordtest methods NT Fire 002 to 007. The corresponding NS standards are listed in Table 8.61.

A non-combustibility test based on IMCO Resolution A.270 is used in place of the NT Fire 001 method adopted in all other Nordic countries which is equivalent to ISO/DIS 1182. The principle of the IMCO test is however similar (see Section 8.2.18.2 and 8.3.4.3).

The ASTM D 2863 oxygen index test recently introduced as Nordtest method NT Fire 013 is only required by Norway at present. Further details are given below.

Linings and coverings are tested to NS 3901 ($\triangleq$ NT Fire 002). The apparatus is shown in Fig. 8.23 and the test specifications are summarised in Table 8.51. In order to be classified as of "low flammability" the test specimen exposed to the propane flame must not ignite in any of three tests of 30 min duration.

In certain cases, the Norwegian Building Regulations (Rundskriv H-17/73 [5]) specify determination of the oxygen index of linings to ASTM D 2863. It is used to compare materials in doubtful cases or to provide additional data on a material intended for a specific application.

Coverings are tested to NS 3902 (≙ NT Fire 003) and NS 3903 (≙ NT Fire 004). The apparatus is illustrated in Fig. 8.24 and the test specifications are given in Table 8.52.
    A covering is classified as fire retardant if:

- the temperature of the fire gases does not exceed NKB limiting curve *1* (see Fig. 8.25), individual values and the mean value of smoke density do not exceed the value specified in NS 3903 by more than 50% and 10%, respectively,
- the combustible material content does not exceed 25% by weight,
- the mean and individual increases in temperature beneath the chipboard do not exceed 280 °C and 300 °C, respectively in tests of 10, 20 and 30 min according to NS 3902.

NS 3903 is an additional method for testing finishes for use in ships or offshore platforms. For such applications, the above limiting values of fire gas temperature and smoke density must not be exceeded.
    The fire performance of roof coverings is tested by NS 3905 (≙ NT Fire 006), that of floor coverings by NS 3906 (≙ NT Fire 007). Diagrams and test specifications are given in Fig. 8.26 and Table 8.55, respectively. The requirements are satisfied in both cases if the burnt length of surface and charred area of the underlying combustible material do not exceed 55 cm and 100 cm^2, respectively.

ASTM D 2863-77. Oxygen index test (≙ NT Fire 013)

The oxygen index is determined by the US Standard ANSI/ASTM D 2863-77 [16] procedure which has been introduced as Nordtest Method NT Fire 013 [13]. The apparatus is illustrated in Fig. 8.30 and the test specifications are summarised in Table 8.62.

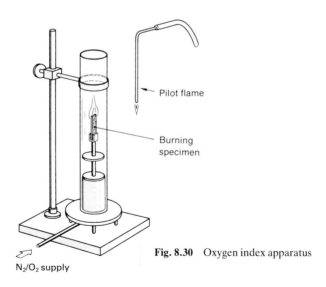

Pilot flame

Burning specimen

N$_2$/O$_2$ supply

Fig. 8.30 Oxygen index apparatus

Preliminary tests are first carried out in order to ascertain the approximate O$_2$/N$_2$ ratio required for the material under investigation. This is reached when the material burns at a uniform slow rate after ignition. The oxygen content of the O$_2$/N$_2$ mixture is then lowered until the test specimen just continues to burn. At the next lower O$_2$ concentration (a reduction of 0.2% in the oxygen content) the test specimen must extinguish. The ratio O$_2$/(O$_2$+N$_2$) is multiplied by 100 and designated the oxygen index.

Table 8.62   Oxygen index test specifications

Specimens	10 specimens 150 mm × 6 mm × 3 mm
Specimen position	clamped vertically
Ignition source	gas pilot flame
Test duration	until the minimum oxygen concentration of an O_2/N_2 mixture required to sustain combustion is reached
Results	expressed as $n = \dfrac{100 \times O_2}{O_2 + N_2}$ [%]

Circular H-17/73 of 2. 4. 1973 of the Norwegian Communal and Labour Ministry [5] specifies the oxygen index test as well as the NS 3901 test for exterior coverings of combustible material and for combustible insulation for use in single storey single family dwellings.

Only those exterior coverings which are of "low flammability" by NS 3901 and which meet the requirements relating to oxygen index and ignition temperature shown in Fig. 8.31 are permitted to be used in buildings of up to four storeys.

Combustible insulation for use in single storey single family dwellings must exhibit an oxygen index of at least 15%.

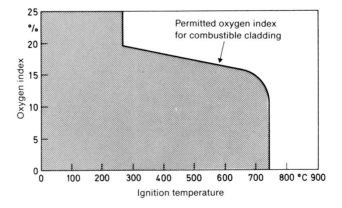

Fig. 8.31   Ignition temperature as a function of oxygen index

Sweden

The Swedish fire protection classification of building materials and components is laid down in the SBN approval regulations [11]. A summary is given in Table 8.63.

Nationally adopted Nordtest methods

With the exception of SIS 650082 (see below; testing materials <3 mm thick for low flammability) all the methods used in Sweden for ascertaining the fire performance of building materials are identical to Nordtest methods NT Fire 001 to 007. The corresponding SIS standards are listed in Table 8.63.

Table 8.63   Swedish Building Regulations fire protection classification

Material	Classification	Test methods SIS	≙ NT Fire
Building materials	non-combustible	–	001
	combustible		
Buildings materials	low flammability		
	<3 mm	650082	–
	>3 mm	024821	002
Linings	flame protecting		
–non-combustible		024822	003
–combustible parts		024822	003
		and	
		024823	004
Surface finishes	class 1	024823	004
	class 2		
	in cases of doubt large-scale test to Meddelande 123		
Roof coverings		024824	006
Floor coverings		024825	007

Building materials are tested for non-combustibility according to NT Fire 001 which is identical to ISO/DIS 1182 (see Section 8.2.18.2).

SIS 024821 (≙ NT Fire 002) is the method used for establishing low flammability for materials >3 mm thick. The apparatus and test specifications are shown in Fig. 8.23 and Table 8.51, respectively. The material is classified of low flammability if in three tests:

– the specimen which is not flamed does not ignite within 15 min,
– after removing the ignition source, the flamed specimen extinguishes within 1 min and both specimens cease to glow within 3 min (for testing and classification of building materials <3 mm thick see below).

The fire performance of non-combustible linings is tested by SIS 024822 (≙ NT Fire 003) and those with combustible constituents are also tested by SIS 024823 (≙ NT Fire 004). The NT Fire 003 fire resistance test is not discussed in this book. A non-combustible lining is considered to be flame protecting if for a least 10 min:

– it does not burn with a visible flame,
– it does not separate, even partially, from the substrate,
– the temperature of the substrate does not exceed 270 °C at any point or 250 °C on average.

In addition to the NT Fire 003 test, linings with combustible constituents must also be tested to NT Fire 004 and classified as class 1 surface finishes.

The tendency of surface finishes to ignite and to develop smoke is tested by SIS 024823 (≙ NT Fire 004). The apparatus is illustrated in Fig. 8.24 and the test specifications are summarised in Table 8.52. Classification is made in classes 1 and 2:

– Class 1 (slight tendency to ignite and develop smoke) is achieved if, within 10 min in three tests, the mean smoke gas temperature/time curve does not exceed limiting curve 1 by

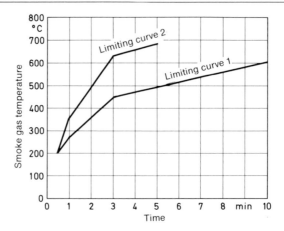

Fig. 8.32   Limiting smoke gas temperature curves according to SBN

more than 30 s in all (see Fig. 8.32) and the area between the experimental and limiting curves does not exceed 15 (°C · min). The mean and individual values of smoke density must not exceed 10 and 50, respectively (100 corresponds to total absorption).

– Class 2 (moderate tendency to ignite and develop smoke) is achieved if, within 5 min in three tests, the measured mean smoke gas temperature/time curve does not exceed limiting curve 2 by more than 30 s in all (see Fig. 8.32) and the area between the experimental and limiting smoke gas temperature curves is not more than 15 (°C · min). The mean and individual values of smoke density must not exceed 30 and 95, respectively (100 corresponds to total absorption).

If these procedures give doubtful results, the State Testing Institute's Meddelande 123 large scale test can be used to clarify matters.

Fire spread on roof coverings is tested by SIS 024824 (≙ NT Fire 006). The apparatus is shown in Fig. 8.26 while the test specifications are summarised in Table 8.55. A roof covering is considered to shield the substrate from spreading fire (flying brands) and not to spread fire per se if

– a maximum of 55 cm of the roof covering and
– a maximum of 30 cm of the substrate

measured from the centre of the ignition source are damaged.

The fire performance and smoke development of floor coverings are tested by SIS 024825 (≙ NT Fire 007). The apparatus is shown in Fig. 8.26 and the test specifications are summarised in Table 8.55. A floor covering meets the Swedish requirements if

– the damaged length measured from the centre of the ignition source does not exceed 55 cm,
– the smoke gases do not exceed a value of 30 in the first 5 min and 10 subsequently (100 corresponds to total absorption).

SIS 650082. Test for assessing low flammability building materials <3 mm thick

Low flammability building materials <3 mm thick are tested to SIS 650082 [17]. The apparatus is illustrated in Fig. 8.33 and the test specifications and SBN classification are summarised in Table 8.64.

Table 8.64   Specifications for testing low flammability building materials <3 mm thick

Specimens	3 specimens 5 cm × 30 cm (if necessary 3 samples each in warp and weft directions)
Specimen position	vertical in combustion box 30 cm × 30 cm × 76 cm
Ignition source	Bunsen burner, luminous flame: 38 mm long, 19 mm below lower edge of specimen
Test duration	flame applied for 12 s, test terminated when flame and incandescence extinguished
Conclusions	classified as of low flammability according to SBN if 5 of 6 specimens – burn on average $\leqq$ 2 s and in no case >3 s – average burnt length $\leqq$ 90 mm and in no case >115 mm

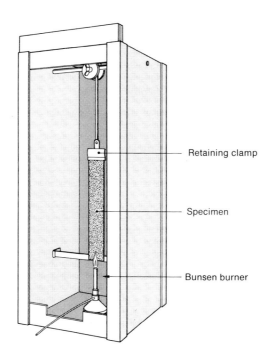

Retaining clamp

Specimen

Bunsen burner

Fig. 8.33   Apparatus for testing low flammability building materials less than 3 mm thick

Official approval

The tests described above for determining the fire performance of building materials can only be carried out by the officially licensed test institute in each country with the exception of Iceland where materials are sent to Denmark for testing due to the lack of a suitable establishment.

The Institutes are:
– Dansk Institut for Prøvning og Justering (DPJ)
  (previously Statsprøveanstalten)
  Amager Boulevard 108
  DK-2300 København S
  Denmark
– Valtion teknillinen tutkismuskeskus (VTT)
  Palotekniikan laboratorio
  (State Technical Research Centre)
  Kivimiehentie 4
  SF-02150 Espoo 15
  Finland
– Norges branntekniske Laboratorium
  N-7034 Trondheim-NTH
  Norway
– Statens Provningsanstalt
  Laboratoriet för brandteknik
  Box 857
  S-50115 Borås
  Sweden

The test organisation issues a report (DK and N: Prøvningsattest, SF: Tutkismusselostus, S: Provningsrapport) which is recognised in all the Nordic countries.

The material is classified on the basis of the test report according to national regulations. The NKB classification has not yet been introduced in any Nordic country.

The authorities in each Nordic country issue type approvals based on the test reports. Such approval which includes marking and inspection is not mandatory and is issued only on application. In practice type approval is almost always requested since it is stipulated by most local authorities and is a major selling point.

Type approval is obtained by submitting the test report to the national authorities and providing evidence of the existence of an inspection agreement with the relevant recognised test institute. The procedures vary slightly from country to country and are summarised below:

Denmark

Details of type approval procedure are given in a Building Ministry Circular [18] and in [19]. Application should be made to:

Boligministeriets godkendelsessekretariat
for materialer og konstruktioner
Postbox 54
DK-2970 Hørsholm
Denmark

Type approvals are valid for three years and a list is published annually with quarterly supplements which are sent to all building authorities.

The inspection specified in the type approval is carried out under contract by the Dansk Institut for Prøvning og Justering. Two independent inspections are generally made each year. In certain cases quality controls are required and test reports must then be submitted quarterly to the test institute.

Finland

Applications for type approval should be made to

Sisäasiainministeriö
Kaavoitus – ja rakennusosasto
(Ministry of the Interior, Dept of Building and Planning)
P Box 230
SF-00131 Helsinki 13
Finland

Type approvals are usually valid for 5 years and a list is published annually (in 1980 under the title "Rakennusalan tyyppihyväksyntäluettelo 1980").

Type approval is carried out by the technical fire laboratory of the VTT. Inspections are made once or twice a year but in special cases an additional inspection test is carried out. Each inspection is reported to the Ministry of the Interior. Summarised reports are not issued.

Iceland

The type approvals of the other Nordic countries, and in particular of Denmark, form the basis for inspection in Iceland since no fire testing is carried out there. The body responsible for compliance with the regulations is the State Authority for Fire Protection:

Brunamálastofnun ríkisins
Laugaveg 120
IS-105 Reykjavik
Iceland.

Norway

Application for fire type approval of building products consisting wholly or partly of plastics or of new materials or designs which are not covered by existing building regulations should be made to

Kommunal – og arbeidsdepartementet
Kontoret for bygnings – og brannvesen
P.O. Box 8112
Oslo-Dep.,
N-Oslo 1
Norway

In the case of all other building materials and components, applications should be sent to:

Statens branninspeksjon
P.O. Box 498 – Sentrum
N-Oslo 1
Norway

Type approvals are valid for 5 years. A list of approved building materials and products is issued at regular intervals and is revised annually. The list consists of three separate sections:

- Building materials and constructions. The latter include finished parts such as wall claddings, combustible insulation, roof coverings etc.
- Building products. This group includes special building components such as fire shutters, floor coverings, fire retardant linings, linings for exterior walls in special purpose buildings, combustible roof coverings etc.
- Building components.

The list is contained in a publication entitled "statlige byggebestemmelser" (state building regulations) issued by

A/S byggtjeneste
Postboks 1575 Vika
N-Oslo 1
Norway

The products mentioned in the "Building materials and constructions" section are approved by the "Kommunal- og arbeidsdepartementet" (Communal and Labour Ministry) and the products in the other two sections by the "Statens branninspeksjon" (State Fire Inspectorate).

The above products are inspected annually by the Norwegian Technical Fire Laboratory in a similar manner to Denmark (loc. cit.).

Sweden

Application for type approval should be made to

Statens planverk
Box 22027
S-10422 Stockholm
Sweden.

Type approvals are generally valid for 5 years, and are listed in "Approval list B, type approved, fire protection" published annually.

Quality control and independent inspection are laid down contractually with the "Statens Planverk" (State Planning Authority) as detailed in the SBN approval regulations [11].

Type approved materials which are inspected nationally are also accepted by the authorities in the other Nordic countries.

Future developments

Nordtest methods NT Fire 001 to 007 are being revised in order to eliminate ambiguities although the actual tests will remain unchanged. NT Fire 001 will reflect the amendments between ISO 1182 and ISO/DIS 1182. The additional methods NT Fire 010 to 013 [13] have not yet been incorporated in the various building regulations. NT Fire 012 and 013 are particularly interesting. The former is identical to the ASTM E 662-79 NBS smoke chamber test for solid materials while NT Fire 013 corresponds to the determination of oxygen index by ASTM D 2863-77.

The work of ISO/TC 92 relating to fire test methods has aroused considerable interest in the Nordic countries. Providing the resulting methods find widespread international acceptance they will replace existing Nordic test procedures.

The following changes will take place in the near future in the individual Nordic countries:

Denmark

A revised edition of the Danish building regulations is planned.

Finland

It is planned to issue a completely revised edition of the building regulations. Appropriate regulations covering quality control and independent inspection of building materials are also in preparation and will be published as "Tyyppihyväksyntäohjeet, rakenteellinen paloturvallisuus" (type approval regulations, structural fire protection).

Iceland

A fire laboratory for small scale fire tests will shortly be built at the Building Research Institute in Reykjavik (Rannsóknastofnun Byggingaridnadarins). Iceland will therefore be able to play a more active role in the Nordtest programme.

Norway

The building regulations are being revised but no firm publication date has been fixed (further details from Norges Byggstandardiseringsgråd, Københavngaten 10, Oslo 5). A new regulation for the classification of building materials based on NKB Publication No. 29 is also being drawn up and should be incorporated in the new building regulations.

Sweden

A "class 3" with a limiting curve *3* in line with NKB (see Fig. 8.25, c.f. Fig. 8.32) is planned for testing the fire performance of surface finishes. The smoke development requirements correspond to those for class 2.

References for 8.2.9

[1] Bygningsreglement 1977. Issued by the Boligministeriet, Slotsholmgade 12, DK-1216 København K (Version in English: Building Regulations, 1977).
[2] Suomen rakentamismääräyskokoelma Issued by the Ministry of the Interior, Hallituskatu 4E, 00170 Helsinki 17.
[3] Byggingarreglugerd. Stj. tid. B, nr. 292/1979, sbr. rg. nr. 298/1979.
[4] Stjórnartídindi B 23-1978, 8. 6. 1978. 455. Nr. 269 Reglugerd um brunavarnir og brunamál.
[5] Bygningslov. 18. 6. 1965. Supplemented by: Veiledning til Byggeforskrifter, 1. 8. 1969 and Rundskriv H-17/73, 2. 4. 1973. Kommunal- og arbeidsdepartementet, Oslo.
[6] Svensk Byggnorm 1975. Statens Planverk. Fack S-104 22 Stockholm.

[7]   Coordinated Nordic fire technical classes. Guidelines for Nordic building regulations. NKB-publication No. 29. June 1977. .

[8]   The National Building Act and Regulations. Boligministeriet. July 1965.

[9]   Bekendtgørelse af Byggelov. Boligministeriets lovbekendtgørelse no. 361. 17. 7. 1972.

[10] Københavns bygnings- og administration vedtoegter. Københavns Magistrat.

[11] SBN. Godkännande Regler. 1975: 9. Brandskydd. Statens Planverk.

[12] Statens Planverk. Publikation nr. 12. Svensk Byggnorm-Upplysning. SBN-U 37: 18. Brandteknisk Klassificering.

[13] Nordtest method. Nordtest, box 5103, S-10243 Stockholm 5.
      – NT Fire 001. Building materials. Non-combustibility test. March 1976.
      – NT Fire 002. Materials – coverings and linings: Ignitability. March 1976.
      – NT Fire 003. Coverings: Resistance to fire. March 1976.
      – NT Fire 004. Surfaces: Tendency to fire spread and smoke development. March 1976.
      – NT Fire 005. Fire-resistance tests on elements of building construction. March 1976.
      – NT Fire 006. Roof coverings: Resistibility to spreading fire. March 1976.
      – NT Fire 007. Floorings: Resistibility to spreading fire and smoke development. March 1976.
      – NT Fire 008. Door and shutter assemblies: fire resistance. March 1978.
      – NT Fire 009. Glazed elements: fire resistance. March 1978.
      – NT Fire 010. Fire dampers: Efficiency to prevent fire spread. June 1980.
      – NT Fire 011. Dust clouds: Minimum explosible dust concentration. June 1980.
      – NT Fire 012. Smoke generated by solid materials: Specific optical density. June 1980.
      – NT Fire 013. Plastics – Candle-like combustion: Minimum oxygen concentration. June 1980.

[14] Tillaeg 7, 9. 4. 1979 – Bygningsreglement, 1977. Aendrede Klassifikationskrav for
      – brandmaessigt egnede gulvbelaegninger
      – brandmaessigt egnede tagbeklaedninger.

[15] Dansk Standard. DS 1058.3. February 1977. Brandteknisk prøvning. Materialer. Beklaedninger og overflader. Antaendelsestemperatur og flammespredning.

[16] ANSI/ASTM D 2863-77. Standard method for measuring the minimum oxygen concentration to support candle-like combustion of plastics (oxygen index).

[17] Svensk Standard SIS 650082. 1966. Textilvaror. Bestämning av brandhärdighet hos vävnader.

[18] Cirkulaere om boligministeriets godkendelsesordninger for materialer og konstruktioner m.v. til byggeri og for materiel m.v. til vand- og afløbsinstallationer. 20. 11. 1978.

[19] A. Alderson: Denmark. Product approval, quality control and building control procedures. HMSO, London, 1974.

8.2.10 German Democratic Republic

Statutory regulations

Fire protection requirements in the German Democratic Republic (GDR) have their legal foundation in the Brandschutzgesetz (Fire Protection Law) [1]. The implementation of these legal requirements is covered in Regulation no 9/74 of the Staatliche Bauaufsicht (StBA) (State Building Inspectorate) [2] and individual sections of TGL 10685 Bautechnischer Brandschutz (Structural fire protection) [3].

Classification and testing of the fire performance of building materials and components

The following GDR standards lay down procedures for classifying and testing the fire performance of building materials and components:

- TGL 10685/11 Determination of the combustibility group of building materials
- TGL 10685/12 Determination of the degree of fire spread of building structures
- TGL 10685/13 Determination of the fire resistance of building structures.

The Bauakademie der DDR (GDR Building Academy) and the Amt für Standardisierung, Meßwesen und Warenprüfung (ASMW) (Authority for Standardisation, Metrology and Product Testing) are responsible for these standards*.

In the GDR it is assumed that, since the fire performance of building materials is determined mainly in laboratory tests, no general predictions can be made on the course of a real fire but only on material and test procedure-dependant fire properties. Consequently, the fire resistance and fire propagation of finished structures are now investigated in full scale tests under the most realistic conditions possible. The contribution to fire propagation of building structures containing combustible materials is determined by TGL 10685/12.

Regulation 9/74 – Fire Protection in Buildings – [2] defines the classification of building structures in various fire propagation grades. The fire performance of building materials plays no significant role in this as it is virtually included in fire propagation. The combustibility of building materials is regarded as a material property of importance only as a selection

Table 8.65   Determination of combustibility group according to TGL 10685/11

Combustibility group Designation	Abbreviation	Test apparatus
combustible with high flame spread	br-gFA	Plattenrahmen
combustible with moderate flame spread	br-mFA	
low combustibility	sbr	Brandschacht
non-combustible	nbr	Furnace

* Available from Staatsverlag der DDR, Bereich Standardversand, Postfach 1068, DDR-701 Leipzig.

criterion in the manufacture of building materials and the development of building structures. Further details on the evaluation of fire test procedures will be found in [4] and [5]
(Sections "Brandtechnische Eigenschaften" and "Bautechnischer Brandschutz").

Determination of combustibility group of building materials by TGL 10685/11

Three test methods the "Plattenrahmen", "Brandschacht" and Furnace tests, are used to
determine the combustibility of building materials according to TGL 10685/11. The resulting
classifications are shown in Table 8.65. The apparatus for the Plattenrahmen combustibility
test is illustrated in Fig. 8.34 and the test specifications are summarised in Table 8.66.

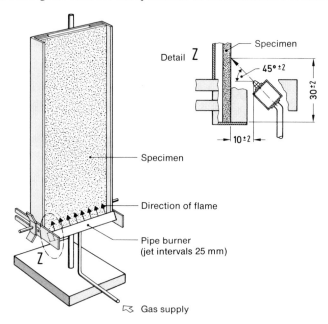

Fig. 8.34 Plattenrahmen apparatus

Table 8.66 Combustibility test specifications for building materials

Specimens	3 specimens 500 mm × 190 mm × ≦ 30 mm
Specimen position	vertical
Ignition source	gas pipe burner with 8 jets, heat flux to specimen 2.8 kW ± 0.35 kW
Test duration	1 min
Conclusions	classification in group – br-gFA if the flames extend beyond the upper edge of the specimen – br-mFA if the flames do not extend beyond the upper edge of the specimen

The Brandschacht apparatus illustrated in Figs. 8.35 and 8.36 is used to test "low combustibility" of building materials. Test specifications are summarised in Table 8.67.

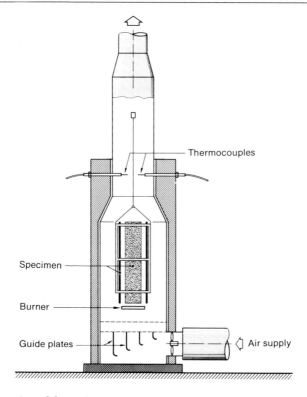

Fig. 8.35 Brandschacht (after [5], p. 46)

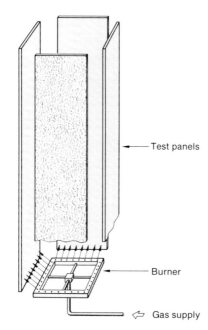

Fig. 8.36 Position of test panels and burner in the Brandschacht (after [5], p. 46)

Table 8.67   Specifications for testing "low combustibility" of building materials

Specimens Specimen position Ignition source	3×4 specimens 1000 mm × 190 mm × ≦ 30 mm vertical at right angles to each other quadratic gas burner with 32 jets each of 3.5 mm diameter heat flux to specimens: 24.4 kW ± 1.4 kW		
Test duration Conclusions	10 min "low combustibility" classification achieved if:		
		mean value	individual value

	– max. temperature 600 mm above
	  upper edge of specimen
	– afterflame time, max.
	– afterglow time, max.
	– proportion of undamaged
	  specimen, minimum
		250 °C
		5 s
		30 s
		
		15 %
			260 °C
			7 s
			35 s
			
			10 %

Non-combustibility is tested in the 750 °C furnace in a similar fashion to ISO/R 1182-1970 (see Section 8.2.18.2). The apparatus is shown in Fig. 8.37 and the test specifications are given in Table 8.68.

Table 8.68   Non-combustibility test specifications for building materials

Specimens Specimen position Radiation source Test duration Conclusions	5 cylindrical specimens, diameter 45 mm, height 50 mm, volume 80 cm^3 vertical in sample holder electrical furnace heated to 750 °C 20 min classification "non-combustible" achieved if – temperature rise 12.5 mm from furnace wall and within test specimen not greater than 50 K – burn time not greater than 10 s

Determination of the fire propagation grade of elements of construction by TGL 10685/12

The TGL 10685/12 standard for determining the degree of fire propagation involves defined test fires. Elements of construction (Bauwerksteile) in the sense of this standard are exterior walls, roofings, exterior claddings, internal walls and their linings, ceiling linings, piping and floors. The tests described below enable these to be classified in the following fire propagation grades (fa):

– no fire propagation (ofa)
– moderate fire propagation (mfa)
– high fire propagation (gfa)
– very high fire propagation (sgfa)

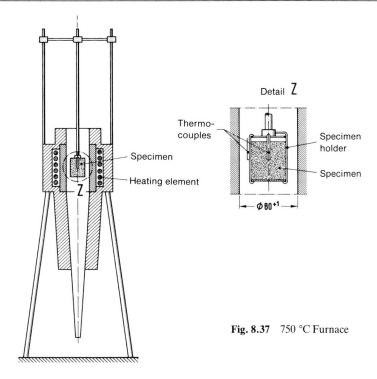

Detail Z

Thermo-
couples

Specimen
holder

Specimen

Specimen

Heating element

Ø 80⁺¹

Fig. 8.37   750 °C Furnace

Five criteria are established in the tests:

– deterioration, e.g. through charring, flaking, burning
– burning droplets
– heat development
– smoke development
– falling away

Three types of test rig are used:

– fire propagation furnaces
– fire rooms
– open air tests

In the test fires in the fire propagation furnaces, the burner flames are adjusted so that they do not touch the test specimen.

The following fuels are used in the fire propagation furnace, fire room and open air tests:

– standard fire wood (NBH), i.e. pine cut in billets 40 mm × 110 mm × 600 mm,
– standard wood shavings (NBS), i.e. shavings up to 3 mm in size, mixed with diesel fuel (DK) in the ratio 1:1.5 by weight.

The *fire propagation furnaces* are of two types shown in Figs. 8.38 and 8.39. Exterior walls are tested in the wall furnace while roofings are tested in the roof furnace. The corresponding test specifications are listed in Table 8.69.

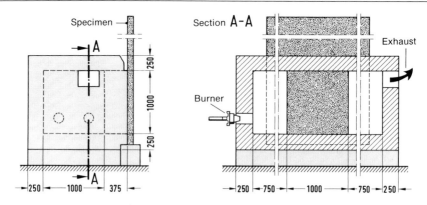

Fig. 8.38   Wall furnace

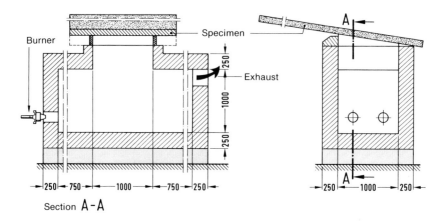

Fig. 8.39   Roof furnace

Table 8.69   Fire propagation furnace test specifications

Specimens	one or two specimens 2 m × 2.5 m × usual thickness
Specimen position	wall furnace: vertical
	roof furnace: corresponding to intended slant of roof
Ignition source	two diesel fuel burners, temperature-time dependence as specified in TGL 10685/13
Test duration	30 min
Conclusions	depending on test performance, classification in fire propagation grades ofa to sgfa, if ofa or mfa is achieved in the roof furnace test, the chamber test is dispensed with (see below)

Roofings are tested for fire propagation grades gfa and sgfa from below using the fire chamber illustrated in Fig. 8.40. The test specifications are listed in Table 8.70.

Table 8.70 "Chamber" test specifications

Specimen	1 specimen 2 m × 2.5 m
Specimen position	corresponding to intended slant of roof
Ignition source	20 kg standard fire wood primed with 400 ml petrol
Test duration	test fire burns for 5 min
Conclusion	classification in fire propagation grade gfa or sgfa

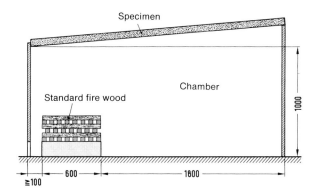

Fig. 8.40 Layout for the "Chamber" test for roofing

Fire room tests are carried out to determine the fire propagation grade of internal or separating walls, ceiling linings, pipes, ducts and flooring. Smoke development is also determined qualitatively with smoke measuring rods. Smoke is considered to obscure vision when the reference marks on the rod in the fire room are no longer recognisable. The fire room is illustrated in Fig. 8.41, the positions of the various building structures are shown in Figs. 8.42 to 8.46 and Table 8.71 lists the test specifications.

Table 8.71 Fire room test specifications for elements of construction

Specimens	one or two specimens 2 m × 2 m (floors 1 m × 2 m)
Specimen position	see Figs. 8.42 to 8.46
Ignition source	– mfa to sgfa 10 kg NBH[1] and 200 ml petrol
	– ofa, mfa 10 kg NBS + DK[2] (floors 500 g NBS[3])
Test duration	15 min with NBH test fire, for grade ofa, room is heated for 15 min with DK with temperature-time dependence as per TGL 10685/13 (floor 15 min NBS test fire)
Conclusion	classification in fire propagation grades ofa to sgfa

[1] standard fire wood
[2] diesel fuel
[3] standard wood shavings

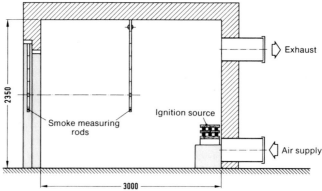

Fig. 8.41   Fire room

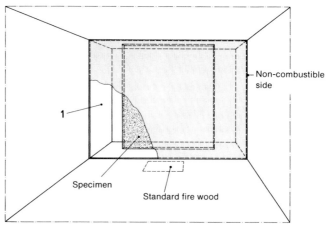

1: Gap between specimen and side of fire room is enclosed with non-combustible
    material

Fig. 8.42   Test layout for interior or separating walls

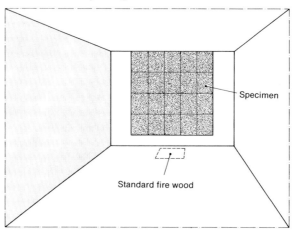

Fig. 8.43   Test layout for interior wall linings

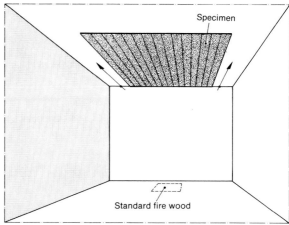

Fig. 8.44 Test layout for ceiling coverings and false ceilings

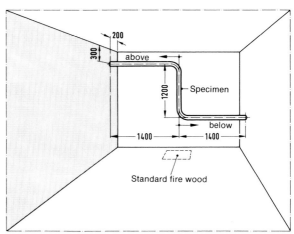

Fig. 8.45 Test layout for pipes and conduits

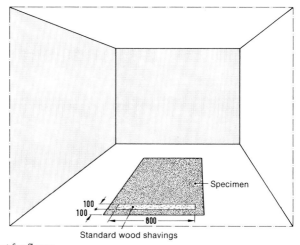

Fig. 8.46 Test layout for floors

Open air tests on roofings, exterior walls and exterior wall claddings are carried out using appropriate mountings. A roof mounting is shown in Fig. 8.47 and the corresponding test specifications are summarised in Table 8.72.

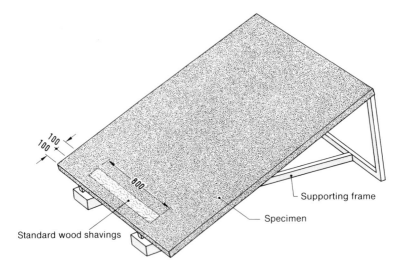

100
100

800

Supporting frame

Specimen

Standard wood shavings

Fig. 8.47   Open air test layout for roofing

Table 8.72   Open air test specifications for roofing

Specimens	one or two specimens 2 m × 2.5 m
Specimen position	corresponding to intended slant of roof
Ignition source	500 g standard wood shavings
Test duration	15 min
Conclusions	classification in fire propagation grades ofa to sgfa

The fire propagation grade of exterior walls is tested from inside and outside using the wall mount. Exterior wall claddings and weather domes are also tested by this means. The set up is shown in Fig. 8.48 and the test specifications are listed in Table 8.73.

Table 8.73   Open air test specifications for exterior walls

Specimens	one or two specimens 2 m × 2.5 m
Specimen position	vertical
Ignition source	20 kg standard fire wood and 400 ml petrol
Test duration	15 min
Conclusions	classification in fire propagation grades ofa to sgfa

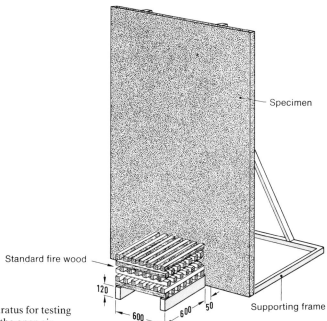

Fig. 8.48 Apparatus for testing
exterior walls in the open air

The interpretation of the various test results described in detail in TGL 10685/12,
pp. 15–19 is fairly extensive and enables classification in the four fire propagation grades
mentioned above.

Official approval

The tests for determining the combustibility group of building materials and the fire propagation grade of building structures are carried out by the following test stations licensed by
the GDR State Building Inspectorate (Staatliche Bauaufsicht des Ministeriums für
Bauwesen).

– Bauakademie der DDR   (combustibility group of building materials,
  Institut für Baustoffe   fire propagation grade of elements of construc-
  Abteilung Kunststoffe   tion)
  DDR-7021 Leipzig
  Essener Str. 38

– Institut für Bergbausicherheit   (combustibility group of building materials, fire
  DDR-9200 Freiberg   resistance of elements of construction)
  Reiche Zeche

– Amt für Standardisierung, Meßwesen   (combustibility group of building materials, fire
  und Warenprüfung   resistance of elements of construction)
  Fachabteilung Bauwesen
  Fachgebiet Bauelementeprüfung
  DDR-8027 Dresden
  Georg-Schumann-Str. 7

A test report giving the classification achieved is issued for the respective element of construction. Providing the requirements relating to fire propagation grade are satisfied, this document serves as the basis for specifying permitted uses. At present, the classified elements and linings are listed in the appendices to Regulation No. 9/74 [2]. A new version will come into force when TGL Blatt 10685/07 is issued. Building materials and elements of construction are not required to carry approval marks.

Future developments

The GDR fire protection requirements and test standards for structural fire safety are being revised. They are contained in TGL sections (Blätter) 10685/01 to 09 (requirements) and TGL 10685/11 to 13 (test procedures). All the revised sections should come into force in the near future.

The following revised structure is planned for the sections of TGL 10685 relating to fire protection requirements:

Section 01 Terms
Section 02 Fire load
Section 03 Fire stops, fire gaps between buildings
Section 04 Evacuation of people
Section 05 Water supplies for fire fighting, fire brigade access
Section 06 Fire hazard classes (BGKL)
Section 07 Fire resistance classes (FWKL), fire performance groups
Section 08 Size of fire compartments
Section 09 Removal of smoke and heat

The following major changes are foreseen for test standards TGL 10685/11 to 13:

TGL 10685/11: "Determination of the combustibility group of building materials":

– non-combustibility: the test temperature will be increased from 750 °C to 825 °C in accordance with CMEA standard 382-76 (equivalent to ISO Recommendation DIS 1182),
– low combustibility: propane will be used in place of town gas in the test fire in accordance with CMEA draft standard, the area of validity will be specified,
– combustibility: propane will be used instead of town gas in the test fire.

TGL 10685/12: "Determination of the fire propagation grade of elements of construction":

– evaluation of the criteria of fire propagation as well as dripping and smoke development with discriminating test procedures,
– the floor test will be dispensed with,
– abolition of the tests for exterior walls and roofings with the present fire propagation furnace according to the temperature/time curve, instead only standard fire wood will be used,
– test duration to be standardised at 20 min (15 min burning, 5 min afterflaming),
– the criterion "length of deterioration" will be replaced by "temperature increase".

TGL 10685/13: "Determination of fire resistance of elements of construction":
The test procedure is being revised in accordance with CMEA standard 1000-78.

References for 8.2.10

[1] Brandschutzgesetz of 19. 12. 1974 (GBI. I No. 62, p. 575).
[2] Vorschrift No. 9/74 of Staatliche Bauaufsicht des Ministeriums für Bauwesen: Bautechnischer Brandschutz, 10. 6. 1974.
[3] TGL 10685. Bautechnischer Brandschutz.
      Blatt 1: Begriffe. December 1963.
      Blatt 3: Brandschutzkonstruktionen in Bauwerken. December 1963.
      Blatt 4: Brandgefahrenklassen. Evakuierungswege für Menschen in Bauwerken, Zugänge und Zufahrten der Feuerwehr. April 1971.
      Blatt 5: Löschwasserversorgung. December 1963.
      10685/11: Bestimmung der Brennbarkeitsgruppe von Baustoffen. November 1975.
      10685/12: Bestimmung des Feuerausbreitungsgrades von Bauwerksteilen. June 1978.
      Blatt 13: Bestimmung des Feuerwiderstandes von Baukonstruktionen. April 1965.
[4] C. Hildebrand: Bewertung der Brandprüfverfahren für brennbare Werkstoffe und daraus gefertigte Bauelemente. UB wissensch.-techn. Beilage (1975), p. 56.
[5] C. Hildebrand: Der Baustoff Plast. 4. Ed., VEB Verlag für Bauwesen, Berlin, 1976.

8.2.11 USSR

Statutory regulations

The functions of the Russian State Fire Inspectorate are defined in order No. 52/654 of 1936. This body is responsible for working out technical fire precautions such as fire safety standards, regulations and technical requirements and monitoring their implementation. All fire protection standards and technical principles are agreed with the fire department of the Ministry of the Interior and confirmed by the State Committee of the Soviet Council of Ministers for Construction.

Standards and regulations concerning the building sector in the USSR are published in a four part work. Structural fire protection is dealt with in Part II of the SNiP ("Sovietskie Normy i Pravila" = Soviet Standards and Regulations). Section A "General Standards" of Part II is subdivided into chapters; Chapter 5, "Fire protection requirements/principles of planning", governs the use of building materials and structures.

Fire protection standards relating to the building sector are divided as follows:

– Fire resistance classes of buildings
– Fire protection structures
– Smoke and heat outlets
– Explosion shutters and pressure relief panels
– Fire safety in the internal and general planning of buildings
– Evacuation of people from buildings
– Water supplies for fire fighting
– Fire protection in heating and ventilation systems.

GOST 12.1.004-76 [1] contains the general fire protection requirements. Further information is given in references [2–4].

Classification and testing of the fire performance of building materials and structures

According to SNiP II-A.5-70, Para. 2.2, building materials are classified in the following classes:

– non-combustible
– low combustibility
– combustible
    low flammability
    highly flammable

This regulation also defines the use of combustible linings in buildings.

SNiP II-A.20-69 lays down the fire performance requirements for building materials used in theatres.

Wood is a frequently used building material. SNiP III-V.7-69 and SNiP I-V.28-62 prescribe ([2], p. 119) the use of flame retardants, cladding and plastering to prevent wooden structures catching fire. This topic is not dealt with further in this book (see also [5], Fire protection of wood).

Various methods are utilised for testing the fire performance of building materials and structures.

The non-combustibility of building materials is tested in accordance with ST SEV 382-76 which corresponds to ISO/R 1182 (see also [4], p. 76 and [5]).

The combustibility of plastics commonly used in the building sector is tested by various procedures laid down in GOST 17088-71 [6] such as the fire tube (rapid test), spread of flame and calorimeter methods. In certain cases the GOST 21793-76 [7] method of determining the oxygen index is used to compare the burning behaviour of various plastics. This GOST test is basically similar to ASTM D 2863.

The surface spread of flame of products such as plastics, painted and varnished linings on combustible or non-combustible substrates, textiles and films is determined according to Appendix 20 of GOST 12.1.017-80 [8] which also includes tests for measuring smoke evolution and toxicity of fire gases (Appendices 19 and 21).

Tests for determining the combustibility of structures are also carried out in the USSR [5]. Further information on fire protection and individual test methods is given in several comprehensive works [2−5].

Unfortunately it was not possible to obtain confirmation that GOST standards and test methods apply to the building sector as indicated in the literature quoted at the end of this section (especially [5]). The GOST 17088-71 test methods are probably no longer in use but are listed here for completeness.

ST SEV 382-76. Non-combustibility test for building materials

The ST SEV 382-76 test is equivalent to ISO/R 1182-1970. The non-combustibility furnace is illustrated in Fig. 8.37 and the test specifications are summarised in Table 8.68 in Section 8.2.10.

GOST 17088-71. Calorimeter, fire tube and spread of flame methods for determining the combustibility of plastics

Calorimeter method

The GOST 17088-71 calorimeter method [6] for determining the combustibility of plastics was developed by the Central Scientific Research Institute in Moscow. A detailed description in German is given by *Thater* [9], p. 69. The apparatus is illustrated in Fig. 8.49 and the test specifications are summarised in Table 8.74.

Table 8.74   Calorimeter test specifications

Specimens	10 specimens 75 mm × 35 mm × ≦ 10 mm (textiles, films: 80 mm × 45 mm × ≦ 1 mm)
Specimen position	vertical in frame 80 mm × 45 mm, specimen suspended 15 mm above upper edge of gas burner
Ignition source	− electric heating element consisting of 2 coils with outputs of 20−25 W and 400−450 W − gas burner with 1 mm diameter jet, flow rate 0.1−0.15 l/min
Test duration	gas burner ignited 15 s after switching on heating elements, test terminated if specimen ignites or after heating electrically for max. 10 min, several tests with differing periods of electrical heating (1, 2, 4, 6, 10 min) are carried out
Conclusion	determination of the combustibility value based on test performance and classification in the relevant combustibility group (see below)

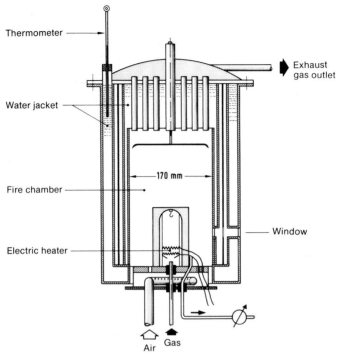

Fig. 8.49   Calorimeter test apparatus

The combustibility value is calculated by dividing the heat given out by the specimen during combustion by the heat supplied to the specimen by the ignition sources. The classification is based on the highest combustibility value obtained in the tests (further details of the calculation are given in [6]).

Combustibility classification is shown in Table 8.75.

Table 8.75   Classification in combustibility groups

Combustibility value	Combustibility group
≦0.1	non-combustible
>0.1–≦0.5	low combustibility
>0.5	combustible
>0.5–≦2.1	low flammability

Fire tube method

According to GOST 17088-71, the fire tube method serves as a rapid means of determining the combustibility of plastics. It was previously used as an acceptance test for evaluating combustible materials in accordance with the Soviet building regulations. The test rig is illustrated in Fig. 8.50 and the test specifications are summarised in Table 8.76.

Table 8.76   Fire tube test specifications

Specimens	6 specimens 150 mm × 35 mm × ≦ 10 mm
	(textiles, films: 155 mm × 45 mm × ≦ 1 mm)
Specimen position	vertical in fire tube, lower end protrudes 5 mm
Ignition source	Bunsen burner, flame height 40 mm
Test duration	until specimen flames, max. 2 min
Conclusions	classified as combustible if
	– specimen burns independently for more than 60 s
	– weight loss >20%
	– two or more of the six specimens burn

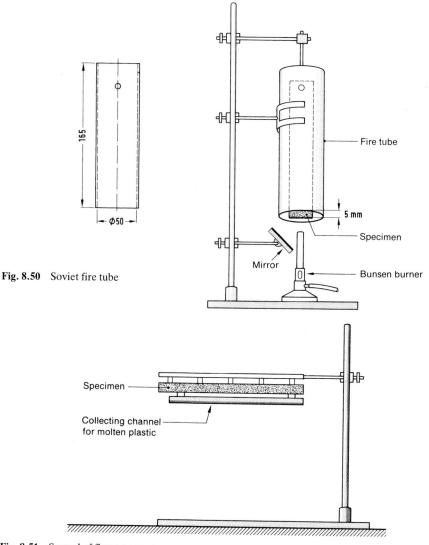

Fig. 8.50   Soviet fire tube

Fig. 8.51   Spread of flame apparatus

The weight loss of the combustible material during burning or glowing as well as the duration of burning (or glowing) are recorded.

Spread of flame method

The GOST 17088-71 spread of flame method is used to investigate highly flammable plastics. The apparatus and test specifications are shown in Fig. 8.51 and Table 8.77, respectively.

Table 8.77   Spread of flame test specifications (GOST 17088-71)

Specimens	6 specimens 300 mm × 40 mm × ≦ 10 mm
	(for textiles and films: max. thickness 1 mm)
Specimen position	horizontal with collecting channel for molten plastic below
Ignition source	small gas burner or alcohol flame, upper edge of burner 10 mm below
	specimen
Test duration	gas flame applied for 2 min, alcohol flame applied for 2.5 min, test
	terminated if specimen extinguishes when ignition source removed
Conclusion	specimen classified as highly flammable if it is completely consumed

GOST 21793-76. Determination of oxygen index for plastics

The oxygen index of plastics is determined in certain cases to compare the combustibility of plastics, e.g. in quality control. The GOST 21793-76 [7] method is basically similar to ASTM D 2863 (see Fig. 8.30 and Table 8.62 in Section 8.2.9 for a diagram of the apparatus and a summary of the test specifications, respectively).

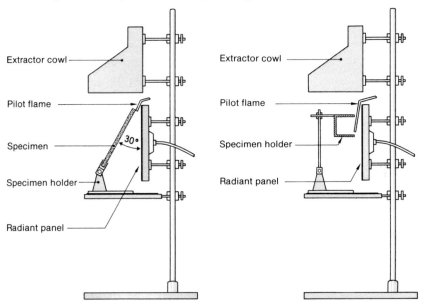

Fig. 8.52   Spread of flame test apparatus
left: Set up for linings, *right:* Set up for textiles and films

GOST 12.1.017-80. Determination of the spread of flame index of materials, smoke formation coefficient of solids and the toxicity of combustion products of polymers

Spread of flame index

The spread of flame index, i.e. the tendency of materials (e.g. finished articles such as linings, textiles and films) to spread flame over a surface is determined according to GOST 12.1.017-80 [8] Appendix 20. The test apparatus and specifications are shown in Fig. 8.52 and Table 8.78, respectively.

Table 8.78   Spread of flame test specifications (GOST 12.1.017-80)

Specimens	5 specimens 140 mm × 320 mm × usual thickness, specimens marked at 30 mm intervals starting 20 mm below top edge
Specimen position	– linings: specimen surface orientated at 30° to vertical radiator surface, distance of top edge of specimen from radiator surface: 70 mm – textiles and films: specimen surface vertical but displaced 40° towards radiator surface, distance of specimen edge to radiator surface 80 mm

Ignition source	– gas infra-red radiator with vertical radiant panel 250 mm × 470 mm, surface temperature: 900 ± 25 °C
	– gas pilot flame, flame length 10–12 mm
	Flame position to
	  – linings: horizontal
	  – textiles and films: vertical

Test duration	until flame front no longer spreads but max. 10 min
Conclusion	depending on test performance, classification in various flame formation indices (see below)

The following criteria are recorded during the test:

– the time t_b (in s) required for the upper region of the specimen to catch fire using a continuously burning pilot flame,
– the times t_1, t_2 . . . t_n (in s) elapsed until the flame reaches specific sections of the surface of the specimen,
– the distance (in mm) travelled by the flame front during the test,
– the maximum temperature (°C) of the smoke gases,
– the time elapsed (in s) until the maximum temperature is reached.

The duration of the test depends on the times necessary for the maximum advance of the flame front and the maximum temperature to be reached.

The flame spread index I is computed for each specimen from the results. Materials are divided into the following classes:

$I \leqq 1$ materials which do not spread flame
$1 < I \leqq 20$ combustible materials which spread flame slowly
$I > 20$ combustible materials which spread flame rapidly

Smoke formation coefficient of solids

The smoke formation coefficient of solids is determined according to GOST 12.1.017-80 Appendix 19. A diagram of the apparatus, test specifications and material classification are given in Section 9.2.2.1.

Toxicity of combustion products

The characteristic value of the toxicity of combustion products of polymeric materials is determined according to GOST 12.1.017-80 Appendix 21.

The materials under test are decomposed in a furnace at temperatures between 600 and 850 °C. 6 to 10 small animals (mice, rats, guinea pigs, rabbits) are exposed to the decomposition gases for 5 min in an undefined test chamber. The LD_{50} value is determined by, for example, the methods of *Litchfield, Wilcoxon* and *Kerber*. In addition, CO, CO_2, HCl, HCN and toluene diisocyanate, HCHO and HF are determined analytically.

Determination of the combustibility of building structures

In the USSR the combustibility of building structures is determined with the fire propagation furnace [5] heated in accordance with the internationally accepted ISO 834 standard temperature-time curve. The test specifications for walls, ceilings, linings and other building elements are given in Table 8.79.

Table 8.79 Test specifications for the combustibility of building structures

Specimen	1500 mm × 1500 mm
Specimen position	vertical
Irradiated zone of specimen	900 mm × 900 mm, calibration marks 500 mm above and to the side of the irradiated zone
Ignition source	burner operated as per standard temperature-time curve
Test duration	15 min
Conclusion	classification in various combustibility groups depending on fire propagation

Building structures are graded in individual combustibility groups using the combustibility value K determined from the test:

- K = 0. The structure is classified as non-combustible. Partial destruction and deterioration including glowing of the specimen in the irradiated zone are not taken into account.
- $0 < K \leqq 1$. The structure is classified as of low combustibility. Burning in the irradiated zone is permitted.
- K > 1. The structure is classified as combustible.

Official approval and future developments

No information could be obtained on these two points. Initial approaches regarding fire protection in buildings should be directed to the

Administration for Foreign Relations of the
Ministry of the Interior of the USSR, Moscow.

Queries on the Soviet GOST standards are dealt with by

GOST
Leninski Prospekt 9
Moscow.

References for 8.2.11

[1] GOST 12.1.004-76. Fire protection. General requirements.

[2] *M. J. Roitman:* Grundlagen der Brandschutz-Normierung im Bauwesen. Translated from the Russian. Staatsverlag der DDR and Verlagsgesellschaft Rudolf Müller, Köln-Braunsfeld. 1974.

[3] *M. W. Alexejev, M. J. Roitman, P. G. Demidov, N. A. Tarasov-Agalakov:* Grundlagen des Brand-schutzes. Translated from the Russian, Staatsverlag der DDR, Berlin, 1976.

[4] *W. T. Monachov:* Test methods for the fire hazard of materials (Russ.) 2nd revised edition, Chimia, Moscow, 1979.

[5] *G. P. Teslenko:* Reducing the fire risks of plastics. Fire International, 64 (1979) 6, p. 28; paper given at the International Symposium on Fire Risk Evaluation in Industry, Swedish Fire Protection Association, Stockholm, May 1979.

[6] GOST 17088-71. Plastics. Methods of determining combustibility.

[7] GOST 21793-76. Plastics. Method of determining oxygen index.

[8] GOST 12.1.017-80. Explosion and fire hazard of oil products and chemical organic products.

[9] *R. Thater:* Brennverhalten von Plastformstoffen. VEB Verlag für Grundstoffindustrie, Leipzig, 1968.

8.2.12 Hungary

Statutory regulations

The statutory regulations for structural fire protection in Hungary are contained in Standard MSZ 595 "Fire protection of buildings" [1]:

MSZ 595	Fire protection of buildings
MSZ 595/1-79	Definitions
MSZ 595/2-79	Classification of the combustibility of building materials
MSZ 595/3-79	Fire resistance requirements of building structures
MSZ 595/4-79	Medium and high rise buildings

Sections 1 to 4 came into force on 1. 1. 1980. Section 2, which covers the classification of building materials, lists the prescribed test standards (see below) and contains a summary of materials classified with the aid of these tests. Section 4 lays down the areas of application of the materials classified in accordance with Section 2 in medium and high rise buildings. Sections 5 to 7 deal with the evacuation of buildings, fire compartments and the calculation of fire resistance limits.

The "Országos Tüzvédelmi Szabályzat", OTSZ (State Regulation for Fire Protection) details, in conjunction with MSZ 595, general regulations for erecting and operating structural works. Further standards cover fire precautions in skyscrapers, theatres and cinemas.

Classification and testing of the fire performance of building materials

According to MSZ 595/2-79 building materials are divided into the following groups:

- nem éghető   (non-combustible)
- éghető   (combustible)

The latter are subdivided into:

- nehezen éghető   (low combustibility)
- közepesen éghető (moderately combustible)
- könnyen éghető   (highly combustible)

Classification of building materials and components is made on the basis of tests conforming to MSZ 14800 Sections 1, 3 and 4 [2]. MSZ 14800 Section 2 was introduced as CMEA Standard MSZ KGST 382-76 on 1. 7. 1979 [3].

The individual standards are:

- MSZ 14800/1 lap-67. Fire resistance tests. Evaluation of the fire resistance limits of structures.
- MSZ KGST 382-76 (previously MSZ 14800/2-69). Fire protection standards for the combustibility of structures. Classification of building materials as "non-combustible" materials.
- MSZ 14800/3 lap-69. Fire resistance tests. Classification of building materials in combustibility classes by testing for "low combustibility".
- MSZ 14800/4 lap-74. Fire resistance tests. Classification of building materials in combustibility classes by testing for "moderate combustibility".

MSZ 14800/1 which covers the fire resistance of building components is not dealt with. A comprehensive review of fire performance of building materials and details of the situation in Hungary can be found in the monograph on the combustibility of plastics by *Pál* and *Macskásy* ([4], p. 171 ff, in Hungarian).

A further Building Ministry standard, MSZ-04 103-77 "Investigation of fire spread on façades" [5], is prescribed for certain applications in MSZ 595/3 and 4.

Testing the non-combustibility of building materials according to MSZ KGST 382-76

The MSZ KGST 382-76 (previously MSZ 14800/2-69) non-combustibility test is basically similar to ISO/R 1182-1970. The non-combustibility furnace and test specifications (cf. Fig. 8.37 and Table 8.68) are discussed in Section 8.2.10.

Testing building materials for "low combustibility" and "moderate combustibility" according to MSZ 14800/3-69 and MSZ 14800/4-74

These tests largely resemble the DIN 4102 Part 1 (Section 8.2.2) and TGL 10685/11 (Section 8.2.10) Brandschacht test shown in Fig. 8.35. The test specifications which are summarised in Table 8.80 differ somewhat from the German version.

Table 8.80   Specifications for testing "low combustibility" and "moderate combustibility" of building materials

Specimens	5 × (low combustibility) or 3 × (moderate combustibility) four speci-mens 1000 mm × 190 mm × usual thickness
Specimen position	vertical, perpendicular to each other
Ignition source	quadratic gas burner with 32 jets, gas supply 72 l/min with 5000 kcal/Nm^3 or 85 l/min with 4200 kcal/Nm^3
Test duration	10 min (low combustibility) 2 min (moderate combustibility)
Conclusions	classification "low combustibility" (after 10 min) or "moderate combustibility" (after 2 min) achieved if: − the unconsumed length of specimen is at least 15 mm − the mean smoke gas temperature does not exceed 250 °C − the weight loss of the specimen is max. 80%

For floorings to be classified as "moderately combustible" the residual length of undamaged specimen must be at least 300 mm. The material is glued to an asbestos cement panel. If the above requirements are not satisfied the material is classified as "highly combustible".

MSZ 595/2-79 precludes the use of building materials which exhibit an ignition temperature <150 °C according to MSZ-09-400 42-77 (this test corresponds to the ASTM D 1929 Setchkin ignition test, details of which are given in Section 8.2.14).

MSZ-04 103-77. Fire propagation test for façades

In this standard, vertical fire propagation and its limiting values on lightweight façades, combustible wall claddings and façades with large areas of glass are determined by means of a model fire test using a defined test fire. The standard applies to wall structures for buildings of at least two storeys. The layout of the test building is shown in Figs. 8.53 to 8.55 and test specifications are summarised in Table 8.81.

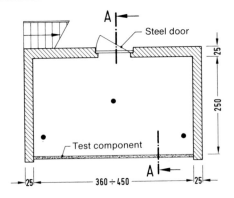

Fig. 8.53   Plan of ground floor of test building (fire room)

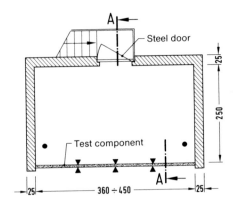

Fig. 8.54   Plan of upper storey of test building (observation level)

Table 8.81   Specifications for testing fire propagation on façades

Specimen	one test component 6.5 m high × 3.6 to 4.5 m wide × usual thickness
Position of specimen	vertical
Ignition source	wood crib (fire load depends on type of building and contents, see below), ignition with 10 kg fuel oil
Test duration	until maximum fire propagation but max. 90 min
Conclusion	depending on test performance classification in fire propagation limits T_f 1.50 to T_f 0.00 (see below)

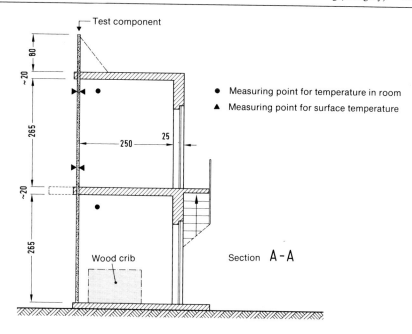

Fig. 8.55 Cross section of test building (section A−A)

The fire tests are carried out in a two storey test building (Fig. 8.55) with the test component built into the front wall. A wood crib is located on the ground floor. If the test component is intended for use in dwellings, hotels or communal buildings, the fire load must be at least 160 Mcal/m². In order to simulate conditions in all other buildings, the fire load consists of the amount of combustible material found there. The fire load is converted to "wood equivalents" with the aid of the fire load value q,

$$q = \frac{\sum_{i=1}^{n} (G_i \cdot f_i)}{40\ 000 \cdot F_p}$$

where

n = number of types of material
f_i = calorific potential (kcal/kg) of all combustible material in room
G_i = mass (kg) of combustible matter
F_p = surface area (m²) of room (fire compartment)

The wood crib is placed 30 to 50 cm away from the wall under test and must cover at least 50% of the floor. The crib is set alight with the help of 10 kg fuel oil contained in a trough slid under it. Thermocouples located in the fire room measure whether the prescribed temperatures of 300 °C and 600 °C are reached after 10 min and 15 min respectively. The temperature in the fire room is measured with three thermocouples; the temperature on the test wall surface with three inside and three outside thermocouples and that in the upper storey with two thermocouples. The test is continued until maximum fire spread or at the most for 90 min following ignition.

The results enable the façades tested to be classified in the classes listed in Table 8.82.

Table 8.82   Classification of fire propagation on façades

Class	Fire spread limit [min]
T$_f$ 1.50	≧90
T$_f$ 1.00	60–90
T$_f$ 0.75	45–60
T$_f$ 0.50	30–45
T$_f$ 0.25	15–30
T$_f$ 0.00	<15

The fire spread limit is the time elapsed until one of the following events occurs:

– Flames or hot smoke gases penetrate between the façade and ceiling as shown by wadding (placed in the gap between the façade and the floor of the upper storey) bursting into flame or incandescing.
– The temperature rise on the inner face of the façade averages 140 °C or is 180 °C at one measuring point.
– Flames or hot gases penetrate the test wall in the upper storey.
– A curtain made of combustible material located in the upper storey is set on fire by the glazed surface breaking.
– The fire on the surface of the front wall spreads to the ceiling of the upper storey.

Official approval

In Hungary, fire performance tests on building materials and structures are carried out by the official test institute for the building industry:

Epitésügyi Minőségellenőrző Intézet (ÉMI)
(Institute for Quality Control in Building)
H-1502 Budapest, Pf. 69
Diószegi ut 37

This organisation issues a test certificate, which is fully accepted by the authorities, detailing the test results and classifying the material in accordance with MSZ 595/2-79.

All building materials and structures require an "ÉMI applications permit" covering combustibility. It is valid for 5 years and is obtained by producing the test certificate. In the case of standard products, it is preferable to establish a product specification laying down the most important material properties. The user of such a product is entitled to have it checked by the ÉMI and if the properties differ from the specification the manufacturer is liable to pay compensation.

If no product specification exists and the product is manufactured for five years, it must be resubmitted do the ÉMI for renewal of the applications permit. Every 2 to 3 years the ÉMI summarises the results of fire tests in:

Épitőanyagok éghetősége, épületszerkezetek tüzállósága
(Combustibility of building materials, fire resistance of building structures)

available from the

Épitésügyi Tájékoztatási Központ (ÉTK)
(Building Information Centre).

6 volumes have appeared up to 1980.

Future developments

Additional statutory regulations in the series MSZ 595 dealing with the evacuation of buildings, fire compartments and the calculation of fire resistance limits are in preparation.

Further test methods for determining the combustibility of building materials and structures are under development as additional sections of MSZ 14800. A draft standard for testing building materials on the basis of the critical stage of radiant thermal energy (using the Pyrowerke, Hannover, test radiator) has been withdrawn.

ÉMI is working intensively on smoke development and toxicity of fire gases and hopes to issue relevant standards for the building sector over the next few years. The ISO smoke box (see Section 9.2.3.2) is favoured for smoke density measurements while fire gas toxicity will be determined by chemical analysis rather than biologically.

References for 8.2.12

[1] Építmények tűzvédelme.
   - MSZ 595/1-79 Fogalommeghatározások.
   - MSZ 595/2-79 Építőanyagok éghetőségi csoportosítása.
   - MSZ 595/3-79 Épületszerkezetek tűzállósági követelményei.
   - MSZ 595/4-79 Középmagas és magas épületek.
[2] Tűzállósági vizsgálatok.
   - MSZ 14800/1. lap-67 Épületszerkezetek tűzállósági határértékének vizsgálata.
   - MSZ 14800/3. lap-69 Épitési anyagok éghetőségi csoportba sorolása a "nehezen éghetőség" vizsgálatával.
   - MSZ 14800/4-74. Épitési anyagok éghetőségi csoportba sorolása a "közepesen éghetőség" vizsgálatával.
[3] MSZ KGST 382-76 Tűzállósági vizsgálat a "nem éghető" épitési anyagok csoportjának meghatározására.
[4] *Pál, Károlyné* and *Macskásy, Hugó:* A műanyagok éghetősége (Combustibility of plastics). Műszaki Könyvkiadó, Budapest, 1980.
[5] MSZ-04 103-77. Tüzterjedés vizsgálata épülethomlokzaton.

8.2.13 Czechoslovakia

Statutory regulations

Health and safety at work as well as fire protection in Czechoslovakia are governed by a range of laws, government decrees, proclamations and other mandatory directives issued by certain authorities and institutions.

The requirements of fire protection in buildings are described in a comprehensive series of legally binding standards which deal with the regulations, classification and tests concerning the fire performance of building materials and components. The standards contain requirements relating to fire proof structures, escape routes, separation of buildings, division of buildings into fire compartments, etc. Preventative measures such as sprinklers, smoke and heat extractors and fire alarms are also described. These requirements form a unified concept for the fire protection of buildings.

ČSN 73 0802 "Fire protection of buildings, general regulations" is the fundamental standard for fire precautions and contains a summary of all the important relevant requirements. This standard is supplemented by others covering various types of building such as dwellings, hospitals and factories etc. [1].

Classification and testing of the fire performance of building materials

The Czechoslovak fire protection standards are divided into five groups.

– project standards [1],
– test standards [2],
– evaluation standards [3],
– object standards [4],
– special standards outside the 73 08 series [5].

The project standards concern structural fire protection requirements and have already been mentioned in the introduction. The test and evaluation standards are discussed in more detail below while the object and special standards listed under [4] and [5] are mentioned for the sake of completeness.

The various standards concerning testing and evaluation of the fire resistance of building components lie outside the scope of this book and are not dealt with.

ČSN 73 0823 defines five fire classes for building materials (Table 8.83).

Table 8.83   ČSN 73 0823 fire classes for building materials

Fire class	Designation
A	non-combustible
B	not easily combustible
C1	low combustibility
C2	moderately combustible
C3	easily combustible

Classification is made on the basis of performance in tests laid down in ČSN 73 0853 (see below) which also contains a list of materials which can be classified without testing. These include inorganic materials such as asbestos, concrete etc. in class A, polystyrene-concrete in class B, wood and plastics building materials conforming to certain ČSN standards in classes C1 and C2 and non-standardised combustible building materials in class C3.

ČSN 73 0853 however no longer reflects latest developments and is being gradually replaced by three new standards. The first of these, ČSN 73 0861 (test of non-combustibility of building materials) based on ISO/R 1182, was introduced on 1. 1. 1980. Test results from ČSN 73 0853 can be utilised until 1. 1. 1986.

ČSN 73 0861. Non-combustibility test for building materials

The ČSN 73 0861 non-combustibility test for building materials is identical to CMEA Standard ST SEV 382-1976 corresponding to ISO/R 1182. A diagram of the non-combustibility furnace and test specifications are given in Section 8.2.10, Fig. 8.37 and Table 8.68.

ČSN 73 0853. Combustibility test for building materials

The ČSN 73 0853 combustibility test for building materials is carried out with the Landman burner illustrated in Fig. 8.56. The test specifications are summarised in Table 8.84.

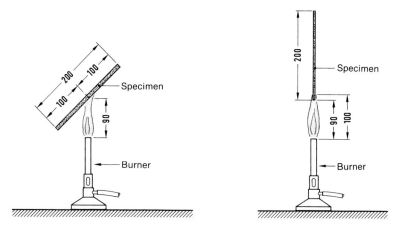

Fig. 8.56 Landman burner for testing the combustibility of building materials
left: Test layout for panels and light building materials, *right:* Test layout for films

The specimens are weighed and, depending on the materials, positioned at 45° (panels and light building materials) or vertically (films) 90 mm above the upper edge of the burner. A 100 mm long non-luminous flame is applied for 10 min. The time that the specimen continues to burn, incandesce or glow independently is measured, and the % weight loss during the test is determined. The behaviour of the material during the test is also taken into account in classifying the material. The arithmetic mean of the results from 10 tests are used to classify the material as shown in Table 8.85.

Table 8.84   ČSN 73 0853 combustibility test specifications for building materials

Specimens	10 specimens 200 mm × 100 mm
Specimen thickness	– films 0.1 mm to 3 mm
	– panels 3 mm to 10 mm
	– light building materials 10 mm to 100 mm
Specimen position	– panels and light building materials 45° to horizontal
	– film vertical
Ignition source	coal gas laboratory burner (flow 2 l/min)
	flame temperature 1000 °C to 1100 °C ($\triangleq$ 4000 kcal/m^3), non-luminous flame 100 mm high, the upper edge of the burner is sited 90 mm below the middle of the test specimen tilted at 45° or 90 mm below the bottom of the vertically positioned test specimen
Test duration	flame applied for 10 min to specimen, test continues until afterflame, afterglow or charring of specimen cease
Conclusion	classification in combustibility classes A to C3 (see below) depending on test performance

Table 8.85   Classification of materials according to ČSN 73 0853

Combustibility grade	Behaviour of the material during test	Afterglow, charring [min]	Weight loss [%]
A non-combustible	no burning, incandescence or charring	0	$\leqq$ 2
B not easily combustible	mainly incandescence or charring	$\leqq$ 3	$\leqq$ 5
C1 low combustibility	slow ignition and combustion, extinguishes within 2 min of removal of ignition source	$\leqq$ 10	$\leqq$ 10
C2 moderately combustible	burns, extinguishes within 5 min of removal of ignition source	$\leqq$ 20	$\leqq$ 50
C3 easily combustible	burns rapidly and is completely consumed within 10 min of flame application, continues to burn for more than 5 min after ignition source has been removed	> 20	> 50

Official approval

In Czechoslovakia certain products are evaluated, approved and checked by a system of state test stations operating in user interests. The Office for Standardisation and Metrology (ÚNM) is the central administrative body for state testing and licenses the state test stations.

Two state test stations (SZ) are active in the building sector:

SZ 204 – Technical Building Test Institute Prague
    TZÚS
    Washingtonova ul. 25
    ČS-113 33 Praha 1

and

SZ 205 – Technical Building Test Institute Bratislava
TZÚS
Lamačská 8
ČS-809 42 Bratislava

Two research institutes are concerned with evaluation of certain types of building materials and products to a limited extent:

SZ 227 – Building Research Institute Prague
Výzkumný ústav pozemních staveb (VÚPS)
Pražská ul. 16
ČS-102 21 Praha 10 – Hostivař

and

SZ 238 – Building Research Institute Ostrava
Slavíkova ul. 1744
ČS-708 00 Ostrava-Poruba

The fire performance of building materials is tested in the fire laboratory at the Building Research Institute (VÚPS) in Veselí nad Lužnicí. Testing is usually carried out within four weeks and a test report issued two weeks later. This test report is accepted by the authorities and its validity is unlimited unless a new or modified test method is introduced or the test report is withdrawn. The test reports are listed by the Building Research Institute and the most important are published in a monthly bulletin. The Czechoslovak Building and Architecture Centre also issues a catalogue containing the fire characteristics of building materials and components.

Fire performance tests on building materials are usually carried out together with tests of other important properties of the material. Depending on the results of the tests, the product is classified in one of three quality grades or is rejected by the state test station. Products which have the first or second quality grade conferred on them are granted the right to use the relevant quality marking by the SZ. The results of these procedures are published regularly. The state test station makes random checks on the properties of approved products to ensure that they meet those of the sample and manufacturers must also maintain continuous quality control of their products.

Future developments

Various modifications will be made in the near future to the test and evaluation standards in Czechoslovakia relating to the standards for fire resistance of building components and combustibility of building materials.

ČSN 73 0851 (Determination of the fire resistance of building structures) will be revised to bring it into line with CMEA standard ST SEV 1000-1978.

ČSN 73 0855 (Determination of the fire resistance of exterior walls) based on CMEA standard ST SEV 1000-1978 will replace ČSN 73 0851 for testing walls.

ČSN 73 0856 (Determination of the fire resistance of suspended ceilings) is in preparation.

Various standards for testing and evaluating the combustibility of building materials are being revised or introduced. Evaluation standard ČSN 73 0823 (Combustibility of building materials) is being fundamentally revised and will take into account test standards

ČSN 73 0861 (introduced on 1. 1. 1980), 73 0862 and 73 0863 which will supersede ČSN 73 0853.

ČSN 73 0862 [6] describes a test method for determining heat release during combustion of a test specimen in relation to time. It is based on the British BS 476: Part 6 fire propagation test (Section 8.2.5) and will be used to classify building materials in various combustibility classes.

ČSN 73 0863 (Determination of the surface spread of flame of building materials) [6] follows the aims of GDR Standard TGL 10685/12 (Section 8.2.10) with different test methods. Full scale tests on exterior walls, suspended ceilings and floorings are compared with results from model fire tests.

Smoke development and toxicity are not considered in the Czech fire protection standards nor are relevant standards planned in the near future. However a test programme on this subject is being worked out by the fire laboratory of the Slovak Authorities for Fire Protection.

References for 8.2.13

[1] ČSN (Czech State Standard) Fire protection of buildings.
ČSN 73 0802. General Provisions. 1. 4. 1977.
ČSN 73 0831. Assembly rooms.
ČSN 73 0833. Appartments. 1. 4. 1977.
ČSN 73 0835. Hospitals.
ČSN 73 0837. Individual garages and blocks of garages. 1. 1. 1978.
ČSN 73 0838. Large garages. 1. 11. 1978.
ČSN 73 0839. Car repair shops and petrol stations. 1. 11. 1978.
ČSN 73 0840. Industrial premises. 1. 11. 1978.
ČSN 73 0842. Agricultural premises. 1. 11. 1978.
ČSN 73 0843. Premises for telecommunications. 1. 10. 1979.
ČSN 73 0844. Warehouses. 1. 7. 1978.
ČSN 73 0849. Historical buildings. 1. 11. 1978.
[2] ČSN 73 0851. Determination of the fire endurance of structures. 1. 7. 1971.
ČSN 73 0852. Determination of the fire endurance of fire shutters. 1. 3. 1976 (based on ISO/DIS 834).
ČSN 73 0853. Determination of the combustibility of building materials. 1. 7. 1971.
ČSN 73 0855. Determination of the fire endurance of external walls.
ČSN 73 0856. Determination of the fire endurance of suspended ceilings.
ČSN 73 0861. Combustibility test for building materials – non-combustible materials. 1. 1. 1980 (based on ISO/R 1182).
[3] ČSN 73 0818. Staffing of buildings. 1. 1. 1973.
ČSN 73 0821. Fire endurance of structures. 1. 10. 1974.
ČSN 73 0823. Combustibility of building materials. 1. 1. 1973.
ČSN 73 0824. Calorific value of combustible materials. 1. 9. 1980 (revision of standard of 1. 1. 1973).
[4] ČSN 73 0872. Protecting buildings from the spread of fire via ventilation systems. 1. 10. 1979.
ČSN 73 0875. Electric fire alarms.
[5] ČSN 73 0135. Drawings for fire protection in buildings. 1. 7. 1972.
[6] ČSN 73 0862. Determination of the combustibility of building materials.
ČSN 73 0863. Determination of the surface spread of flame of building materials.

8.2.14 United States of America

Statutory regulations

The fifty states which make up the USA all have their own differing constitutions. Apart from special cases, where federal regulations apply (see below), there are no nationally valid mandatory building codes or regulations defining structural fire protection requirements. These requirements are contained in some 20,000 more or less different local building codes resulting in particular problems on implementation.

A range of Model Building Codes has, however, been developed by various organisations and is brought up to date every two or three years by new editions or supplements. Their use is favoured in, but not restricted to, the following regions:

- The West: the Uniform Building Code issued by the International Conference of Building Officials (ICBO) [1].
- The Middle West: the BOCA Basic Building Code issued by the Building Officials and Code Administrators International Inc. [2].
- The South: the Standard Building Code issued by the Southern Building Code Congress International, Inc. (SBCC) [3].
- The North East: the National Building Code previously issued by the American Insurance Association (AIA) [4] and now issued by the National Conference of States for Building Codes and Standards (NCS BCS).

These model building codes are favoured in the areas where they originate and are adopted in full or in part in state or city building regulations, although this is not mandatory. Fire precautions are dealt with comprehensively in these model building codes.

Many building authorities also use the non-regional NFPA 101 "Code for Safety to Life from Fire in Buildings and Structures" of the National Fire Protection Association (NFPA) which also covers fire precautions.

In addition, certain building regulations issued by the Federal Agencies apply nationwide, for instance the Minimum Property Standards of the Department of Housing and Urban Development (HUD) and the regulations of the Department of Health and Human Services (HHS) (previously called the Department of Health, Education and Welfare [HEW]).

Both departments have financed various construction projects. The HUD Department sets minimum requirements for dwellings which must be met in order to obtain Federal Mortgage Insurances. Since the latter are frequently taken up, developers usually comply with these Minimum Property Standards. Building projects financed by the HHS Department must meet the "Minimum Requirements of Construction and Equipment for Hospital and Medical Facilities".

All the above building codes contain similar structural fire protection measures such as regulations on escape routes, fire resistance of building components, precautions against the spread of fire and smoke, the fire performance of combustible building materials and finished parts, fire alarms, extinguisher systems and the classification of buildings into different categories of fire hazard (public buildings, cinemas, hospitals, etc).

The Consumer Product Safety Commission (CPSC), a further Federal Agency is concerned with the combustibility of certain materials and issues regulations and associated test methods. Floor coverings can only be sold if they comply with CPSC regulations and pass certain fire tests [5].

Useful reviews of the numerous American building regulations are given in [6] (Vol. 2, Chap. 7 and Vol. 7, Chap. 5) and in [7]. Up to date details can be obtained from the latest editions or amendments of the four Model Building Codes mentioned above.

Classification and testing of the fire performance of building materials

In addition to fire tests on building materials and components in general in the USA, there are requirements relating to specific materials such as plastics and wood. For example besides the general methods for determining the combustibility of plastics, special tests are required for rigid foams and films.

As a result of the multitude of building regulations, there is no unified system of testing and classification. However, in practice nearly all fire test methods have been issued by the American Society for Testing and Materials (ASTM) and have, in the main, been officially confirmed as American National Standards by the American National Standards Institute (ANSI) with the designation ANSI/ASTM. Many of these standard test methods were developed by Underwriters' Laboratories Inc. (UL) a major American test institution.

As in other countries, fire testing and classification are based on certain parameters such as non-combustibility, fire resistance, ignition temperature, flame spread, smoke development, etc.

The various parameters are tested by the following ASTM methods:

- ANSI/ASTM E 119-79. Fire tests of building construction and materials.
- ASTM E 136-79. Behavior of materials in a vertical tube furnace at 750 °C.
- ANSI/ASTM E 84-79a. Surface burning characteristics of building materials.
- ANSI/ASTM E 162-78. Surface flammability of materials using a radiant heat energy source.
- ANSI/ASTM D 2843-77. Density of smoke from the burning or decomposition of plastics.
- ANSI/ASTM E 662-79. Specific optical density of smoke generated by solid materials.
- ANSI/ASTM D 1929-77. Ignition properties of plastics.
- ANSI/ASTM D 635-77. Rate of burning and/or extent and time of burning of self-supporting plastics in a horizontal position.
- ANSI/ASTM D 568-77. Rate of burning and/or extent and time of burning of flexible plastics in a vertical position.
- ASTM D 2859-76. Flammability of finished textile floor covering materials.
- ANSI/ASTM E 648-78. Critical radiant flux of floor-covering systems using a radiant heat energy source.

All ASTM Standards issued as American National Standards are contained in the Annual Book of ASTM Standards available from the American Society for Testing and Materials, 1916 Race Street, Philadelphia, Pa 19103, USA.

Of the above standards, ASTM E 119-79 (identical to UL 263, UBC Standard 43-1, NFPA 251) refers to the determination of the fire resistance of building components and is not discussed in this book.

The non-combustibility of building materials is determined according to ASTM E 136-79 which differs considerably from ISO 1182 as regards test apparatus and specifications.

Interior finishes such as wall, ceiling and some floor coverings are classified in all building regulations on the basis of the flammability parameter, surface spread of flame, using the ASTM E 84-79a tunnel test. In certain cases such as the HUD regulations, the surface flammability of materials is determined by ASTM E 162-78 using a radiant heat source. This method is not otherwise used in the construction field.

Smoke development is considered in the building regulations too. A distinction is made between solid materials in general (tested with the NBS smoke density chamber according to NBS Technical Note 708 or ASTM E 662-79) and plastics in particular (tested with the XP2 chamber according to ASTM D 2843-77). Smoke development is also considered in ASTM E 84-79a and ASTM E 162-79. Details of these methods are given in Section 9.2.

Specific groups of building materials also have to satisfy building regulation requirements. The fire performance of wood, for example, is investigated by various methods [8, 9] which are, however, not discussed here. The building regulations contain the following specific test methods for plastics: ignition properties of plastics to ASTM D 1929-77 and the rate of burning of plastics in horizontal and vertical positions to ASTM D 635-77 and ASTM D 568-77, respectively. Rigid foams are tested increasingly not just according to ASTM E 84-79a but also by the so-called corner tests. These large-scale tests were developed by various bodies and are favoured by insurers such as Factory Mutual. This type of large scale test is however not likely to be incorporated in the principal American building codes.

The fire performance of floor coverings is determined by the ASTM D 2859-76 methenamine pill test which simulates a burning cigarette and also by ASTM E 84-79a. The National Bureau of Standards (NBS) developed the NBSIR 75-950 (ASTM E 648-78 or NFPA 253) radiation test which enables floor coverings to be tested under more realistic conditions. The method has been officially incorporated in building regulations, e.g. in BOCA under 704-7 – Floor covering.

Attention is also drawn to Underwriters' Laboratories UL 992 [10] which is a scaled down (8 ft) version of the ASTM E 84-79a tunnel test with the specimen positioned on the floor. This particular method has not been incorporated in building codes but is in use in Canada (see Section 8.2.15).

For the sake of completeness, test methods for determining the fire performance of roofing [11] and fire tests for fire resistant doors and windows [12, 13] are mentioned here although they are not discussed in this book nor are various other tests required on occasion by local officials.

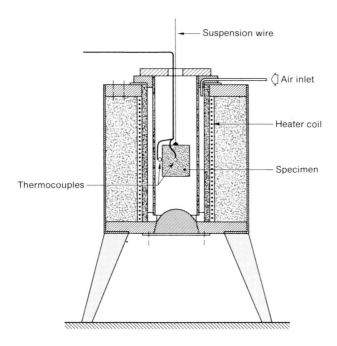

Fig. 8.57   750 °C tube furnace

ASTM E 136-79. Determination of combustion characteristics of building materials

The ASTM E 136-79 test for determining the combustion characteristics of building materials differs from ISO 1182 (Section 8.2.18) as is evident from Fig. 8.57 and the test specifications given in Table 8.86. Certain building codes (e.g. UBC Standard 4-1, Sec. 410. Non-combustible material, tests) specify this method.

Table 8.86   Test specifications for determining the combustion characteristics of building materials by ASTM E 136-79

Specimens	minimum of 4 samples 38 mm × 38 mm × 51 mm
Specimen position	vertical
Ignition source	electric furnace heated to 750 °C
Test duration	until thermocouples reach maximum temperature or specimen fails test
Conclusions	passed if at least 3 of the 4 specimens
	– do not cause a rise in furnace temperature of more than 30 °C
	– do not burn after the first 30 s
	– do not cause a temperature rise in the furnace or burn when weight loss exceeds 50%

ASTM E 84-79a. Surface burning characteristics of building materials

The ASTM E 84-79a test is identical to UL 723 (UL developed this method), NFPA 255 and UBC Standard 41-1. The apparatus, known as the Steiner tunnel is illustrated in Fig. 8.58 and the test specifications are summarised in Table 8.87.

Table 8.87   Steiner tunnel test specifications

Specimens	at least 1 sample 0.51 m × 7.32 m × usual thickness
Specimen position	horizontal under tunnel roof
Ignition source	2 gas burners with 5.3 MJ/min output located 190 mm below specimen at a distance of 305 mm from and parallel to the fire end of the test chamber
Test duration	10 min
Conclusion	determination of flame spread and "Flame Spread Classification" (FSC), measurement of smoke density

Two preliminary tests are carried out after calibrating the apparatus. A first run is made with a standard red oak specimen to obtain numerical values of 100 for flame spread and smoke density. In the second preliminary test an asbestos cement specimen is tested in order to obtain zero values for these same parameters.

In the actual main test, the contribution of the material under test to smoke development and flame spread is measured and the material classified on the basis of the results. Details of smoke density measurement are given in Section 9.2.2.2.

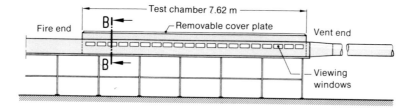

Section **B - B**

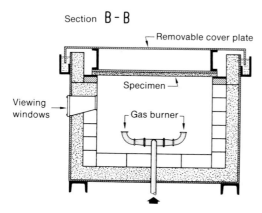

Fig. 8.58   25 ft Steiner tunnel

In order to obtain the Flame Spread Classification (FSC) of the material the distance travelled by the flame front is plotted as a function of time. If the total resultant area A_T under the flame spread time – distance curve $\leqq 97.5$ (ft · min), then

$$FSC = 0.515 \cdot A_T$$

If A_T is greater than 97.5 (ft · min), then

$$FSC = \frac{4900}{195 - A_T}$$

The determination of spread of flame with the 25 ft tunnel test forms the basis of classifying "Interior Finishes" contained in all the building codes. The classification characteristics used to differ from code to code but now largely agree. The Interior Finish classifications of the principal building codes are quoted here as an example.

– Life Safety Code, NFPA 101 Section 6-2.1.5:

Class	Flame spread
A	0 − 25
B	26 − 75
C	76 − 200

– Uniform Building Code (UBC) (issued by ICBO) Section 4204, Table 42-A:

Class	Flame spread
I	0 – 25
II	26 – 75
III	76 – 200

Smoke density must not exceed 450. Plastics are also covered; flame spread must not be more than 200 and smoke density is limited to 450 (or 75 by ASTM D 2843-77). In the codes listed here, rigid foam plastics must, depending on the application, exhibit flame spread ≤ 25 or ≤ 75 and smoke density ≤ 450.

– Basic Building Code (issued by BOCA) Section 904.2, Table 16 A:

Class	Flame spread
I	0 – 25
II	26 – 75
III	76 – 200

– Standard Building Code (issued by SBCC) Section 704 – Restrictions on Interior Use of Combustible Materials:

Class	Flame spread	Smoke density
A	0 – 25	
B	26 – 75	≤ 450
C	76 – 200	

– National Building Code (issued by NCS BCS) Section 810.3, Uses of Interior Finishes:

Depending on the type of building or use in particularly exposed areas (e.g. escape routes) Flame Spread 75 or 200.

– HUD Section 405-8.2 and -8.3 or Table 4-5.4:

Depending on the type of building or use in particularly exposed areas, flame spread 0–25, 0–75 or 0–200. Floors as well as walls and ceilings are also included.

– HHS section 8.15: F. Interior Finishes:

Maximum Flame Spread 25 or 75. The smoke density (max. 450) is determined by NBS TN 708 (see Section 9.2.2.1).

This list demonstrates the complexity of the American Building Codes and resultant difficulties in assigning the correct classification for all applications and materials despite the wide measure of agreement.

ASTM E 162-78. Test for surface flammability of materials using a radiant heat energy source

The apparatus for the ASTM E 162-78 surface flammability test is shown in Figs. 8.59 and 8.60 while the test specifications are summarised in Table 8.88.

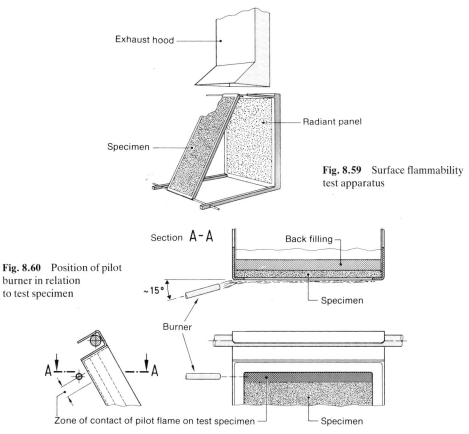

Exhaust hood

Radiant panel

Specimen

Fig. 8.59   Surface flammability test apparatus

Section **A-A**   Back filling

Fig. 8.60   Position of pilot burner in relation to test specimen

~15°

Specimen

Burner

A ---⊕--- A

Zone of contact of pilot flame on test specimen

Specimen

Table 8.88   ASTM E 162-78 radiant panel flame spread test specifications

Specimens	4 specimens 150 mm × 460 mm
Specimen position	at an angle of 30° to vertical, distance from radiant panel: upper (150 mm long) edge 120 mm, lower edge 340 mm
Ignition sources	– vertical gas radiant panel 300 mm × 460 mm, operating temperature 670 °C
	– gas pilot burner, 230 mm long porcelain tube, 6 mm diameter, mounted horizontally at an angle of 15 to 20° to specimen; flame length 150 to 180 mm, applied to upper edge of specimen from a distance of 32 mm
Test duration	until the 380 mm reference mark is reached or maximum of 15 min
Conclusions	Flame Spread Index calculated from measured flame spread and heat evolution, measurement of smoke development

A minimum of four specimens are exposed to the thermal energy of the radiant panel and a pilot flame for a maximum of 15 min. The times necessary for the flame front to reach reference marks situated at intervals of 76 mm are recorded. The term "flashing" is used if the flame front advances from one reference mark to another in less than 3 s. The heat evolution due to the smoke gases, the level of smoke development (see section 9.2.1.1) and flaming drops are also recorded.

The Flame Spread Index I_s is the product of the Flame Spread Factor F_s and Heat Evolution Factor Q:

$$I_s = F_s \cdot Q$$

F_s is obtained by plotting distance against time required to reach each reference mark. These points are joined to one another and give a line from which F_s is calculated (details are given in Section 9.2 and Appendix A 1.5 in E 162−78).

Q is calculated from $Q = \frac{CT}{\beta}$ where C is a constant for converting into metric units, T is the maximum observed thermocouple temperature difference between the temperature time curve of the test specimen and that of an asbestos cement calibration specimen, β is a constant for the apparatus (value approx. 40 $\frac{°C}{kW}$). The ASTM E 162-78 test is only mentioned in the regulations of the HUD Minimum Property Standards under 405-8.3 "Flame Spread Tests" and has no other significance as a test method in the building sector.

Test methods for plastics

ASTM D 1929-77. Test method for ignition properties of plastics

The ignition properties of plastics are tested by ASTM D 1929-77 using the Setchkin furnace which is similar to that described in ASTM E 136-79 (see Fig. 8.57 and Table 8.86). There are, however, certain modifications in order to accommodate plastics. Thus the specimens are not in the form of a block suspended by a wire in the furnace, but are tested as granules (in the case of thermoplastics) or as 20 mm × 20 mm squares (in the case of thermosets) weighing approximately 3 g and placed in a pan. The test specifications differ considerably from those of ASTM E 136-79 and are given in Table 8.89.

Table 8.89   ASTM D 1929-77 test specifications for self-ignition and flash-ignition temperatures

Specimens	minimum of 5 specimens each for self-ignition and flash-ignition temperatures by procedure A, fewer for short procedure B
Specimen position	pan containing 3 g of specimen suspended in furnace
Ignition sources	– electric furnace which can be heated to 750 °C
	– pilot flame above furnace opening (only used in the determination of flash-ignition temperature)
Test duration	until no further ignition of the test specimen occurs at the minimum temperature measured
Conclusions	determination of the self-ignition and flash-ignition temperatures of plastics

The test is explained using Procedure A: initially the flash-ignition temperature is determined approximately in 3 tests with low (25 mm/s), moderate (50 mm/s) and high (100 mm/s) air flow rates with a temperature rise of 600 °C/h. The air temperature at which the decomposition gases are ignited by the pilot flame is noted. The second approximation occurs with the air flow which gave the lowest ignition temperature in the preliminary test at a temperature increase of 300 °C/h.

The actual determination of the flash-ignition temperature is made at constant furnace temperature which should be 10 °C below the ignition temperature established in the preliminary tests. If ignition occurs, runs are carried out lowering the temperature each time by 10 °C until ignition no longer occurs within 30 min.

The self-ignition temperature is determined as above but without the pilot flame.

This test is a laboratory method and is only mentioned in special cases in building regulations. Thus, for example, UBC Section 5207 lays down that domelights must not fall out of their holders at temperatures less than 200 °F below their flash-ignition temperature as determined by UBC Standard No 52−3 (≙ ASTM D 1929).

ASTM D 635-77. Rate of burning of plastics in a horizontal position

The ASTM D 635-77 method is used to test rigid plastics in a horizontal position. The apparatus has already been illustrated in Fig. 8.18 in Section 8.2.5 (BS 2782, Method 508 A). The test specifications differ somewhat and are summarised in Table 8.90.

Table 8.90   ASTM D 635-77 test specifications for burning rate of plastics

Specimens	10 specimens, 125 mm × 12.5 mm × usual thickness, reference mark 100 mm from free end of specimen
Specimen position	longitudinal axis (125 mm) horizontal, transverse axis inclined at 45° to horizontal
Ignition source	Bunsen burner with 25 mm long blue flame
Test duration	flame applied for 30 s
Conclusions	− if 100 mm mark reached, determine mean rate of burning in cm/min − if 100 mm mark not reached, determine mean burning time in s and mean extent of burning in mm various classifications according to building code (see below)

This test method forms the basis for classifying the burning behaviour of plastics in various building codes especially the Basic Building Code, Uniform Building Code and Standard Building Code. According to these regulations only those plastics which exhibit a maximum rate of burning of 6.35 cm/min for a thickness >1.27 mm are permitted.

Such plastics are classified in class C-2 according to the Basic Building Code and in CC2 by the other two codes. Plastics for more rigorous requirements must exhibit a maximum burning rate of 2 cm/min or extinguish before the reference mark is reached.

The whole of Chapter 26 of the Standard Building Code is devoted to plastics. Section 2601 deals with the classification of their burning behaviour. Test specimens less than 1.27 mm thick must, in addition, be tested to ASTM D 568-77 (see below) which limits use to those plastics which are not completely consumed in under 2 min.

ASTM D 568-77. Rate of burning of plastics in a vertical position

The rate of burning of vertically positioned plastics is tested by ASTM D 568-77. The test equipment is shown in Fig. 8.33, Section 8.2.9 "Sweden". The test specifications are summarised in Table 8.91.

Table 8.91   ASTM D 568-77 test specifications for burning rate of plastics

Specimens	10 specimens 25 mm × 450 mm, reference mark 70 mm below the upper suspended end of the specimen
Specimen position	suspended vertically from a clamp
Ignition source	Bunsen burner with 25 mm long flame
Test duration	flame applied until specimen ignites, max. 15 s
Conclusions	– if reference mark reached, calculation of mean burning rate in cm/min
	– if reference mark not reached, determination of mean burning time and mean extent of burning
	classification in classes A to D according to the Standard Building Code

The classification of plastics tested according to this standard has already been described above.

Floor coverings

ASTM D 2859-76. Methenamine pill test

This method was introduced as DOC-FF-1-70 and DOC-FF-2-70 by the Consumer Product Safety Commission in 1970 and was subsequently adopted as ASTM D 2859-76. Since the test simply involves igniting a methenamine tablet placed on the specimen, no diagram is shown. The test specifications are listed in Table 8.92.

Table 8.92   ASTM D 2859-76 methenamine pill test specifications

Specimens	8 specimens 230 mm × 230 mm
Specimen position	horizontal, 230 mm × 230 mm steel plate with a 205 mm diameter cut-out is laid over the specimen
Ignition source	methenamine tablet lit with a match
Test duration	until flames extinguish or reach the inner edge of the steel plate
Conclusions	passed if charred area $\geqq$ 25.4 mm from inner edge of steel plate

ASTM E 648-78. Flooring radiant panel test

The fire performance of floor coverings is investigated by the ASTM E 648-78 (previously NBSIR 75-950) or NFPA No 253 flooring radiant panel test. A diagram of the apparatus is given in Fig. 8.3 in Section 8.2.2, while the test specifications are summarised in Table 8.93.

The test is carried out by exposing the test specimen to the radiation and applying the pilot flame for 10 min to the narrow edge nearest the radiant panel. Subsequently the flame is swung up so that it burns 50 mm above and parallel to the specimen. If the specimen has ignited the test is continued until the flames extinguish, otherwise it is terminated after 10 min.

The furthest advance of the flame front is measured after the test has ended using the curve shown in Fig. 8.61 obtained with a blank sample. This distance is converted into the critical radiant heat flux in W/cm^2 required for ignition.

Table 8.93   ASTM E 648-78 flooring radiant panel test specifications

Specimens	3 specimens 250 mm × 1050 mm × usual thickness
Specimen position	horizontal
Ignition sources	– gas radiator 305 mm × 457 mm operating temperature up to 815 °C, inclined at 30° to horizontal, lower edge 140 mm above test specimen, radiant flux on sample from source 1.0 to 0.1 W/cm² – pivotable propane pilot flame, inner blue flame cone 13 mm long, applied perpendicular to long edge in the middle of the narrow edge nearest to the radiant panel, pilot flame can be swung up parallel to specimen at a height of 50 mm
Test duration	10 min exposure to flame and radiation, if no ignition, flame swung up and radiation continued for 10 min, if ignition occurs, test continued until flames extinguish
Conclusions	determination of the mean critical radiation flux

Both the BOCA Basic Building Code and Section 704.7 of the Standard Building Code require floor coverings to be tested in this way. Depending on the application, the material must be resistant to heat fluxes of 0.22 or 0.45 W/cm².

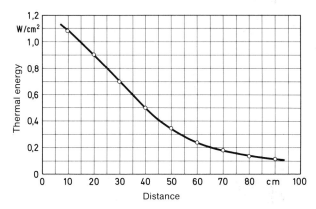

Fig. 8.61   Standard radiant heat energy flux profile

Official approval

No officially appointed institutions for establishing the fire performance of building materials and components exist in the USA. In theory anybody could run a test laboratory and carry out fire tests using methods (e.g. to ANSI) laid down in the various building codes. It is, however, at the discretion of individual authorities to recognise such tests.

There are many well known test institutes whose tests are usually recognised by the authorities. A distinction is made between those which are state run (Universities, e.g. the University of California, Berkeley, California 94720), those which are run as "Not-for-Profit" organisations with state and private management and finally those "Profit" organisations which operate on a purely private basis. Further details of these organisations are available from the Society of Fire Protection Engineers, 60 Batterymarch Street, Boston, Massachusetts 02110.

These organisations and their test laboratories are equipped to varying degrees to test materials. While many only carry out the relevant tests and issue test reports, certain organisations set up inspection and quality control agreements with manufacturers of products which have passed the tests. The product then carries the marking of the test organisation. Marked products are favoured by the authorities.

The Underwriters' Laboratories Inc (UL), one of the largest "Not-for-Profit" organisations testing the fire performance of building materials and components is an important example of the latter group. UL publish annually a Building Materials Directory listing and classifying tested and inspected materials (further details on UL test and approval procedures are given in Section 8.4.3.1).

Future developments

The US Model Building Codes are being continuously revised and extended. Individual test methods have, however, hardly changed and there are no modifications in the pipeline.

In the area of floorings, fire performance requirements will be adopted or included in modified form in the next editions or supplements of the Building Codes. New requirements will be included in the Basic Building Code (testing probably in accordance with ASTM E 648). Modifications will be made to the Standard Building Code while the Uniform Building Code will probably remain unchanged.

There are no plans to introduce the corner test methods for foams in the Model Building Codes.

The regulations and tests relating to smoke development and toxicity of fire gases are likely to stay as they are in the short term.

References for 8.2.14

[1]   Uniform Building Code. 1979 Edition. International Conference of Building Officials (ICBO). 5360 South Workman Mill Road, Whittier, California 90601.
[2]   The BOCA Basic Building Code/1978. Seventh Edition. Building Officials & Code Administrators International, Inc. 1313 East 60th St., Chicago, Illinois 60637. "1980 Supplement" (new address 17926 South Halsted Street, Homewood, Illinois 60430).
[3]   Standard Building Code. 1979 Edition. Southern Building Code Congress International, Inc. 900 Montclair Road, Birmingham, Alabama 35213.
[4]   The National Building Code. 1976 Edition. American Insurance Association. Engineering and Safety Service, 85 John Street, New York, N.Y. 10038 (The National Building Code has since been issued by the National Conference of States on Building Codes and Standards, Inc. (NCS BCS), 481 Carlisle Drive, Herndon, VA 22070).
[5]   I. A. Benjamin, S. Davis: NBSIR 78-1436. Flammability Testing for Carpet. April 1978. Final report.
[6]   National Materials Advisory Board: Fire Safety Aspects of Polymeric Materials, Technomic Publishing Co., Inc., Westport, 1979.
      – Volume 2. Test Methods, Specifications and Standards.
      – Volume 7. Buildings.
[7]   C. J. Hilado: Handbook of Flammability Regulations. Technomic Publishing Co., Inc., Westport, 1975.
[8]   ANSI/ASTM E 69-50 (reapproved 1975). Combustible Properties of Treated Wood by the Fire-Tube Apparatus.
[9]   ASTM E 160-50 (reapproved 1975). Combustible Properties of Treated Wood by the Crib Test.
[10] UL 992–1976. Test Method for Measuring the Surface Flame Propagation Characteristics of Flooring and Floor Covering Materials.
[11] ANSI/ASTM E 108–78. Fire Tests of Roof Coverings.
[12] ANSI/ASTM E 152–78. Fire Tests of Door Assemblies.
[13] ANSI/ASTM E 163–79. Fire Tests of Window Assemblies.

8.2.15 Canada

Statutory regulations

Fire protection is dealt with generally in the National Fire Code of Canada [1] while those aspects relevant to building are covered in the National Building Code of Canada (NBC) [2] and its supplements [3, 4]. These codes serve as a model for the 10 Canadian Provinces and 2 Territories and have been adopted in their entirety in mandatory regulations by the latter. The 10 Provinces have incorporated them in local building regulations with various amendments. The codes define minimum requirements and local building regulations are generally more demanding.

The Provincial Advisory Committee to the National Building Code (PACNBC) which liaises between the Provinces and the Associate Committee on the National Building Code consists of a representative from each Province and Territory appointed by the Ministers responsible for building regulations. One of its aims is to harmonise the changes in the NBC proposed by the Provinces [5].

Classification and testing of the fire performance of building materials and components

The fire performance requirements of building materials and components are contained in the National Building Code of Canada (NBC) and its amendments [2, 3]. Part 3 "Use and Occupancy" divides buildings into various categories such as theatres, hospitals, dwellings, hotels, department stores etc. Fire resistance requirements of building components and fire performance requirements of combustible materials such as interior finishes are laid down in a further section. The permitted flame spread ratings and smoke developed classifications (for example for interior finishes) are tabulated in the supplements. A summary of all the test methods contained in the NBC is given at the end of the supplements.

The fire test methods cited in the NBC were all developed by the Underwriters' Laboratories of Canada (ULC). The following standards relate to the fire resistance of building components [6–13]:

– ULC – S 101 Fire endurance tests of building construction and materials
– ULC – CAN 4 – S 104 Fire tests of door assemblies
– ULC – CAN 4 – S 105 Fire door frames
– ULC – CAN 4 – S 106 Fire tests of window and glass block assemblies
– ULC – S 107 Fire resistance of roof covering materials
– ULC – S 110 Fire ducts
– ULC – S 111 Fire tests for air filter units
– ULC – S 112 Fire dampers.

They are not dealt with further.

The non-combustibility of building materials is tested by ULC-CAN 4 – S 114 – 78 [14] which differs somewhat from ISO/R 1182 although it is derived from it.

Several methods for testing the fire performance of combustible materials are prescribed in the NBC. The most important method used for testing interior finishes is ULC – S 102 – 1978 [15] which is practically identical to the American ASTM E 84-79a method. Two further methods for evaluating floor coverings, ULC – S 102.2 – 1978 [16] and light diffusers, ULC – S 102.3 – 1979 [17] are derived from ULC – S 102. An additional test for non-melting building materials, ULC – S 127 [18], is contained in the latest (1979) version of ULC – S 102 but is not yet specified in the NBC. It is used if other tests give ambiguous results. In certain cases, the NBC requires fabrics and films to be flame tested to ULC – S 109 [19].

The test methods listed here are discussed in detail below and, where necessary, the resultant classifications according to NBC are given.

These standards may be obtained from:

> The Canadian Standards Association (CSA)
> 178 Rexdale Blvd.
> Rexdale, Ontario
> M9W 1R3

and

> Underwriters' Laboratories of Canada (ULC)
> 7 Crouse Road
> Scarborough, Ontario
> M1R 3A9

Determination of the non-combustibility of building materials to ULC – CAN 4 – S 114 – 78

The non-combustibility of building materials is determined to ULC – CAN 4 – S 114 – 78 [14] based on ASTM E 136 (see Section 8.2.14). The Canadian method differs somewhat to ASTM E 136 and the apparatus is therefore shown in Fig. 8.62 and the test specifications are summarised in Table 8.94.

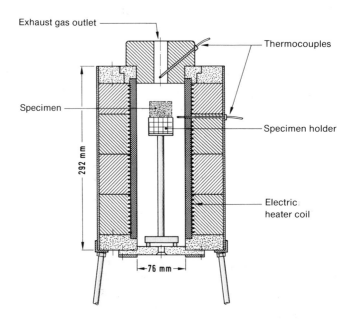

Fig. 8.62   Non-combustibility furnace

Table 8.94   Test specifications for determining the non-combustibility of building materials to ULC – CAN 4 – S 114 – 78

Specimens	3 specimens 38 mm × 38 mm × 51 mm
Specimen position	vertical
Ignition source	electric furnace heated to 750 °C (1380 °F)
Test duration	max. 15 min
Conclusions	passed if
	– at least 3 specimens do not contribute on average more than 18 °C (65 °F) to the temperature rise
	– no specimen burns 30 s after the start of the test
	– no specimen exceeds a maximum weight loss of 20%

ULC – S 102 – 1978. Test for surface burning characteristics of building materials

The surface burning characteristics of building materials are tested by ULC – S 102 – 1978 [15]. However, this is based on the 1979 version which is not yet included in the NBC. ULC – S 102 is more or less identical to ASTM E 84-79a. The apparatus and test specifications correspond to those given in Fig. 8.58 and Table 8.87 respectively, in Section 8.2.14. The experimental results, however, are evaluated differently. The results from at least three runs are used to determine the Flame Spread Classification as FSC_1, FSC_2 and FSC_3. The distance travelled by the flame front is plotted graphically as a function of time. If the total area A_T under the flame spread time-distance curve is

– $\leqq 97.5$ (ft · min) then
$$FSC_1 = 0.564 \cdot A_T \tag{1}$$

– > 97.5 (ft · min) then
$$FSC_1 = \frac{5363}{195 - A_T} \tag{2}$$

With certain materials the flame front may advance rapidly during the initial stages of the test and subsequently slow or even fail to reach the end of the specimen. In such cases the flame spread is calculated according to the following equation which takes such behaviour into account:

$$FSC_2 = 28.2 \frac{d}{t} \tag{3}$$

where t is the time in minutes required by the flame front to travel d ft where a marked slow down of the flame front occurs.

If the flame spread behaviour is such that it is difficult to ascertain the point at which the speed of the flame front starts to decrease, then FSC_3 is determined by consideration of test results obtained according to ULC – S 127 (see below) (see also appendix 3 of ULC – S 102 – 1979).

Besides flame spread, the contribution to smoke development is also determined as in ASTM E 84-79a (further details are given in Section 9.2.2.2).

In contrast to ASTM E 84-79a, the contribution to heat release is also evaluated. As with smoke development, heat release is computed by comparing the area under the curve from the material under test with that from red oak. The area obtained from the latter is arbitrarily set at 100 and that from asbestos is set equal to 0.

Interior finish materials are classified according to NBC [2] subsections 3.1.10 and 3.1.11 and supplements subsection 3.1 [3], on the basis of the Flame Spread Ratings and Smoke Developed Classification obtained. These subsections also contain classifications of floorings according to ULC – S 102.2 and of light diffusers to ULC – S 102.3. The Flame Spread Ratings and Smoke Developed Indices are listed in tables in the NBC supplements under section 3.1. The upper figure refers to the permitted flame spread and the lower figure to the permitted smoke development. For example $\frac{25}{50}$ indicates a flame spread of 0 to 25 and smoke development of 0 to 50. $\frac{150}{300}$ indicates flame spread of 75 to 150 and smoke development of 100 to 300. The classes of flame spread and smoke development are defined in Table 8.95.

Table 8.95   Grades of flame spread and smoke development

Flame spread number	range	Smoke development number	range
25	0– 25	50	0– 50
75	26– 75	100	51–100
150	76–150	300	101–300
X[1]	>150	X[1]	>300
X[2]	>300	X[2]	>500

[1]   For walls and ceilings according to ULC – S 102
[2]   For floors according to ULC – S 102.2

ULC – S 102.2 – 1978. Test for surface burning characteristics of floor coverings and miscellaneous materials

The surface burning characteristics of floorings and miscellaneous materials are tested according to ULC – S 102.2 – 1978 [16]. The test rig is identical to the Steiner tunnel described in ULC – S 102–79, but in this case the test specimen lies on the floor and both burners are directed downwards at an angle of 45° to the specimen. Diagrams are shown in Section 8.2.14 and in Fig. 8.63.

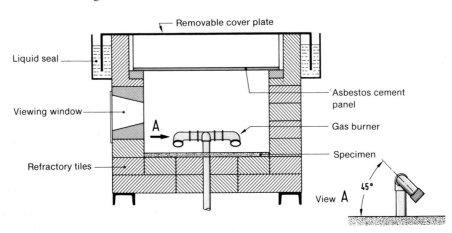

Fig. 8.63   Modified Steiner tunnel for testing floor coverings and miscellaneous materials

The test specifications are similar to those described in ULC – S 102 – 1979 with the following differences:

The specimen lies on the floor of the tunnel and is therefore narrower; its dimensions are 0.44 m × 7.32 m × usual thickness. The tunnel is calibrated as described in Section 8.2.14 by swinging the burner up and carrying out measurements on asbestos and red oak specimens fixed to the ceiling.

The values obtained from the tests (see Section 8.2.14) are used to compute the Flame Spread Classification, Fuel Contribution and Smoke Density.

This method is also suitable for materials which cannot be tested when fixed to the ceiling such as thermoplastics and loose fill materials.

ULC – S 102.3 – 1979. Fire test for light diffusers and lenses

The tendency of light diffusers and lenses to become loose and fall out of their holders is assessed by ULC–S 102.3–1979 [17] using the Steiner tunnel described in ULC–S 102–1979 and ASTM E 84-79a.

The test procedure is similar to ULC – S 102 – 1979 except that two tests are carried out on specimens half the size (12 ft ≙ 3.66 m). In one case the specimen is simply placed on the ledges of the furnace and in the second it is clamped in position. Note is made of whether and when the specimens fall from position and whether or not ignition occurred before the material fell from position.

ULC – S 127 – 1978. Corner wall test for flammability characteristics of non-melting building materials

The ULC – S 127 – 1978 corner wall test method [18] is used in addition to the ULC – S 102 – 1979 and ULC – S 102.2 – 1978 tunnel tests when these methods do not give clear data on the advance of the flame front. The test rig is illustrated in Figs. 8.64 and 8.65 and the test specifications are summarised in Table 8.96.

Table 8.96   ULC – S 127 – 1978 corner wall test specifications

Specimens	inside of the fire test chamber consisting of ceiling, two walls and canopy lined with test material
Fire chamber	cube-shaped with internal dimensions of 1.30 m, canopy measures 0.52 m from top to bottom, cutout 47.5 cm × 15 cm in front canopy (see diagram)
Ignition source	cylindrical tray, diameter 22 cm, depth 14 cm, filled with sand and ceramic beads, copper tube with 48 holes, from which natural gas with a heat output of 2 MJ/min flows, located in lower part of bead layer, gas ignited by a small burner located above the sand bed, the tray is positioned on the floor in the corner formed by the two walls
Test duration	until the flames issue beneath the canopy or the cotton thread stretched 2.54 cm beneath breake, maximum 5 min after lighting the ignition source
Conclusions	determination of time t until flame issues beneath the canopy or the cotton thread breaks and determination of Flame Spread Classification FSC_3

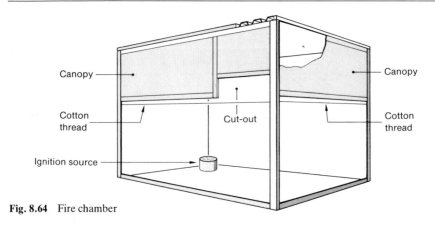

Fig. 8.64   Fire chamber

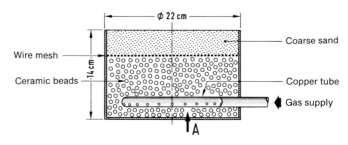

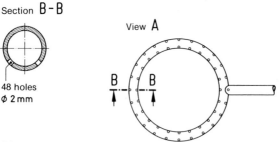

Fig. 8.65   Ignition source

The time t at which flames appear from beneath the canopy or the cotton thread breaks is recorded and is converted to the Flame Spread Classification FSC_3 with the aid of a graph. The ordinate of the graph is the Flame Spread Classification FSC_2 according to ULC – S 102 and S 102.2 which is related to "t", represented by the abscissa, by the relationship

$$FSC_3 = 51.47\, t^{-1.215} \tag{4}$$

(further details are given in ULC – S 127 – 1978 Fig. 3 and Appendix A).

ULC – S 109 – 1969. Flame tests of flame-resistant fabrics and films

The ULC – S 109 – 1969 [19] method for flame testing of flame resistant fabrics and films ($\triangleq$ US method NFPA 701) involves two tests with ignition sources of differing intensity (small and large flame). In both cases the flame is applied vertically to the specimen with a Bunsen burner.

The apparatus for the small flame test corresponds to that shown in Fig. 8.33 in Section 8.2.9. The test specifications are summarised in Table 8.97.

Table 8.97 Small flame test specifications

Specimens	10 specimens 70 mm × 254 mm × usual thickness 5 specimens in direction of warp and 5 in direction of weft, the specimens are clamped in a metal frame so that an area 50 mm × 254 mm is tested
Specimen position	vertical in combustion chamber 305 mm × 305 mm × 760 mm, lower end of specimen 19 mm above tip of burner
Ignition source	Bunsen burner with luminous 38 mm long flame with air supply shut off, burner located vertically beneath specimen or at an angle of 25° from the vertical if dripping expected
Test duration	flame applied for 12 s, afterflame time and charring noted
Conclusions	passed if – afterflame time $\leqq$ 2 s – no burning drops or material falling – length of char due to vertical flame spread and afterglow does not exceed specified limits (see below)

Charring of the specimen caused by vertical flame spread and afterglow must not exceed the values given in Table 8.98. The length of char is determined by tearing.

Table 8.98 Classification of fabrics and films by their extent of destruction

weight of material [$g \cdot m^{-2}$]	mean tear length of material (10 specimens) [mm]	maximum tear length of material (individual specimens) [mm]
> 340	90	115
$\leqq$ 340 – >200	115	140
$\leqq$ 200	140	165

The large flame test is similar to the small flame test but employs flat and folded specimens, up to 2 m long. Normally, however, flat specimens need not be longer than 760 mm and folded specimens not longer than 1065 mm in order to establish compliance with the test requirements. The maximum lengths are necessary when it is desirable to ascertain the extent of destruction following a failed test. The specifications for the large flame test are given in Table 8.99.

Table 8.99 Large flame test specifications

Specimens	– flat: 10 specimens 127 mm × 762 mm or if necessary up to 2134 mm – folded: 4 specimens 635 mm × 762 mm or if necessary up to 2134 mm each specimen is folded lengthwise four times so that the folds are approx. 127 mm apart
Test stack	305 mm × 305 mm × 2134 mm on 305 mm high supports, open at top and bottom
Specimen position	vertical, bottom of specimen 100 mm above tip of burner, folded speci- mens set up with folds approx. 12.7 mm apart
Ignition source	Bunsen burner with 280 mm long oxidising flame, burner vertical under specimen or at angle of 25° to vertical if dripping expected
Test duration	flame applied for 2 min, afterflame time and length of char noted
Conclusions	passed if – afterflame time $\leqq$ 2 s – no burning drops or falling material – length of char due to vertical flame spread and afterglow does not exceed 254 mm

Official approval

The only Canadian Institution carrying out fire tests on building materials and components is

Underwriters' Laboratories of Canada (ULC)
7 Crouse Road
Scarborough, Ontario, Canada
M1R 3A9

ULC are a non-profit organisation accredited by the Standards Council of Canada [20, 21] to carry out fire tests on building materials and components, issue test reports, enter into inspection agreements and grant test marks for inspected products. ULC also issue an annual "List of Equipment and Materials" consisting of Volume I "General" and Volume II "Building Construction". These contain lists and classifications of tested and inspected products. Further details on the test and approval procedures of ULC are given in Section 8.4.3.1.

Future developments

The National Fire Code and National Building Code, revised in 1980, and the fire test procedures specified therein are continuously amended and extended. No major changes are, however, envisaged. As regards determination of smoke development and toxicity of fire gases, international developments and in particular finalisation of the work of ISO/TC 92 are awaited and no national activities exist. Consideration is being given to increasing the number of test institutes accredited by the Standards Council of Canada for fire testing and inspection of building materials and components.

References for 8.2.15

[1] National Fire Code of Canada 1980. Fourth Edition. National Research Council of Canada, Ottawa, NRCC No. 17306.
[2] National Building Code of Canada 1980. Eighth Edition. National Research Council of Canada, Ottawa, NRCC No. 17303.
[3] The Supplement to the National Building Code of Canada 1980. First Edition. National Research Council of Canada, Ottawa, NRCC No. 17724.
[4] Administrative Requirements for Use with the National Building Code 1980. National Research Council, Ottawa, NRCC No. 17725.
[5] Use of the National Building Code by Provinces and Municipalities. NBC News, Vol. 3, No. 1, March 1978.
[6] ULC – S 101 – 1977. Standard Methods of Fire Endurance Tests of Building Construction and Materials.
[7] ULC – CAN 4 – S 104 – 77. Standard Method for Fire Tests of Door Assemblies.
[8] ULC – CAN 4 – S 105 – 79. Standard Specification for Fire Door Frames Meeting the Performance Required by CAN 4 – S 104 – 77.
[9] ULC – CAN 4 – S 106 – 79. Standard Method for Fire Tests of Window and Glass Block Assemblies.
[10] ULC – S 107 – 1969. Test Method for Fire Resistance of Roof Covering Materials.
[11] ULC – S 110 – 1970. Standard for Fire Ducts.
[12] ULC – S 111 – 1977. Standard Method of Fire Tests for Air Filter Units.
[13] ULC – S 112 – 1976. Standard of Fire Dampers.
[14] ULC – CAN 4 – S 114 – 78. Standard Method of Test for Determination of Non-Combustibility in Building Materials.
[15] ULC – S 102 – 1978. Standard Method of Test for Surface Burning Characteristics of Flooring, Floor Covering and Miscellaneous Materials.
[16] ULC – S 102.2 – 1978. Standard Method of Test for Surface Burning Characteristics.
[17] ULC – S 102.3 – 1979. Standard Method for Fire Tests of Light Diffusers and Lenses.
[18] ULC – S 127 – 1978. Standard Corner Wall Method of Test for Flammability Characteristics of Non-Melting Building Materials.
[19] ULC – S 109 – 1969. Standard for Flame Tests of Flame-Resistant Fabrics and Films.
[20] Criteria and Procedures for Accreditation of Testing Organizations. Can-P-4, June 1978, Standards Council of Canada. 350 Sparks Street, Ottawa, K1R 7S8.
[21] Criteria and Procedures for Accreditation of Certification Organizations. Can-P-3, October 1977, Standards Council of Canada.

8.2.16 Australia

Statutory regulations

The Commonwealth of Australia consists of the Australian Capital Territory where the capital, Canberra, is situated and the States of Victoria, New South Wales, Queensland, Northern Territories, Western Australia, South Australia and Tasmania.

The States are largely independent as far as legislation is concerned and all have their own differing building codes so that structural fire protection also varies. The individual building regulations are [1–6]:

– Uniform Building Regulations   (Victoria)
– Ordinance No. 70   (New South Wales)
– Building Act 1975   (Queensland)
– Uniform Building By-Laws   (Western Australia)
– Building Act and Regulations   (South Australia)
– Building Regulations 1978   (Tasmania)

In order to deal with this plethora of legislation, the Federal Government set up the Interstate Standing Committee for Uniform Building Regulations. The Committee, now known as the Australian Uniform Building Regulation Coordinating Council has drawn up the Australian Model Uniform Building Code (AMUBC) which will gradually be incorporated in the building regulations of individual States. Indeed it has already been adopted by some States.

The situation regarding fire protection – and in particular the use of combustible materials – is still confused. Only New South Wales has adopted the relevant AMUBC regulations although some of the other states use parts. Thus the use of combustible materials is not regulated in some states whereas in others certain building materials such as roof sheeting and foams (EPS and PUR) are restricted. The use of combustible materials also depends on the type of building. There are 10 groups of building such as apartments, hotels, shops and hospitals arranged in order of increasing hazard.

Classification and testing of the fire performance of building materials

The test methods used to ascertain whether building materials and components meet the fire requirements laid down in the building regulations are described in Australian Standard AS 1530, Parts 1 to 4*. Polystyrene foam used for thermal insulation is subject only to AS K 156-1965.

AS 1530 "Fire Tests on Building Materials and Structures" is divided into the following sections [7]:

– Part 1 – Combustibility Test for Materials
– Part 2 – Test for Flammability of Materials
– Part 3 – Test for Early Fire Hazard Properties of Materials
– Part 4 – Fire-Resistance Test of Structures.

AS 1530 Parts 3 and 4 are being revised at present. Part 3 (DR 79151 [8]) is being revised editorially but the test methods will remain unchanged while Part 4 (DR 79152 [9]) is being brought into line technically with ISO 834.

---

* available from the Standards Association of Australia (SAA), Standards House, 80 Arthur Street, North Sydney, NSW.

The Australian Building Regulations refer to AS 1530 Parts 1 to 3 and, in special cases to Part 4, for evaluating the fire performance of building materials. While Part 1 only enables an opinion on combustibility or non-combustibility to be made, various indices used in Parts 2 and 3 enable fire performance to be gradually differentiated. Part 2 applies to thin flexible materials such as roof sheeting, curtains or wallcoverings while Part 3 covers all other combustible building materials. AS 1530 Part 4 is a test for determining the fire resistance of building components and is not dealt with in this book. In one specific case however, it is of importance for combustible building materials. AMUBC Amendment no. 14 [10] permits the use of such materials even if they have not satisfied AS 1530 Part 3 according to [10] provided they are protected on all sides by non-combustible material and pass the 10 min furnace test. In this test, 1 m sq. specimens of such composite systems are heated for 10 min up to approx. 700 °C according to the AS 1530 Part 4 time/temperature curve. This is not a determination of fire resistance as such but a demonstration that the composite system can contain a fire for 10 min.

Martin and *Dowling* review Australian fire tests contained in regulations and standards [11].

AS 1530, Part 1. Combustibility test

The AS 1530 test for combustibility or non-combustibility is essentially the same as ISO/DIS 1182. Consequently the apparatus and test specifications are discussed in Section 8.2.18.2.

AS 1530, Part 2. Flammability test

The flammability of building materials – in this case fabrics and films – is tested by AS 1530, Part 2 – 1973. A diagram of the apparatus and test specifications are given in Fig. 8.66 and Table 8.100, respectively.

Table 8.100 Flammability test specifications

Specimens	6 specimens 535 mm × 75 mm
Specimen position	stretched over a slightly convex frame at 3° to 4° to the vertical
Ignition source	alcohol flame (0.1 ml pure alcohol in copper container) 13 mm below lower edge of specimen
Test duration	max. 160 s
Conclusion	flammability index ≦ 26 according to AMUBC and Ordinance 70 (NSW)

If the material has an asymmetric weave six specimens are tested in the warp and six in the weft direction. If both sides have differing surface structure then two sets of six specimens are tested.

The material stretched over the frame is ignited by burning 0.1 ml pure alcohol in a copper container 13 mm below the lower edge of the specimen. The temperature of the fire gases is measured by thermocouples positioned 570 mm above the top edge of the specimen in a flue. Observations are made for a maximum of 160 s after igniting the alcohol. If the flame does not reach the highest (21st) mark, the maximum flame height is noted. The tempera-

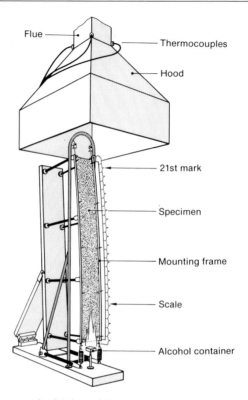

Fig. 8.66   Flammability apparatus for fabrics and films

ture of the smoke gases is measured every 5 s over a period of 180 s by the thermocouples. The following are also recorded:

- the time required by the flame to reach the 21st mark if this occurs before 160 s have elapsed,
- the area between the recorded temperature curve for the combustion gases and the ambient temperature curve over the 180 s period.

Certain factors, calculated from the test data are used to compute the flammability index and thus classify the material. These are: speed factor, heat factor and spread factor and are calculated as follows:

– *Speed factor:* The speed factor S is expressed as:

$$S = (60 - \frac{3\,t}{8})$$

where t is the time in s required by the flame to reach the 21st mark. The mean value from six tests is used in the equation. If the flame does not reach the 21st mark on any one specimen the speed factor is recorded as 0.

– *Heat factor:* The heat factor H is obtained from:

$$H = 0.24 \cdot A$$

where A is the mean value determined from six tests of the area between the temperature curve of the combustion gas and the ambient temperature curve over the 180 s test period.

– *Spread factor:* The spread factor E is only calculated if the speed factor S equals 0.

$$E \ = \ \frac{20}{9} \ (D-3)$$

where D is the mean scale mark (0–21) reached by the flame determined for six specimens.

The flammability index (I) is obtained via one of the following equations:

$$I \ = \ H + E \text{ or}$$
$$I \ = \ H + S$$

The expression H + E is used if the flame does not reach the 21st mark and H + S if it does reach this mark.

AS 1530, Part 3. Early fire hazard test

The early fire hazard of building materials is tested by AS 1530, Part 3 – 1976. The apparatus is illustrated in Fig. 8.67 and the test specifications are given in Table 8.101.

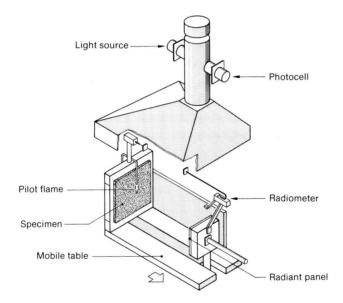

Light source
Photocell
Pilot flame
Radiometer
Specimen
Mobile table
Radiant panel

Fig. 8.67 Early fire hazard test apparatus

The specimen mounted in the specimen holder is first irradiated for 30 s from a distance of 850 mm. The specimen is then moved progressively closer to the radiant panel every 30 s in decreasing steps of twice 200 mm, twice 50 mm, twice 20 mm, 8 steps of 10 mm and finally 11 steps of 5 mm. At this point 12.5 min have elapsed and the specimen is 175 mm away from the radiant panel. The test is continued for a further 7.5 min and thus terminates when a total of 20 min have elapsed.

Table 8.101 Early fire hazard test specifications

Specimens	6 specimens 600 mm × 450 mm × usual thickness
Specimen position	vertical mobile specimen holder, positioned parallel to radiant panel, moved during test from 850 mm to 175 mm towards radiant panel
Ignition sources	– vertical gas radiator 300 mm × 300 mm, radiation intensity 850 mm from radiator: 2.47 kW/m^2
	– two gas pilot flames at a distance of 15 mm from specimen, length of luminous portion of flame 12 mm: first pilot flame 50 mm above centre of test specimen, second variable for igniting decomposition gases
Test duration	20 min
Conclusions	spread of flame and smoke developed indices required for permitted use under the building regulations

If the specimen ignites, movement towards the radiant panel is halted. The radiation intensity from flames on the specimen surface is recorded every 3 s during the test with a radiometer. A photocell is located in the flue for determining smoke development. The light absorption values are also recorded every 3 s. Exact details, a diagram of the apparatus and the test specifications are given in Section 9.2.2.2.

The time elapsed from the start of the test until the material ignites is recorded. Ignition is considered to have occurred if the flame causes an increase in radiation intensity of 0.1 kW/m^2 during a 10 s period as measured with the radiometer. The test results enable four indices to be established for the material. These are: Ignitability, Heat Evolved, Spread of Flame and Smoke Developed.

– *Ignitability:* The index number for the ignitability is 20 minus the time in minutes until ignition of the material. If five or more specimens do not ignite the Ignitability Index is 0.

– *Heat Evolved:* The heat evolved for each sample is calculated from the integral of a period of 2 min after ignition of the difference between the instantaneous radiation intensity and that just before ignition. The index number is determined from the integral radiation intensity as shown in Table 8.102. If five or more specimens fail to ignite, the Heat Evolved Index is set equal to 0.

Table 8.102 Index numbers for heat evolved

Index number	Value of radiation intensity integral [kW · m^{-2} · s]
0	<25
1	25–< 50
2	50–< 75
3	75–<100
4	100–<125
5	125–<150
6	150–<175
7	175–<200
8	200–<225
9	225–<250
10	≧ 250

– *Spread of Flame:* If the radiation intensity increases by more than 1.4 kW/m^2 from the time of ignition and in less than 203 s, the time to ignition is recorded. The Spread of Flame Index is determined from this time (Table 8.103). If five or more specimens fail to ignite or the radiation intensity increases by less than 1.4 kW/m^2 within 203 s, the Spread of Flame Index is set equal to 0.

Table 8.103   Spread of flame index numbers

Index number	1.33 × average time for radiation intensity to increase by 1.4 kW/m^2 [min]
0	$\geq 4\frac{1}{2}$
1	$4 \; - <4\frac{1}{2}$
2	$3\frac{1}{2} - <4$
3	$3 \; - <3\frac{1}{2}$
4	$2\frac{1}{2} - <3$
5	$2 \; - <2\frac{1}{2}$
6	$1\frac{1}{2} - <2$
7	$1 \; - <1\frac{1}{2}$
8	$\frac{1}{2} \; - <1$
9	$\frac{1}{6} \; - <\frac{1}{2}$
10	$<\frac{1}{6}$

– *Smoke Developed:* see Section 9.2.2.2.

A report listing the indices obtained based on test performance is issued. The ignitability indices run from 0–20 while the other indices run from 0–10. In practice only the Smoke Developed and Spread of Flame indices are considered in the various building regulations and for the approval of building materials.

AS K 156 – 1965 Appendix F. Determination of flammability

The various Australian Codes only permit the use of polystyrene foam (EPS) as an insulating material in buildings if it satisfies the determination of flammability test in Appendix F of AS K 156 – 1965 [12]. The procedure is based on BS 2782: Method 508 A though the test specifications are different. The apparatus is illustrated in Fig. 8.18 of Section 8.2.5 and the test specifications are summarised in Table 8.104.

Table 8.104   Determination of flammability test specifications

Specimens	three to five specimens 200 mm × 25 mm × 12 mm, reference marks at 50 mm and 75 mm parallel to the free end of the specimen
Specimen position	long side (200 mm) horizontal, short side (25 mm), inclined at 45° to horizontal
Ignition source	Bunsen burner (approx. 20 mm non-luminous flame)
Test duration	flame applied to free end of specimen until the 50 mm mark is reached either by melting or burning, specimen observed until flame extinguishes
Conclusion	classified as "self-extinguishing" if the 75 mm mark is not reached

Official approval

According to the various Building Codes, one or more of the tests described above must be carried out in order to ascertain the fire performance of building materials. The tests can be performed by any chosen institution approved by the National Association of Testing Authorities, Australia (NATA). Approval involves regular inspection of the test institution and especially of the test laboratories by NATA experts. A NATA directory [13] listing recognised test institutions is published annually. Institutes which test fire performance of plastics are not listed separately but the following NATA approved organisations carry out such tests.

– Australian Wool Testing Authority (AWTA)
  Textiles Testing Division
  24 Robertson Street
  Kensington VIC 3031

  Tests: AS 1530, Parts 2 and 3

– The Broken Hill Pty. Co. Ltd. (BHP)
  Melbourne Research Laboratories
  245-273 Wellington Road
  Clayton VIC 3168

  Tests: AS 1530, Parts 3 and 4

– Commonwealth Sugar Refineries Ltd. (CSR)
  Building Materials Research Division
  Oulton Avenue
  Concord West NSW 2138

  Tests: AS 1530, Parts 2 and 3

– Experimental Building Station (EBS)
  Department of Construction
  82-101 Dehli Road
  North Ryde NSW 2113
  P.O. Box 30 Chatswood 2067

  Tests: AS 1530, Parts 1 to 4.

The test laboratory issues a NATA Endorsed Report containing the test results. This document is sufficient proof of the fire performance of the building material. Building materials are not marked or inspected in Australia.

Future developments

Parts 3 and 4 of AS 1530 are being revised and the new editions should be available shortly.

AS K 156 – 1965 Appendix F "determination of flammability" is referred to in various building regulations as a method of determining the fire performance of polystyrene foam used for thermal insulation. This test will probably be withdrawn and be replaced by AS 2122.1–1978 "determination of flame propagation" [14] which will be used to test whether all rigid foams used as thermal insulation such as EPS, PUR, PIR, UF and PF are flame retardant.

AS 2122.1 is based on the ASTM 3014 Butler chimney test and is being developed by several organisations under the aegis of the Division of Building Research of the CSIRO (Commonwealth Scientific and Industrial Research Organisation), the largest Australian research organisation.

The oxygen index test (AS 2122, Part 2) [15] has a certain importance in the quality control of plastics. It is not however mentioned in the building regulations and is therefore not mandatory.

The present specifications for plastic pipes do not contain any test specifications concerning fire performance. Incorporation of the AS 1530, Part 3 early fire hazard test in these specifications in the future is under consideration.

Floor coverings are increasingly considered as part of a building and are thus increasingly included in building codes. No special test method is planned in Australia but the American flooring radiant panel test (NBSIR 75-950) already used in several countries (e.g. Federal Republic of Germany) will probably be on the short list.

No work is being done on smoke density and toxicity of fire gases pending developments in ISO.

References for 8.2.16

[1]   Uniform Building Regulations. Victoria, 1974. Reprint No. 1 with Amendments (up to No. 363/1978).
[2]   Ordinance No. 70. New South Wales. Building. Reprint 28th June, 1979.
[3]   Building Act 1975. Queensland. Brisbane, 1978.
[4]   Western Australia. Uniform Building By-Laws, 1974.
[5]   Building Act and Regulations. South Australia. January 1978.
[6]   Statutory Rules 1978 No. 135. Building Regulations 1978. Tasmania.
[7]   AS 1530. Fire tests on Building Materials and Structures
       – Part 1 – 1976: Combustibility Test for Materials.
       – Part 2 – 1973: Test for Flammability of Materials.
       – Part 3 – 1976: Test for Early Fire Hazard Properties of Materials.
       – Part 4 – 1975: Fire-Resistance Test of Structures.
[8]   Draft for Comment. September 1979. DR 79151. (Revision of AS 1530, Part 3 – 1976.)
[9]   Draft for Comment. September 1979. DR 79152. (Revision of AS 1530, Part 4 – 1975.)
[10]   The Australian Model Uniform Building Code, Amendment No. 14, April 1977.
[11]   *K. G. Martin, V. P. Dowling:* Australian Fire Tests in Standards and Regulations. Paper at Interflam, 27 to 29. 3. 1979, Guildford, England.
[12]   AS K 156 – 1965. Expanded Polystyrene for Thermal Insulation.
[13]   1979 NATA Directory (Status at 1. 6. 1979, available from the National Association of Testing Authorities, Australia. 688 Pacific Highway, Chatswood, NSW, 2067).
[14]   AS 2122.1 – 1978. Combustion propagation Characteristics of plastics. Part 1 – Determination of Flame Propagation Following Surface Ignition of Vertically Oriented Specimens of Cellular Plastics.
[15]   AS 2122.2 – 1978. Combustion propagation Characteristics of plastics. Part 2 – Determination of Minimum Oxygen Concentration for Flame Propagation Following Top Surface Ignition of Vertically Oriented Specimens.

8.2.17 Japan

Statutory regulations

The Building Standards Law came into force on 16 November 1950. The aim of this legislation is "to protect the lives, health, and wealth of citizens, and thus contribute to the prosperity of the community, by laying down guidelines and standards for plots of land, building design, furnishing and use". Structural fire protection is covered by this law and various official announcements and guidelines. The 48 Prefectures have their own additional local regulations.

The Ministry of Construction has issued various directives laying down permitted uses of building materials including restrictions on the use of interior linings introduced on 1 May 1969. These limits vary depending on the size and type of building or structure – these are divided into 10 classes and include theatres, assembly halls, hospitals, hotels, department stores, ground floor recreation rooms, garages, high rise buildings more than 31 m high, underground shopping precincts, etc.

Classification and testing of fire performance of building materials

Three ministerial directives cover the classification and testing of the fire performance of building materials:

– Announcement No. 1828 for non-combustible building materials [1].
– Announcement No. 1231 for semi-non-combustible and fire retardant building materials [2].
– Announcement No. 101 for fire retardant plastics for roofing [3].

Announcement No. 1231 contains smoke development and toxicity tests as well as fire tests.

The methods for ascertaining the fire safety parameters described in the building ministry directives and the resultant classifications are laid down in the following standards [4]:

– JIS A 1301 Method of fire test for wooden structural parts of buildings.
– JIS A 1302 Method of fire test for non-combustible structural parts of buildings.
– JIS A 1304 Method of fire resistance test for structural parts of buildings.
– JIS A 1311 Method of fire protecting test of fire door for building.
– JIS A 1312 Method of fire test for roof of buildings.
– JIS A 1321 Testing method for "incombustibility*" of internal finish material and procedure of buildings.
– JIS A 1322 Testing method for "incombustibility*" of thin materials for buildings.

Only JIS A 1321 and JIS A 1322 which relate to the fire performance of building materials are discussed in this book. JIS standards are published by the Japanese Standards Association, 1–24, Akasaka 4 Chome, Minato-ku, Tokyo 107, Japan.

---

* The term "incombustibility" used in the English translation of Japanese Standards is retained in order to prevent confusion with "non-combustibility" in the sense of ISO 1182.

JIS A 1321. Method for testing non-combustible, semi-non-combustible and fire retardant building materials

Building materials are classified in the fire classes shown in Table 8.105 with the help of the test methods described in this standard. Further tests (hole test, toxicity test) are specified by Announcement No. 1231 as shown in Table 8.105. The hole and face tests are described later in this section while the toxicity test is discussed in Section 9.3.

Table 8.105 JIS A 1321 classification of building materials

Fireproof class	Designation	Test methods
1	non-combustible	elementary material test and face test
2	semi-non-combustible	face test, hole test[1] and gas toxicity test[1]
3	fire retardant	face test and gas toxicity test[1]

[1] The hole and gas toxicity tests are not listed in JIS A 1321 but are required by Announcement No. 1231

Building materials are tested for non-combustibility by the elementary material test using an electric furnace operating at 750 °C. The apparatus is similar to the ASTM E 136 equipment described in Section 8.2.14 but the test specifications differ somewhat and are therefore listed in Table 8.106.

Table 8.106 Elementary material test specifications for non-combustibility

Specimens	3 specimens 40 mm × 40 mm × 50 mm
Specimen position	vertical
Ignition source	electric furnace heated to 750 °C
Test duration	20 min
Conclusions	passed if no specimen causes a rise in the furnace temperature greater than 50 °C

The face test is based on BS 476: Part 6 (see Section 8.2.5). It enables materials to be classified in the three "fireproof" classes on the basis of test performance. The apparatus is illustrated in Fig. 8.68 and the test specifications are summarised in Table 8.107.

Table 8.107 Face test specifications

Specimens	3 specimens 220 mm × 220 mm × $\leq$ 15 mm
Specimen position	vertical, 35 mm away from electric heater
Ignition sources	– town gas pilot flame – electric heater operated by calibrated control (see below), switched on 3 min after start of test in addition to pilot flame
Test duration	10 min (classes 1 and 2) or 6 min (class 3)
Conclusions	classification in fireproof classes 1 to 3 (see below) depending on test performance

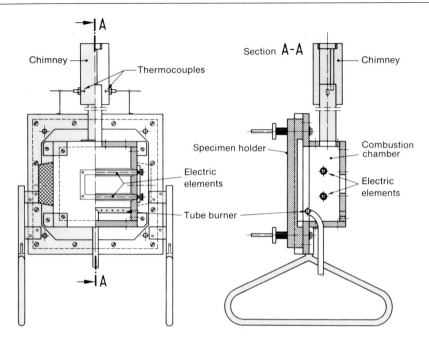

Fig. 8.68   "Face test" apparatus
left: Front view (exterior) (interior), *right:* Side view

Before starting the actual test, the furnace is adjusted by calibrating the electric heater and pilot flame so that the temperature of the gases leaving the furnace have the time-temperature dependence shown in Table 8.108.

Table 8.108   Gas temperature as a function of time

Time [min]	1	2	3	4	5	6	7	8	9	10
Gas temperature [°C]	70	80	90	155	205	235	260	275	290	305

Table 8.109   Test times for classification in various "fireproof" classes

"Fireproof" classification	Heating time pilot flame only [min]	Heating time with pilot flame and electric heater [min]	Total heating time [min]
Class 1	3	7	10
Class 2	3	7	10
Class 3	3	3	6

The test specimen is first subjected for 3 min to the gas pilot flame. Subsequently the electric heater is also switched on and the test carried out as shown in Table 8.109.

At the end of the test, classification is made on the following criteria:
In order to be classified in "fireproof" classes 1 to 3 no specimen must

– melt right through its entire thickness, show continuous cracks more than one tenth of thickness or exhibit deformation detrimental to fire protection,
– afterflame for more than 30 s.

In addition, in order to qualify for "fireproof" class 1 the gas temperature curve obtained in the test must not exceed the standard time-temperature curve (obtained by adding 50 °C to the gas temperature calibration curve).

Materials are classified in "fireproof" classes 2 and 3 if, within three minutes of the start of the test, the experimental gas temperature curve exceeds the standard time temperature curve as follows:

The area (°C · m) enclosed by the gas temperature curve and the standard time-temperature curve should not exceed 100 and 350 for classification in fireproof classes 2 and 3, respectively.

JIS A 1231 includes a test for smoke development which is also a factor in the classification. A diagram of the apparatus, test specifications for determining smoke development and the resultant classification are given in Section 9.2.2.2. According to JIS A 1321, all the criteria listed in Table 8.110 must be satisfied.

Table 8.110   Criteria for classification in "fireproof" classes 1 to 3

"Fireproof" class	Test duration [min]	Melting, cracks, deformation	Afterflame time [s]	Area consisting of measured minus standard gas temperature curve at 3 min [°C · min]	Smoke emission coefficient per unit area C_A
1	10	not permitted	$\leqq 30$	0	$\leqq 30$
2	10	not permitted	$\leqq 30$	$\leqq 100$	$\leqq 60$
3	6	not permitted	$\leqq 30$	$\leqq 350$	$\leqq 120$

Ministry of Construction Announcement No. 1231 [2] requires two further tests, the so-called hole test and gas toxicity test, in addition to those of JIS A 1321.

The hole test employs the same apparatus and procedure as the face test. The specimens are of the same dimensions, but differ from those in the latter by having three 25 mm diameter holes drilled vertically in the 180 mm × 180 mm face. The test is passed if

– afterflame does not persist for more than 90 s,
– the area obtained from the measured minus the standard gas temperature curve is less than 150 (°C · min),
– the smoke emission coefficient C_A does not exceed 60.

Details of the gas toxicity test are given in Section 9.3. Two test specimens are compared with a standard sample of red lauan wood. The test is passed if the mean incapacitation time of test animals is greater when testing the specimens than when using the standard sample.

JIS A 1322. Test for "incombustibility" of thin materials for buildings

This procedure is used to investigate the burning behaviour of curtains, carpeting and other thin materials and is prescribed in local building codes. The apparatus is illustrated in Fig. 8.69 and the test specifications are listed in Table 8.111.

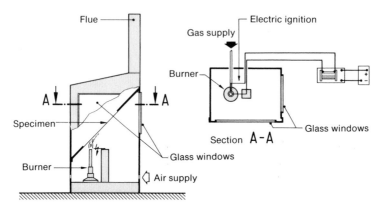

Fig. 8.69   Test apparatus for thin materials

Table 8.111   Test specifications for the burning behaviour of thin materials

Specimens	3 × 6 specimens 300 mm × 200 mm × usual thickness
Specimen position	inclined at 45°, 50 mm above tip of burner
Ignition source	gas Meckel burner (internal diameter 20 mm), lit by electric induction coil, flame height: 65 mm
Test duration	flame applied for 10 s, 20 s, 30 s, 1 min, 2 min and 3 min
Conclusions	classification in building material classes 1 to 3 (see below) depending on charred length, afterflame time and afterglow

The test specimen is mounted stress-free in a holder and tested at an angle of 45°, 50 mm above the burner tip. The gas burner is ignited electrically with an induction coil and the flame height adjusted to 65 mm. The flame is applied to the sample for 10 s, 20 s, 30 s, 1 min, 2 min and 3 min. The charred length, afterflame time and duration of afterglow are meas-

Table 8.112   Classification of burning behaviour of thin building materials

Building material class	Charred length [mm]	Afterflame time [s]	Afterglow time [min]
1	< 50	<1	≦1
2	<100	<5	≦1
3	<150	<5	≦1

ured. Other phenomena occurring during the test such as flaming drops and falling material while burning are recorded. Afterflame time is considered to be the time during which the specimen continues to burn once the burner is removed. Afterglow is specified as flameless combustion 1 min after removal of the burner. The charred length is defined as the maximum charred or destroyed section in the longitudinal direction of the holder.

The burning behaviour of thin materials is classified according to test performance as shown in Table 8.112.

Official approval

The fire performance of building materials is classified with the aid of the above tests performed by the following officially recognised test institutes to whom materials should be submitted:

- Building Research Institute, Ministry of Construction.
  1 Tatehara, Oho-Machi, Tsukuba-Gun
  Ibaraki-Ken, 305 Japan
- Forestry and Forest Product Institute, Ministry of Agriculture,
  Forestry and Fisheries.
  1 Matsunosato, Kukizaki-Mura,
  Ibaraki-Ken, 300-12 Japan
- Japan Testing Center for Construction Materials.
  1804 Inari-cho, Soka-Shi, Saitama-Ken, 304 Japan.
- General Building Research Corporation.
  Fujishirodai 5-125, Suitashi, Osaka, 565 Japan
- Tokyo Fire Department.
  3–5, Otemachi 1-Chome, Chiyoda-Ku, Tokyo, 100 Japan
- Hokkaido Building Research Institute.
  8, 1-Chome, 4-Jo 24-Ken, Nishi-Ku,
  Saporo-Shi, Hokkaido, Japan

A test report is issued and, if the test results are satisfactory official approval can be requested from the Building Center of Japan. This organisation passes it on for consultation to the Evaluation Committee of Fire Protection Performance appointed by the Ministry of Construction. Provided a positive decision is reached, the material is officially approved by the Ministry of Construction which informs the manufacturer and local authorities (for further details see [5]).

Official approval remains valid as long as the standards on which it is based are unchanged. Officially approved building materials and structures are listed in seven volumes of the "List of Approved Fire Endurance Structures and Fire Preventive Materials" as follows:

Volume 1:   Fire endurance structures – class A – walls.
Volume 1-A: Fire endurance structures – class A – columns, floors, beams and roofs.
Volume 2:   Fire endurance structures – class B.
Volume 2-A: Fire doors.
Volume 3:   Fire preventive materials – class 1 – non-combustible.
Volume 4:   Fire preventive materials – class 2 – semi-non-combustible.
Volume 5:   Fire preventive materials – class 3 – fire retardant.

All new materials which have been officially approved are periodically added to this list. An inspection agreement is entered into with the Building Center of Japan and the relevant Construction Ministry Commission. The latter's inspectors ensure that the manufacturer's production and quality control facilities maintain product quality at a high level. In addition, random checks are made by the inspectors. If the reported results of quality control and independent inspection are satisfactory the manufacturer has the right to mark his product with the Ministry of Construction seal of approval.

Another way of obtaining official approval for building materials is via the processing associations. The processor submits the material via his association to the Building Research Institute. A test report is sent back to the Association which applies for official approval from the Building Center of Japan. The application is registered at this Center and passed on via the Building Research Institute to the Building Ministry for a further expert opinion. If successful the Building Ministry grants official approval which is communicated to local authorities and to the applicant via the processing association. The latter is responsible for quality control and reports in April of each year to the Ministry of Construction.

Future developments

The regulations and test methods relating to fire performance of building materials are unlikely to change in the near future. Intensive efforts are being made in the field of smoke development of plastics where a draft JIS standard has been published. Further details are given in Section 9.2.3.3.

When completed, the work of ISO/TC 92 (see Section 8.2.18.2) will probably be adopted only in part in Japanese building standards. Besides the ISO 1182 non-combustibility test which already forms part of the Japanese test procedures, the DP 5657 ignitability test may be adopted after its introduction as an ISO standard. The flame spread and heat release tests are not under active discussion. Existing mandatory Japanese smoke density tests are considered adequate so that the ISO smoke chamber test is unlikely to be adopted.

A directive on fire doors is expected shortly and will involve a test similar to that of JIS A 1311.

References for 8.2.17

[1] Non-combustible building materials conforming to the Building Standards Law. Announcement No. 1828 of the Ministry of Construction, December 1970.
[2] Semi-non-combustible building materials and fire retardant building materials conforming to the Building Standards Law. Announcement No. 1231 of the Ministry of Construction, 25. 8. 1976.
[3] Fire retarded plastics for roofs (semi-fire retardant). Announcement No. 101 of the Ministry of Construction, January 1970.
[4] Japanese Industrial Standard (JIS) (published by the Japanese Standards Association).
    – JIS A 1301 – 1975: Method of Fire Test for Wooden Structural Parts of Buildings.
    – JIS A 1302 – 1975: Method of Fire Test for Non-combustible Structural Parts of Buildings.
    – JIS A 1304 – 1965: Method of Fire Resistance Test for Structural Parts of Buildings.
    – JIS A 1311 – 1966: Method of Fire Protecting Test of Fire Door for Building.
    – JIS A 1312 – 1959: Method of Fire Test for Roof of Buildings.
    – JIS A 1321 – 1970: Testing Method for Incombustibility of Internal Finish Material and Procedure of Buildings.
    – JIS A 1322 – 1966 (Reaffirmed 1973): Testing Method for Incombustibility of Thin Materials for Buildings.
[5] Approval of fire preventing materials conforming to the Building Standards Law. Announcement No. 214 of the Ministry of Construction.

8.2.18 International Organization for Standardization (ISO)

8.2.18.1 Introduction

As far as fire testing is concerned, one of the main activities of ISO is the development of standards relating to fire performance of building materials and components. This work forms the foundation for replacing empirical test methods with procedures which will enable the most important technical fire parameters to be assessed systematically.

Due to the importance of fire tests relevant to the building sector, ISO is covered at this point in the book. A brief introduction to the aims and structure of the organisation and to the Technical Committees (TC) concerned with fire testing is given and the various relevant standards enumerated. Finally, the work of TC 92 "Fire Tests on Building Materials, Components and Structures" is described in detail.

Aims and structure of ISO

The objectives of ISO are to promote worldwide standards to facilitate the exchange of goods and services and to encourage mutual cooperation within the sphere of intellectual, scientific, technological and economic activities. The results of the technical work of ISO are published as "International Standards".

ISO work is carried out via some 2,000 technical bodies. More than 100,000 experts from all over the world participate in this work which has resulted in the publication of almost 4,000 ISO standards.

A member body of ISO is the national body appointed by the relevant government as the responsible standards organisation. Member bodies have full voting rights on any technical committee, are eligible for Council membership and occupy a seat in the General Assembly.

At January 1980, there were 71 member bodies. Over 70% of ISO member bodies are government institutions or organisations incorporated under public law. The rest have close links with public administrations in their respective countries.

A correspondent member is usually an organisation in a developing country which does not yet have its own national standards organisation. Correspondent members do not play an active role in the technical work but are kept fully informed. At January 1980 there were 16 correspondent members. ISO members are listed in [1] (pp. X to XVIII). Details are also given in Section 10.4.

Technical work

The technical work of ISO is carried out via Technical Committees (TC). The ISO Council decides whether a TC should be established and lays down its terms of reference. The actual work programme is drawn up by the TC itself.

Member bodies wishing to play an active role in the work of TC's or SC's (sub-committees) are designated as P (participating) members. They are entitled to vote and must attend meetings as frequently as possible. Member bodies wishing only to be informed about the work of TC's or SC's are designated as O (observer) members.

The International Standards are developed by the TC's. Initially a Draft Proposal (DP) is circulated within the relevant TC and must pass through several stages prior to acceptance as an International Standard. This procedure is intended to ensure that the end result is acceptable to as many countries as possible.

When the TC has reached agreement, the DP is sent to the Central Secretariat for registration as a Draft International Standard (DIS). The DIS is then circulated to all ISO members and, provided 75% vote in favour, it is sent to ISO Council for acceptance as an International Standard. An International Standard may be used as such or after incorporation in national standards.

Technical Committees concerned with fire protection

Several of the 178 TC's listed in the 1980 ISO Catalogue are concerned with the combustibility or fire performance of materials. They are listed below together with International Standards issued by them.

ISO/TC 21. Equipment for fire protection and fire fighting

– ISO 3941 – 1977. Classification of fires.

ISO/TC 22. Road vehicles

– ISO 3795 – 1976. Determination of burning behaviour of interior materials for motor vehicles.
   This standard is based on FMVSS 302, further details of which are given in Section 8.3.

ISO/TC 35. Paints and varnishes

– ISO 3679 – 1976. Rapid test for determination of flashpoint.
– ISO 3680 – 1976. Rapid test for determination of danger classification by flashpoint.

ISO/TC 38. Textiles

Up to now no standards relating to burning behaviour have been introduced. The methenamine pill test based on ASTM D 2859−76 (see Section 8.2.14) will shortly be issued as ISO 6925.

ISO/TC 41. Pulleys and belts

– ISO/R 340 – 1963. Flame resistance of conveyor belts – specifications and method of test.

ISO/TC 45. Rubber and rubber products

This TC has issued ISO 3582 together with TC 61. Details are given below under TC 61.

ISO/TC 61. Plastics

– ISO 181−1981. Determination of flammability characteristics of rigid plastics in the form of small specimens in contact with an incandescent rod.
   This standard is based on the Schramm-Zebrowski glowbar test (see Section 8.4).
– ISO 871−1980. Determination of temperature of evolution of flammable gases (decomposition temperature) from a small sample of pulverized material.
– ISO 1172−1975. Textile glass reinforced plastics – determination of loss on ignition.
– ISO 1210−1982. Determination of flammability characteristics of plastics in the form of small specimens in contact with a small flame.
   A Bunsen flame is applied at 45° to a horizontally positioned specimen.

- ISO/R 1326 – 1970. Determination of flammability and burning rate of plastics in the form of film.

  ISO/R 1326 is also being revised and is available as ISO/DIS 1326, Determination of flammability of plastics in the form of film and sheet. This standard is basically similar to ASTM D 568 described in Section 8.2.14.

- ISO 3582 – 1978. Cellular plastic and cellular rubber materials – laboratory assessment of horizontal burning characteristics of small specimens subjected to a small flame.

  ISO 3582 is based on ASTM D 1692 (now withdrawn) in which a flame is applied to the bottom of a foam specimen by a swallow tail burner.

- ISO/DP 4589. Laboratory method of test to assess oxygen index values for the burning characteristics of small vertical specimens after ignition by a small flame or incandescent surface.

  This draft standard is based on the ASTM D 2863 oxygen index test described in section 8.2.9, "Norway".

ISO/TC 92. Fire tests on building materials, components and structures

These test methods relating to buildings are dealt with in detail in Section 8.2.18.2.

ISO/TC 94. Personal safety – Protective clothing and equipment

- ISO 2801 – 1973. Clothing for protection against heat and fire – General recommendations for users and for those in charge of such users.

ISO/TC 136. Furniture

TC 136 has set up Working Groups WG 4, Fire Tests, in Sub-Committee SC 1 Test Methods. WG 4 will work out a test method for determining the burning behaviour of upholstered furniture.

ISO/TC 138. Plastics pipes, fittings and valves for the transport of fluids

This includes an ad-hoc Fire Group (ISO/TC 138/WG 1) which is concerned with problems of testing the fire performance of plastics pipes.

The Coordinating Committee for Fire Tests (CCFT) – new designation: TAG 5 – coordinates all the fire protection activities of ISO. All the TC's mentioned above were present at its first session in November 1978. The object of this committee is to find a common path for solving problems relating to the development and adoption of fire test methods for which the various TC's are responsible.

8.2.18.2 ISO/TC 92. Fire tests on building materials, components and structures

ISO/TC 92 was established in 1961 to develop test methods for ascertaining the fire performance of building materials and components. Individual topics are investigated by Working Groups (WG). Up to the 11th Plenary Session of ISO/TC 92 held in Sydney from 6 to 13. 9. 1979 these were as follows:

WG 2. Combustibility and heat release.
WG 3. Fire resistance: doors, shutters and glazed elements.

WG   4. Ignitability, flame spread and smoke generation.

WG   6. Fire test terminology.

WG   7. Advisory and liaison.

WG   9. Chimneys and flues.

WG 10. Measuring instruments and techniques.

WG 11. Fire resistance: general requirements.

WG 12. Toxic hazards in fires.

WG 13. External exposure roof tests.

WG 14. Ventilation ducts.

(WG 15. Classes of fire resistance).

These Working Groups consist of nominated experts and not of representatives of ISO member bodies. They are therefore unable to approve DP's, DIS's or Technical Reports (TR), a task which is in fact the responsibility of the TC's. The resultant approval procedure is both difficult and time-consuming but has now been somewhat simplified by the replacement of WG's with Sub-Committees (SC) which can approve test methods up to the DIS stage. The TC's function is then limited to coordination, controlling the work programme, formal approval and processing documents after the DIS stage.

As a result the plenary session in Sydney voted to reorganise ISO/TC 92 and to set up the following three Sub-Committees:

TC 92/SC 1: Reaction to fire,

TC 92/SC 2: Fire resistance and fire tests for building components,

TC 92/SC 3: Toxic hazards in fire.

SC 1 consists of WG 2 and WG 4, SC 2 of WG 3, WG 11, WG 13, WG 14 and SC 3 of WG 12. WG 6, WG 7, WG 10 and the newly formed WG 15 continue to report directly to TC 92 so that a heterogeneous structure exists.

Reorganisation will take place in several stages and until it is complete the existing set up will remain in force.

ISO/TC 92 is carrying out comprehensive studies within the sphere of the WG's and SC's to establish methods for testing the fire performance of building materials and components. The work on "reaction to fire" tests is discussed below with the exception of secondary fire effects. Smoke development of fire gases is dealt with extensively in Section 9.2 and toxic hazards are discussed in Section 9.1. Fire resistance tests, i.e. ISO 834 "Fire resistance tests on elements of building construction" and two amendments [2], ISO 3008 "Door and shutter assemblies" [3] and ISO 3009 "Glazed elements" [4] are mentioned here for completeness but are not otherwise discussed.

TC 92 has been concerned for some time with the significance of "reaction to fire" tests and in 1975 published Technical Report 3814 [5] describing the development of methods for measuring the fire performance of building materials. In addition to various observations on "fire philosophy" and on the historical development of fire testing, the report introduces the concept of test methods which delineate the most important factors affecting the initiating fire such as ignitability, flame spread and heat release as well as secondary fire effects. These test methods enable the contribution of building materials to the development of a fire to be assessed during their own decomposition. Two further Technical Reports – TR 6585, "fire hazard and the design and use of fire tests" [6] and TR 6543, "development of tests for measuring toxic hazards in fire" [7], which extended the concept contained in TR 3814, appeared in 1979. "Fire philosophy" and the historical development of fire testing are discussed in greater detail in Chapter 7 and in Chapter 8.

In order to support and advise ISO/TC 92, various liaisons with other international organisations exist in addition to links within ISO (see under CCFT). These are:

- CCE: Commission of the European Communities.
- CEI Bois: European Confederation of Woodworking Industries.
- UN/ECE/HBP: United Nations Economic Commission for Europe – Committee for Housing, Building and Planning.
- EFI: European Flooring Institute.
- EURIMA: European Insulation Manufacturers Association.
- IMCO: Inter-Governmental Maritime Consultative Organization.
- CIB/14:   Conseil International du Bâtiment.
- EUROGYPSUM: Working Community of the European Gypsum Industry.

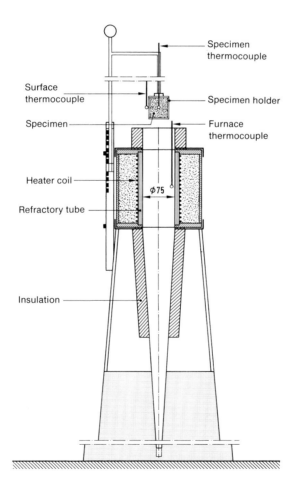

Fig. 8.70   Non-combustibility furnace

ISO 1182. Non-combustibility test

The non-combustibility of building materials is tested by ISO 1182–1979 [8]. In many countries the earlier ISO/DIS 1182 or ISO/R 1182 versions of this method are still used. These versions differ to varying degrees but are basically similar. The apparatus is illustrated in Fig. 8.70 and the test specifications are summarised in Table 8.113.

Table 8.113   ISO 1182 non-combustibility test specifications

Specimens	5 cylindrical samples, diameter 45 mm, height 50 mm, volume 80 cm³
Specimen position	vertical in specimen holder
Radiation source	electric furnace heated to 825 °C
Test duration	20 min
Conclusions	passed if all five specimens on average
	– cause a temperature rise of not more than 50 °C as measured by the thermocouples in the test specimen, on the specimen surface and in the furnace
	– do not burn for longer than 20 s
	– do not suffer a weight loss of more than 50%

Difficulties occur when placing the test specimen in the furnace since this act is associated with a temperature rise irrespective of whether the specimen contains combustible components or not. Consequently Working Group ISO/TC 92/WG 2 Non-combustibility is revising ISO 1182.

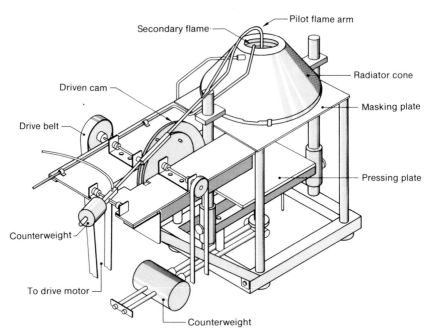

Fig. 8.71   Ignitability test apparatus

ISO/DP 5657. Ignitability of building materials

ISO/DP 5657 ignitability of building materials [9] is the first of a series of test methods intended to describe precisely the various aspects of reaction to fire of building materials. This draft proposal was published at the end of 1980 as a Technical Report (TR). The ignitability apparatus is shown in Figs. 8.71, 8.72 and 8.73 while the test specifications are summarised in Table 8.114.

Table 8.114   ISO/DP 5657 ignitability test specifications

Specimens	max. five specimens 165 mm × 165 mm × ≦ 70 mm for each radiation intensity: 5, 4, 3, 2 and 1 W/cm^2
Specimen position	horizontal, the test specimen is masked so that a circle 140 mm in diameter is irradiated
Ignition sources	– radiator cone consisting of heating coil with variable radiation intensity (1 to 5 W/cm^2), lower rim of cone 22 mm above test specimen
	– moveable ignition device which can apply 10 mm long propane flame to the test specimen every 4 s for 1 s through the centre of the radiator cone from a distance 10 mm above the specimen (working position), rest position above cone
	– secondary flame above radiator cone for reigniting pilot flame if it extinguishes
Test duration	until specimen ignites, max. 15 min
Conclusions	if specimen does not ignite within 15 min, result for tested level of irradiance given as "no ignition", lower levels of irradiance are considered "not tested"

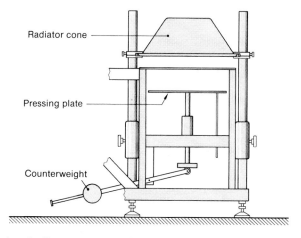

Fig. 8.72   Mounting of radiator cone on specimen support frame

The ignitability test apparatus consists of a radiator which can be operated at irradiance levels of 1 to 5 W/cm^2 and a support framework which enables specimens up to 70 mm thick to be tested horizontally. The specimen is clamped by means of a pressure plate and counter-

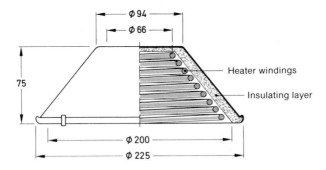

Fig. 8.73   Details of radiator cone

weight against a masking plate with a 140 mm diameter cut out. This locates the specimen 22 mm below the bottom rim of the cone.

The radiator is calibrated prior to the test by placing a non-combustible board with a radiometer at its centre in the specimen position. A calibration curve (radiation intensity in W/cm^2 against power input to radiator in W) is obtained.

The specimen is clamped in position for the test, the radiation intensity adjusted to 5 W/cm^2 and the ignition device set in motion. The last consists of a small propane burner which is moved from its rest position above the cone aperture to its working position inside the cone every 4 s and applies a flame for 1 s to the specimen at a height of 10 mm.

The test is continued until the specimen ignites or for a maximum of 15 min. If none of the five specimens is ignited, the test is considered to have been passed ("no ignition") for 5 W/cm^2 and tests at lower levels of irradiance are dispensed with. If ignition occurs, tests are repeated down to the lowest level of irradiance if necessary.

Table 8.115   ISO/DP 5658 spread of flame test specifications

Specimens	800 mm × 155 mm × $\leq$ 40 mm, three specimens for each orientation (wall, floor, ceiling)
Specimen position	end of exposed area nearest radiator at a distance of 100 mm
	– wall: 450 mm side of radiant panel horizontal, specimen vertical, long (800 mm) horizontal side at 45° to radiant panel
	– floor: 450 mm side of radiant panel vertical, specimen horizontal and located centrally in the plane of the bottom of the radiant panel, long (800 mm) side at 90° to radiant panel
	– ceiling: 450 mm side of radiant panel vertical, specimen horizontal and located centrally in the plane of the top of the radiant panel, long (800 mm) side at 90° to radiant panel
Ignition sources	– vertical variable propane radiant panel 300 mm × 450 mm, radiation intensity 6.2 W/cm^2, surface temperature 750 °C
	– variable propane pilot flame, length 80 mm, impinges on specimen 20 mm from edge nearest to radiator
Test duration	test terminated when flame front extinguished or reaches end of specimen
Conclusions	the maximum distance in mm of flame travel and the time to extinction if the end of the specimen is not reached are recorded

ISO/DP 5658. Spread of flame of building materials

The ISO/DP 5658 spread of flame test [10] enables materials to be tested in horizontal (floor and ceiling) and vertical (wall) orientations. Round-robin vertical spread of flame tests have been carried out in ISO/TC 92/WG 4/TG 3 and the results will be published in a Draft Technical Report. The spread of flame test apparatus is illustrated in Figs. 8.74, 8.75 and 8.76 and the test specifications are summarised in Table 8.115.

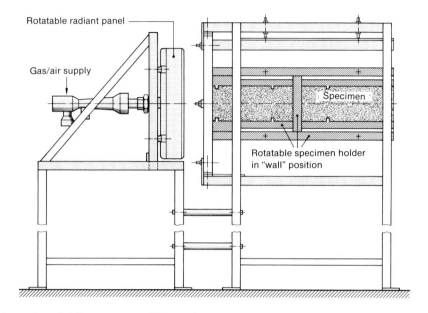

Fig. 8.74   Spread of flame apparatus (side view)

The radiant panel is calibrated prior to the test using the specimen irradiation levels given in Table 8.116.

Table 8.116   Required irradiation levels at test specimen

| Distance of measuring point from radiator [mm] | Required irradiation level | | |
	45° wall position [W/cm^2]	floor position [W/cm^2]	ceiling position [W/cm^2]
50	3.03	1.24	1.63
150	2.38	0.70	0.90
250	1.67	0.45	0.57
350	1.10	0.29	0.37
450	0.70	0.19	0.25
550	0.44	0.13	0.17
650	0.28	0.10	0.12
750	0.18	0.09	0.09

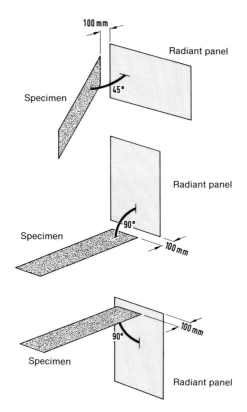

Fig. 8.75   Orientations of specimen and radiant panel
top: Wall position, *centre:* Floor position, *bottom:* Ceiling position

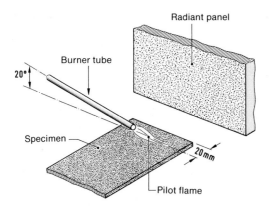

Fig. 8.76   Position of pilot flame

When the radiant panel has reached equilibrium temperature the pilot flame is positioned so that it impinges on the specimen at an angle of 20° to its surface, 20 mm from the edge nearest the radiator. About 50 mm of flame should be in contact with the specimen. The specimen is loaded into the holder and the times taken by the flame front to reach the 100, 150, 200 mm etc. marks up to maximum travel are recorded.

The test is terminated when the flame front is extinguished or the end of the specimen has been reached.

Substantial experience has so far been obtained with wall position tests. Extended round-robin tests are also planned for the floor and ceiling positions.

Rate of heat release

Within ISO/TC 92/WG 2, the heat release group has drawn up Document ISO/TC 92/WG 2 N 148 [11] which will form the basis of ISO/DP 5660. The major difficulties which have occurred in this work make it unlikely that the apparatus described in the Document [11] will be developed further. A piece of proven test equipment – the OSU Calorimeter developed by *Smith* in the USA – is preferred. A review of the various calorimeters available in the USA is given in [12] (p. 36 and 50 ff).

Since the heat release group has not yet reached a decision, a description of the test procedure is dispensed with here.

The calorific potential of building materials is determined by ISO 1716 [13] and is mentioned for completeness. The test is carried out in a high pressure bomb calorimeter.

Secondary fire effects

Smoke development and toxicity of fire gases have been comprehensively investigated by ISO/TC 92/WG 4 and WG 12. Two draft proposals for determining the smoke development of fire gases, ISO/DP 5659 smoke generated by solid materials (NBS smoke chamber) and ISO/DP 5924 smoke generated by building materials (ISO smoke chamber) have been issued. The development of methods for testing toxicity of fire gases is the subject of a technical report [7]. Details of the apparatus and test specifications for ISO/DP 5659 and ISO/DP 5924 are given in Section 9.2.

8.2.18.3 Future developments

The objectives of ISO, namely to promote the development of standards and thus facilitate international cooperation are vigorously supported by various TC's working on fire protection. Thus ISO/TC 61 (plastics) is in the process of developing and revising numerous laboratory test methods in order to complete a comprehensive set of standards for quality control (see above under ISO/TC 61). The experience of ISO/TC 61 in this field could be a major aid to other TC's.

ISO/TC 92 is concerned with developing systematic test methods to quantify the most important structural fire parameters. The work on ignitability and flame spread are already well advanced but must be supported by further round-robin tests.

Work has only just started on heat release and much time and effort will have to be expended on establishing a test procedure. As far as secondary fire effects are concerned, a great deal of experience has been accumulated with smoke density measurements by means of a comprehensive series of tests. The advances made here are described in Section 9.2. Besides a technical report on the development of test methods little progress has been made on the subject of toxicity of fire gases.

ISO/TC 136 is considering developing methods for testing the burning behaviour or fire performance (there is no clear agreement on this) of upholstered furniture. On account of the topicality of this problem, it is intended to develop relevant test procedures shortly.

References for 8.2.18

[1]   ISO-Catalogue. 1980 (International Organization for Standardization, Case postale 56, CH-1211 Genève 20).
[2]   ISO 834−1974. Fire Resistance Tests. Elements of Building Construction.
      Amendment 1, 1. April 1979.
      Amendment 2 (Draft), 15. September 1979.
[3]   ISO 3008−1976. Fire Resistance Tests. Door and Shutter Assemblies.
[4]   ISO 3009−1976. Fire Resistance Tests. Glazed Elements.
[5]   ISO/TR 3814−1975. The Development of Tests for Measuring "Reaction to Fire" of Building Materials.
[6]   ISO/TR 6585−1979. Fire Hazard and the Design and Use of Fire Tests.
[7]   ISO/TR 6543−1979. The Development of Tests for Measuring Toxic Hazards in Fire.
[8]   ISO 1182−1979. Fire Tests – Building Materials. Non-Combustibility Test.
[9]   Draft Proposal ISO/DP 5657. Fire Tests. Reaction to Fire. Ignitability of Building Products. ISO/TC 92/WG 4 N 300. February 1979.
[10] Draft Proposal ISO/DP 5658 (Preliminary proposal). Fire Test. Reaction to Fire. Spread of Flame of Building Materials. ISO/TC 92/WG 4 N 243. June 1977.
[11] Document No. ISO/TC 92/WG 2 N 148. Fire Test. Reaction to Fire. Rate of Heat Release. July 1977.
[12] National Materials Advisory Board. Fire Safety Aspects of Polymeric Materials. Volume 2: Test Methods, Specifications, and Standards. Technomic Publishing Co., Inc., 1979. 265 Post Road West, Westport, CT 06880, USA.
[13] ISO 1716−1973. Building Materials – Determination of Calorific Potential.

8.3 Transportation, transport and storage of hazardous materials

D. I. Hans-Joachim Bönold

Nowadays plastics are considered as essential materials in all vehicles. In the past their use was determined mainly on the grounds of their production advantages over metallic materials, e.g. rapid, cost saving manufacture of complex mouldings and reduced assembly costs, and by consumer demands for more comfort and better design. Today the significant weight savings required for energy conservation, more stringent industrial and traffic safety requirements, low maintenance and running costs can frequently be achieved only by the increased use of plastics.

Plastic tanks and vessels are used increasingly for storing and transporting hazardous materials. Their long term corrosion resistance and stability to many chemicals are important factors in an increasingly environmentally conscious world. Here too, the low weight of plastics results in savings in energy and costs.

8.3.1 Motor vehicles

Approximately 7 to 10% by weight, i.e. 60 to 100 kg, of a modern, medium size car consists of plastics. This can be broken down roughly into: polyurethane (PUR) 28%, polyvinyl chloride (PVC) 25%, acrylobutadiene styrene (ABS) and styrene polymers 15% and polypropylene 14%. The quest for lower fuel consumption and the desire for safety, corrosion resistance and comfort will lead to increased application of plastics in the automotive field. Modern technology will enable reinforced thermoplastics and thermosets to be used on a wider scale for mass produced body parts. Following more than a decade of testing in competition cars, high density polyethylene (HDPE) fuel tanks are being installed in large numbers in mass produced cars.

8.3.1.1 Statutory regulations

The object of safety legislation is to guarantee the user a minimum level of protection. Performance requirements are generally laid down in safety standards to prevent development being impeded by construction regulations. These standards reflect the state of the art and can be relatively easily brought into line with technical advances in safety.

Legal provisions often refer to relevant standards such as those of ISO, DIN etc. Such safety standards are, however, still relevant even if they are not specifically mentioned since "state of the art" levels of safety can be guaranteed only if the appropriate standards, rules and guidelines are complied with.

The Straßenverkehrsgesetz (StVG) (Road Traffic Act), Straßenverkehrsordnung (Road Traffic Order) and Straßenverkehrs-Zulassungs-Ordnung (StVZO) (Road Traffic Licensing Regulations) [1] form an important part of Federal German traffic legislation. The StVZO lays down the conditions for vehicles to be used on roads. Besides the licensing procedure for motor vehicles and trailers, Part III contains the construction and use regulations, § 30 of which states:

Vehicles must be so constructed and equipped that

1. their normal operation neither harms nor endangers, hinders or disturbs anyone more than necessary,

2. the occupants are protected as far as possible from injury, particularly in accidents and the extent and consequence of injuries should remain as slight as possible.

This fundamental requirement provides the Kraftfahrt-Bundesamt (KBA) (Federal Motoring Authority) and officially recognised experts with the basis for testing vehicles for approval and for updating technical requirements. Fire safety is also included. Of course international harmonisation has resulted in an increasing transfer of responsibilities to international committees and in particular to those of the European Community (EEC) and the United Nations Economic Commission for Europe (ECE).

The aim of harmonising technical regulations within the EEC is to remove technical trade barriers between member states. EEC Directives are established by the General Directorate for the Internal Market of the Commission of the European Community (Table 8.117). The adoption of approval directives in national legislation must normally occur within 18 months. EEC type approval will be granted for complete vehicles but since some directives have not yet been finalised, partial type approvals are being issued in the interim.

Table 8.117   Principal committees for motor vehicles in the European Community

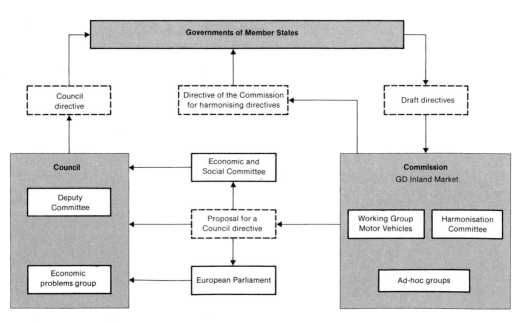

The UN Economic Commission for Europe has an Inland Transport Committee (ITC) in which the SC 1 Standing Committee "Road Transport" is concerned with developing unified regulations relevant to safety. The "Vehicle Construction" Working Party (WP 29) is responsible for technical regulations and has appointed "Rapporteur Groups" which include experts from industry, to deal with specific questions (Table 8.118). The work is based on the Agreement of 20. 3. 1958 on the "Adoption of uniform conditions of approval and reciprocal recognition of approval for motor vehicles equipment and parts".

Table 8.118   Principal committees within the Economic Commission of the UN for motor vehicles

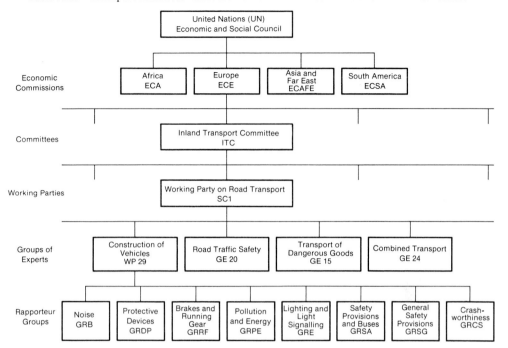

Regulations finalised by the Working Party are implemented if two states declare their use to the UN Secretary General. It is significant that such provisions are adopted not only by the parties to the agreement but also by other countries. The technical provisions of a particular ECE agreement are then declared as authoritative in the national legislation.

At present 42 regulations have been issued by the UN General Secretariat in New York including No. 34 "Uniform provisions concerning the approval of vehicles with regard to the prevention of fire risks" [2], Annex 5 of which contains the test regulations for plastic fuel tanks.

Besides regulations, ECE working parties can also draw up "Recommendations" for example for materials for use in vehicle interiors [3].

The US Federal Motor Vehicle Safety Standards (FMVSS) based on the US Safety Act occupy a special position in the regulations of other countries due to the importance of European and Japanese motor industry exports to the US. The process of issuing a new safety standard commences with an announcement in the Federal Register (FR). Interested parties thus have the opportunity to express their opinion, raise objections or suggest additions which are then dealt with in a "Notice of Proposed Rule Making". The intended deadline is fixed at the start.

The US regulations cover not only vehicles and components which are already in use but also accelerate new developments which are thought to be particularly important for vehicle safety. This dynamic legislation enables rapid changes and amendments to be made so that new technical trends can be put into practice relatively rapidly.

Besides the FMVSS, the Motor Carrier Safety Regulations (MCSR) for motor vehicles have limited validity for interstate and cross-border traffic.

8.3.1.2 Technical fire protection requirements and tests

All safety requirements including those in the field of fire protection must be orientated towards real accident situations. Statistical and phenomenological analyses are used to establish the required levels of performance. Sensible performance standards should be laid down in safety regulations taking into account technical and financial limitations.

Fire incidents are relatively rare in motor vehicles compared to the large number of accidents. According to a survey of accidents carried out by the German HUK-Verband (Association of Liability Insurance, Accident and Traffic Underwriters) involving 28,936 vehicles and 40,464 casualties, only 64 fires were reported [4]. This represents 0.24% of the accidents investigated. It is nevertheless significant that the number of deaths in fire incidents is 10 times greater than in accidents which did not result in fires.

The cause of fire is usually difficult to ascertain. It can be assumed, however, that in the incidents included here, leaking fuel ignited by short circuits, sparks or hot exhausts was a prime source. The survey does not include fire incidents which did not involve personal injuries. According to *Trisko* [5] these are usually due to carburettor fires, short circuits or to careless handling of smokers requisites and naked flames. The increasing incidence of arson is also noteworthy.

Fire spreads relatively slowly in a vehicle as long as large quantities of fuel do not escape. Thus the Allianz-Zentrum für Technik, Ismaning near Munich (Allianz Insurance Company Centre of Technology) reported flash-over in the interior of a car only some 5 to 10 minutes after leaking fuel had ignited in the engine compartment [6].

The fire risk in motor vehicles can be further reduced by the following measures:

– The fuel system must remain leak-free even if it is distorted in an accident. In particular no fuel should penetrate the passenger compartment.
– Materials and components in the passenger cabin should not contribute to rapid fire propagation.
– The passenger compartment must protect the occupants for an adequate period from external flames.
– Electrical wires must be safely routed and batteries and components must be firmly anchored.

Materials and components for use in car interiors

Specific requirements for materials and components in the interiors of cars, trucks and buses were first established by the US National Highway Transport Safety Administration (NHTSA) and brought into force as Federal Motor Vehicle Safety Standard (FMVSS) 302 in 1972 [7]. Specimens taken from the passenger compartment are clamped horizontally and subjected for 15 s to a Bunsen flame. The rate of flame spread, measured over a distance of 254 mm, should not exceed 4 in/min (101.6 mm/min) for any of the specimens (Fig. 8.77). The specimen thickness must correspond to that of the component and should not exceed ½ in (12.7 mm). The test specifications are summarised in Table 8.119.

The test procedure has been adopted by all countries with a significant automotive industry and also forms the basis of ISO Standard 3795 [8] established by ISO/TC 22/SC 16 to provide international unified test conditions for such components. In common with German Standard DIN 75200 [9], ISO 3795 does not contain any explicit requirements. These are laid down in legal provisions or conditions of supply.

According to the Federal German "Richtlinien zu § 30 StVZO über die Verwendung schwerentflammbarer Werkstoffe im Kraftfahrzeugbau" (§ 30 StVZO Guidelines for the use of low flammability materials in motor vehicle construction), the maximum permitted rate of flame spread for interior components subject to mandatory testing is 110 mm/min

Table 8.119   FMVSS 302 test specifications for flammability of materials for vehicle interiors

Specimens	5 specimens, 356 mm × 100 mm × usual thickness reference marks 38 mm, 292 mm, measured length 254 mm
Specimen position	horizontal
Ignition source	Bunsen burner, 9 mm diameter 38 mm high flame applied to edge of specimen
Duration of flame application	15 s
Result	rate of flame spread over measured length, maximum permitted rate of flame spread 4 in/min (101.6 mm/min)

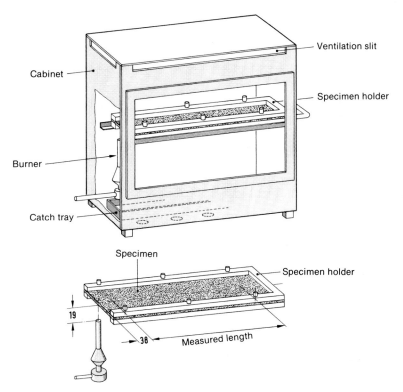

Fig. 8.77   US Safety Standard FMVSS 302 rate of flame spread test for motor vehicle interior components

[10]. Proof must be furnished when the new vehicle is tested for type approval by officially recognised experts.

In Japan, JIS D 1201 [11] for interior components of motor vehicles includes a fire retardant test corresponding to ASTM D 2863-77 [12] (see Section 8.2.9, Fig. 8.30 and Table 8.62) as well as a test based on FMVSS 302 (flammability test method). The tests should be carried out on artificially weathered, aged specimens.

According to JIS, materials are classified in four groups based on rate of flame spread and in five groups based on fire retardation index (Table 8.120). However, at present the Japanese Ministry of Transport (MOT) only specifies the flammability test method to FMVSS 302.

Table 8.120   Classification according to JIS D 1201–1973

| *Classification according to rate of flame spread* | |
Classification	Flame spread / evaluation
Slow burning I	<50 mm/min
Slow burning II	50 to <75 mm/min
Slow burning III	75 to <100 mm/min
Self extinguishing	all specimens extinguish before the first reference mark, or the flame extinguishes at burn length ≦ 50 mm and burning time ≦ 60 s
Classification according to fire retardation index	
Classification	Fire retardation index
Fire retardant I	>30
Fire retardant II	>27 to 30
Fire retardant III	>24 to 27
Fire retardant IV	>21 to 24
Fire retardant V	≦21

The Japanese standards also require smoke density to be determined and the test equipment thus includes a device which measures obscuration across a 500 mm long light path using a photocell (for further details see Section 9.2.2.2 "JIS A 1321 and JIS D 1201 Smoke production tests").

Bodywork

Only in the Federal Republic of Germany are fire protection requirements laid down for bodywork and body components made of plastics. According to the § 30 StVZO Guidelines relating to the use of low flammability materials in vehicle construction, sheet components of vehicle assemblies enclosing the passenger compartment must be tested to DIN 53438 Part 3 [13]. Painted specimens of representative thickness must satisfy "Evaluation Class F1". The test is also intended to ensure that vehicles with plastic bodies cannot be set alight by small ignition sources such as matches and lighters.

Proof that materials conform to the requirements must be furnished when applying for type approval.

Fuel tanks

The use of plastic fuel tanks raises the question of their approval and evaluation from the point of view of fire safety. The Federal German Minister of Transport has appointed the "Fachausschuß Kraftfahrzeugtechnik" (FKT) (Motor Vehicle Technology Committee) to develop safety requirements and tests for such tanks [14, 15, 16]. This task is performed by the "Sonderausschuß Feuersicherheit" (Fire Safety Committee) of the FKT in close cooperation with the plastics industry (Table 8.121) and the results have been published in the "Prüfvorschriften des FKT-SA Feuersicherheit" (FKT-SA fire safety test specifications) [17]. These test conditions have been incorporated in ECE Regulation No. 34 [2] which is currently applied by all European countries with a significant automotive industry.

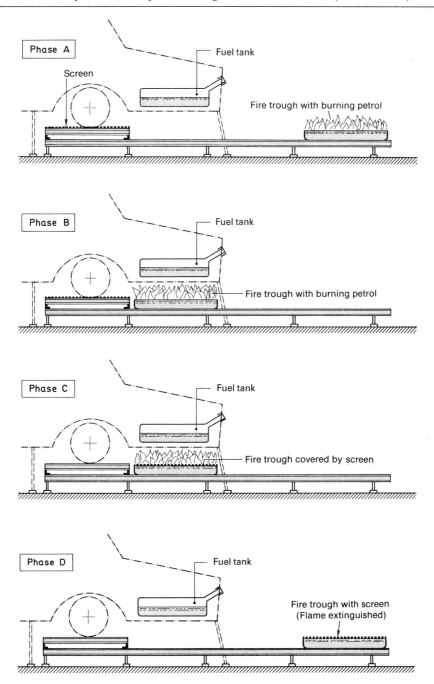

Fig. 8.78   Testing the fire performance of plastic fuel tanks according to the regulations of the Fire Safety Committee of the FKT

Table 8.121   Cooperation of Committees in the Federal Republic of Germany

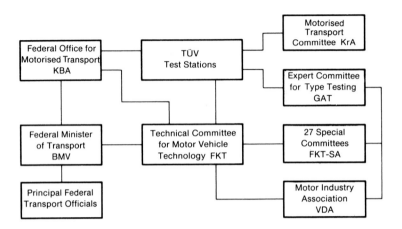

The principal tests and requirements for plastic fuel tanks are summarised in Table 8.122.

The fire performance test is illustrated schematically in Fig. 8.78. The fuel tank is filled with fuel to 50% of its nominal capacity and installed in a test rig or in the vehicle assembly which should include any parts which may affect the course of the fire in any way. The filler pipe is closed and the venting system should be operative. Flame is applied to the fuel tank in four phases from an open fire trough filled with petrol:

– Phase A (Preheating)
  The fuel in the fire trough is ignited and burns for 60 s.
– Phase B (Direct flame exposure)
  The fuel tank is subjected to the flames of the fully developed fuel fire for 60 s.
– Phase C (Indirect flame exposure)
  Immediately after completing Phase B, a defined screen is placed between the fire trough and the tank. The latter is subjected to this reduced fire exposure for a further 60 s.
– Phase D (End of test)
  The fuel trough covered by the screen is brought to the initial position. The tank and fire trough are extinguished.

The requirements of the test are met if, at the end of the test, the tank is still in its mount and does not leak.

In the Federal Republic of Germany, the Federal Minister of Transport (BMV) has nominated the "Technische Prüfstelle für den Kraftfahrzeugverkehr beim TÜV Berlin e. V." (TÜV Berlin motor traffic test station) to test fuel tanks according to the FKT provisions and ECE Regulation 34. Table 8.123 lists other authorities and technical services in states applying ECE-R 34. Outside Europe ECE-R 34 tests are recognised in Japan and Australia providing they are fully documented by photographs or film records.

The US National Highway Traffic Safety Administration (NHTSA) is considering incorporating the ECE-R 34 Appendix 5 technical fire protection requirements for plastic fuel tanks in US Traffic Law, Standard No. 301-75 "Fuel System Integrity" [18]. A decision on this is still awaited.

Table 8.122 Requirements and tests for plastic fuel tanks according to the test regulations of the Fire Safety Committee of the FKT

Test Specification No.	Parameter	Type and quantity of contents	Test conditions			Minimum requirement
			Temperature [°C]	Time / pressure	Other	
1	Impact resistance	coolant 100%	−40 °C	−/−	Impact mass: 150 N Work energy storage: 30 Nm	no leak of fluid
2	Mechanical strength	water 100%	65 °C (53 °C)*	8 h/1.5 bar (5 h/1.3 bar)*	–	watertight and serviceable
3	Fuel permeability	petrol 50%	1. 40 °C 2. 23 °C	after 4 weeks storage: 8 weeks testing:		quantity lost: 1. <20 g/d 2. <10 g/d
4	Resistance to fuel	1. repeat of tests 1 and 2 after carrying out test 3 2. supplemented by comparative measurements on test rods				As 1 and 2 No significant deviation
5	Resistance to fire	petrol 50%	defined flame effect from outside (petrol fire)	2 min	test on built-in tank	No leaks in operating position and stays in mounting
6	Resistance to high temperatures	water 50%	95 °C	1 h	ventilation system open	no leaks, dimensionally stable

* different criteria according to ECE-R 34

Table 8.123   ECE-Regulation 34. User states, Authorities and Technical Services

ECE- Test mark	User state	Date introduced	Responsible Traffic Authority	Responsible Technical Service
E 2	France	10. 9. 78	1)	1)
E 3	Italy	1. 11. 76	2)	7)
E 5	Sweden	1. 7. 75	3)	3)
E 11	Great Britain	1. 7. 75	4)	8)
E 17	Finland	13. 2. 78	5)	–
E 18	Denmark	18. 11. 79	6)	–
E 14	GDR	28. 6. 81	9)	–
E 19	Rumania	5. 6. 81	10)	–

1) Ministère de l'équipement
   Direction des routes et de la circulation routière
   Sous-Direction de la réglementation des
   véhicules
   6, Rue du Théâtre
   F-75015 Paris
2) Ministero dei Trasporti e dell'Aviazione Civile
   Direzione Generale MCTC – Dir. Centrale IV –
   Divisione 41
   Via Nomentana 591
   I-00141 Roma
3) Statens Trafiksäkerhetsverk
   (Swedish Road Safety Office)
   Fack
   S-781 86 Borlänge
4) The Department of Transport
   Vehicle and Component Division
   St. Christopher House
   Southwark Street
   London SE 1 OTE
5) Liikenneministeriö
   Tieliikenneosasto
   Etalá Esplanadi 16, Box 235
   SF-00131 Helsinki 13

6) Ministry of Justice
   Road Safety Division
   Købmagergade 48
   Postbox 2131
   DK-1015 Copenhagen K
7) Centro Superiore Ricerche e Prove
   Autoveicoli e Dispositivi del
   Ministero dei Trasporti
   Viale delle Province 155
   I-00162 Roma
8) Department of the Environment
   Vehicle Engineering Division
   St. Christopher House
   Southwark Street
   London SE 1 OTE
9) VEB Wissenschaftlich-Technisches
   Zentrum Automobilbau
   Kauffahrtei 45
   Postfach 1034
   DDR-9010 Karl-Marx-Stadt
10) Ministerul Industriei
   Constructiilor de Masini
   Directia Generală Tehnică
   Calea Victoriei nr. 133
   R-71102 Bucuresti

Plastic windows

An ECE Regulation covering windows made of safety glass and glass-like materials is in preparation. Until this is finalised, the national rules covering testing of these components will remain in force.

In the Federal Republic of Germany, the conditions are laid down in the "Technische Anforderungen an Fahrzeugteile bei der Bauartprüfung nach § 22a StVZO" [19] (Technical requirements for vehicle components in the type test according to § 22a StVZO). Technical fire requirements are given in Part II No. 29 "Safety glass made of glass-like materials (rigid and flexible plastics)" (Fig. 8.79 and Table 8.124).

The "Staatliches Materialprüfungsamt Nordrhein-Westfalen", Dortmund-Aplerbeck has been nominated as the Federal German test station for safety glass.

In the USA, the requirements of FMVSS 302 also apply to plastic windows in convertible hoods.

Table 8.124   Test specifications for windows of glass-like materials

Rigid plastics:	
Specimens	3 specimens, 150 mm × 13 mm × usual thickness
	calibration marks at 10 mm and 100 mm
Specimen position	longitudinal axis horizontal
	transverse axis inclined at 45°
Ignition source	Bunsen burner, flame height 15 to 20 mm
Duration of flame application	30 s
Conclusion	rate of flame spread over measured length, maximum permitted rate of flame spread: 90 mm/min

Flexible plastics:		
Specimen	1 specimen 300 mm × 20 mm × usual thickness	
Specimen position	vertical	
Ignition source	benzene (C_6H_6) drop	
Conclusion	rate of burning, maximum permitted values:	
	Thickness of film [mm]	Area rate of burning [cm^2/s]
	0.1 to 0.25	$\leqq 6.0$
	0.25 to 0.5	$\leqq 3.0$
	0.5 to 1.5	$\leqq 1.5$

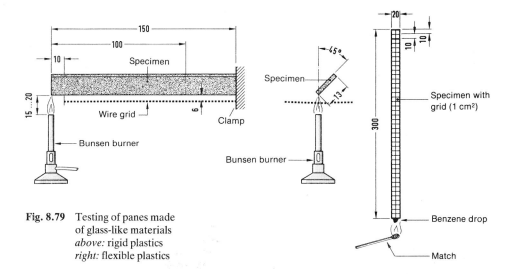

Fig. 8.79   Testing of panes made of glass-like materials
above: rigid plastics
right: flexible plastics

8.3.1.3 Future developments

The continuing development of fire safety specifications will in future be based on unification of regulations within the framework of the UN and of the European Communities. In addition, more stringent requirements are expected for bus seating and in fact public operators have already started to make demands in this direction.

Limitation of smoke and toxic gas emissions has been investigated by ECE Report Group GRSG 1978 and is not considered significant.

References for 8.3.1

[1]   Straßenverkehrs-Zulassungs-Ordnung (StVZO) as in the Announcement of 15. 11. 1974, BGBl. I, p. 3193.

[2]   United Nations agreement concerning the adoption of uniform conditions of approval and reciprocal recognition of approval for motor vehicle equipment and parts – Uniform provisions concerning the approval of vehicles with regard to the prevention of fire risks.

[3]   ECE Recommendation: Flammability of materials intended to be used inside road vehicles. Trans/SC 1/WP 29/78, Annex 4.

[4]   Innere Sicherheit im Auto – Das Unfallgeschehen und seine Folgen. Issued by: HUK Verband der Haftpflicht-, Unfall- und Kraftverkehrsversicherer e. V., Hamburg, 1975.

[5]   *E. M. Trisko:* Fire J. (1975) 3, p. 19.

[6]   *M. Danner, D. Anselm:* Der Verkehrsunfall (1977) 12, p. 229.

[7]   Title 49 – Transportation § 571.302. Standard 302: Flammability of interior materials (valid Sep. 1972). US-Federal Register Vol. 36, No. 232.

[8]   International Standard ISO 3795 (1976): Road vehicles – Determination of burning behaviour of interior materials for motor vehicles.

[9]   DIN 75200 (Sep. 1980): Bestimmung des Brennverhaltens von Werkstoffen der Kraftfahrzeuginnenausstattung.

[10] FKT-Sonderausschuß "Feuersicherheit": Richtlinien zu § 30 StVZO über die Verwendung schwerentflammbarer Werkstoffe im Kraftfahrzeugbau – April 1977.

[11] Japanese Industrial Standard JIS D 1201 – 1973: Test method for flammability of organic interior materials for automobiles.

[12] ANSI/ASTM D 2863−77: Standard method for measuring the minimum oxygen concentration to support candle-like combustion of plastics (oxygen-index).

[13] DIN 53438 Part 3 (April 1977): Prüfung von brennbaren Werkstoffen. Verhalten beim Beflammen mit einem Brenner, Flächenbeflammung.

[14] *H. Wolf, G. Stecklina:* Materialprüfung 17 (1975) 6, p. 205.

[15] *W. Becker, H. J. Bönold, M. Egresi:* Materialprüfung 17 (1975) 6, p. 203.

[16] *W. Becker, H. J. Bönold, M. Egresi:* Fire Prevention Sci. & Technol. 21 (1979) 5, p. 3.

[17] FKT-Sonderausschuß "Feuersicherheit": Untersuchungen zur Beurteilung der Gebrauchsfähigkeit von Kraftstoffbehältern aus Kunststoffen – Prüfvorschriften – April 1977.

[18] Advanced Notice of Proposed Rulemaking. Federal Motor Vehicle Safety Standards, fuel system integrity, plastic fuel tanks. Federal Register Vol. 34, No. 113, 11. 6. 1979.

[19] Technische Anforderungen an Fahrzeugteile bei der Bauartprüfung nach § 22a StVZO, 5. 7. 1973 (VkBl p. 559).

8.3.2 Rail vehicles

Decisive factors in the increased usage of plastics in railways, tramways, elevated and underground systems and modern tracked transport systems are the requirement for light-weight construction in the interests of higher payloads and for more efficient use of energy, low maintenance costs, corrosion resistance and improved comfort.

Although the high fire risk steam locomotive is largely a thing of the past, most fires still occur in traction units [1]. The main causes are excess oil and grease mixed with dirt and dust ignited by sparks from short circuits or overheated bearings, explosion of oil switches and high voltage step selectors.

Due to its high flashpoint, diesel fuel rarely ignites. Even so there are numerous potential sources of fire in diesel drive units and locomotives, one of the most frequent being fuel dripping from leaky oil pipes onto hot exhausts and rapidly moving mechanical components. Such fires are usually localised and rarely result in injuries since they are detected and fought by trained personnel at an early stage. Cleanliness and regular inspection are the most effective fire precautions in this field.

The risk of ignition by short circuits is relatively low in passenger carriages provided installations are suitably fused. The only significant fire hazards are heating and catering facilities in sleeping and dining cars operated by poorly trained staff.

Passenger-induced ignition hazards are a different matter. Matches, cigarettes, etc. care-lessly thrown away are still a common cause of fire particularly on local routes. Small apertures and slits in covers over hollow spaces, bogies, etc. are a tempting means of getting rid of glowing cigarettes and matches. Fed by draughts, rubbish, dust and paper, a smoulder-ing fire can remain undetected and only flare up after several hours. Hundreds of cigarette ends, for example, have been found in tram bogies amid heaps of grease-saturated paper and tickets and have often caused extensive fires. Arson is also increasingly frequent.

The development of a fire is often assisted by litter under seats. Wall and ceiling cladding can also contribute to rapid surface spread of fire. If such fires occur en route, they can be a major hazard to passengers particularly if they spread rapidly to adjacent compartments or carriages.

Fire risks in rail vehicles are not determined solely by design or interior materials but also by operating conditions. For example, a tram which stops every few minutes and in which passengers are under the supervision of staff represents a different level of hazard to a sleeping car in a long distance train. While the fire brigade and help can be on the spot within a few minutes in the case of inner city traffic, fires on long journeys frequently have to be fought with on-board equipment. Evacuation of carriages requires more time and is frequently made more difficult by cuttings, tunnels and viaducts.

Fire tests on exact mock-ups of train compartments and carriages have shown that small ignition sources such as glowing tobacco products or burning matches seldom result in the interior fittings catching fire [2]. In contrast, fires caused by flammable liquids spread relatively rapidly. Their spread to several compartments is favoured by continuous corridors and the low fire endurance of compartment doors and partitioning. Slipstream and ventila-tion can considerably accelerate fire propagation. Fire tests and investigations of actual fire incidents have shown, moreover, that high levels of smoke emission can occur with the fully developed fire.

8.3.2.1 Statutory regulations

Technical legal provisions for rail vehicles vary from country to country and with the type of vehicle. In addition, operators frequently stipulate that various specifications laid down in conditions of purchase must be met.

In the Federal Republic of Germany, the construction and operation of tramways, elevated and underground railways, suspension and cable cars are governed by the "Straßenbahn-Bau und Betriebsordnung" (BOStrab) (Tramway Construction and Operation Order) [3]. The "Länder" technical supervisory authorities supervise the execution and construction of operating facilities and rolling stock and issue acceptance certificates.

The Federal German Railways (DB) are responsible for the safety of their installations in accordance with § 38 of the Federal Railway Act [4]. No other authorities are involved in inspection, certification, etc.

Unification of regulations in order to meet the requirements of international rail transport, is important particularly for those countries connected by a railway network. European and Asian railway administrations are represented in the "Union Internationale des Chemins de Fer" (UIC) which is establishing the UIC Code covering regulations, recommendations and uniform conditions of supply for rail vehicles [5].

8.3.2.2 Technical fire protection requirements and tests

In the Federal Republic of Germany, the fire protection requirements for trams are based on § 30 of the Tramway Construction and Operation Order which lays down that the structure of carriages must guarantee "state of the art" protection for passengers. In particular they must consist of low flammability (schwerentflammbar) materials. This term is not defined in the order and it is left up to the Technical Inspectorate to put this requirement in concrete form. The fire protection requirements are frequently similar to those of the German Federal Railways. In other instances materials and components in rail vehicle interiors must meet US Federal Motor Vehicle Safety Standard 302 (FMVSS 302).

Table 8.125 Test specifications for materials and components in German Federal Railways' rolling stock and installations

Specimens	10 specimens: 300 mm × 100 mm × usual thickness (maximum 160 mm)
Specimen position	vertical (V-test) horizontal (H-test)
Ignition source	Bunsen burner with fishtail jet, flame temperature 950 °C inclination: V-test: 45° H-test: 65° flame applied to surface, 20 mm from end of specimen
Flame application	V-test: 3 min H-Test: 2 min if the specimens continue to burn after shutting off the burner, a further test is carried out in which the specimen is extinguished after flame application is terminated
Conclusions	Combustibility grade: B 1 to B 4 Smoke development grade: Q 1 to Q 4 "Drippability" grade: T 1 to T 4

The provisions concerning fire performance testing of materials and components for use in German Federal Railways' installations and rolling stock are given in DV 899/35 – Instruction Sheet [6] which specifies:

– Testing of fire performance if the "Institut für Bautechnik, Berlin" has not issued a test certificate proving compliance with class A (non-combustible) or B1 (low flammability) building materials as defined by DIN 4102 Part 1 [7].

- Testing of smoke development.
- Testing for flaming drops.

Fire performance and secondary fire effects are tested in the DB Brandschacht (Fig. 8.80, Table 8.125).

Evaluation of fire performance – combustibility grade

Specimens are classified into combustibility grades as shown in Table 8.126. Mouldings which differ from the prescribed dimensions are not classified but the fire performance in such cases must be described.

Table 8.126   Classification in combustibility grades

Combustibility grade	Behaviour of specimen	Burnt surface [%]
B 4 (non-combustible)	as a result of natural properties does not burst into flame, also does not char or ash	
B 3 (slightly combustible)	bursts into flame with difficulty, does not burn on its own or only hesitantly, burns and chars only with additional heat supply at a low rate	up to 75
B 2 (combustible)	when brought to ignition temperature, bursts into flame and generally burns rapidly or on its own	76 to 90
B 1 (highly combustible)	bursts into flame very easily and burns rapidly with a large flame without additional heat source	91 to 100

Evaluation of smoke development – smoke development grade

Sight obscuration during combustion is measured by a densitometer incorporated in the exhaust gas collector duct of the DB-Brandschacht. The percentage attenuation of the light source is recorded for classifying specimens in smoke development grades as shown in Table 8.127.

Table 8.127   Classification in smoke development grades

Smoke development grade	Behaviour of specimen	Permitted sight obscuration in Brandschacht [%]
Q 4	smokes very slightly	≦10
Q 3	smokes and soots moderately	11 to 40
Q 2	smokes and soots strongly	41 to 70
Q 1	smokes and soots very strongly	71 to 100

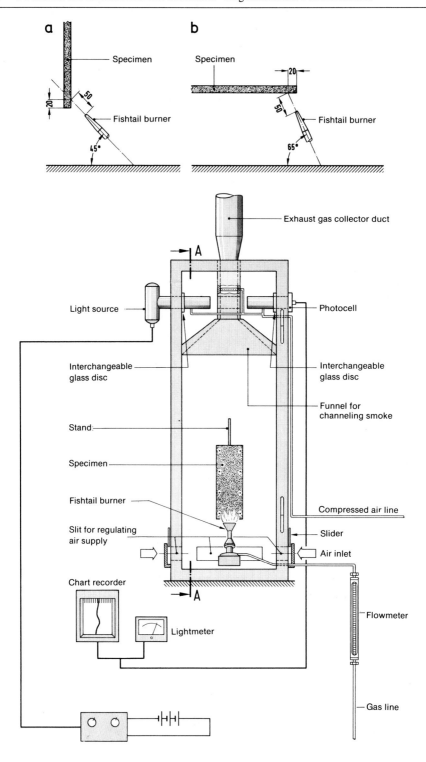

a
Specimen
20
50
Fishtail burner
45°

b
Specimen
20
50
Fishtail burner
65°

Exhaust gas collector duct
A
Light source
Photocell
Interchangeable glass disc
Interchangeable glass disc
Funnel for channeling smoke
Stand
Specimen
Fishtail burner
Compressed air line
Slit for regulating air supply
Slider
Air inlet
Chart recorder
A
Flowmeter
Lightmeter
Gas line

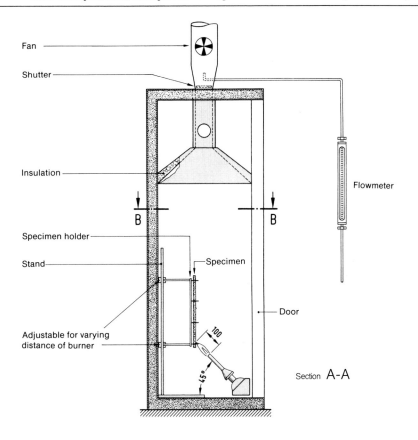

Fan

Shutter

Insulation

Flowmeter

B   B

Specimen holder

Stand   Specimen

100

Adjustable for varying
distance of burner

45°

Door

Section A-A

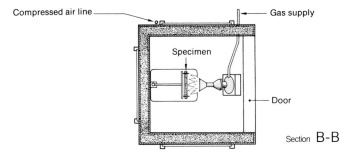

Compressed air line   Gas supply

Specimen

Door

Section B-B

Fig. 8.80   German Federal Railways' (DB) Brandschacht
        a: vertical specimen position (V-test), *b:* horizontal specimen position (H-test)

Evaluation of dripping – "drippability" grade

Distortions of the specimen during the fire test as well as the occurrence of flaming or nonflaming drops are evaluated as shown in Table 8.128.

Table 8.128   Classification in "drippability" grade

"Drippability" grade	Behaviour of specimen
T 4	does not distort or soften, no drops formed
T 3	strong distortion, softens in parts or forms drawn out threads in place of drops
T 2	non-flaming drippings
T 1	flaming drippings

Testing of seat cushions and back rests

The DB-Merkblatt (DB Instruction Sheet) specifies that comparably shaped specimens must be used in tests for seat cushions and backrests in the DB-Brandschacht. The combustibility is not classified.

Minimum Requirements

The minimum requirements for fire performance and secondary fire effects of materials and building components are laid down in the following annexes to the DB Instruction Sheet:

– Annex 1 (Anhang 1): Memorandum (Merkbuch) A for construction work [9].
– Annex 2 (Anhang 2): Memorandum B for rolling stock, tanks and containers [10].

These completely preclude the use of building materials which are highly flammable (leichtentflammbar) as defined in DIN 4102 Part 1. Furthermore, materials and building components which emit highly corrosive combustion products must not be used in operationally important structures and rooms (e.g. signal boxes, telecommunications rooms, machine rooms).

Tests are carried out in the Chemistry Department of the "Bundesbahn-Versuchsanstalt" (Federal Railways Research Institute) in Munich which issues DB Test Certificates. Application should however be made to the Bundesbahn Zentralamt (BZA) in Minden.

8.3.2.3 International fire performance tests and requirements

Instruction Sheet 564.2 VE of the UIC Code [5] contains fire prevention and fire fighting regulations for rail vehicles used on international routes. The tests and requirements recommended for passenger carriages are listed in Table 8.129.

It is also suggested that dripping, smoke development and toxicity of combustion products should be noted though no test methods are given.

The UIC instruction sheet also contains recommendations on the structural layout of passenger carriages such as the provision of steel fireproof bulkheads between ceiling and roof at maximum intervals of 11 m.

Fire performance testing of seats according to UIC instruction sheet 564.2 VE, Appendix III

The UIC provides a choice of two procedures for testing seats (Fig. 8.81). In method A, a piece of newspaper folded into the shape of a cushion is filled with crumpled paper up to a

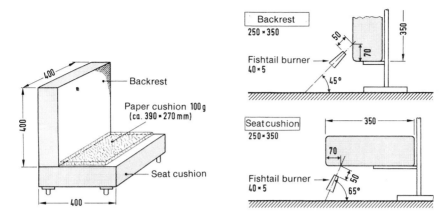

Fig. 8.81 Testing of the fire performance of seats according to UIC Instruction Sheet 564.2 VE, Appendix III
left: method A, *right:* method B

Table 8.129 Fire performance test methods suggested by the UIC

Application	Test method		Requirement
curtain material	DIN 66082	[11]	V − c
	IMCO (Flame spread)	[12]	$I \leqq 20$
	NF G 07-113	[13]	Class B
	Oxygen index	[14]	$\geqq 28$
seats	Instruction sheet 564.2 VE,		Method A
	Appendix III		Method B
laminates	DV 899/35		B 3
	ST 447	[15]	maximum of two "unsatisfactory"
			specimens
	Oxygen index		$\geqq 35$
	IMCO (Flame spread)		$I \leqq 35$
partitions	DV 899/35		B 3 (burnt area $\leqq$ 65%)
	ST 481	[16]	"satisfactory"
	IMCO (Flame spread)		$I \leqq 75$
floor coverings	ISO/DIS 6925	[17]	afterflame time $\leqq$ 5 s
			least distance of damaged
			area from reference circle $\geqq$ 80 mm
electric conductors	UIC Instruction Sheet 895 VE		conditions as per § 2.4.4.3.1
glass fibre reinforced unsaturated polyester resin moulding materials (GRP)	DV 899/35		B 3
			afterflame time <30 s
	ST 447		"satisfactory"
	Oxygen index		$\geqq 26$
	IMCO (Flame spread)		$I \leqq 60$

prescribed weight and is then set on fire. A defined pilot flame is used in method B. Both procedures are intended to simulate arson (Table 8.130).

Table 8.130   Specifications for fire performance testing of seats according to UIC Instruction Sheet 564.2 VE, Appendix III

	Method A	Method B
Specimen	complete seat with backrest or mock-up 400 mm × 400 mm	mock-up 250 mm × 350 mm backrest and seat cushion
Ignition source	100 g newspaper in shape of cushion	fishtail Bunsen burner 40 mm × 5 mm
Test duration	ignition source burns for approx. 5 min	backrest: 3 min seat cushion: 2 min
Requirements	extinction of flame in ≦ 10 min no burning drops	afterflame time ≦ 1 min no burning drops

Method A is carried out in a draught-free room while Method B should take place in an undefined combustion chamber.

Besides the internationally accepted tests mentioned here, each national railway administration uses a range of additional fire tests (Table 8.131). If no details are given in the technical conditions of supply the relevant authorities should be consulted.

Table 8.131   Other fire performance tests for rail vehicles

Country	Test method		Used for
France Requirements of the Société Nationale des Chemins de Fer (SNCF)	ST 447 ST 481 NF P 92-507	[18]	coated particle board in passenger carriages wooden parts building components, seats
Great Britain Requirements of the British Railway Board	BS 476, Part 7 BS 3424, Method 17 BR 541 A BR 602 ASTM D 1692*	[19] [20] [21] [22]	decorative wall linings coated boards upholstery GRP laminates foam plastics
USA Guidelines of the Urban Mass Transportation Administration (UMTA) [25]	ASTM E 162 FAR § 25.853(b) NBS Flooring radiant panel test NBSIR 74–495 NFPA Standard no. 258 (1974)	[23] [24]	seat covers, insulation, wall and ceiling linings cushion material carpeting smoke density measurement

* withdrawn without replacement

8.3.2.4 Future developments

The worldwide energy crisis will lead to a reduction in private traffic and to the expansion of local rapid tracked-transport systems, particularly in the industrialised countries. Due to the lack of land in congested city centres, modern transport systems will run underground or on elevated sections. Both involve higher potential risks to passengers in the event of fire. Over the last few years the number of fires caused by negligence or arson has risen considerably. The following primary objectives must be borne in mind when selecting suitable designs and materials particularly in underground systems:

- Low ignitability and flame spread for materials and composites used as surface finishes as well as seats.
- Fire propagation must be retarded by fire resistant partitions between compartments and to safeguard escape routes.
- The spread of fire to adjacent carriages or to trains standing on neighbouring tracks must be prevented.
- Escape routes must be kept free of dangerous amounts of smoke and toxic combustion gases until passengers are rescued.

These requirements are seldom taken into account by existing fire regulations. Safety concepts must consider not only possible fire precautions but also operating conditions of rolling stock. Criteria should be established in large scale and model tests and suitable uniform international test procedures developed.

References for 8.3.2

[1]   E. Oettli: Magazin für den Feuerwehrmann No. 7 (1979), p. 218.
[2]   I. Oikawa: Fire experiments of coach. Quarterly Reports Vol. 15, No. 3 (1974).
[3]   Verordnung über den Bau und Betrieb der Straßenbahnen (Straßenbahn-Bau- und -Betriebsord-nung – BOStrab) of 31. 8. 1965, BGBl I, p. 1513.
[4]   Bundesbahngesetz of 13. 12. 1951, BGBl I, p. 955.
[5]   UIC Code Vol. V – Vehicles. Union Internationale des Chemins de Fer. Secrétariat Général, Paris.
[6]   Deutsche Bundesbahn: Merkblatt für die Prüfung des Brandverhaltens fester Stoffe (valid from 1. 12. 1972). DV 899/35.
[7]   DIN 4102 Teil 1: Brandverhalten von Baustoffen und Bauteilen – Baustoffe. Begriffe, Anfor-derungen und Prüfungen. May 1981.
[8]   TL 918433 (Draft) June 1980: Anforderungen an das Brennverhalten von Werkstoffen – Zulas-sungsbedingungen. Technische Lieferbedingungen.
[9]   Deutsche Bundesbahn: Merkbuch A für Bauwerke (valid from 1. 12. 1972). DV 899/35/I.
[10] Deutsche Bundesbahn: Merkbuch B für Fahrzeuge, Behälter und Container (valid from 1. 12. 1972). DV 899/35/II.
[11] DIN 66082 (December 1980): Kennwerte für das Brandverhalten textiler Erzeugnisse.
[12] DDR-Schiffs-Revision und Klassifikation (DSRK) Part IV. Brandschutz. 1975.
[13] NF G 07-113 (December 1978): Textiles, Comportement au feu. Méthode de classement en fonction de la surface brûlée.
[14] ASTM – D 2863 (1977): Flammability of plastics using the oxygen index method.
[15] ST 447 (March 1980): Spécification technique pour la fourniture de panneaux stratifiés, à surface décorée, à base de matières plastiques thermodurcissables.
[16] ST 481 (May 1975): Spécification technique pour la fourniture de bois ignifugés pour matériel roulant.

[17] International Standard ISO/DIS 6925: Textile floor coverings – Burning behaviour – Tablet test at ambient temperature.
[18] NF P 92-507 (October 1975): Classement des matériaux utilisés dans la construction.
[19] BS 476: Part 7 (1971): Fire tests on building materials and structures – Surface spread of flame tests for materials.
[20] BS 3424, Method 17 (1973): Methods of test for coated fabrics.
[21] BR: British Railway Standards – British Railway Board.
[22] ASTM D 1692 (1978): Rate of burning or extent of burning of cellular plastics using a supported specimen by a horizontal screen (Standard withdrawn without replacement).
[23] ASTM E 162 (1978): Surface flammability of materials using a radiant heat energy source.
[24] Federal Aviation Regulations Part 25, § 25.853, Amendment 25–32 (May 1972).
[25] National Materials Advisory Board: Fire safety aspects of polymeric materials. Vol 8. Land transportation vehicles. Technomic Publ. Co., Inc., Westport, 1980.

8.3.3 Aircraft

A modern wide-bodied jet such as the Boeing 747 contains some 4,000 kg of plastics. Approximately 2,000 kg of this are used in structural applications, mainly in the form of glass reinforced types, and as much again in compartments occupied by passengers and crew [1]. In addition, up to 8,600 kg of combustible materials including maintenance materials, provisions and hand baggage are stored in the cabins. To this must be added some 39,000 kg of freight, usually in metal containers and approximately 30,000 kg of fuel in wing and fuselage tanks [2].

A survey of transport aircraft accidents [3] indicated that between 1955 and 1974 53,000 persons were involved, including some 11,000 fatalities, 2,650 of which were caused by fire. Approximately 75% of accidents occur on the runway or within a radius of 3,000 m of the airport. By far the largest number of fatalities occur as a consequence of crash landings in this area, i.e. when planes land short of or overshoot the runway on take-off.

Large quantities of fuel are frequently released during crashes and are ignited by short circuits or heat. Such fires can develop fully within 1 to 3 min and because of the low fire endurance of the aircraft fuselage, occupants have only a few minutes in which to escape.

Fires during flight occur mainly in the galleys as a result of electrical faults or overheating. It is noteworthy that smokers materials are a frequent cause of cabin fires. Other commonly cited causes include faults in the electrical and oxygen supply systems [4].

Fires started by small ignition sources in the cockpit or cabin can generally be successfully tackled with on-board equipment. Exceptions include fires which develop unnoticed in inaccessible compartments or toilets. In 1973, for example, a fire in a toilet in an aircraft at Paris-Orly resulted in the death of 119 passengers.

Fires also occur in aircraft while on the ground, mainly during maintenance work on the electrical and oxygen supply systems. Such incidents usually do not result in casualties and can, as a rule, be brought under control relatively easily.

Technical fire requirements for materials used in aircraft can therefore only make a limited contribution to risk reduction.

In view of the frequency of fires occurring on impact, much attention should be devoted to fuel storage. Mechanically resistant fuel tanks with foam fillings as well as modification of the physical properties of the fuel can limit the formation of ignitable fuel-air mixtures and the spillage of combustible liquids to a certain extent. The US Army has achieved considerable success in this respect. High strength fuel tanks with self-sealing connections (dry breakaway fuel fittings) have been used for years in helicopters and have led to a significant reduction in the incidence of fire following impact.

In fires passengers should be protected for as long as possible from heat, smoke and toxic gases by suitable measures such as division into fire compartments and the use of fire resistant partitions in front of concealed fuselage areas and spaces where a high fire risk exists. These measures should be supplemented by fire alarm systems and effective automatic extinguishing equipment.

The ignitability, combustibility and secondary fire effects of materials, fire endurance of structural components and measures for detecting and fighting on-board fires are regrettably often considered as separate problems. The only effective way of reducing fire risk, particularly in air transport, appears to be the introduction of safety systems which take adequate account of all aspects of fire protection. Large scale fire tests under operating conditions are a prerequisite for more effective fire regulations in aviation. They must take into account the types of accident which pose a particular hazard for occupants. The majority of tests involve small ignition sources simulating the start of a fire during flight. As a rule they do not enable any predictions to be made on the behaviour of structures exposed to large ignition sources.

8.3.3.1 Statutory regulations

Besides specifications agreed for operational reasons between manufacturers and purchasers of aircraft, aeroplanes and the materials used in their construction must comply with national and international regulations. Compliance is monitored by the national air transport authority of the country in which the aircraft is registered. Most countries have adopted wholly or in part the Federal Aviation Regulations (FAR) [6] of the US Federal Aviation Administration (FAA), as the basis for ensuring airworthiness. From time to time the Regulations are amended to reflect the latest technical developments. The FAA is advised by experts from the US Aerospace Industries Association (AIA), the US Air Transport Association (ATA), the International Civil Aviation Organization (ICAO) and the International Air Transport Association (IATA).

The following FAR regulations apply in the Federal Republic of Germany until further notice [5]:

FAR Part 23 – Airworthiness Standards: Normal, utility and acrobatic category airplanes

FAR Part 25 – Airworthiness Standards: Transport category airplanes

FAR Part 27 – Airworthiness Standards: Normal category rotorcraft

FAR Part 29 – Airworthiness Standards: Transport category rotorcraft

FAR Part 33 – Airworthiness Standards: Aircraft engines

The regulations cover the airworthiness tests required for type approval by the "Luftfahrt-Bundesamt Braunschweig" which grants a "Verkehrszulassung" (traffic permit) and issues an airworthiness certificate.

8.3.3.2 Technical fire protection requirements and tests

The terminology of technical fire protection is defined in FAR Part 1. It should be noted however that the terms employed, such as "fire-proof", "fire resistant", "self-extinguishing" and "flash resistant" often have different meanings in other standards and regulations, a situation which can cause confusion.

The methods used to test the materials and components in the cabins and holds of transport aircraft are described in Appendix F of FAR, Part 25. They are based to some extent on US Federal Test Method Standard No. 191 [7, 8].

The requirements for military aircraft are largely similar. In the Federal Republic of Germany they are covered by Airworthiness Regulation LTV 1500-850 [9] which makes considerable use of test rigs laid down in German Standards (DIN).

Airline and manufacturers' specifications which contain fire performance requirements based mainly on those of the FAR must also be complied with. They often contain, however, additional requirements particularly relating to smoke emission and toxicity of combustion products.

Requirements for materials and parts used in crew and passenger compartments in transport aircraft are given in FAR § 25.853. They also apply to other aircraft where appropriate.

The test procedures for proving compliance with the requirements are given in Appendix F to FAR Part 25. These tests are generally carried out on test specimens taken from or simulating the components used. Composites must be tested as such.

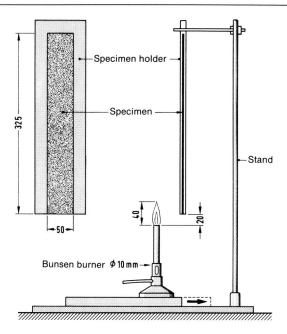

Fig. 8.82   FAR Part 25 testing in a vertical position

Vertical test

The test for demonstrating that materials are "self-extinguishing" is illustrated schematically in Fig. 8.82. The test specifications and requirements are summarised in Table 8.132. The test is carried out in a draught-free cabinet according to Federal Test Method Standard 191, Method 5903.2. The mean of three results is obtained.

Table 8.132   FAR Part 25 specifications for vertical test

Specimens	3 specimens, exposed surface 50 mm × 325 mm thickness: ≦ minimum thickness in use		
Specimen position	vertical		
Ignition source	Bunsen or Tirrill burner, 10 mm diameter, 843 °C 40 mm flame height		
		Class (a):	*Class (b):*
Flame application		60 s	12 s
Requirements	burn length	≦ 150 mm (6 in)	≦ 200 mm (8 in)
	afterflame time	≦ 15 s	≦ 15 s
	flame time of drippings	≦ 3 s	≦ 5 s

Horizontal test

Components are tested in a horizontal position when proof must be obtained that a maximum permitted rate of flame spread is not exceeded (Fig. 8.83 and Table 8.133). The test is carried out in a draught-free cabinet according to Federal Test Method Standard 191, Method 5906. The mean of three measurements is evaluated.

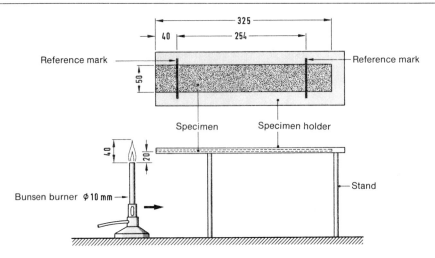

Fig. 8.83   FAR Part 25 testing in a horizontal position

Table 8.133   FAR Part 25 specifications for horizontal test

Specimens	3 specimens, exposed surface 50 mm × 325 mm thickness: ≦ minimum thickness in use reference marks: 40 mm and 294 mm
Specimen position	horizontal
Ignition source	Bunsen or Tirrill burner, 10 mm diameter, 843 °C 40 mm flame height
Flame application	15 s
Test distance	254 mm (10 in), 40 mm (1.5 in) of the specimen should burn before the timing device is started
Requirements	

	Class (b−2):	Class (b−3):
maximum permitted rate of flame spread	62.5 mm/min (2.5 in/min)	100 mm/min (4 in/min)

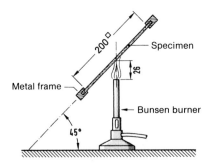

Fig. 8.84   FAR Part 25 testing at 45°

Forty five degree test

Certain parts used in cargo and baggage compartments (FAR § 25.855) must be tested at an inclination of 45° (Fig. 8.84 and Table 8.134) as well as vertically. The test is carried out in a draught-free cabinet and the mean of three measurements evaluated.

Table 8.134   FAR Part 25 specifications for forty five degree test

Specimens	3 specimens, exposed surface 200 mm × 200 mm thickness: ≦ minimum thickness in use
Specimen position	at 45° to horizontal
Ignition source	Bunsen or Tirrill burner, 10 mm diameter, 843 °C 40 mm flame height
Flame application	30 s
Requirements	no penetration of specimen
	afterflame time ≦ 15 s
	glow time ≦ 10 s

Sixty degree test

Insulation, electric conductors and cables must be "self-extinguishing". The test is illustrated in Fig. 8.85 and the test specifications and requirements are summarised in Table 8.135. The test is carried out in a combustion cabinet according to Federal Test Method Standard 191 (with the cabinet door open) or in a test chamber approximately 300 mm × 300 mm × 600 mm high with open top and side.

Table 8.135   FAR Part 25 specifications for sixty degree test

Specimens	3 specimens stretched taut, exposed length 610 mm
Specimen position	inclined at 60° to horizontal
Ignition source	Bunsen or Tirrill burner, 10 mm diameter, 955 °C, inclined at 30° to horizontal, 75 mm flame height
Flame application	30 s
Requirements	burn length ≦ 76 mm (3 in)
	afterflame time ≦ 30 s
	flaming time of drippings ≦ 3 s

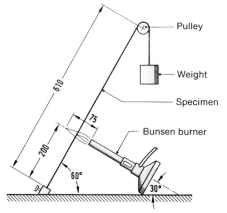

Fig. 8.85
FAR Part 25 testing at 60°

"Fireproof" and "fire resistant" tests

Main flight controls, engine assemblies and other parts of the airframe which lie in fire risk zones or adjacent areas as well as fire bulkheads, claddings and shielding subject to heat must be made of fireproof materials or be fire resistant. The terms are defined in FAR Part 1 as follows:

– "Fireproof"

with respect to materials and parts used to confine fire in a designated fire zone means the capacity to withstand at least as well as steel in dimensions appropriate for the purpose for which they are used, the heat produced when there is a severe fire of extended duration in that zone.

– "Fire resistant"

a) with respect to sheet or structural members means the capacity to withstand the heat associated with fire at least as well as aluminium alloys in dimensions appropriate for the purpose for which they are used.

b) with respect to fluid-carrying lines, fluid system parts, wiring, air ducts, fittings and powerplant controls means the capacity to perform the intended functions under the heat and other conditions likely to occur when there is a fire at the place concerned.

Table 8.136   FAR Part 23 "fireproof" and "fire resistant" test specifications

Specimens	250 mm × 250 mm for flat specimens or 5 × outside diameter for hoses
Specimen position	horizontal
Ignition source	burner applied to specimen over an area of approx. 125 mm × 125 mm, temperature 1093 °C ± 28 °C, with hose pipes, the flame must be approx. as wide as the outside diameter of the hose
Flame application	*"fireproof"*: 15 min *"fire resistant"*: 5 min
Requirement	tested part must be in working condition after test

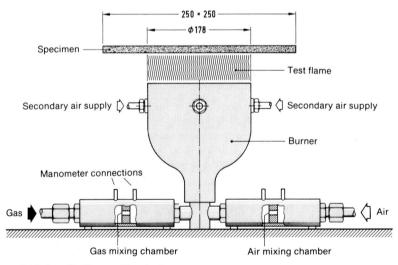

Fig. 8.86   FAR Part 23 "fireproof" and "fire resistant" tests

The basis of the fireproof and fire resistant test is described in FAR § 23.1191 (fire bulkheads). Further details particularly as regards test rigs are not given. The layout is illustrated in Fig. 8.86 and the test specifications and requirements are summarised in Table 8.136.

Certain mandatory fire equipment is tested by ad-hoc methods as well as by the methods described above. This applies particularly to the effectiveness against smoke of bulkheads between passenger and crew compartments and cargo and baggage compartments as well as to smoke detectors, fire alarms and automatic extinguishers.

Smoke density and toxicity of thermal decomposition products

Various FAA proposals and drafts in the last few years have been devoted to requirements and test procedures relating to smoke emission and toxicity (Notice of Proposed Rule Making [NPRM] No. 74−38, 75−3) [10, 11].

At a public hearing on materials for aircraft interiors in November 1977 in Washington, it was emphasised that smoke density and toxicity should not be dealt with as separate problems. A higher level of safety can be achieved only if new safety standards include more stringent requirements for fuel systems and flight safety equipment as well as on the fire performance of materials and on their secondary fire effects.

The NPRMs mentioned above were withdrawn in August 1978 [12].

8.3.3.3 Technical fire requirements in the conditions of supply of the aviation industry – additional requirements relating to smoke density and toxicity of combustion products

Technical fire requirements are also included in the material specifications of the airlines or aircraft manufacturers. As a rule they correspond to those of FAR. Compliance must be demonstrated with the same or similar test methods and equipment. The relevant test conditions of Lufthansa Specification 25-00.2-01 [13] are summarised in Table 8.137.

Additional requirements are often specified or evidence from standard or modified tests is required in order to evaluate secondary fire effects. Airbus Industrie, for example, specifies an additional test for smoke density and toxicity of combustion products for materials used in all A 300 models [14]. The basic layout of the test chamber used for this corresponds to the Aminco NBS smoke chamber. In contrast to NBS Technical Note No. 708, Appendix II, the specific optical density Ds is determined at 90 s and 4 min and, in the case of electrical wiring, within 20 min. For parts in the pressurised area of the fuselage the following limiting values should not be exceeded:

– Ds 100 within 4 min for textiles, air ducts, insulation and coverings.
– Ds 100 within 90 s of the start of the test, and
– Ds 200 between 90 s and 4 min for interior ceiling and wall panels, window reveals, partitions, cabin walls, luggage lockers, seat cushions, carpets and elastomeric and thermoplastic components.
– Ds 15 within 20 min for all electrical wire and cable insulations.

The toxicity of all parts used in the pressurised area of the fuselage must be tested with the NBS smoke chamber equipped with three gas sampling probes. These pass through the top of the chamber and reach half way down the smoke chamber (Fig. 8.87).

The samples required for determining toxicity should be taken at the same time as the smoke density is measured. "Dräger Tubes" are used for analysis. Analysis for hydrogen chloride (HCl) and hydrogen fluoride (HF) is made directly during the test and other toxic

Table 8.137 Fire performance test conditions for aircraft interior materials according to Deutsche Lufthansa specifications

Requirement class	Specimen[1] size [mm] / position	Flame exposure time [s]	Flame temperature [°C] / height [mm]	Afterflame time [s]	Burning time of drippings [s]	Evaluation Burn length [mm]	Burn rate [mm/min]	Afterglow time [s]
Fire resistant FIR I	318 × 375 / 45°	30	843 / 38	≦ 15	–	no penetration	–	≦ 10
Fire resistant FIR 2	318 × 375 / 45°	30	843 / 38	≦ 15	–	no penetration	–	≦ 10
	368 × 76 / vertical	12	843 / 38	≦ 15	≦ 5	≦ 203	–	–
Self-extinguishing SE 1	368 × 76 / vertical	60	843 / 38	≦ 15	≦ 3	≦ 152	–	–
Self-extinguishing SE 2	368 × 76 / vertical	12	843 / 38	≦ 15	≦ 5	≦ 203	–	–
Self-extinguishing SE 3	914 long / 60°	30	954 / 76	≦ 30	≦ 3	≦ 76	–	–
Flame resistant FLR 1	356 × 102 / horizontal	15	843 / 38	–	–	–	≦ 63	–
Flame resistant FLR 2	356 × 102 / horizontal	15	843 / 38	–	–	–	≦ 102	–

–: not evaluated
[1] Specimen thickness ≦ usual thickness

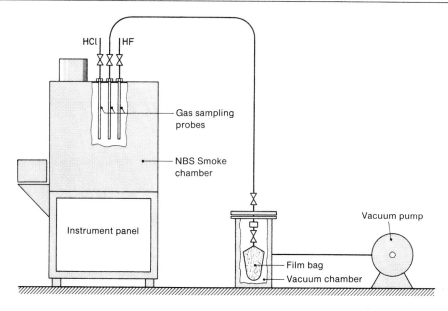

Fig. 8.87   Airbus Industrie material test specification: Analytical measurement of toxicity with the NBS smoke chamber

components are determined from a gas sample taken from a film bag filled with the help of a vacuum pump during the test. Analysis of thermal decomposition products resulting from flaming and non-flaming conditions is carried out. Samples taken at a given time should not exceed the concentrations summarised in Table 8.138.

Table 8.138   Limiting values of toxic smoke gas components as specified in Airbus Industrie material test specification

Smoke gas components		Maximum concentration after	
		1.5 min [ppm]	4 min [ppm]
Hydrogen fluoride	(HF)	30	30
Hydrogen chloride	(HCl)	50	500
Hydrogen cyanide	(HCN)	100	150
Sulphur dioxide	(SO$_2$)	50	100
Carbon monoxide	(CO)	3000	3500
Nitrous gases	(NO + NO$_2$)	50	100

8.3.3.4 Future developments

The efforts of the air traffic authorities to establish comprehensive technical fire requirements for transport aircraft received considerable impetus as a result of the mysterious airplane catastrophe in Riyadh in 1980 when 301 people burnt to death after a Saudi-Arabian Lockheed L 1011 Tristar made a successful emergency landing. Large scale tests being carried out in the USA are intended to assess all the components influencing the fire performance of aircraft. Although evaluation of the tests will take some time, they should result in comprehensive safety requirements which will include far-reaching structural measures for fire protection and increased fire performance requirements of materials. These requirements will be issued by the FAA initially as a Notice of Proposed Rule Making in the US Federal Register and will doubtless be adopted by air traffic authorities in other countries.

References for 8.3.3

[1] *E. F. Schiantarelli:* Kunststoffe im Flugzeugbau. Gottlieb Duttweiler Institut. Monatszeitschrift (1971) 5, p. 43.
[2] Flugzeuge und Brände. NFPA-Seminar Geneva. Fire International Dec. 1976, p. 18.
[3] *Taylor:* Fire fuel and survival. A study of transport aircraft accidents 1955–1974. AGARD Conference Proceeding No. 166, Rome, 1975.
[4] National Materials Advisory Board: Fire safety aspects of polymeric materials. Vol. 6. Aircraft: Civil and military. Technomic Publ. Co., Inc., Westport, 1977.
[5] Bundesanzeiger No. 90, 14. May 1965 and NFL B 75/65.
[6] Federal Aviation Regulation (FAR). Airworthiness Standards. Department of Transportation, Federal Aviation Administration.
[7] Federal Test Method, Standard No. 191: Flame resistance of cloth, vertical. Method 5903.2, 9. 7. 1971.
[8] Federal Test Method, Standard No. 191: Burning rate of cloth, horizontal. Method 5906, 31. 12. 1968.
[9] LTV 1500-850. Luftfahrt-Tauglichkeits-Vorschrift: Brandverhalten von Luftfahrt-Werkstoffen. Bundesamt für Wehrtechnik und Beschaffung, January 1974.
[10] Advanced Notice of Proposed Rulemaking No. 74–38, 39 FR 450 44, 30. 12. 1974.
[11] Notice of Proposed Rulemaking No. 75–3, 40 FR 6508, 12. 2. 1975.
[12] Withdrawal of Proposed Rulemaking, 43 FR 37703, 24. 8. 1978.
[13] Material Specification 25-00.2-01: Requirements for flammability and fire containment testing of aircraft cabin interior equipment and materials. Deutsche Lufthansa, Hamburg, 1. 2. 1979.
[14] Airbus Industrie: Material Test Specification No. ATS-1000.001, 1979.

8.3.4 Ships

During the 1977 West European Conference on Marine Technology (WEMT) in London, 8 papers out of 16 on "Safety at Sea" were devoted entirely to fires on board ship. This clearly demonstrates the continuing topicality, despite far reaching safety measures, of fire protection on ships. The number of total losses of sea going vessels due to fire or explosion has scarcely diminished over the last 25 years although strict safety regulations allow little scope for the use of combustible materials in ships.

The use of plastics on ships which conform to the International Convention for the Safety of Life at Sea is limited largely to furniture, decor, claddings, substructures, ceilings and to insulation in loading, post and baggage compartments. Insulation of cold storage on freighters and of tanks on gas tankers is, however, still a major application of foam plastics since these materials are easy to manipulate, can be worked by modern processes and, in the case of closed cell structures, absorb little moisture.

Glass fibre reinforced unsaturated polyester moulding materials (GRP) are frequently used in canal and leisure craft, small fishing and special purpose vessels. Their resistance to corrosion and weathering, low maintenance costs and easy handling make them superior in many ways to traditional materials such as wood and steel. This is particularly true if the high cost of moulds and slipways can be offset against large production runs. Thermoplastics as well as thermosets are used in the manufacture of small sports and leisure craft.

Every year in Hamburg harbour, some 50 to 70 fires occur on all types of craft including 20 to 30 sea going vessels [1]. Excluding fires during building and repair which frequently result from inadequate safety precautions, one of the most common causes is careless handling of smokers materials, etc. in ship's living quarters. In the experience of the Hamburg Fire Brigade it is almost impossible to bring such fires rapidly under control unless they are extinguished in the initial phase. The following reasons are given [1]:

– Ships cabins generally have relatively low ceilings and are of small volume for economic and design reasons.
– Compared to houses the fire load density is high because personal possessions such as clothing and linen are kept in a relatively small space together with cupboards and beds.
– Only outside cabins have windows and these are frequently small.
– Corridors are usually low and narrow and false ceilings conceal service lines of all kinds.

The rapid spread of the initiating fire is considered to be caused particularly by the low ceiling height. If flames penetrate the corridor the fire can spread rapidly due to long flame tips. Increasing levels of smoke occur at the same time. The spread of smoke and fire is favoured by their natural tendency to rise and by mechanical ventilation and air conditioning installations. In this respect the development of a ship fire is comparable to that in a building.

Fire fighting is facilitated by the presence of trained personnel but may be hindered by structural features. As a result much store is set on automatic fire alarm and extinguisher systems particularly in sea going vessels complemented by display systems on the bridge and by automatic and manual remote controlled bulkhead doors. The bulkheads must remain sealed against smoke and fire for a sufficient time even when subjected to high temperatures.

8.3.4.1 Statutory regulations

Most states apply the 1974 International Convention for the Safety of Life at Sea (SOLAS) [2] to sea going vessels on voyages to foreign countries. The Convention achieved legal status in the Federal Republic of Germany at the beginning of 1979 [3]. The Appendix to the

Convention contains safety regulations for the construction and operation of sea going vessels.

The International Convention permits additional national regulations, for example in the Federal Republic of Germany the "Schiffssicherheitsverordnung" (SSV) (Ship Safety Order) [4] also applies. Part A of the SSV contains regulations common to both; additional regulations for ships covered by SOLAS 1974 and regulations for certain ships outside the scope of SOLAS are given in parts B and C, respectively.

International rules for fishing vessels over 24 m in length are the subject of the Torremolinos International Convention [5] which has still not been universally ratified.

Besides various other IMCO recommendations and codes, the provisions of the ships' classification bodies and national safety regulations must also be complied with.

In the Federal Republic of Germany sea going vessels fall under the "Bundesverkehrsministerium, Abteilung Seeverkehr", Hamburg (Federal Ministry of Transport, Shipping Division). The "Deutsches Hydrographisches Institut" (German Hydrographic Institute) and the "See-Berufsgenossenschaft" (SBG) Hamburg are responsible for implementing the International Convention and the SSV. The latter organisation relies on Germanic Lloyd to deal with technical problems and inspection abroad.

The area of validity of inland navigation regulations is frequently dependent on the individual waterway. As a rule, requirements are adopted or mutually recognised by the riparian states. The technical requirements for ships navigating the Federal Rhine Waterway are subject to the "Rheinschiffs-Untersuchungsordnung" (RheinSch UO) which came into force on 26 March 1976 [6]. According to this regulation, testing of inland shipping is carried out by Schiffsuntersuchungskommissionen (shipping commissions) at the "Länder" shipping authorities. These commissions issue test certificates. Certificates from other Rhine riparian states or Belgium are recognised.

Inland ships which are registered with one of the classification bodies must also comply with its provisions.

8.3.4.2 Technical fire protection requirements

Sea going vessels

Technical fire requirements are contained in Chapter II-2 of SOLAS 1974, which lays down that hulls and superstructures must be divided into main vertical zones by divisions (class "A"). Other divisions (classes "B" and "C") are intended for protecting certain areas of the vessel. Divisions should adequately delay the spread of a fire. The materials used and the fire endurance of the divisions are subject to certain requirements including protection against smoke and flames. Furthermore, the side of the structural element away from the fire must not become dangerously hot for a defined fire exposure. Endurance is indicated in the type designation (Table 8.139).

Hatches and doors in divisions must provide the same level of fire safety and prevent the passage of smoke and flames as effectively as the divisions in which they are incorporated.

The minimum requirements for elements of construction are determined by the purpose and layout of the holds. They are summarised in tables in SOLAS 1974.

According to the definition in SOLAS Chapter II-2 Regulation 3, non-combustible materials should not ignite or evolve combustible gases when heated to 750 °C. All other materials are deemed "combustible" and their use is restricted by additional regulations particularly in living quarters and working areas. Exposed surfaces, in corridors and stairwells, for example, must exhibit "low fire spread characteristic" and the primary deck coverings in living quarters, control stations, stairs and corridors must be made of "not readily ignitable" materials.

Table 8.139 SOLAS 1974 requirements for divisions on sea vessels

Division class	Material	Component requirement
A (Bulkheads, decks)	steel or equivalent material and non-combustible insulation	1. Protection against smoke and fire penetration: 2. Permitted temperature rise: 1 h average $\leqq$ 139 K maximum $\leqq$ 180 K for class "A 60" in 60 min for class "A 30" in 30 min for class "A 15" in 15 min for class "A 0" in 0 min
B (Bulkheads, decks, claddings, panelling)	non-combustible materials	1. Protection against flame penetration: 2. Permitted temperature rise: ½ h average $\leqq$ 139 K maximum $\leqq$ 225 K for class "B 15" in 15 min for class "B 0" in 0 min
	non-combustible and combustible materials	1. Protection against flame penetration: 2. Permitted temperature rise: ½ h average $\leqq$ 139 K maximum $\leqq$ 225 K for class "B 30" in 30 min
C	non-combustible materials	No further requirements

The test methods for "low fire spread characteristic" and "not readily ignitable" materials differ from country to country and only limited mutual recognition exists.

Fishing vessels

Three design concepts are permitted (Table 8.140) for fishing vessels over 55 m in length which are subject to the Torremolinos International Convention [5].

Table 8.140   Construction methods for fishing vessels according to the Torremolinos International Convention

Method	Requirements	
	internal bulkheads	fire alarm and extinguisher systems
I F	non-combustible materials class "B" or "C" divisions	not required
II F	no requirements	automatic fire indicator and extinguisher systems
III F	for living quarters <50 m²: no requirements for living quarters >50 m²: sections with class "A" and "B" divisions	automatic alarm and indicator systems

Non-combustible materials are prescribed for enclosing bulkheads for engine rooms, control stations and for protecting stairs and corridors for all three methods.

Structures made of combustible materials such as wood and GRP are permitted for fishing vessels up to 55 m in length. However, surface finishes of glass fibre reinforced plastics in living quarters and working areas, control stations and engine rooms must be manufactured with permitted fire retardant resins or be protected with permitted fire protection coatings or non-combustible materials.

The fire endurance of decks and bulkheads must be substantiated by the Normal Fire Test [7]. IMCO Resolution A.270 [8] and IMCO Guidelines A.166 [9] and A.214 [10] apply to the requirements "non-combustible", "low flame spread characteristic" and "not readily ignitable".

The Torremolinos International Convention also points out the hazards of smoke and toxic combustion products [11]; however, no test procedure is given.

Inland ships

According to the "Rheinschiffs-Untersuchungsordnung" only passenger ships are subject to technical fire requirements on the Federal Waterways [6]. In this case, divisions and doors between corridors and cabins and between cabins must be fire retardant (feuerhemmend) and spaces above ceilings and behind wall panelling must be blanked off at least every 10 m by fire resistant structural components. No special demands are made on the fire performance of deck and steering rooms or on the "non-combustibility" or on the characteristic "not readily ignitable" of the insulating materials used in them.

Sports boats

The only technical provisions in the Federal Republic of Germany governing the use of plastics in sports and leisure craft are contained in classification regulations. According to these, the Germanic Lloyd reserves the right to insist on "self-extinguishing" behaviour for GRP laminates used in certain components in yachts. No test procedure is given for this property [12].

The European Communities are concerned with guidelines for water craft as part of their efforts to eliminate technical trade barriers. The "Sicherheit der Sportboote" (Sports boat Safety) Working Group of the "Schiffsbautechnische Gesellschaft" (STG) (Technical Ship-building Association) also deals with fire protection of sports craft. The outcome of discussions in this committee will determine whether additional fire safety regulations for sports and leisure craft will be drafted and passed by the Federal Minister of Transport.

Yachts with paid crews or paying passengers are treated by the SSV as passenger vessels or special craft, and are subject to the relevant technical fire requirements.

Rescue equipment

SOLAS 1974 does not prescribe fire protection tests for rescue equipment such as life boats, life rafts, life belts and vests. Special directives imposed by the authorities often apply to mandatory rescue equipment and these take into account particular conditions of use.

Enclosed GRP lifeboat for tankers, for example, have been subjected for approximately 10 min to the effects of an open liquid fire [13] while the outer skin was wetted by water spray equipment. The test led to the conclusion that GRP life boats can provide sufficient protection to the crew against flames, heat and smoke in an oil fire and they thus conform to the relevant IMCO recommendation.

Life jackets are covered by the test and registration conditions of the "See-Berufsgenossenschaft" [14].

8.3.4.3 Technical fire tests

Fire test procedures for divisions – IMCO Resolution A.163 (ES IV)

Class "A", "B" and "F" divisions with prescribed fire endurance as well as bulkheads and doors in divisions are tested according to IMCO Resolution A. 163 (ES IV) [7] which specifies heating a furnace chamber in a defined manner with a gas or oil burner. The test component is built into an opening in the furnace chamber. The principle of the test for vertical divisions is illustrated in Fig. 8.88 and the test specifications and requirements are summarised in Table 8.141.

Table 8.141   IMCO Resolution A.163 (ES IV) fire test procedures for divisions

Specimen	size: at least 4.65 m² length of side: one side at least 2.44 m (including joints and door frames)
Specimen position	bulkheads and doors vertical, decks horizontal
Ignition source	gas or oil heated furnace chamber, temperature profile conforms to IMCO standard time/temperature curve (Fig. 8.89)
Flame application	class "A" divisions: 60 min class "B" divisions: 30 min class "F" divisions: 30 min
Conclusions	1) detection of flammable gases with swab 25 mm away over a period of 30 s 2) measurement of temperature rise with thermocouples on surface (see Table 8.139)

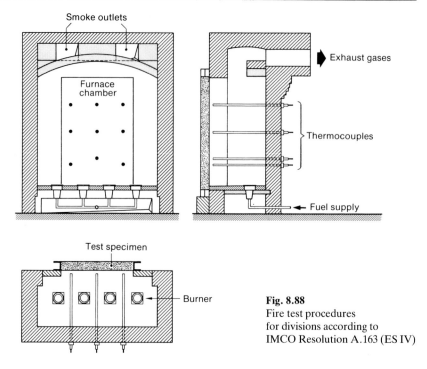

Fig. 8.88
Fire test procedures
for divisions according to
IMCO Resolution A.163 (ES IV)

The temperature in the furnace chamber is measured with thermocouples. The test rigs for decks are similar in concept but the test specimen is built horizontally into the upper part and the furnace chamber heated via the side walls.

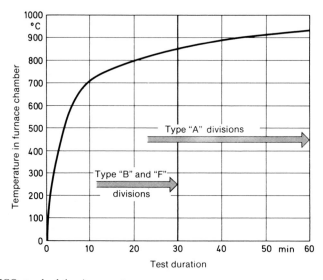

Fig. 8.89   IMCO standard time/temperature curve

Test for qualifying materials as "non-combustible" – IMCO Resolution A.270 (VIII)

Materials and components which must be proved non-combustible are tested according to IMCO Resolution A.270 VIII [8].

The test and evaluation are similar to those of ISO/DIS 1182.2 (see Section 8.2.18.2). The test specimen is introduced into a vertical cylindrical furnace chamber at 750 °C. The temperature in the furnace chamber and on the specimen surface are measured. A further thermocouple is located in the centre of the specimen (Fig. 8.90). The test specifications and requirements are contained in Table 8.142.

Table 8.142   IMCO Resolution A.270 (VIII) non-combustibility test specifications

Specimens	diameter 45 mm, height 50 mm, volume 80 cm^3
Specimen position	vertical, along axis of furnace chamber
Ignition source	electric furnace heated to 750 °C
Test duration	20 min
Conclusions	test passed if:
	temperature rise on furnace thermocouple $\leqq$ 50 K
	temperature rise on surface thermocouple $\leqq$ 50 K
	continuous burning time $\leqq$ 10 s
	average weight loss $\leqq$ 50%

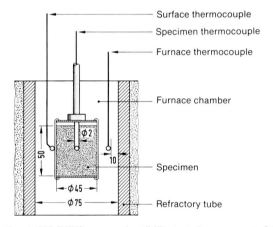

Fig. 8.90   IMCO Resolution A.270 (VIII) non-combustibility test. Arrangement of thermocouples

Test for "low flame spread characteristic" – IMCO Resolution A.166 (ES IV)

For substantiating "low flame spread characteristic", IMCO Resolution A.166 (ES IV) refers to national test methods for determining spread of flame on building components [9]. Smoke development must also be evaluated.

In the Federal Republic of Germany, use is made of the "Brandkanal" (fire tunnel) technique intended to reproduce approximately on a reduced scale the actual situation in ships' corridors (Fig. 8.91). The test is carried out by the Hamburg Building Materials Test Station.

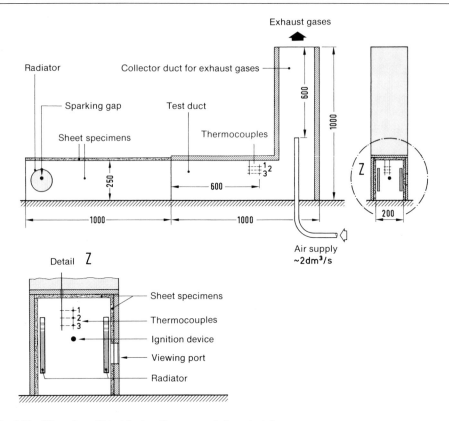

Fig. 8.91   "Brandkanal" test for low flame spread characteristic

The specimens are arranged as part of the test duct like a tunnel with their external surface facing inwards. Specimens less than 10 mm thick, paints and coatings are tested on non-combustible carrier plates, e.g. of asbestos cement (Table 8.143). The test run with the worst result is evaluated.

Table 8.143   SBG "Brandkanal" test specifications

Specimens	3 specimens 1000 mm × 250 mm × usual thickness (if necessary on non-combustible carrier plate)
Specimen position	one specimen horizontal, two specimens vertical in the form of a tunnel
Ignition source	2 quartz radiators each rated at 1 kW, 1 cm from the surface of the vertical specimens
Test duration	10 min
Conclusions	test passed if:
	residual length $\geqq$ 150 mm
	exhaust gas temperature $\leqq$ 200 °C
	ignition, burning time and smoke may also be taken into account

Table 8.144 Further methods for testing "low flame spread characteristic"

User state	Shipping authority/test institute	Test method/requirement
GDR	DDR Schiffs-Revision und Klassifikation (DSRK)	as USSR
Great Britain	Department of Trade, Marine Division	Spread of flame index I $\leqq$ 20 BS 476: Part 7 [15], Class 2
Italy	Registro Italiano Navale (RINA)	Guida per la Classificazione di Materiali Combustibili (similar to ASTM E 162)
Sweden	National Swedish Administration of Shipping and Navigation	Nordtest Method NT Fire 004 "Surfaces: Tendency to fire spread and smoke development" Limiting curve of the Statsprøveanstalten Copenhagen (Form B.R 512 D)
USSR	Shipping Register of the USSR	Spread of flame index according to GOST 12.1.017-80, Appendix 20 (see Section 8.2.11) (at present as a Recommendation to IMCO). I $\leqq$ 20
USA	Department of Transportation, United States Coast Guard	US Coast Guard Specification 164.012 Interior finish for merchant vessels Test to ASTM E 84 Flame spread $\leqq$ 20 ft Smoke development $\leqq$ 10%

According to IMCO guidelines, "low flame spread characteristic" is generally determined by the national methods used for determining spread of flame on building materials and components. In other cases, special tests based on the standardised methods have been developed by shipping registration authorities and institutes. Current methods are tabulated in Table 8.144.

Test method for qualifying materials as "not readily ignitable" – IMCO Resolution A.214 (VII)

According to IMCO Resolution A.214 (VII), primary deck coverings should be tested by exposing one face using the IMCO standard time/temperature curve [10]. The test apparatus consists of a furnace chamber heated by an oil or gas burner. The specimens are mounted on a 5 mm steel plate and positioned horizontally steel-side down above a cut out above the furnace chamber. The ignitability and extent of burning of the deck covering are measured during exposure to heat from the furnace chamber.

The smoke density is measured in a further test, using the smoke gas collector equipped with a densitometer illustrated in Fig. 8.92. It is placed on the surface of the test specimen and the attenuation of the directed light ray is measured over a period of 30 min and converted to optical density. Samples of gas are taken at regular intervals during the test in order to investigate the type and quantities of toxic fire gases (Table 8.145).

In the Federal Republic of Germany, the test is carried out on the small test rig according to DIN 4102 Part 8 [16]. The test equipment used in other countries operates on the same principle.

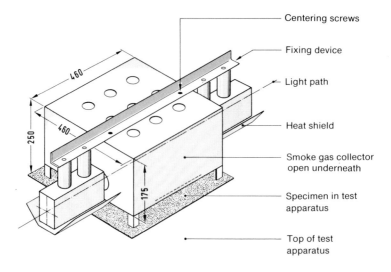

Fig. 8.92   Smoke density measurement during testing of deck coverings according to IMCO Resolution A.214 (VII)

Insulating materials

Technical fire requirements for thermal and sound insulation materials are not specifically mentioned in the 1974 International Convention but organic insulating materials may not be used in non-combustible divisions. Additional requirements are, however, frequently specified in national regulations.

Table 8.145   IMCO Resolution A.214 (VII) specifications for testing primary deck coverings

Specimens	3 specimens 650 mm × 650 mm (± 100 mm) × usual thickness
Specimen position	horizontal over furnace chamber
Ignition source	gas or oil heated furnace chamber operated according to IMCO
	standard time/temperature curve
Test duration	1. two tests of 15 min each
	2. one test of 30 min
Evaluation	1. detection of ignitable gases using a defined gas burner during the
	15 min test
	2. measurement of smoke density at intervals during the 30 min test
Results	burning time $\leqq$ 10 s
	optical density
	gas concentration as a function of test time

The "Schiffssicherheitsverordnung" (Ship Safety Order) in the Federal Republic of Germany permits the use of approved "low flammability" insulating materials according to DIN 4102 Part 1 [17] provided the substructure is non-combustible and the insulation is covered with non-combustible material. This does not apply to control stations, machine rooms, and leisure and working areas where non-combustible insulating materials must be used.

Testing must be carried out according to DIN 4102 Part 1 at an approved institute and must show that the insulating material can be classified in building material class B1, taking into account its built-in state. In addition, a critical animal test must demonstrate that foams

Table 8.146   Other requirements and tests for qualifying deck coverings and insulating materials as "not readily ignitable"

Country	Requirement	
	Deck covering	Insulating material
Great Britain	Not readily ignitable – IMCO Resolution A.214 (VII)	Merchant Shipping Notice M 592: 1. Depending on area of application, covering with non-combustible materials 2. Testing by Fire Research Station "Fire Propagation Test"
USA	US Coast Guard Specification 164.006 Evaluation in "Smoke test" and "Fire resistance and integrity test" by Underwriters' Laboratories, Northbrook	US Coast Guard Notice 8-80: 1. Covering with non-combustible materials 2. No tests or approvals procedure
USSR	Not readily ignitable – IMCO Resolution A.214 (VII)	No special requirements
Sweden	Not readily ignitable – IMCO Resolution A.214 (VII)	No special requirements

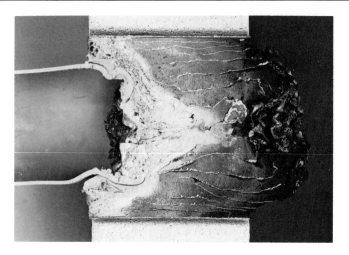

Fig. 8.93   Sleeve through a division for a plastic pipe after testing to IMCO Resolution A.270 (VIII)

do not give rise to decomposition products of greater toxicity than those from comparable natural materials such as wood and cork.

Requirements and tests for deck coverings and insulating materials applicable in other countries are summarised in Table 8.146.

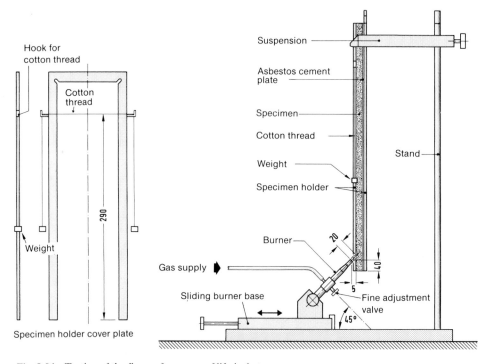

Fig. 8.94   Testing of the fire performance of life jackets

Miscellaneous

Apertures in divisions such as for *pipe and cable sleeves* must show the same fire endurance as the actual division. The test is based on the IMCO Resolution A.270 (VII) method. Fig. 8.93 shows a sleeve through a division for a polypropylene pipe after single-sided exposure to fire. The pipe has been rapidly and completely squashed by several layers of an intumescent material in the sleeve which foams under the influence of heat. The aperture is completely filled by non-combustible foam effectively preventing the passage of smoke and flames.

No special technical fire requirements are demanded for *rescue equipment* by the International Convention. However, in the Federal Republic of Germany, the effects of flame on life jackets must [14] be tested according to DIN 54332 [18]. Freely suspended specimens of the buoyancy material and outer jacket material including straps and cords must not ignite during a 5 s application of flame (Fig. 8.94, Table 8.147).

Table 8.147 Specifications for testing life jackets

Specimens	length 340 mm, width 104 mm, usual thickness
Specimen position	vertical, freely suspended
Ignition source	small burner directed to the surface at an angle of 45° for 5 s
Conclusion	passed if no ignition

The International SOLAS Convention includes technical fire protection requirements for *furniture and furnishings* in passenger vessels for more than 36 passengers. Only furniture with limited fire hazard can be used in cabins, lounges, offices or other living accommodation. The requirements are as follows:

- Desks, wardrobes, dressing tables, secretaires, etc. must consist entirely of non-combustible materials. Combustible veneers not more than 2 mm thick may be used on working surfaces.
- Free standing furniture such as chairs, sofas and tables must be manufactured with a non-metallic frame.
- The flame spread of hanging textiles such as curtains must not exceed that of a 0.8 kg/m^2 wool material.
- The flame spread of floor coverings must not exceed that of a comparable woollen material.

The "See-Berufsgenossenschaft Hamburg" refers to DIN 51960 [19] and DIN 51961 [20] for testing moveable carpeting.

8.3.4.4 Future developments

Within the framework of IMCO, the FPXX sub-committee "Fire Protection" and associated working group for test methods, are continuing to develop technical fire protection requirements and tests for shipbuilding. The aims of the work include further harmonisation of national regulations and uniform test specifications for proving "low flame spread characteristic" and qualifying materials as "not readily ignitable". Relevant proposals have been submitted by the USA and USSR.

The elimination of technical barriers to trade is particularly important due to the international nature of the shipping industry and its suppliers and thus mutual recognition of approvals and tests by IMCO signatories is also desirable. This is a further task for IMCO committees.

The concept of achieving a high degree of fire safety by excluding as far as possible all combustible material proved to be of limited effectiveness after the WEMT 1977 Conference in London. The fire hazard on ships can probably only be reduced if all possible preventive and defensive fire safety measures are sensibly coordinated.

Plastics are indispensable materials in shipbuilding but are considered "combustible" in the terms of the International Convention of 1974. Even so they do not necessarily increase the fire hazard on ships. Due to the rapid development of fires, the installation of sprinklers in living quarters and smoke extractors in escape routes deserve particular emphasis.

References for 8.3.4

[1] *M. Gebhardt:* Erfahrungen aus Bränden in Wohnunterkünften von Seeschiffen. Jahrbuch der Schiffbautechnischen Gesellschaft 71 (1977), pp. 7/11.

[2] International Convention for the Safety of Life at Sea (SOLAS), Inter-Governmental Maritime Consultative Organization (IMCO), 1974.

[3] Verordnung über die Inkraftsetzung des Internationalen Übereinkommens von 1974 zum Schutze des menschlichen Lebens auf See. BGBl. Part II, No. 8, 21. 2. 1979.

[4] Verordnung über die Sicherheit der Seeschiffe (Schiffssicherheitsverordnung – SSV). 3. 10. 1980, BGBl Part I, 1980, No. 62.

[5] Torremolinos International Convention for the Safety of Fishing Vessels, Inter-Governmental Maritime Consultative Organization (IMCO), 1977.

[6] Verordnung zur Einführung der Rheinschiffs-Untersuchungsordnung, 23. 3. 1976, BGBl Part 1, 1976, No. 35.

[7] IMCO Resolution A.163 (ES IV): Recommendation for fire test procedures for "A" and "B" – class division.

[8] IMCO Resolution A.270 (VIII): Recommendation on test method for qualifying marine construction materials as non-combustible.

[9] IMCO Resolution A.166 (ES IV): Guidelines to the evaluation of fire hazard properties of materials.

[10] IMCO Resolution A.214 (VII): Improved provisional guidelines on test procedures for primary deck coverings.

[11] Torremolinos International Convention for the Safety of Fishing Vessels. 1977. Attachment 3. Recommendation 8: See guidance concerning the use of certain plastic materials.

[12] Germanischer Lloyd: Vorschriften für den Bau und die Klassifikation von Yachten. Vol. I, 1972.

[13] *Seemann:* Schiff u. Hafen 17 (1965) 12, Preprint.

[14] Bekanntmachung des BMV über Prüfungs- und Zulassungsbedingungen für Rettungswesten. 25. 10. 1977, VkBl. 1978, Vol. 5.

[15] British Standard 476: Part 7: 1971: Fire tests on building materials and structures. Surface spread of flame tests for materials. British Standards Institution.

[16] DIN 4102 Part 8: Brandverhalten von Baustoffen und Bauteilen. Kleinprüfstand (Draft September 1977).

[17] DIN 4102 Part 1: Brandverhalten von Baustoffen und Bauteilen. Baustoffe – Begriffe, Anforderungen und Prüfungen. May 1981.

[18] DIN 54332: Prüfung von Textilien. Bestimmung des Brennverhaltens von textilen Fußbodenbelägen. February 1975.

[19] DIN 51960: Prüfung von organischen Bodenbelägen – Prüfung des Brennverhaltens. August 1975.

[20] DIN 51961: Prüfung von organischen Bodenbelägen. Oberflächenveränderung durch Einwirkung glimmender Tabakwaren (Draft October 1978).

8.3.5 Transport and storage of hazardous materials

Containers made of plastics have been successfully used for many years for storage and transport. Their resistance to corrosion and many chemicals as well as light weight are particular advantages over metal containers.

Polyethylene petrol canisters have proven themselves over more than 10 years in cars. Glass fibre reinforced unsaturated polyester tanks on vehicles have been used successfully for almost 20 years for transporting flammable and non-flammable liquids and have demonstrated ample strength in normal traffic conditions and in accidents.

Fire tests have been carried out on model [1, 2] and full size tanks [3, 4] in order to assess the relative risks of tanks and containers in the realistic conditions of a fire. For example, tanks made of GRP, steel and aluminium approximately half filled with fuel oil or naphtha were exposed for approximately 30 min to a liquid fuel fire (Figs. 8.95 to 8.100).

The tests led to these conclusions:

- The rapid increase in internal pressure in steel and aluminium tanks can force out jets of burning liquid under high pressure within a few minutes. People in the vicinity including fire fighters are put at risk by such "flame throwers".
- Steel tanks may rupture or aluminium tanks may melt if the fire continues for any length of time. This represents a further hazard to the surroundings and may result in the fire spreading rapidly.
- Even if the tanks are not destroyed by flames, dangerous and flammable liquids can leak out of sealing points and contaminate ground water or sewers.
- Steel or aluminium tanks are difficult to extinguish in fires. Leaking gas can reignite on hot metal parts. Extinction is comparatively long and dangerous.

These risks are far lower with GRP tanks. They remain leak-free considerably longer and their fire endurance is determined primarily by shape, size and supports. The storage and transport of flammable and hazardous liquids in glass fibre reinforced plastic tanks generally involve less risk than in conventional aluminium or steel tanks.

Containers made of thermoplastics such as polyethylene petrol canisters have been tested by the "Bundesanstalt für Materialprüfung". The fuel vapour/air mixture issuing from the open filler nozzle was ignited. Even after one hour the burning fuel vapour did not cause any leaks in the canister [5]. The use of suitable plastic containers and tanks for transporting and storing hazardous materials does not generally increase the fire risk. The low thermal conductivity of plastics compared to that of metallic materials can, in fact, result in higher fire endurance particularly if low boiling point flammable liquids are being carried.

8.3.5.1 Statutory regulations

Plant for storing hazardous materials is subject to differing legal requirements in each country. In the Federal Republic of Germany, the "Order relating to installations for storing, loading and transporting flammable liquids on land" (VbF) [6], which stipulates that plastic tanks used for storing dangerous flammable liquids must be approved according to type, applies.

Plant operators must apply to the relevant authorities for the necessary tests which are based on the "Technical rules for flammable liquids" (TRbF) drawn up by the "Deutsche Ausschuß für brennbare Flüssigkeiten" (DAbF) (German committee for flammable liquids) and proclaimed by the "Bundesminister für Arbeit" (BMA) (Federal Minister of Labour). These regulations contain technical safety requirements for materials, manufacture, design, equipping, testing and operation of plant.

Fig. 8.95   Steel tank

Fig. 8.96   Aluminium tank

Fig. 8.97   GRP tank

Figs. 8.95 to 8.97   Comparative tests on the behaviour of various types of tank, start of test; tests carried out in Moreton/England

Fig. 8.98   Steel tank

Fig. 8.99   Aluminium tank

Fig. 8.100   GRP tank

Figs. 8.98 to 8.100   Comparative tests on the behaviour of various types of tank, flames applied for 4 min; tests carried out in Moreton/England

The transport of hazardous goods in Europe is subject to the international requirements of cross-border traffic. Various national regulations which are generally in line with the international provisions also apply and are reviewed in Table 8.148.

Table 8.148   International and Federal German provisions for the carriage of dangerous goods

Mode of transport	International provisions		Federal German provisions	
Sea	IMDG-Code	[7]	GGV See	[13]
Rail	RID	[8]		
	SMGS	[9]	GGV E	[14]
	(CMEA countries only*)			
Road	ADR	[10]	GGV S	[15]
Inland Waterways	ADNR	[11]	ADNR (introduced by all riparian	
			Rhine states and Great Britain)	
Air	IATA (RAR)	[12]	Luftverkehrsgesetz	[16]
			Bekanntmachung des BMV	[17]

* also valid after and in transit through the USSR from the West

The standard international European contracts and the national regulations based on them governing the carriage of dangerous goods employ the RID system of classification (Table 8.149) [18].

Class 9, "other dangerous materials and objects" is found only in the Federal Republic of Germany's regulations for carriage by road. The designation "restrictive class" signifies that only the listed dangerous goods can be carried under specified conditions. All other goods belonging to these classes cannot be carried unless special permission is granted.

Table 8.149   RID System of classification for dangerous goods

Class		Designation of individual classes
1a	(restrictive class)	explosive materials and objects
1b	(restrictive class)	objects loaded with explosives
1c	(restrictive class)	ignition materials, fireworks etc.
2	(restrictive class)	compressed or liquified gases and gases dissolved under pressure
3	(non restrictive class)	ignitable liquid substances
4.1	(non restrictive class)	ignitable solid substances
4.2	(restrictive class)	self-igniting substances
4.3	(restrictive class)	substances which emit flammable gases in contact with water
5.1	(non restrictive class)	igniting (oxidising) substances
5.2	(restrictive class)	organic peroxides
6.1	(non restrictive class)	poisonous substances
6.2	(restrictive class)	noxious or contagious substances
7	(restrictive class)	radioactive substances
8	(non restrictive class)	corrosive substances
9	(non restrictive class)	other dangerous materials and objects (only GGV S)

"Non restrictive class" dangerous goods are either named or described in greater detail. They can be carried under the conditions of carriage laid down for these classes. Goods which are neither mentioned nor described more closely are not considered as dangerous goods in the sense of this provision and can be transported without any special conditions.

The classifications of the International Maritime Dangerous Goods Code (IMDG) [7] and of the IATA Restricted Articles Regulations (RAR) [12] relating to carriage by sea and air respectively differ somewhat. Many national regulations are also in force for the transport of dangerous goods.

8.3.5.2 Technical fire protection requirements

Few technical fire requirements covering packaging used in the carriage of dangerous goods are contained in the regulations mentioned above. Exceptions include heating tests for all containers used for transporting radioactive materials. The "Regulation for the Safe Transport of Radioactive Materials" of the International Atomic Energy Agency (IAEA) has been adopted almost unchanged in national and international provisions for all modes of transport. According to this it is considered satisfactory if the thermal energy penetrating a sample package is less than if the whole package is subjected to a temperature of 800 °C for 30 min at a radiation factor of 0.9. An absorption coefficient of 0.8 is assumed for the outside of the package.

Proof can be analytical or experimental. Test methods are defined in the IAEA guideline [19]. The necessary tests are carried out by the "Bundesanstalt für Materialprüfung" (BAM), Berlin (Table 8.150).

GRP tanks used for transport and above ground storage of flammable liquids must withstand a half hour fire test in order to meet Federal German regulations. The test method is also valid for the following rules:

TRbF 404: Guidelines for above ground tanks made of glass fibre reinforced unsaturated polyester resin moulding material, used for storing fuel oil and diesel fuel (August 1972).

TRbF 411: Guideline for tanks made of glass fibre reinforced plastics on vehicles and for mobile tanks of glass fibre reinforced plastics for conveying flammable liquids (February 1974).

Federal Minister of Transport Guideline for tanks made of glass fibre reinforced unsaturated polyester resin or epoxy resin moulding materials (GRP) (25. 7. 75). Compliance with this guideline is a condition for obtaining approval in accordance with

§ 4 GGV E
§ 11 GGV S
§ 3 GGV See

Table 8.150   Heating test according to IAEA guidelines

Test method	Exposure conditions
Open fire	fuel oil fire, duration of exposure 30 min
Furnace Test I	furnace, uniform temperature curve as per ISO R 834, duration of exposure 35 min
Furnace Test II	furnace, temperature 800 °C (constant), exposure 30 min

Compliance with the requirements must be substantiated by the following test:

The tank, half filled with fuel oil as per DIN 51603, is placed approximately 400 mm above the surface of the fuel (fuel oil and petrol – to facilitate ignition). The width and length of the fuel trough should exceed those of the tank by 300 mm.

The amount of fuel should be metered so that the flames burn for at least 30 min in wind-shielded conditions. After 30 min continuous exposure the flames should be extinguished. The tank must still be completely free from leaks in the portion filled by liquid. The test can be dispensed with if comparable tank designs have already been shown to have adequate resistance to flames.

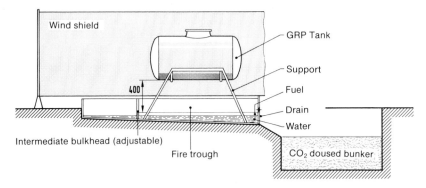

Fig. 8.101 Testing of GRP tanks exposed to fire, fire test rig of the "Bundesanstalt für Material-prüfung" (BAM), Berlin

The test rig (Fig. 8.101) in Lehre near Braunschweig used by the "Bundesanstalt für Materialprüfung" (BAM) Berlin is suitable for testing containers and tanks up to 2 m × 5.5 m. The dimensions of the fire trough can be altered and it can also be opened from the side so that its contents can run into a CO_2 doused bunker. Wind shields fixed to the sides reduce the influence of wind on tests carried out in the open air. The test specifications are summarised in Table 8.151.

Table 8.151 Specifications for testing GRP tanks exposed to fire

Specimen	tank, 50% filled with fuel oil
Specimen position	in working position, approximately 400 mm above surface of liquid in fire trough
Ignition source	fuel oil fire
Test duration	30 min
Conclusion	passed if tank leak-free in portion filled with liquid

8.3.5.3 Future developments

Fire safety tests on containers used for conveying flammable and dangerous substances have shown that their resistance depends less on the materials from which they are constructed than on their overall design and their mounting on a vehicle. Tests should therefore not be limited to ignitability and fire propagation of materials and wall sections. The results of such investigations cannot give any information on the fire risk in a transport accident.

Over the last few years tanker fires and explosions which have occurred in road and rail accidents (sometimes with drastic consequences), have mainly involved metallic tanks. This confirms the results of the large scale tests described above.

In cooperation with industry, test institutes in several countries are trying to improve and modify technical fire testing. Where necessary the changes will be incorporated in the relevant regulations and thus reduce the residual risk despite the increase in freight.

References for 8.3.5

[1]   F. Ch. Jarczyk: Kunststoffe 59 (1969), pp. 432/440.
[2]   Richardson, Butterworth: Reinforced fiberglass plastic tank trailers for gasoline transportations. Reprint without source reference.
[3]   Royal Armament Research and Development Establishment: Engulfment fire tests on road-tanker sections. RARDE Technical Report 7. 1975.
[4]   W. Becker, H. J. Bönold, M. Egresi: Prüfung des Brandverhaltens von Tanks und Behältern zur Lagerung, Bevorratung und zum Transport brennbarer Flüssigkeiten. 5th International Fire Protection Seminar, Karlsruhe, 1976.
[5]   F. Schulz: Verhalten von Kunststoffkanistern unter Brandeinwirkung – unter besonderer Beachtung von mit brennbaren Flüssigkeiten gefüllten Behältern. 2nd International Fire Protection Seminar, Karlsruhe, 1964.
[6]   Verordnung über Anlagen zur Lagerung, Abfüllen und Beförderung brennbarer Flüssigkeiten zu Lande (VbF). 27. 2. 1980, BGBl. I, p. 173.
[7]   IMDG-Code. International Maritime Dangerous Goods-Code.
[8]   RID. International convention concerning the carriage of goods by rail.
[9]   SMGS. Original title: Soglaschenije Meshdunarodnoje Grusovoje Ssobschtschenige.
[10] ADR. European agreement concerning the international carriage of dangerous goods by road.
[11] ADNR. European agreement concerning the international carriage of dangerous goods by inland waterways.
[12] IATA Restricted Articles Regulations (available from the International Air Transport Association, Geneva).
[13] GGV See: Verordnung über die Beförderung gefährlicher Güter mit Seeschiffen. 5. 7. 1978, BGBl. I, p. 1017.
[14] GGV E: Verordnung über die Beförderung gefährlicher Güter mit der Eisenbahn. 23. 8. 1979, BGBl. I, p. 1502.
[15] GGV S: Verordnung über die Beförderung gefährlicher Güter auf der Straße. 23. 8. 1979, BGBl. I, p. 1509.
[16] Luftverkehrsgesetz (1. 8. 1922 version in Announcement of 15. 3. 1974). BGBl. I, p. 721.
[17] Bekanntmachung des Bundesministers für Verkehr über die Erlaubnis zum Mitführen gefährlicher Güter in Luftfahrzeugen. 31. 5. 1968, L 5 – 582 – 38 P/67.
[18] G. Hommel: Handbuch der gefährlichen Güter. Springer Verlag 1974.
[19] Advisory material for the application of IAEA Transport Regulations. International Atomic Energy Agency, Vienna, 1973.

8.4 Electrical engineering

Dr. Hans-Wilhelm Schiffer

Plastics have made a significant contribution to the rapid advances in electrical engineering in the last few years. They offer significant advantages over traditional inorganic insulating materials such as glass, ceramics and mica, including outstanding electrical insulation properties, low electrical losses, easy fabrication and cost effective processing. Plastics are also used increasingly as structural elements in technical electrical products.

It cannot be denied, however, that the use of plastics in electrical products entrains special fire precautions. Judicious selection of materials and design can, nevertheless, ensure that electrical products do not cause or spread fire under operating conditions or in the event of a fault or when exposed to an external flame.

Potential ignition sources in electrical products result primarily from the use of electrical energy and include overheated conductors arising from bad connections, arcing and tracking. Special fire tests described below have been developed in order to simulate as closely as possible actual ignition risks.

Fire tests in the electrical industry can be divided into those involving materials and those involving finished components. Testing of materials provides comparative data on combustibility under specific test conditions and, due to the low mass of the sample, can generally be carried out in a normal laboratory fume cabinet. In order to obtain reproducible results, test conditions, i.e. pretreatment, dimensions and position of the specimen, duration and intensity of exposure to the ignition source, etc. should be specified in as much detail as possible. The results of material tests are generally quoted as numerical values or as classifications in combustibility classes.

Combustibility tests on materials are used mainly in product development and quality control. The results enable chemists working on improving the fire safety of plastics to compare the combustibility of modifications of chemically similar polymers. In quality control, material tests serve to evaluate the uniformity of a particular property of a product, in this case, the combustibility.

Data from combustibility tests assist the development engineer to select materials when designing new products. The results of material tests can, however, give only a limited prediction of the fire performance of the plastic in the finished product. Important parameters such as the interaction of various materials and the design of the finished component cannot be included in standard material tests. Design has a considerable influence on the parameters determining the course of a fire such as shape and surface finish, ventilation at the seat of the fire, heat transfer by convection, radiation and conduction as well as fire spread due to the fall of burning drops.

The interaction of all related material and design factors can only be investigated by tests on assemblies. Special fire tests developed for finished components as well as for standard test specimens are intended to quantify the potential fire hazard due to faulty or improperly used electrical equipment by simulation of such conditions. For instance, special test ignition sources have been developed (see Section 8.4.1.2). The aim of tests on finished components is a) to demonstrate that the design of a product will not cause a fire in the event of a fault or improper use, or b) to estimate the fire hazard from the actual course of the initial phase of a fire and so enable suitable measures to be taken.

Full scale model fire tests simulating working conditions as closely as possible are carried out in addition to tests on materials and assemblies specified in standards and other regulations. Model fire tests are required where standard tests do not provide an adequate assessment of the fire hazard in the proposed application or in the absence of standard test procedures or requirements. Special facilities have been set up by plastics manufacturers [1–3] in order to carry out such large scale tests without polluting the environment with smoke.

8.4.1 Federal Republic of Germany

8.4.1.1 VDE regulations

Electrical safety requirements in the Federal Republic of Germany are laid down in the VDE (Verband Deutscher Elektrotechniker) regulations. The VDE is a voluntary association of electrical technologists set up in 1893 to establish independently and irrespective of pressure groups the safety rules necessary for protection against electrical hazards. From the first regulation on low voltage equipment issued some three years after the founding of the organisation, VDE regulations have grown to over 10,000 pages.

The German Standards Committee (DNA) and VDE established the German Technical Electrical Commission (DKE) on 13. 10. 1970 in order to unify and rationalise technical electrical standards. Under an agreement between the DKE and VDE, VDE regulations will continue but be incorporated in DIN Standards together with those standards drawn up by the Electrotechnical Standards Committee. Eventually all VDE regulations will probably become part of the DIN Standards [4].

Since the VDE regulations are based on civil law they do not have the status of binding legal provisions such as state laws or the safety regulations of the underwriters for statutory accident insurance. They are, however, accepted as standard technical practice and are thus often referred to in legal provisions and safety regulations [5, 6] although there is no legal obligation to comply with them. However, in the case of failure or an accident involving equipment which deviates from VDE regulations, proof must be furnished that the design is at least equal to accepted standard technical practice [7].

The "VDE-Prüfstelle" (VDE Test Station) was set up in 1920 to give manufacturers the opportunity of having their electrical products tested independently for compliance with the VDE regulations and to publicize products which conform. The various approval marks available to the VDE Test Station are protected by the German Patent Office and international registration and can only be utilised with the express permission of the VDE Test Station.

The VDE insignia are the VDE mark for installation equipment, domestic appliances, etc., the VDE marker thread and cable mark for insulated wiring and cables for high voltage and telecommunication installation and Funkschutz mark (protection of wireless communication) and Electronic test mark.

The VDE has also been granted a protected European test mark [8].

Application for permission to use a VDE test mark is not limited to VDE members. Application forms may be obtained from the VDE Test Station.[1]

The "VDE-Prüfstelle" differentiates between the "Zeichenprüfung" (mark test), "Gutachten" (expert opinion) and "Informations-Prüfung" (information test). The mark test has as its aim the right to carry a VDE mark. Permission is granted if, besides the

---

[1] Address: VDE Prüfstelle, Merianstraße 28, D-6050 Offenbach

relevant test result, various other organisational and legal conditions are met. These include production inspection facilities. Mark approval gives the manufacturer the right to mark all products which are the same as the ones tested. The VDE mark indicates that the products conform to the VDE regulations in all properties relevant to safety, consequently there is no VDE mark for individual properties such as fire safety.

An expert opinion applies only to the product submitted for test and does not grant the right to use the VDE mark. This also applies to the information test which only extends to a specific property of the product.

Four categories of VDE testing exist [9]:

Category 1. Tests in accordance with full VDE regulations
Category 2. Tests in accordance with drafts of VDE regulations
Category 3. Tests allowing deviations from VDE regulations
Category 4. Tests based on provisional rules of the VDE Test Station.

Category 1 is the normal case. Testing to drafts as per Category 2 is possible with the authorisation of the relevant Committee of the DKE. Category 3 includes those tests where the VDE Test Station has discovered that the technical product does not comply completely with VDE regulations but is technically safe. Products for which no current or draft VDE regulations exist are tested according to category 4 [10]. The provisional rules are published in the Elektrotechnische Zeitschrift (ETZ).

8.4.1.2 Fire safety tests in the VDE regulations

The safety provisions of the VDE regulations for electrical equipment and installations contain fire safety tests and requirements. In addition some VDE regulations contain fire safety test methods which are not related to any particular field of application. The DKE committees responsible for equipment safety are obliged to select suitable methods from these when laying down safety tests, and to specify performance requirements taking into consideration the potential fire risk of the electrical product in use. The aim is to limit as far as possible the number of fire safety tests contained in the VDE regulations for various areas of application in the interests of rationalisation and to use only those methods which prove technically satisfactory.

The duality of material and component testing is reflected in the allocation of respon- sibilities to the Standards Committees within the DKE. Sub-Committee UK 831.2 "Temper- ature Effects and Combustibility" in Technical Field 8 "Materials of Electrical Technology" has been responsible since 1981 for testing the combustibility of materials. Fire tests on finished components are however developed by UK 131.3 "Ignition Sources" in Technical Field 1 "General Electrical Engineering" and the associated working groups.

Test methods for materials
Glow bar test

One of the oldest and most important methods for testing the combustibility of materials in electrical engineering is the glow bar test developed by *Schramm* and *Zebrowski* and pub- lished in 1932 as VDE 0305 "Guidelines for determining the glow resistance of insulating materials". In 1943 it was adopted with other material tests as the "glow resistance test" in VDE 0302 "Guideline for mechanical and thermal testing of solid insulating materials". It remained valid in this form until it was replaced in 1970 by the current version in VDE 0304, Part 3 [11].

According to VDE 0304, Part 3, a horizontally clamped specimen is ignited at one end with an electrically heated silicon carbide rod (the glow bar). The burnt length or burning rate are determined depending on whether the flames extinguish or continue to burn after the ignition source is removed. The test apparatus is illustrated in Fig. 8.102.

The glow bar is run at 960 °C, a temperature which ensures that all organic insulating materials encountered in practice will be ignited. Since 960 °C is the melting point of pure silver, attainment of this temperature can be easily checked by laying a small piece of silver foil on the glow bar.

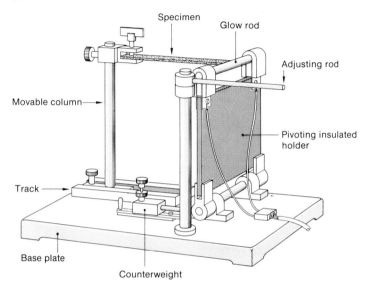

Fig. 8.102 VDE 0304 glow bar apparatus

Materials are divided into three main categories, classes I, II and III, based on test performance. Classes II and III consist of three and two sub-groups, respectively. Test specifications are summarised in Table 8.152.

Other evaluation criteria than in VDE 0304 apply in the original *Schramm* and *Zebrowski* "glow resistance test" (VDE 0302). The specimen is extinguished at the end of the ignition period (3 min) and the weight loss during burning and the spread of flame are determined. Classification is made in six quality grades using the product of the weight loss and the flame spread. *Pohl* and *Wörner* have shown that the specimen weight loss is not a suitable parameter for differentiating the combustibility of thermoplastic and thermosetting insulating materials [12], hence the impetus for revising the original test method [13] which is now outmoded.

The glow bar test has also been issued independently by the Plastics (FNK) and Materials Testing (FNM) Standards Committees of the German Standards Board (DNA) as DIN 53459 [14]. The May 1975 edition of this standard largely agrees with VDE 0304, Part 3 with the exception of the specimen width which is 10 mm instead of 15 mm. A round-robin test amongst members of the FNK/FNM 4.10 (now FNK 104) working group has shown that the difference in width does not affect classification by this method.

DIN 53459 is being revised again with the following probable changes: the comments on class I will be replaced by the statement: "The length destroyed by the effects of heat should not exceed 5 mm". Materials will be classified in class II a if the mean flame spread is $5 \, \text{mm} < \bar{s} \leqq 10 \, \text{mm}$ [15].

Table 8.152   VDE 0304 glow bar test specifications

Specimens	5 specimens 120 mm × 15 mm × 4 mm, if non-uniform results are obtained, a further set of 5 specimens is tested, reference marks 25 mm and 95 mm from edge of specimen to which ignition source is applied
Specimen conditioning	24 h in standard atmosphere (23 °C/50% relative humidity)
Specimen position	horizontal
Ignition source	electrically heated silicon carbide bar, 8 mm diameter, 100 mm exposed length with metallised contacts at ends, bar temperature 960 °C ± 5 K
Application of ignition source	3 min
Conclusion	classification of insulation materials in following classes: *Class I* Insulation materials which do not exhibit any visible flame Comment: Insulating material exhibiting a weak flame at the point of ignition which disappears within 2 s of removing the glow bar also fall into this category *Class II* Insulation materials which extinguish before the second mark is reached Class II is sub-divided into: II a insulation materials with a mean spread of flame $\bar{s} \leq 10$ mm II b insulation materials with a mean spread of flame 10 mm $< \bar{s} \leq 30$ mm II c insulation materials with a mean spread of flame 30 mm $< \bar{s} \leq 95$ mm *Class III* Insulation materials for which the flame front reaches the second mark Class III is sub-divided into: III a insulation materials with a mean rate of spread of flame $\bar{v} \leq 0.5$ mm/s III b insulation materials with a mean rate of spread of flame $\bar{v} > 0.5$ mm/s

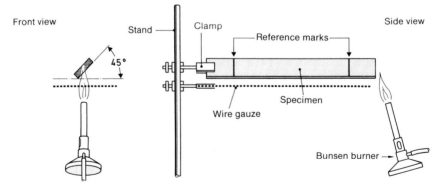

Fig. 8.103   VDE 0318, Part 1a combustibility test layout

Flame test

A flame test, based on the HB test according to UL 94 (see Section 8.4.3.2) using horizon-tally positioned test specimens can be considered as an alternative to the glow bar test and has been incorporated in various German electrical standards, e.g. VDE 0318, Part 1a/..75, Draft 1 and DIN 40802 Part 1 [16, 17]. The apparatus and test specifications are given in Fig. 8.103 and Table 8.153, respectively.

Table 8.153   VDE 0318, Part 1a combustibility test specifications

Specimens	4 specimens 125 mm × 13 mm × product thickness, mark 25 mm from specimen end to which flame is applied
Specimen position	longitudinal axis horizontal, lateral axis inclined at 45° to horizontal
Ignition source	25 mm non-luminous Bunsen flame
Flame application	30 s
Conclusion	burning time from extinction of burner to extinction of specimen flame, note whether burn length extends beyond measuring mark

Combustibility test for films

The VDE regulations contain special combustibility tests for films. Thus, according to VDE 0340, Part 1/5.75 self-adhesive insulating tapes must be tested by two different methods, the Bunsen burner test and the ignition leaflet test [18]. Figs. 8.104 and 8.105 and Tables 8.154 and 8.155 show the apparatus and test specifications, respectively.

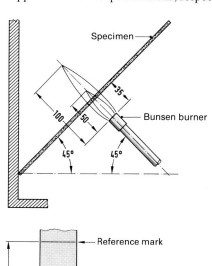

Fig. 8.104   VDE 0340,
Part 1 Bunsen burner test layout

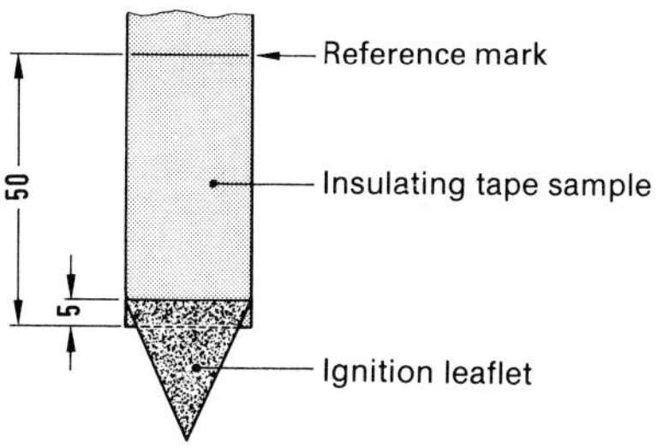

Fig. 8.105   VDE 0340,
Part 1 ignition leaflet test set-up

Table 8.154   VDE 0340, Part 1 Bunsen burner test specifications

Specimens	three 300 mm long copper tubes, outside diameter 10 mm, wall thickness 1 mm, wound with the insulating tape under test, overlap 55 to 65%
Specimen position	longitudinal axis of copper tube inclined at 45° to horizontal
Ignition source	Bunsen burner flame 100 mm long with 50 mm flame nucleus
Flame application	60 s
Conclusion	classification in the following classes:
	Bu 1: flame extinguishes within 10 s of gas supply being switched off
	Bu 2: flame extinguishes within 30 s of gas supply being switched off
	Bu 3: flame burns for longer than 30 s after gas supply is switched off

Freely hanging films are tested by the ignition leaflet method. Difficulties can occur with "oriented" films due to shrinkage during the test.

Table 8.155   VDE 0340, Part 1 ignition leaflet test specifications

Specimens	6 strips 300 mm × 25 mm, reference mark 50 mm above lower edge of specimen
Specimen position	ignition leaflet suspended vertically
Ignition source	ignition leaflet made of regenerated cellulose glued to the lower edge of the film strip, the ignition leaflet is lit with a small flame
Conclusion	classification of the film in the following
	Z1: specimen does not burn up
	Z2/n/m: specimen extinguishes before the reference mark is reached, m millimetres are consumed or charred within n seconds
	Z3/n: specimen does not extinguish before reference mark is reached. It continues to burn or drip for n seconds

Determination of the ignition temperature of decomposition gases

The ignitability of gases liberated during thermal decomposition is an important factor in the combustibility of materials. A distinction is made between the flash-ignition temperature and self-ignition temperature depending on whether after mixing with air, the gases ignite with or without an additional pilot flame. The flash-ignition temperature is generally lower than the self-ignition temperature. Examples of both are given in [13]. Flash and self-ignition temperatures are not absolute quantities since they depend on the geometrical characteristics of the test equipment and in particular on how the decomposition gases are mixed with atmospheric oxygen. They are thus only meaningful if quoted in conjunction with the test method. The data in [13] were obtained by the American ASTM D 1929 *Setchkin* method.

The VDE 0345/8.69 ignitability test for films [19] is the only method in the VDE regulations for determining flash-ignition temperatures. The test apparatus (Fig. 8.106) consists of a bored out copper block containing a thin walled iron cylinder in which clippings of the film are placed. The cylinder is closed with a lid which has a jet to enable gases to escape. The flash-ignition temperature is the maximum block temperature at which the escaping decomposition gases can still not be ignited with a flame.

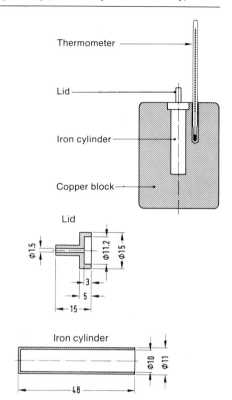

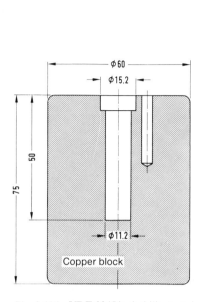

Fig. 8.106 VDE 0345 ignitability test rig

Table 8.156 VDE 0345 ignitability specifications

Specimen	1 g of film clippings
Heating	copper block which can be brought to a specified temperature
Ignition	attempts are made to light the escaping gases with a 5 mm long flame
Conclusion	the material is considered as non-flammable if no flame appears at the jet for at least 15 s for the particular test temperature (block temperature)

Other test methods

Other test methods are frequently mentioned in the VDE regulations in connection with the combustibility of insulating materials. These include the various dimensional stability to heat and tracking resistance tests. Since these methods deal primarily with other material properties rather than combustibility, they are not discussed here.

Methods for testing finished components

Hot mandrel test

Many older VDE specifications require the resistance of organic components in electrical equipment to heat and fire to be tested by the hot mandrel method. This test, developed shortly after the introduction of organic electrical insulators, was based on the premise that

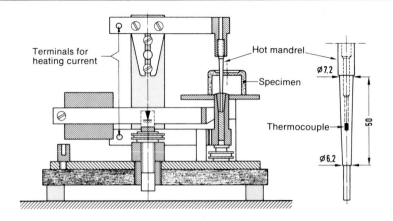

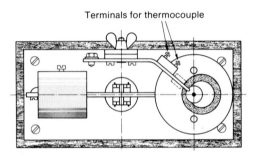

Fig. 8.107   VDE 0470 hot mandrel test apparatus

metal parts embedded in or fixed to the insulating material could overheat due to poor contact. The resulting temperatures could lead to degradation of the insulating material and ignition of the decomposition gases liberated [20].

A conical hole is drilled in the insulating component under test. The conical hot mandrel heated to a specified temperature is pressed into this hole using a specified force. The gases generated during heating of the insulating material must not be ignited by the sparks of a high frequency generator. Originally the maximum depth of penetration, e.g. 2 mm, of the hot mandrel in the insulating component was specified.

It soon became obvious that the method had various technical weaknesses which became even more apparent with the large scale introduction of thermoplastics in electrical equipment. Thermoplastics melt and flow away from the hot mandrel so that the thermal loading on the insulating material is no longer maintained. A partial solution was to move the test specimen manually but this led to poor reproducibility. Finally, VDE 0470 specified that the device for applying force to the mandrel should be blocked in order to prevent motion of the specimen relative to the mandrel [21]. The apparatus and test specifications are shown in Fig. 8.107 and Table 8.157, respectively.

Even in its VDE 0470 form, the hot mandrel test is technically unsatisfactory. The development of better fire safety tests for electrical components was therefore commenced in 1960 and led to the methods of VDE 0471. As a result the hot mandrel test is now obsolete.

Table 8.157   VDE 0470 hot mandrel test specifications

Specimen	insulating component from equipment under test in which a conical hole is drilled such that equal lengths of the hot mandrel protrude from both ends of the hole
Test layout	surface of insulator horizontal, insulating component is pressed against the mandrel with a force of 11.8 N, device for applying force is then locked in order to prevent further movement
Ignition source	the hot mandrel is heated to 300 °C in approx. 3 min and maintained at this temperature to within 10 K for 2 min. Temperature measured with a thermocouple located in the mandrel. Attempts are made to ignite the gas issuing from the upper exit point of the mandrel with 6 mm long high frequency sparks
Test duration	5 min
Conclusion	test passed if decomposition gases cannot be ignited by high frequency sparks

Glow wire test

The glow wire test is one of the methods intended to replace the hot mandrel test. In the case of faults or improper use, overheated metal parts can act as ignition sources. A glowing wire coil is intended to simulate such an ignition source.

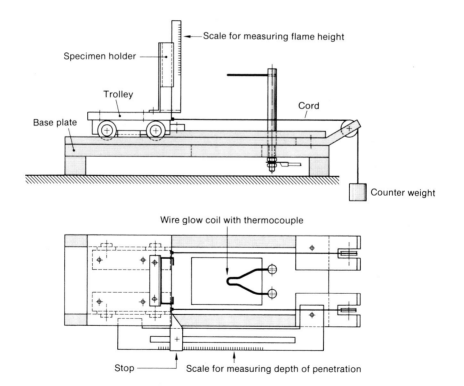

Fig. 8.108   VDE 0471, Part 2 glow wire test apparatus

The basic principles of this method were established as early as 1962 [20]. Since then various reports on experience with the glow wire test have appeared [22–25]. Following two draft versions, the glow wire test was incorporated in the VDE regulations in 1975 as VDE 0471, Part 2 [26].

A typical version of the equipment used in this test is illustrated in Fig. 8.108. The most important component is the glow wire coil consisting of a chrome-nickel alloy (NiCr 8020 to DIN 17470). The tip of the coil is drilled through and contains a miniature thermocouple to measure its temperature. The test specimen is fixed on a trolley and is pressed against the tip of the wire coil with a force of 1 N using a rope pulley. The depth of penetration of the wire coil is limited to 20 mm by stops.

The length of time that the specimen burns and the flame heights are noted. The test specifications are summarised in Table 8.158. The testing of an electrical socket is shown in Fig. 8.109 as an example of this method.

The development of the glow wire test has the same aim as that of the other VDE 0471 test methods, namely to provide technically sound and informative methods for the DKE Commissions responsible for the safety of electrical products which can then be incorporated in their regulations.

Six test temperatures ranging from 450 °C to 960 °C can be used according to VDE 0471, Part 2. The equipment commissions must select the temperature which corresponds to the risk situation for the respective product. The glow wire test is also being developed for international use (see Section 8.4.4).

Table 8.158   VDE 0471, Part 2 glow wire test specifications

Specimen	electrical product or part thereof. As a rule only one test is carried out. If ambiguous data are obtained, two further specimens must be tested
Test layout	the position of the specimen should correspond to the least favourable case in use, glow wire coil horizontal, penetration depth limited to 20 mm, pressing force 1 N

Ignition source	glow wire coil made of chrome-nickel alloy with built-in miniature thermocouple
	Test temperatures:
	    450 °C ± 10 K
	    550 °C ± 10 K
	    650 °C ± 10 K
	    750 °C ± 10 K
	    850 °C ± 10 K
	    960 °C ± 15 K

Application of ignition source	30 s

Conclusions	the test is considered passed if:
	1. the test specimen does not flame, or
	2. flames, incandescence or burning drops in the vicinity of the specimen do not act as an ignition source, where
	    a) any flames more than 30 mm high on the test specimen must extinguish not later than 30 s after switching off the ignition source
	    b) any flames less than 30 mm high on the test specimen must extinguish not later than 60 s after switching off the ignition source
	    c) incandescent processes must end within 60 s of switching off the ignition source

Fig. 8.109   Glow wire test of an electrical socket according to VDE 0471, Part 2

Bad-connection test

Practical experience has shown that unfavourable influences and human error can lead to terminals in electrical equipment with high contact resistance. Over a period of time this can result in overheating and glowing. Such "glowing contacts" can ignite the insulating material in the vicinity of the terminal. The bad-connection test is intended to simulate this hazard.

This phenomenon has been investigated in depth by the VDE Test Station and results reported by *Schwarz* [20]. It was discovered that the point-shaped contact of the parts under electrical tension first leads to low energy ("cold") sparks which form a thin insulating oxide layer on the conductor. With continuing making and breaking of the contact point, e.g. due to vibration or thermal expansion, the semiconducting oxide layer increases in thickness until the unstable "blue spark process" undergoes sudden transition to a stable and continuous "red spark process". An incandescent transition zone is formed between the two parts of the contact. Considerable amounts of heat are liberated which can result in strong heating of the contact parts and their substrate. The semiconducting layer consists of a mixture of various copper oxides.

In the initial development of the bad-connection test, attempts were made to reproduce the state of the red spark process while avoiding the blue spark process. The results of this work led to the publication of the first draft of VDE 0471, Part 3 [27]. Two paths were suggested for reproducing the effect of the semi-conducting layer on the surface of the copper wire. One way is to slide an oxidised steel tube over the copper wire and to conduct the test current from the copper wire to the contact point via the steel tube. Alternatively, the test current can be allowed to pass via a copper wire coated with iron sulphide. The iron sulphide coating is produced by dipping a clean copper wire in a mixture of one part by weight of flowers of sulphur and two parts by weight of iron powder and subsequently holding the wire in a Bunsen flame.

In the VDE 0471, Part 3, Draft 1, bad-connection test the product or subassembly is placed on a base consisting of 5 mm thick plywood with a 1 mm thick pine veneer in the least favourable position of use. Heat should be generated as close as possible to where a glowing contact would occur in practice.

The glowing contact element described above is positioned so that it touches the contact point under test without any noticeable pressure. Terminal screws must not be tightened. A test power loss, which depends on the nominal current of the test specimen, is produced with a power source. The glow process must be maintained for 30 min avoiding vibration and other disturbances. The test is considered as passed if during this time, flames, incandescence or burning drops do not start to act as ignition sources outside the test specimen and the pine veneer does not ignite.

It was soon realised that the test method was deficient. In particular it was impossible to maintain the desired power loss sufficiently accurately using the steel tube or iron sulphide coated glow contact elements during the relatively lengthy test. A British suggestion for producing the expected heat development with an electric heating element was subsequently adopted. A DKE-UK 131.3 Working Group has developed suitable heating elements for various test specimens of differing size. Although this has not completely resolved all the outstanding technical queries, it has been decided to discuss the results of this work as a CEE or IEC proposal and to issue them as VDE 0471, Part 3, Draft 2 [28] in the Federal Republic of Germany. Details are reported in Section 8.4.4.

Short circuit arc test

In the event of a fault, short circuit arcing can occur in electrical products, e.g. if a wire comes adrift from a terminal and touches another conductor at a different potential. The fire hazard due to arcing caused by shorts is certainly less than that due to glowing contacts because circuit breakers or fuses generally shut off the current rapidly. The VDE 0471, Part 4 short circuit arc test [29] was developed to evaluate this hazard.

Schwarz has calculated that the short circuit arc energy of equipment up to 20 A normal rating can be as high as 2100 Ws [20]. Since electrical short circuit tests require complicated apparatus the electrical process has been replaced by the chemical Thermite reaction. The energy content of a Thermite charge can be determined very accurately and its rate of combustion can be accelerated or moderated with suitable additives. VDE 0471, Part 4 specifies that the arcing effect should be simulated with an electrically ignited Thermite charge ("Pyrocapsule") which liberates an energy of 2100 ± 210 Ws within 0.3 to 0.4 s.

Shortly after the test was published, it was realised that there is hardly any requirement for it in practice. Furthermore, the Pyrocapsules proved difficult to obtain and VDE 0471, Part 4 was therefore withdrawn in 1976 without a successor.

Fig. 8.110   VDE 0471, Part 5 flame test (no. 2 test flame)

Flame test

In general, flames are not the primary cause of fires in electrical equipment but occur if electrical components fail. From the point of view of fire propagation it is nevertheless interesting to note how insulating components behave near flames. In addition, flames from outside can affect electrical equipment, e.g. cables and conductors which are exposed to external flames during the initial stage of a fire.

Various different flame tests are contained in the VDE regulations. VDE 0471, Part 5, "Flame Test" was the first attempt to reduce the number of flame tests to a few standard methods [30]. This standard describes three flames: test flames no. 1 (needle flame) and no. 2 (small burner flame) are used to simulate igniting flames which can occur as a result of a technical electrical fault or to reproduce small external flames. Test flame no. 3 (Bunsen type flame) is used to simulate larger igniting flames which may affect the electrical equipment from outside during the initial stage of a fire.

The burner used to produce the no. 1 test flame is a small tube, 0.8 mm outside diameter and 0.15 mm wall thickness e.g. a ground-off hypodermic needle as in DIN 13097 Part 1. The DIN 50051 small burner is used for the no. 2 test flame. Both burners are run on propane. In a vertical position, no. 1 test flame is 12 mm long and no. 2 test flame is 20 mm long. The published version of VDE 0471, Part 5 does not define the no. 3 test flame. A future edition of this VDE regulation will contain details.

Whether an insulating component ignites depends, to a large extent, on how long the flame is applied. Three different times are given in VDE 0471, Part 5. Other times can also be specified should it prove to be necessary for individual electrical products. The VDE 0471, Part 5 test specifications are listed in Table 8.159. A typical application is illustrated in Fig. 8.110.

Table 8.159   VDE 0471, Part 5 flame test specifications

Specimen	electrical product or part thereof. The test is to be carried out on three samples
Specimen position	should correspond to the least favourable case in practice. Usually, the test specimen is positioned above a base specified in the VDE regulations for the product under test
Ignition source	a) needle flame, 12 mm long b) small burner flame, 20 mm long c) Bunsen type burner flame (in preparation)
Flame application	5, 10 or 15 s
Conclusion	test passed if on the specimen a) no flames or incandescence occur or b) the afterflame time is less than 30 s or c) the burnt length does not exceed the value laid down in the VDE standards for the electrical product d) flames as well as falling burning or incandescent material do not act as ignition sources in the vicinity of the test specimen

There are only slight differences in the temperatures of the no. 1 and no. 2 test flames. No. 2 flame possesses superior technical properties, e.g. better stability due to the design of the small burner (DIN 50051). Even so this test flame has hardly been adopted in the VDE regulations in contrast, for example, to standards in the building and textile fields. The no. 1 flame is easier to manipulate inside equipment or components due to the small size of the burner.

Test with tracking current as an ignition source

It is well known that tracking currents do not only cause failure of the insulation of electrical products but can also result in fires under certain conditions.

The DIN 53480/VDE 303, Part 1 tracking resistance test is used to characterise the tracking behaviour of insulators. This method is a pure material test (c.f. [31]) which cannot take into account structural influences. Tracking resistance data can, however, provide the designer with an indication of the tracking behaviour of the insulating material in the finished product. Whether tracking currents actually occur in the product depends not only on the tracking resistance of the material but also on various other factors. These include the distance between the live components in the product, the geometry of the insulating components between, the kind of potential contamination, the nature of the residues, the wettability of the insulator surface and the magnitude of the voltage.

VDE Commission 0474 "Tracking current safety" was set up in 1958 to develop a test for the tracking characteristics of finished components because it was realised that the tracking resistance test cannot completely quantify this phenomenon. The term "tracking current safety" of an electrical appliance is defined as the resistance of an insulating component to tracking under the influence of tracking currents. It takes into account the tracking resistance of the material and the design (size, shape and position of tracking path) [32]. Although the activities of this commission did not lead to a generally applicable test [33], the work of *Kaufmann,* in particular, resulted in fresh insight into the dependence of tracking current on the geometry of the insulating component [32].

The question whether electrical products ignite due to tracking currents is a special aspect of tracking current safety. In 1976 a working group of DKE-UK 131.3 "Ignition Sources" started on the development of a method for testing electrical products, subassemblies and components for ignition by tracking currents. Progress has been such that a first draft of VDE 0471, Part 6 "Test with tracking current as an ignition source" has been issued [34]. A report on the test method and the results of preliminary experiments with model terminals and various components has been recently published [35].

The starting point in the development of the new test method was the realisation by *Kaufmann* [32] that meaningful test results can be obtained only if the test specimen is wetted on all sides by the test solution. This is achieved in VDE 0471, Part 6 with the aid of a spray nozzle. The specimen is placed in the centre of a test chamber (dimensions approximately 450 mm × 330 mm × 300 mm) connected to the power source and sprayed. As soon as the current has reached a set upper limit over the tracking paths being formed, the spray nozzle is shut off. If the tracking current drops below a selected lower limit as the specimen dries, the spray nozzle is switched on again so that the specimen is intermittently sprayed during the test.

The test is considered to have been terminated if one of the following occurs:

a) The tracking current has not exceeded 1 mA after spraying for 1 min and after additional treatment with a special quartz powder and renewed spraying. In this case the component is effectively encapsulated.
b) The tracking current reaches a value of 0.9 A for at least 5 s. In this case the ability of the equipment to function properly would be affected (short circuiting).
c) The test specimen catches fire and burns for longer than 2 s.
d) The maximum test duration of 100 min has elapsed without (b) or (c) occurring.

Since the method is used primarily to test whether tracking currents cause ignition of the insulating component, only case (c) counts as a criterion for failing the test.

Draft VDE 0471, Part 6 specifies three test solutions of differing conductivity and six test voltages ranging from 130 V to 600 V. Selection of these and other parameters such as short circuit current and limiting spray switch currents enables the load on the component in case of a fault to be closely simulated.

Little experience of this method is available at present. Hopefully it will prove suitable for assessing the ignition risks of insulating materials in finished components due to tracking currents.

Test methods for special fields of application

Individual VDE regulations contain various fire safety requirements in addition to other technical safety specifications. Many of these requirements are based on tests on materials and finished components described in Section 8.4.1.2. A few other VDE test methods also exist and these are discussed here.

VDE 0100 "Specification for the erection of electrical power installations with voltages up to 1000 V" [36] is particularly important since it covers a large area of electrical engineering. A reissue of the comprehensive 1973 edition will be published over the next few years [37]. VDE 0100 contains numerous terms such as "ignitable", "low flammability", "flame retardant" and "combustible". These are, however, (with the exception of building material classifications) used without reference to test specifications and are thus purely verbal definitions without any tangible meaning. The term "easily ignitable" is an exception and is defined in VDE 0100 as follows: "Solid materials are defined as easily ignitable if they continue to burn or glow after 10 s exposure to the flame of a match". The physical properties of a match flame are really insufficiently reproducible for test purposes. The match flame should obviously be replaced by a standardised flame such as the needle or small burner flame of VDE 0471, Part 5.

An appropriate definition of the term "easily ignitable" based on a needle or small burner flame already exists in various parts of VDE 0730 "Specification for electric motor-operated appliances for domestic and similar purposes". The switches and temperature controllers of dishwashers, washing machines and refrigerators, for example, must be constructed in such a way that a minimum distance of 35 mm must exist between the insulating components of these parts and easily ignitable parts. In order to ascertain whether parts closer than 35 mm are "not easily ignitable" they are subjected to a needle flame or small burner flame for 10 s. After the flame is removed the specimen must not continue to burn or glow for longer than 15 s. No burning drops must fall on a pine wood veneer under the test specimen.

An unusual flame test in VDE 0441 [38] requires that post insulators made of organic materials with ratings of 1 to 300 kV be exposed to an oxyacetylene flame. The insulator is mounted in the normal position and subjected to a 150 mm long flame 5 times for 15 s with breaks of 15 s. The test is considered to have been passed if the organic material of the insulator extinguishes within 60 s.

A special propane burner, of about the same size as a Bunsen burner, has been developed to test the "flame retardance" of cables, wires and insulated cords to VDE 0472d [39]. This burner can be adjusted to give a defined propane flame of variable height. Jumper wires, connecting stranded wires and connecting cable cores are tested with a 125 mm long flame (test flame A), conductors and cables with a 175 mm long flame (test flame B). The test specifications are detailed in Table 8.160.

Wiring ducts and accessories made of insulating materials (VDE 0604/11.77), wiring conduits and accessories (VDE 0605/7.72) must be tested for "flame retardance" in a similar manner to conductors and cables.

Other completely novel cable test methods were published in 1979 as VDE 0472, Parts 804, 813 and 814 [40−42]. Besides the conventional tests of single cables with the propane gas burner described above, Part 804 contains a large scale test for cableway designated "test type C". The method is derived from the American IEEE 383 specification for cables in nuclear power stations and from the Swedish SS 424 14 75 specification. 3.6 m long pieces of

Table 8.160   Specifications for flame testing cables and conductors to VDE 0472d

Specimen	600 mm long piece of cable or conductor
Test layout	test specimen suspended vertically in a combustion chamber. Two different methods of applying flame
	a) for connector cables, strands or cores, test flame A, burner at 45° to horizontal. Application of flame 100 mm above lower end of test specimen, distance between specimen and tip of burner 30 to 40 mm
	b) for conductors and cables, test flame B, one burner is used for specimens up to 50 mm outside diameter, two burners for thicker specimens. Axes of burners inclined 45° to horizontal, angle between both burner axes 90°. Tip of inner flame cone impinges on specimen 100 mm from lower end
Ignition source	a) test flame A (propane flame) 125 mm long
	b) test flame B (propane flame) 175 mm long, 0.7 mm thick copper wire must be melted in 4 to 6 s by flame
Application of flame	a) until conductor or first layer of sheathing under external sheath becomes visible, though maximum 20 s
	b) duration t in [s] computed by $$t = 60 + \frac{m}{25}$$ m = mass of specimen in g
Conclusion	the test for "flame retardance" is passed if the test specimen has not burned or if any flames have extinguished after the ignition source is removed and if the furthest trace of fire has not reached the upper end of the specimen

cable are assembled in an approximately 25 cm wide cableway in a 4 m high frame. A flame is applied for 20 min to the lower region with a propane ribbon burner 25 cm wide. The test is passed if any flames extinguish themselves and the fire damage does not reach the upper end of the cableway. This is the first pilot scale fire test in the VDE regulations. Special installations similar to those for large scale tests are necessary such as the special fire test houses described in [1] and [3].

VDE 0472, Part 814 is another unusual test for the functional endurance of cables, wires and flexible cords exposed to a flame. The flame from a 60 cm long gas-tube burner is applied to a horizontal live cable 1.2 m long. The test is passed if the series cut-out does not operate during application of the flame (the duration has not yet been fixed).

The range of novel cable tests has been extended by a method for determining the corrosivity of combustion gases. 1 g of crushed sample is weighed into a porcelain boat which is placed in a 60 cm long quartz tube and heated to $750-800$ °C by an annular furnace. The decomposition gases are passed through distilled water whose pH and electrolytic conductivity are measured. The test is passed if the pH does not fall below a prescribed minimum value and the electrolytic conductivity does not exceed a prescribed limiting value.

8.4.2 Western Europe

Most countries have their own regulations relating to fire safety and electrical equipment. It is noteworthy that there are many similarities in the test methods despite the fact that historically the regulations developed separately. The glow bar test, for example, is found in the Spanish UNE 53-035-76, in the French NF T 51-015 and in the British BS 738 standards. This agreement is due, not least, to the work of the international standardisation organisations.

The safety regulations for electrical products in various countries are, in many cases, as comprehensive, as those of the VDE. It is thus impossible to give a review of all the fire safety tests and requirements contained in them. Instead, some of the tests not (or not yet) contained in the VDE specifications are given below.

8.4.2.1 BS 738. Naked flame test and determination of ignition temperature

British Standard 738 [43], first published in 1937, is considered as the basic standard for testing the combustibility of insulating materials for electrical products. In addition to the glow bar test, BS 738 contains the naked flame test. A test specimen 102 mm × 13 mm × 6 mm is clamped horizontally and a flame applied to one side from below. An ignition time, defined as the minimum flame application time for which the test specimen continues to burn after removing the pilot flame, is determined. A Barthel burner run on methyl alcohol is used instead of a gas burner. The burner is correctly adjusted if a 0.7 mm thick copper wire placed in the flame melts within 6 s. The Barthel burner test has been adopted in various other British Standards for electrical engineering (e.g. BS 2848, 3497 and 4145).

BS 738 also contains a test for determining the flash-ignition temperature of the decomposition gases of insulating materials (cf. VDE 0345 in Section 8.4.1.2). A test specimen, 51 mm × 13 mm × max. 13 mm, is suspended along the centre line of a cylindrical electric furnace. The interior of the furnace is 127 mm high with a diameter of 76 mm and is closed on all sides except for a 6.5 cm^2 opening in the top. The furnace is adjusted so that the temperature, as measured by a thermocouple in the interior, increases linearly at a rate of 300 K/h. The minimum interior temperature at which decomposition gases given off by the test specimen can be ignited by a small flame is noted.

8.4.2.2 Oxygen index test

The oxygen index test suggested by *Fenimore* and *Martin* [44] and specified in the American ASTM D 2863 Standard [45] occupies a special place amongst combustibility tests. Details, a diagram of the apparatus (Fig. 8.30) and test specifications (Table 8.62) are given in Section 8.2.9.

While many combustibility tests result in "yes-no" decisions or classification in defined combustibility classes, the oxygen index test expresses performance as a numerical value.

A vertically clamped test specimen is ignited in a controlled variable oxygen-nitrogen atmosphere at its upper end. The oxygen index is defined as the minimum oxygen concentration at which the test specimen just burns, candle-like, from top to bottom.

The oxygen index test is certainly a valuable aid in the development of materials particularly when plastics with the same chemical basis are being compared. Difficulties occur when different types of polymer are being compared, e.g. a polycarbonate which tends to char and polymethyl methacrylate which is non-charring, since carbon formation in the vicinity of the flame can affect the oxygen index.

Caution is also required when using the oxygen index for evaluating the fire safety of materials in finished components since the test conditions such as burning from top to bottom in an artificially enriched oxygen atmosphere do not reflect a real situation. It is thus incorrect to assume that a material with an oxygen index of over 21% could not burn in practice because air only contains 21% oxygen. Such an assumption disregards the fact that burning actually proceeds upwards causing preheating, so that materials with oxygen indexes over 21% will burn in air. Flaming drippings cannot be investigated by this method.

Due to the method's lack of correlation with practice, the working group responsible for fire safety standards for plastics in the German Standards Committee, FNK/FNM 4.10 (now FNK 104) has categorically resisted all attempts to introduce the oxygen index test in the regulations and guidelines for fire precautions [46]. Consequently the oxygen index test has so far not been included in German electrotechnical standards.

In view of this background, it is remarkable that two standards for determining the oxygen index have appeared, BS 2782: Part 1: Methods 141 A to 141 D in Great Britain and NF T 51-071 in France [47, 48]. There is a clear trend towards adopting this technique in electrical equipment standards and in Great Britain it has already been incorporated in BS 9400 for integrated circuits. "Électricité de France" (E.d.F.) which issues its own standards (alongside the official standards organisation, AFNOR, and the "Union Technique de l'Électricité", UTE) recommends the oxygen index test according to NF T 51-071 as a materials test for electrical products in its standard HN 20-E-40 [49]. *Metzger* and *Paris* have reported on practical experience of this method [50].

Other methods for electrical engineering materials recommended by E.d.F. in HN 20-E-40 are flame tests according to UL 94 (see Section 8.4.3.1) which are laid down in NF T 51-072 and tests for determining smoke density, corrosivity and toxicity of fire gases. The tests for the secondary fire effects are discussed in the following section.

8.4.2.3 French test methods for smoke density, corrosivity and toxicity of fire gases

The French "Union Technique de l'Électricité" has published test methods under the designations UTE C 20-452, UTE C 20-453 and UTE C 20-454 [51−53] for determining smoke density and corrosivity and toxicity of fire gases.

Smoke density determination by UTE C 20-452 is based on a method suggested by the American National Bureau of Standards (NBS). Details and diagrams of the apparatus (Figs. 9.5 and 9.6) are given in Section 9.2.2.1. A test specimen with a surface 76×76 mm^2 and a maximum thickness of 25 mm is positioned vertically in a closed chamber with a volume of 510 dm^3 and heated with an infra-red radiator. The radiation intensity at the specimen surface is 2.5 W/cm^2. The smoke gases generated during thermal decomposition of the specimen collect in the chamber and obscure a light beam passing vertically through it. The specific optical density is calculated from the attenuation of light transmission taking into account the volume of the chamber, the length of the light path and the area of the specimen's surface. The decomposition gases can be ignited with a small pilot burner in order to be able to carry out the test under flaming as well as smouldering conditions.

Any melt dripping from thermoplastic materials can be caught, at least partially, in a small trough below the sample. The specific optical density is first calculated as a function of time. Two alternative indices derived from this are suggested as a means of characterising the results. These are "la valeur de l'obscurcissement dû à la fumée (VOF)" and "l'indice de l'opacité des fumées (IOF)". The VOF index gives an indication of the total smoke production and is calculated as the sum of the specific optical densities measured at 1 min intervals. The IOF index, in contrast, is more a measure of the rate of smoke development. It is calculated from the maximum specific optical density, the time elapsed for the specific optical density to reach a value of 16 and the times elapsed for 10%, 30%, 50%, 70% and 90% of the maximum specific optical density to be reached.

It should be noted that a second French standard NF T 51-073 for determining the smoke density of plastics exists [54]. In contrast to the method described above, the test specimen is located in a quartz tube surrounded by a concentric annular furnace which heats the specimen to a selected temperature. Air flows at a specified rate over the specimen. The optical transmission of the smoke-air mixture formed is measured. The method has certain similarities to the previous German technique given in DIN E 53436/37 dating from 1966 (see also Fig. 9.10 in Section 9.2.2.1). Due to the differences in sample geometry, ventilation conditions and sample temperature smoke density measurements by UTE C 20-452 cannot be compared with those by NF T 51-073.

In order to determine the *corrosivity* of fire gases by UTE C 20-453 [52], a mixture of 300 mg of the material in granular form and 100 mg of polyethylene are placed in a closed glass container filled with moist air and heated to 55 °C. The mixture is allowed to fall on a sample holder preheated by an electric furnace where it ignites and burns. The addition of polyethylene ensures that the mixture ignites. A 1 m long, 0.05 mm diameter oxide-free copper wire is wound on a glass support inside the glass vessel. The electrical resistance of the wire is measured as a function of time. After the sample is consumed the temperature of the closed glass vessel is maintained for 2 h at 55 °C alternated by 2 h at 40 °C. The corrosivity of the fire gases is deduced from the increase in the electrical resistance of the copper wire during several cycles.

The method for determining the *toxicity* of the gases by UTE C 20-454 [53] is limited expressly to synthetic materials although it is well known that natural organic materials can also give rise to toxic combustion products. The test specimen is located in a porcelain vessel in a 100 cm long tube heated by a 60 cm long furnace. The furnace temperature can be adjusted to defined temperatures up to 1000 °C. A stream of air is passed over the sample so that thermal decomposition occurs in an excess of oxygen. The decomposition temperatures are 400 °C, 600 °C and 800 °C. The proportions of CO, CO_2, HF, HCl, HBr, HCN, SO_2 and NO_x are determined chemically. It should be noted that toxicologists agree that the toxicity of combustion products of organic materials cannot be determined by analytical methods due to possible synergistic and antagonistic effects and that animal experiments are required. The UTE C 20-454 method can, therefore, only give an indication of the toxic effect of decomposition gases.

8.4.2.4 Cable tests according to NF C 32-070

The technical fire protection tests of NF C 32-070 [55] adopted in France differ in some cases considerably from those used in other countries. The standard differentiates between the combustibility of the cable (réaction au feu) and its fire resistance (résistance au feu). Cables are divided into three combustibility classes: C1, C2 and C3 and two classes of fire resistance: CR1 and CR2.

In order to distinguish between classes C2 and C3, a test is carried out with one or, in the case of thicker cables, two Bunsen burners. The test closely resembles the International IEC 332 standard and the German VDE 0472d test (see Section 8.4.1.2). If the test is passed, the cable is classified as C2 otherwise it is classified in the least favourable class, C3.

Cables used in applications involving stringent fire safety requirements must be of class C1 and must pass a special test developed in France using the apparatus illustrated in Fig. 8.111. A 160 cm length of cable (or bundle of cables in the case of thin cables) is suspended vertically from a frame in a test chamber with internal dimensions 80 cm × 70 cm × 200 cm.

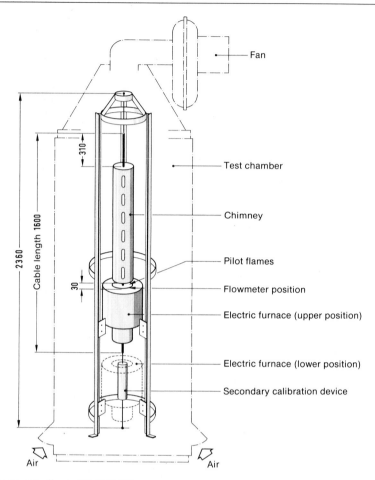

Fig. 8.111   C1 test according to NF C 32-070

An annular furnace which can be slid up and down is fixed to the lower part of the frame. In its top position it surrounds the lower part of the cable and in its lowest position it surrounds a probe for checking its heat output, the secondary calibration device. Two 20 mm long tangential pilot flames are located above the top furnace position, 10 to 15 mm from the surface of the cable. Above the pilot flames, the cable is enclosed concentrically by an 80 cm long metallic chimney which serves to conduct the flames upwards from the cable burning below. A stream of air flowing upwards at approximately 2 m/s is generated with a fan in the flue of the chamber and checked with a flowmeter.

Before the start of the test, the radiation output of the furnace is first adjusted at its upper position by placing a further measuring probe in place of the cable. This is the primary calibration device. Once the output of the furnace as determined by the rise in temperature of this measuring probe has reached the required value, the furnace is slid into the lower position. The cable is then suspended in the test chamber. The actual test starts when the furnace is brought to its upper position again and lasts 30 min during which ventilation is interrupted for 1 min after 10 min. The cable achieves class C1 if in two tests the section of cable above the chimney remains undamaged.

Cables achieve class CR1 for fire resistance by NF C 32-070 if they pass the test described below, otherwise they are classified in class CR2. One or more 70 cm long cables are clamped horizontally in a furnace at least 30 cm long and subjected to a tension of 2 N per mm^2 (copper cross-sectional area). The cables must be able to switch four independent circuits each connected between one side of the cable and a power source via a 0.5 A fuse. On the other side of the cable each circuit has a lamp through which a current of 0.25 A flows. The cable specimens are also subjected to impact twice per minute. The furnace is heated so that its internal temperature rises in accordance with the international standard time/temperature curve (see ISO 834). The temperature is then maintained at 900 °C for 15 min following which the test is terminated. The cable is classified in class CR1 if none of the four fuses or lamps fails. If only one lamp or fuse fails the test can be repeated with a further test specimen (5th circuit).

The NF C 32-070 fire resistance test must be clearly differentiated from fire resistance tests for building components such as ISO 834 although the standard time/temperature curve is used in both. The French method tests the ability of the cable to function under thermal and mechanical loads. In contrast, the fire resistance tests originating in the building industry are intended to ensure that an element, such as a wall, hinders the spread of a fire for an adequate time. Recently, cable ducts through walls, e.g. for sealing fire compartments, have been tested in this way (see for example, VDE 0100y/...76, Draft 1).

8.4.3 USA

In the USA the safety of electrical equipment and installations is governed by the regulations and approval procedures of the Underwriters' Laboratories Inc. (UL). Many international product specifications outside the USA are orientated towards the UL and a brief account of this organisation's activities is therefore given here.

8.4.3.1 Test and approval procedures of the Underwriters' Laboratories

The Underwriters' Laboratories Inc. were founded in 1894 with the aim of carrying out technical safety tests for the protection of people and goods. As a "not-for-profit" organisation, UL is not permitted to pass profits to third parties but must use them to improve and extend their activities in furtherance of this aim [56].

UL first started by carrying out technical fire protection tests. Later their field of activity expanded and today it includes safety tests in the fields of fire protection, electrical engineering, heating and air conditioning, burglary protection, accident prevention, chemical safety and marine technology. UL operate five test stations in Chicago and Northbrook (Illinois), Melville (New York), Tampa (Florida) and Santa Clara (California). Each test station has certain specialities. In addition, responsibilities are divided on a regional basis. European clients should contact Melville due to its location on the American East Coast[2].

UL safety standards test technical safety aspects of products and not characteristics such as suitability for use, value for money, etc. UL regulations are established as follows:

As soon as it is known that new product types for which no regulations exist will have to be tested, a UL employee (Standards Engineer) initiates a draft regulation in cooperation with one of the Engineering Councils attached to various areas of activity of UL and consisting of UL appointed expert advisors.

---

[2] Address: UL Laboratories, 1285 Walt Whitman Road, Melville, L.I., New York, 11746, USA

Once a draft regulation has been drawn up it is presented to an Industry Advisory Conference made up of representatives from Industry whose objections can lead to further drafts. UL draws up a final version of the UL regulation taking into account the comments made. A list of "Standards for Safety" may be obtained from UL.

Three types of UL tests exist: listing, classification and recognition tests. Successful completion of a listing test allows a finished product to carry the UL listing mark which is comparable to the VDE test mark. In contrast, the classification test covers only a few characteristics of the finished product designated by the manufacturer or supplier. It thus does not result in a UL mark being granted.

An important characteristic of the UL Approval System is that individual components or materials can be tested with the aim of obtaining recognition. A component or material cannot, of course, carry a UL mark on its own. However, the testing of a finished product for the purposes of listing is simplified if components and materials which are already UL recognised are used.

Listing, classification and recognition are associated with product monitoring or "Follow-Up Service" which involves inspectors visiting factories on behalf of UL and making random checks whether products from the production line meet the specifications given in the test certificate. There are two different kinds of "Follow-Up Service". The first is the "Unit Charge Program" or "Type L Program". The frequency of visits by inspectors depends on the quantities manufactured. The interval between visits is laid down for each product; at least one visit per month should be made. In the alternative "Fee Program" or "Type R Program" inspections are made at fixed intervals of time irrespective of the quantities produced. As a rule 4 inspection visits per year are made. UL specifies which procedure is applicable for a particular case. The "Fee Program" usually applies in the case of European production facilities.

All approvals granted by UL are published annually in the Product Directories. A register of all components and material for which recognition has been granted is published in March of each year with a supplement in September under the title "Recognized Component Directory". The manufacturers of the tested products receive an extract of this directory in the form of "Recognition Cards" also known as "Yellow Cards". The manufacturer thus has documentary evidence that his product meets the relevant requirements of the UL regulations and that a "Follow-Up Service" is being carried out.

8.4.3.2 UL 94. Flammability tests

UL 94 is one of the most important UL standards relating to fire safety test methods and requirements and contains several fire tests for plastics [57]. The requirements of UL 94 together with a few other tests form the basis for the "Recognition" of plastics as summarised in the "Recognized Component Directory".

UL 94 applies not only to the electrical industry but also to all areas of application except the use of plastics in building. UL 94 is particularly significant for the use of plastics in electrical products since a UL listing of the product frequently requires a favourable flammability classification of the materials used.

In addition to the flammability tests described below, UL 94 also contains a method for determining self-ignition temperature and a further method for ascertaining spread of flame with infrared radiation which corresponds to the ASTM E 162 radiant panel test for building materials. The UL 94 test methods are based on research into the combustibility of plastics (including that of *Perkins* in 1941 [58]) by Underwriters' Laboratories Inc.

Testing for classification in class 94HB

UL 94 contains test procedures for both horizontally and vertically positioned solid plastic test specimens in the form of rods. Successful completion of the horizontal test leads to classification in class 94HB. This test method has already been outlined as a flame test in Section 8.4.1.2. The test layout corresponds to Fig. 8.103. The test specimen is clamped with its longitudinal axis horizontal and a Bunsen flame is applied to its free end. Classification in class 94HB requires that the burning rate of the test specimen should not exceed a maximum value dependent on its thickness or that the specimen extinguishes itself after removal of the flame. The test specifications for the 94HB test summarised in Table 8.161 differ in detail from those of the corresponding VDE test (Table 8.153).

Table 8.161   UL 94 test specifications for classification in class 94HB

Specimens	3 samples 127 mm × 12.7 mm × maximum 12.7 mm with two reference marks 25.4 mm and 101.6 mm from the free end. The thickness should correspond to the minimum for the intended application. If necessary 3.2 mm thick samples should be tested in addition. Depending on test performance, it may be necessary to test a further set of three samples
Specimen conditioning	at least 48 h in 23/50 standard atmosphere
Specimen position	longitudinal axis of sample horizontal, transverse axis inclined at 45° to horizontal
Ignition source	methane or natural gas Bunsen or Tirrill burner with 25 mm non-luminous flame. The longitudinal axis of the burner is tilted at 45° towards the horizontal during application of flame (see Fig. 8.103)
Application of flame	30 s. If the flame reaches the 25.4 mm reference mark on the sample before 30 s have elapsed, the burner is removed
Conclusion	classification in class 94HB if 1. the burning rate between the reference marks does not exceed 38 mm/min in the case of samples $\geqq$ 3 mm thick 2. the burning rate between the reference marks does not exceed 76 mm/min in the case of samples <3 mm thick, or 3. the samples extinguish before the 102 mm mark is reached

Testing for classification in classes 94V-0, 94V-1 and 94V-2

The test for classifying solid plastic rods in classes 94V-0, 94V-1 and 94V-2 is more rigorous than the 94HB test due to the vertical specimen position which results in burning material at the lower end of the sample preheating material above it. Furthermore, the sample must extinguish itself. The test layout is illustrated in Fig. 8.112. A flame is applied twice to the lower end of the vertically suspended test specimen for 10 s. The top class, i.e. 94V-0 is achieved if the mean afterflame time of five samples after 10 applications of the flame does not exceed 5 s. The material is placed in class 94V-1 if the mean afterflame time is less than 25 s. If flaming drippings occur, the material is classified in 94V-2. The ignition of surgical cotton placed below the specimen serves as a criterion for this phenomenon. The test specifications are summarised in Table 8.162.

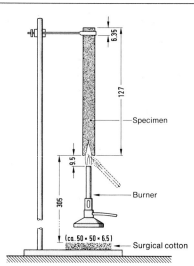

Fig. 8.112 Test layout for classification in classes 94V-0, 94V-1 and 94V-2 according to UL 94

Table 8.162   UL 94 test specifications for classification in classes 94V-0, 94V-1 and 94V-2

Specimens	two sets of 5 specimens 127 mm × 12.7 mm × maximum 12.7 mm. Two sets of specimens of material of the maximum and minimum thickness in the intended application should be used. Depending on test performance it may be necessary to test further sets of samples
Specimen conditioning	a) storage of one set of specimens for at least 48 h in 23/50 standard atmosphere
	b) storage of second set of specimens for 168 h in warm air oven at 70 °C followed by 4 h cooling to room temperature in a dessicator
Specimen position	specimen suspended with longitudinal axis vertical. A horizontal layer of surgical cotton 51 mm × 51 mm × 6 mm is placed 305 mm below the lower edge of the specimen
Ignition source	Bunsen or Tirrill burner with 19 mm high non-luminous flame
Application of flame	twice 10 s for each specimen. The second application starts as soon as the specimen, ignited by the first application, extinguishes
Conclusion	a) classification in class 94V-0 if:
	afterflame time is less than 10 s
	the sum of the afterflame times for 10 applications of the flame does not exceed 50 s
	no burning drops
	samples do not burn up completely
	afterglow does not continue for more than 30 s after removal of ignition source
	b) classification in class 94V-1 if:
	afterflame time ≦30 s after removal of ignition source
	the sum of the afterflame times for 10 flame applications does not exceed 250 s, afterglow does not continue for more than 60 s after removal of ignition source
	other criteria as for a)
	c) classification in class 94V-2 if:
	ignition of surgical cotton by burning drops
	other criteria as for b)

Testing for classification in classes 94HBF, 94HF-1 and 94HF-2[3)]

UL 94 contains a method for testing foam materials similar to the obsolete ASTM D 1692 test. The test apparatus is illustrated in Fig. 8.113. A flame from a special burner is applied to one side of the foam sample lying horizontally on a wire grid. Class 94HBF is achieved if the burning rate does not exceed 38 mm/min. If the specimen extinguishes within 2 s of removal of the ignition source, it is classified in classes 94HF-2 or 94HF-1 depending on whether burning drippings occur. The test specifications are summarised in Table 8.163.

Table 8.163   UL 94 test specifications for classification in classes 94HBF, 94HF-1 and 94HF-2

Specimens	two sets of five specimens 152 mm × 50.8 mm × maximum 12.7 mm with three reference marks 25.4 mm, 57 mm and 127 mm from end of specimen to which flame is applied. Two sets of specimens of the minimum and maximum thickness encountered in the intended application should be tested. Depending on test performance, it may be necessary to test further sets of samples
Specimen conditioning	a) storage of one set of specimens for at least 48 h in 23/50 standard atmosphere b) storage of a second set of specimens for 168 h in a warm air oven at 70 °C followed by 4 h cooling to room temperature in a dessicator
Specimen position	specimen lies horizontally on wire grid of specified mesh horizontal layer of surgical cotton 51 mm × 51 mm × 6 mm placed 305 mm below specimen
Ignition source	Bunsen or Tirrill burner with special jet to give a 47 mm wide flame, height of non-luminous flame: 38 mm
Flame application	60 s

Conclusions	a) classification in class 94HBF if:
	    burning rate between the 25.4 mm and 127 mm marks does not exceed 38 mm/min or, the specimen extinguishes before the 127 mm mark and the requirements for classes 94HF-1 and 94HF-2 are not fulfilled
	b) classification in class 94HF-1 if:
	    afterflame time ≦2 s for at least four of five specimens
	    afterflame time does not exceed 10 s for any specimen
	    no destruction of sample past 57 mm mark
	    no incandescence for more than 30 s after ignition source is removed or past the 57 mm mark
	    no burning drops
	c) classification in class 94HF-2 if:
	    ignition of surgical cotton by burning drops
	    other criteria as for b)

Test for classification in class 94-5V

The test for vertically positioned solid plastic specimens differs from the UL 94V test described above mainly by the five applications of flame to each specimen. The 94-5V test is first carried out on rod shaped specimens (method A) using the arrangement shown in Fig. 8.114. In order to pass the test, the specimens must not continue to burn or incandesce for

---

[3)] withdrawn in the third edition, January 1980

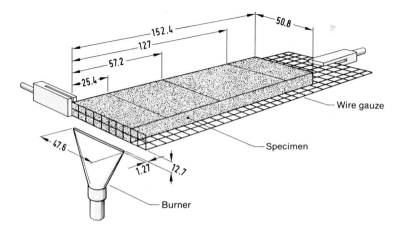

Fig. 8.113   Test layout for classification in classes 94HBF, 94HF-1 and 94HF-2 according to UL 94

Table 8.164   UL 94 test specifications for classification in class 94-5V

Specimens	method A: two sets of five specimens 127 mm × 12.7 mm × maximum 12.7 mm method B: sheets 152 mm × 152 mm × maximum 12.7 mm rod shaped samples and sheets should be tested in the minimum and maximum material thickness for the intended application depending on test performance, further sets of specimens may have to be tested
Specimen conditioning	a) storage for at least 48 h in 23/50 standard atmosphere b) storage for 60 days in hot air oven at 121 °C followed by 4 h cooling to room temperature. Depending on application, other conditioning procedures are permitted
Specimen position	method A: specimen suspended vertically, flame applied to underneath of sample method B: application of flame: a) to lowest corner of vertical sheet b) to lower edge of vertical sheet c) in the centre of outside of vertical sheet d) to centre of the underside of the horizontal sheet e) with flame directed downwards to top surface of sheet
Ignition source	Bunsen or Tirrill burner with axis inclined at 20° to vertical, flame length 127 mm with 38 mm long blue inner cone
Flame application	5 times 5 s with 5 s intervals between
Conclusions	classification in class 94-5V if: rod shaped specimens do not continue to burn or incandesce for more than 60 s after the ignition source is removed for the fifth time no dripping from specimen only slight destruction otherwise further test of sheets according to method B damage to sheets is insignificant from point of view of intended use

longer than 60 s and no plastic parts must drip; a critical requirement for certain thermoplastics. In addition the specimens must be only slightly damaged at the end of the test otherwise sheets of the same thickness are also tested under slightly different conditions (method B). This test is considered passed if the sheets are insignificantly damaged from the point of view of practical use. Details of the test are given in Table 8.164.

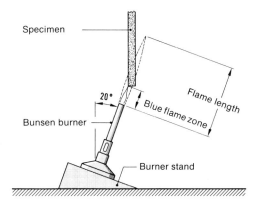

Fig. 8.114   Test layout for classification in class 94-5V (method A) according to UL 94

Testing for classification in classes 94VTM-0, 94VTM-1 and 94VTM-2 [4]

The classification test for classes 94VTM-0, 94VTM-1 and 94VTM-2 was introduced by UL in 1979 [59] for materials which are so thin that they cannot be tested by the UL 94V vertical method. The procedure is similar to the vertical test but instead of rod-shaped solid test specimens, 200 mm long cylindrically wound rolls of film, are used. The film roll is produced by winding a 200 mm × 50 mm strip of film of normal thickness around a 12.7 mm diameter rod. After affixing a piece of adhesive tape to prevent unrolling, the rod is withdrawn and the film roll clamped vertically. Care should be taken to ensure that the adhesive tape is positioned above a reference mark 125 mm from the lower end of the sample in order to prevent it burning and affecting the results. A flame is applied to the lower end of the film roll. The main assessment criteria are the same as in the vertical test for solid specimens, i.e. afterflame time and burning drops. Various differences in detail exist (cf. Tables 8.162 and 8.165). Oriented films are tested longitudinally and transversally to the axis of orientation since shrinkage can significantly affect the results.

8.4.3.3 UL Standards 746A and 746C

The significance of the UL 94 flammability tests for the use of plastics in electrical equipment within the framework of the UL safety concept is clearly demonstrated by the fact that they are referred to in UL 746C which is a fundamental standard for such equipment. UL 746C contains requirements for mechanical, electrical and thermal properties of plastics depending on their application in electrical equipment and appliances, e.g. as carriers for

---

[4] part of UL 94 since third edition, January 1980

Table 8.165   UL 94 test specifications for classification in classes 94VTM-0, 94VTM-1 and 94VTM-2

Specimens	two sets of five film rolls 200 mm long, 12.7 mm internal diameter, marking 125 mm from one end. Depending on test performance further sets of samples may have to be tested
Specimen conditioning	a) storage of first set of samples for at least 48 h in 23/50 standard atmosphere b) storage of second set of samples for 168 h in warm air oven at 70 °C followed by 4 h cooling to room temperature in dessicator
Specimen position	film roll clamped vertically with reference mark 125 mm above bottom of sample, film roll open at top and bottom, horizontal layer of surgical cotton 51 mm × 51 mm × 6 mm located 305 mm beneath bottom of sample
Ignition source	Bunsen or Tirrill burner with 19 mm high non-luminous flame
Flame application	twice 3 s for each sample, the second application starts as soon as the sample extinguishes

Conclusions	a) classification in class 94VTM-0 if:
	    afterflame time ≦10 s
	    sum of the afterflame times for 10 applications of flame does not exceed 50 s
	    no burning drops
	    no material consumed as far as the 125 mm mark
	    sample does not continue to glow for more than 30 s after ignition source is removed
	b) classification in class 94VTM-1 if:
	    afterflame time ≦30 s
	    sum of the afterflame times for 10 applications of flame does not exceed 50 s
	    sample does not continue to glow for more than 60 s after ignition source is removed
	    other criteria as a)
	c) classification in class 94VTM-2 if:
	    ignition of surgical cotton by burning drops
	    other criteria as for b)

live parts or as a material for insulating housings [60]. The interaction of the material properties is considered and the individual requirements are so formulated that in combination they ensure an adequate safety level for the plastic part in the finished product.

Since tests on materials cannot fully assess the influence of the structural make-up of the finished part, UL 746C also includes tests of finished components. For example, housings for electrical appliances must pass a fire performance test as a finished component in addition to the UL 94 classification for the material of which it is made. The flaming conditions depend on the use of the appliance. Portable appliances which are usually operated under supervision, are tested with a 19 mm high Bunsen flame applied twice for 30 s with a break of 1 min. All flames must be extinguished within 1 min after the ignition source is removed. Stationary appliances, in contrast, are tested with a 127 mm high flame applied 5 times for 5 s with intervals of 5 s. After the fifth flame application, the afterflame time must not exceed 1 min. In addition, the housing must retain its ability to function and no flaming drippings should occur.

UL 746C also requires plastics used in electrical equipment to pass two tests with electrical ignition sources. These are the hot wire ignition test and the high current arc ignition test.

Only the relevant requirements are laid down in UL 746C; the actual methods are described in a parallel standard, UL 746A [61]. Both methods have been discussed by *Reymers* [62].

The hot wire ignition test should not be confused with the glow wire test described in Section 8.4.1.2. As a material test, the hot wire ignition test is carried out, not on the finished component, but on a rod shaped test specimen. The test simulates the overloading of a live part in direct contact with the test specimen. Five turns of 0.5 mm thick chrome-nickel wire (80% nickel and 20% chrome) are wound around a 127 mm long, 12.7 mm wide test specimen whose thickness corresponds to the application. The separation between the individual windings should be 6.4 mm. The wire is heated electrically so that 0.26 W is emitted per mm length of wire and then has a temperature of approx. 930 °C. The time when the test specimen ignites is determined. If ignition does not occur, the test is terminated after 120 s. The test is carried out with five test specimens. According to UL 746C plastics used in housings for electrical appliances should not ignite for at least 15 s when tested by this method.

In the high current arc ignition test, a short circuit current of 32.5 A flows through two electrodes, one of which can be moved. The electrodes are pulled apart periodically, generating an arc on the specimen surface 40 times per min. The number of arc ignitions required to set the specimen alight is determined. If it does not burn, the test is terminated after 200 cycles. According to UL 746C plastics for use in appliance housings should survive at least 30 cycles without igniting. The "Recognition Cards" for plastics list not only the UL 94 classification and the mechanical and electrical temperature indices for characterising ageing, discussed by *Reymers* [63], but also the ignition time from the hot wire ignition test and the number of cycles from the high current arc ignition test for several sample thicknesses.

8.4.4 International electrotechnical standardisation

As the commercial links between countries strengthen and markets merge, so the importance of international standardisation increases. The development of international standards is the task of such organisations as ISO and IEC. The former is responsible for all technical fields with the exception of electrical technology. International electrical standards are established by the "International Electrotechnical Commission" (IEC) which was founded more than 70 years ago [64, 65]. The work of the IEC consists of IEC publications in English and French, which practically constitute the international standards, as well as numerous reports from "Technical Committees" (TC), "Sub-Committees" (SC) and "Working Groups" (WG).

For many years a peculiarity of the international scene was the existence of a second international standards organisation in Europe operating in parallel to the IEC, i.e. the "Commission on Rules for the Approval of Electrical Equipment" (CEE) [65] founded in 1926. Since 1978 the IEC has had sole responsibility for international standards thus eliminating duplication and potential disagreements. The new CEE charter which came into force in January 1980 limits its activities to so-called "Conformity Certification" of electrical equipment based on selected IEC standards. The aim of the CEE is to obtain mutual recognition of test results between all member countries. In order to reflect this new objective the name of the organisation was changed to the "International Commission for Conformity Certification of Electrical Equipment" although the abbreviation CEE has been retained. Membership of the CEE and the IEC is open to all countries [66].

Progress towards the elimination of trade barriers can only be achieved if individual national standards and regulations are harmonised or replaced by international standards. In Europe, harmonisation is the responsibility of CENELEC (Comité Européen de Normalisation Électrotechnique).

CENELEC was founded at the start of 1973 by amalgamating CENEL (Comité Européen de Coordination des Normes Électriques) and CENELCOM (Comité Européen de Coordination des Normes Électrotechniques des Pays de la Communauté Économique Européenne). The members of CENELEC are national electrotechnical committees of the member countries of the European Community (EEC), Free Trade Area (EFTA) and Spain. CENELEC's work on harmonisation results either in European standards or harmonisation documents which are then adopted as the national standards by those countries represented in the organisation [67]. In spite of many efforts harmonisation is proving to be very slow in Europe [68]. A list of the principal electrotechnical associations is given in Appendix 10.7.

8.4.4.1 Fire safety test methods in CEE regulations

The CEE ceased to work on standards in 1978 with the result that CEE regulations are no longer being revised. It is thus only a question of time before CEE publications and recommendations become technically obsolete. The test methods contained in them, with one notable exception, CEE Recommendation 5 of May 1971, are therefore not discussed here.

The development of the glow wire test as a replacement for the technically unsatisfactory hot mandrel method has already been reported in Section 8.4.1.2. This work, carried out nationally and within the CEE resulted initially in CEE Recommendation 4 of November 1970, which was the subject of a comparative investigation by *Scherbaum* [23], and finally in CEE Recommendation 5 [69].

The glow wire test is included twice in CEE Recommendation 5. Firstly as a preselection test for parts made of insulating materials and secondly as a test for finished parts for housings in electrical appliances. The bad-connection test is also included. The use of the glow wire test as a preselection test has drawn massive criticism from experts. The fact that the glow wire test is certainly not capable of representing all potential ignition hazards, such as electric arcing, glowing contacts or tracking currents, as well as the requirements contained in this recommendation were particularly criticised. For example, the 960 °C hot wire tip must not penetrate more than 15 mm into the plastic part when pressing against it with a force of 1 N. All unreinforced thermoplastics fail this requirement since they melt and the tip of the hot wire would pass right through the specimen. The limited penetration depth requirement is certainly irrelevant to the fire safety of electrical appliances and is therefore unacceptable.

The intense criticism of CEE Recommendation 5 has resulted in much effort being devoted on a national scale to improving the glow wire and bad-connection tests, and hence this CEE document. Although draft tests were prepared in 1977 and published as DIN 57471/VDE 0471, Parts 100 to 102, Draft 1, due to the reorganisation of the CEE the recommendation was never revised and the draft texts were taken over by the IEC.

8.4.4.2 Fire safety test methods in IEC regulations

Fire safety test methods for materials and finished components are prepared by various IEC standards committees. The "Short Time Tests" (15A) Sub-Committee of the "Insulating Materials" (15) Technical Committee is responsible for test methods for determining the combustibility of materials. IEC-SC 15A presented Document 15A (Central Office) 40 to the member organisations of the IEC for discussion in January 1980 [70]. This harmonisation document will be published as a VDE draft. It includes methods for determining the combustibility of solid electrical insulating materials, i.e. the glow bar test based on VDE 0304, Part 3, and two flame tests with horizontal and vertical rod shaped test specimens based on

UL 94. This is an example of the increasing tendency to adopt UL test methods in IEC regulations, not least because of the active participation of UL representatives on IEC panels.

What minimum requirements should be made on the combustibility of organic materials in electrical appliances? Various older international and national electrotechnical standards, recommend that "fiercely burning" materials such as celluloid should not be used. It is obvious that a description such as "not fiercely burning like celluloid" cannot be used to set a lower safety level. It would be necessary to state at least how the burning behaviour of the material compares with that of celluloid in a test. Experiments by a working group of the former VDE Commission 0471 showed that the burning behaviour of celluloid need not correspond to "fiercely burning". Various types of celluloid burn with a spectacularly large flame but are consumed relatively slowly. Much effort has therefore been devoted to defining in some other way the minimum combustibility requirements for materials used in electrotechnical products. Two alternative test methods are under discussion in the IEC at present. These are the UL 94 horizontal test with solid test specimens for which the specimen thickness and maximum permissible burning rate have yet to be specified and the glow wire test with a probable hot wire temperature of 550 °C.

In 1977 the IEC set up Sub-Committee 50D "Fire Hazard Testing" of the Technical Committee 50 "Environmental Testing" to develop and establish fire safety tests for finished parts. SC 50D was able to base its work on the CEE draft texts published as DIN 57471/VDE 0471, Parts 100 to 102, considered below. This preliminary work enabled two of these test methods, the glow wire and needle flame tests to be finalised for publication at the 45th IEC Annual Conference in Stockholm in summer 1980[5].

VDE Draft 0471, Part 100 (the German translation of CEE draft standard [031-SEC] F102/77) contains instructions for the use of the various fire safety tests for finished parts such as the glow wire, bad-connection and flame tests [71]. One suggestion is to exclude the use of "fiercely burning" materials on the basis of the glow wire test at 550 °C. IEC-SC 50D is in the course of establishing "guidance for the preparation of requirements and test specifications for assessing fire hazard of electrotechnical products" based on this document.

The IEC version of the glow wire test finalised in 1980 is very similar to VDE Draft 0471, Part 101 (CEE [031-SEC] F103/77) [72]. In contrast to the first edition of VDE 0471 [26] (see Table 8.158) various technical changes have been made to the test methods. Thus the glow wire temperature of 450 °C has been deleted. The temperature of 850 °C which was also originally deleted [72] has been restored in the IEC version. Flaming drops from assemblies or components for use in electrical products are tested by determining whether a layer of tissue paper, 200 mm below the test specimen on a 10 mm thick pine board is ignited. Recommendations regarding selection of glow wire temperature (650 °C, 750 °C or 960 °C) for assessing the hazard in different applications are also new.

The IEC version of the needle flame test is basically similar to that in VDE Draft 0471, Part 102. (CEE [031-SEC] F104/77) [73]. The small burner flame in VDE 0471, Part 5 [30] has not been incorporated in the CEE and IEC draft standards. A further test method using a larger flame (Bunsen type burner) is in the course of preparation by IEC-SC 50D.

Section 8.4.1.2 contained a report on the comprehensive German work on the further development of the bad-connection test. The aim of this work was to use small heater elements to simulate the heat build-up expected should a glowing contact occur at screws or clip connections. The results are contained in IEC Document 50D (SEC) 14 and VDE 0471, Part 3, Draft 2 [28]. This IEC document has been submitted to the member organisations of

[5] published as IEC-Publications 695-2-1 and 695-2-2

the IEC for comment. Little experience has been obtained with the new bad-connection test. Comprehensive trials of this method at international level are therefore desirable.

The IEC transferred the "Pilot Function" for fire safety tests on finished components to SC 50D "Fire Hazard Testing" when it was set up. Close cooperation already exists with certain technical committees on questions of fire safety of electrotechnical products, e.g. with IEC TC 61 "Safety of Household Electrical Appliances" on the revision of IEC Publication 553 issued by this committee. This publication reports on fire safety testing and assessment of non-metallic housings and other parts of domestic appliances. It has also appeared as a draft VDE standard [74].

The pilot function concept is novel. Hopefully it will prove itself and in a few years time uniform fire safety test methods and realistic hazard requirements will find their way into IEC regulations due to the pilot function of SC 50D.

8.4.5 Other fire safety test methods

In addition to the tests on materials and finished components described in Sections 8.4.1 to 8.4.4, various test methods which have found wide use outside their intended sphere exist in the field of electrical engineering. These include the ANSI/ASTM D 3713-78 and CSA C 22.2 flame tests which are considered here.

The standards of the Canadian Standards Association (CSA) are arranged according to subject. Part C 22.2 is "Canadian Electrical Code Part II – Safety Standards for Electrical Equipment" which is itself subdivided into more than 140 individual standards corresponding to the various areas of application of electrical equipment.

Besides the UL 94 test methods, some of these standards also contain two flame tests for housings for live parts. One of these tests is carried out by applying a 19 mm high luminous Bunsen flame twice for 30 s with an interval of 1 min to the test component or to a corresponding thick sheet of insulating material. Depending on the type and use of the electrical equipment the test specimen is positioned horizontally or vertically. As a rule the test is passed if the afterflame time after both flame applications does not exceed 1 min and if the test specimen does not exhibit any great damage.

The second CSA C 22.2 flame test requires a 127 mm long Bunsen flame applied obliquely from below to the finished housing or to part of a sheet of insulating material of the same thickness placed vertically. The flame is applied five times for 15 s (see for example [75]). The burner axis is inclined at 20° to the vertical, similar to the arrangement in Fig. 8.114. The pauses between the five flame applications last for 15 s or at least until the test specimen extinguishes. The test is passed if the afterflame times after the first four flame applications do not exceed 30 s and after the fifth application does not exceed 60 s. In addition, the test specimen should not exhibit any holes or other damage which could affect safety. The fall of burning droplets is considered as a negative characteristic.

The combustibility test for polymeric materials described in the American ANSI/ASTM D 3713-78 standard [76] provides a clearer differentiation between the burning behaviour of materials than many other tests. Frequently tests enable only a "yes/no" decision or classification in one of a limited number of flammability classes to be made. The ANSI/ASTM D 3713-78 test, in contrast, provides a so-called Ignition Response Index (IRI).

In order to determine the IRI, a 20 mm long Bunsen flame is applied for 5 s to the underneath of a vertically clamped specimen 127 mm × 13 mm × thickness corresponding to that found in practice but not exceeding 13 mm. If the specimen does not continue to burn or incandesce for longer than 30 s and is not completely consumed and if a layer of surgical cotton placed 305 mm beneath the specimen is not ignited by the burning drops during this time, then a further test of 10 s is carried out. The procedure is repeated with new specimens increasing the duration of flaming by 5 s each time to a maximum of 60 s. The maximum duration of flaming for which these criteria are fulfilled is thus ascertained for 10 separate tests.

The Ignition Response Index is made up of a number corresponding to the maximum flaming time in seconds, the letters B for "Burning" or DI for "Dripping Ignition" and the specimen thickness. Thus "IRI = 35 B at 2 mm" implies that a 2 mm thick test rod flamed for 35 s fulfills the above criteria, but at 40 s flaming continues to burn or glow for longer than 30 s. "IRI = 20 DI at 4 mm" indicates that 4 mm thick specimens do not form burning drops when flamed for 20 s though they will at 25 s. The description "IRI = D at 2 mm" indicates that the sample drips but that the surgical cotton is not ignited. In this case no flame application time is quoted. The Ignition Response Index has proved to be a useful aid for characterising the combustibility of plastics particularly in product development.

8.4.6 Future developments

Increasing internationalisation of technical electrical standards due to harmonisation will result in the transfer of the development of fire safety test methods and requirements to international committees. There is a trend towards elimination of the distinction between tests on materials and finished parts. The use of material tests for preselection when evaluating finished parts will become increasingly common, not least due to the active role played by UL representatives on IEC committees.

Work on national electrical standards will only be effective in future if the results can be communicated sufficiently early to the relevant IEC committee so that they can be incorporated in national safety regulations via IEC publications as a result of harmonisation.

References for 8.4

[1] H. W. Schiffer, H. Mohr: Kunststoffe im Bau 13 (1978), p. 9.
[2] W. Klöker, H. Niesel, F. H. Prager, H. W. Schiffer, O. Bökenkamp, H. G. Klingelhöfer: Kunststoffe 67 (1977), p. 438.
[3] W. Delekat: GIT, Fachz. f. d. Lab. 23 (1979), p. 928.
[4] M. Lehmann: DIN-Mitt. 58 (1979), p. 220.
[5] W. Jeiter: ETZ-B 26 (1974) 6, p. 122.
[6] M. Nöthlichs, W. Jeiter, P. Stürk: Rechtsvorschriften im Bereich der Elektrotechnik, Neue staatliche und berufsgenossenschaftliche Rechtsvorschriften für elektrische Betriebsmittel, Texte und Erläuterungen. Erich Schmidt Verlag, Berlin, 1979.
[7] K. Brinkmann, R. Leber, G. Niehage: ETZ-A 93 (1972), p. 687.
[8] H. Walther: Die VDE-Prüfstelle. VDE-Schriftenreihe Heft 22, Berlin, 1970.
[9] A. Warner: ETZ-A 93 (1972), p. 693.
[10] Verfahren zur Erteilung von VDE-Zeichengenehmigungen. ETZ-B 26 (1974) 18, M 123.
[11] VDE 0304, Part 3/5.70: Bestimmungen für Prüfverfahren zur Beurteilung des thermischen Verhaltens fester Isolierstoffe. Part 3: Brennverhalten.
[12] D. Pohl, Th. Wörner: ETZ-B 19 (1979), p. 558.
[13] J.-F. Flatz, D. Pohl, E. Rickling: Kunst- und Isolierstoffe bei hohen Temperaturen und Flammeneinwirkung. ETZ-Report 1 „Brandsicherheit elektrischer Anlagen", p. 9, Berlin, 1970.
[14] DIN 53459, May 1975: Prüfung mit Kunststoffen. Beurteilung des Verhaltens während und nach Berührung mit einem Glühstab.
[15] DIN-Mitt. 58 (1979), p. 725.

[16] VDE 0318, Part 1a/...75, Draft 1, and DIN 7735, Part 1a, Draft Dec. 1975: VDE-Bestimmung für die Schichtpreßstoff-Erzeugnisse Hartpapier, Hartgewebe und Hartmatte. Prüfverfahren.

[17] DIN 40802, Part 1, Feb. 1976: Metallkaschierte Basismaterialien für gedruckte Schaltungen. Prüfung.

[18] VDE 0340, Part 1/5.75, and DIN 40633, Blatt 1, May 1975: VDE-Bestimmung für selbstklebende Isolierbänder. Kunststoffbänder.

[19] VDE 0345/8.69: Bestimmungen für Isolierfolien der Elektrotechnik.

[20] K. H. Schwarz: ETZ-B 14 (1962), p. 273.

[21] VDE 0470/1.61: Regeln für Prüfgeräte und Prüfverfahren.

[22] D. Pohl: ETZ-A 86 (1965), p. 14.

[23] R. Scherbaum: ETZ-B 24 (1972) 4, M 29.

[24] H. W. Kahnau, W. Kieninger: ETZ-B 26 (1974), p. 663.

[25] H. W. Kahnau, W. Kieninger: ETZ-B 28 (1976), p. 2.

[26] VDE 0471, Part 2/4.75, and DIN 57471, Blatt 2: VDE-Bestimmungen für die feuersicherheitliche Prüfung von elektrotechnischen Erzeugnissen, ihren Baugruppen und Teilen. Glühdrahtprüfung.

[27] VDE 0471, Part 3/...70, Draft 1: Bestimmungen für die feuersicherheitliche Prüfung von elektrotechnischen Erzeugnissen, ihren Baugruppen und Teilen. Part 3 Glühkontaktprüfung.

[28] VDE 0471, Part 3/...80, Draft 2, and DIN IEC 50D (SEC) 14: Prüfung mit einer schlechten Verbindung.

[29] VDE 0471, Part 4/10.73: Bestimmungen für die feuersicherheitliche Prüfung von elektrotechnischen Erzeugnissen, ihren Baugruppen und Teilen. Part 4: Kurzschlußlichtbogenprüfung (test withdrawn in 1976 without replacement).

[30] VDE 0471, Part 5/9.75, and DIN 57471, Part 5, Sept. 75: VDE-Bestimmung für die feuersicherheitliche Prüfung von elektrotechnischen Erzeugnissen, ihren Baugruppen und Teilen. Prüfung mit Flammen.

[31] H. Suhr: Z. f. Werkstofftechnik 3 (1972), p. 434.

[32] W. Kaufmann: ETZ-A 83 (1962), p. 801.

[33] W. Kaufmann: ETZ-A 83 (1962), p. 280.

[34] VDE 0471, Part 6/...80, Draft 1, and DIN 57471, Part 6, Draft November 1980: Feuersicherheitliche Prüfung von elektrotechnischen Erzeugnissen, ihren Baugruppen und Teilen. Prüfung mit Kriechstrom als Zündquelle.

[35] H. Finger, W. Holl, W. F. Kampe, D. Link: ETZ 101 (1980), p. 1268.

[36] VDE 0100/5.73: Bestimmungen für das Errichten von Starkstromanlagen mit Nennspannungen bis 1000 V.

[37] H. W. Kahnau, W. Rudolph: ETZ 101 (1980), p. 303.

[38] VDE 0441, Part 99/...78, Draft 1, and DIN IEC 36 C.28. Draft July 1978: Prüfungen an Innenraum-Stützisolatoren aus organischen Werkstoffen für Netze mit Nennspannungen von mehr als 1000 V bis einschließlich 300 kV.

[39] VDE 0472d/12.77: Leitsätze für die Durchführung von Prüfungen an isolierten Leitungen und Kabeln.

[40] VDE 0472, Part 804/...79, Draft 1, and DIN 57472, Part 804, Draft Oct. 1979: Prüfung an Kabeln und isolierten Leitungen. Flammwidrigkeit.

[41] VDE 0472, Part 813/...79, Draft 1, and DIN 57472, Part 813, Draft Oct. 1979: Prüfung an Kabeln und isolierten Leitungen. Korrosivität von Brandgasen.

[42] VDE 0472, Part 814/...79, Draft 1, and DIN 57472, Part 814, Draft Oct. 1979: Prüfung an Kabeln und isolierten Leitungen. Funktionserhalt bei Flammeneinwirkung.

[43] BS 738: Non-ignitable and self-extinguishing properties of solid electrical insulating materials (including classification and methods of test).

[44] C. P. Fenimore, F. J. Martin: Mod. Plast. 43 (1966), p. 141.

[45] ANSI/ASTM D 2863–77: Standard method for measuring the minimum oxygen concentration to support candle-like combustion of plastics (oxygen index).

[46] Der Limiting-Oxygen-Index-Test nach ASTM D 2863 – Eine kritische Beurteilung des Prüfverfahrens für das Brandverhalten von Werkstoffen. Kunststoffe 64 (1974), p. 153.

[47] BS 2782: Part 1: Methods 141 A to 141 D: 1978. Plastics, Part 1: Thermal properties. Method 141 A: Oxygen index of combustion of a rigid bar of 10 mm × 4 mm nominal cross section. Method 141 B: ...

[48] NF T 51-071, May 1977: Matières plastiques, réaction au feu, détermination de l'indice d'oxygène.

[49] Électricité de France, Document de Normalisation HN 20-E-40, Sept. 1977: Méthodes de laboratoire pour apprécier le comportement au feu des matériaux synthétiques utilisés dans la construction électrique.

[50] G. Metzger, M. Paris: Caoutchoucs et Plastiques 581 (1978), p. 69.

[51] UTE C 20-452, Oct. 1976: Détermination de l'opacité des fumées en atmosphère non renouvelée.

[52] UTE C 20-453, Oct. 1976: Détermination de la corrosivité des fumées.

[53] UTE C 20-454, April 1978: Méthode d'essai pour l'analyse et le dosage de gaz nocifs dégagés par pyrolyse ou combustion des matériaux de synthèse utilisés en électrotechnique.

[54] NF T 51-073, Sept. 1977: Matières plastiques, comportement au feu, méthode d'essai pour la mesure de l'opacité des fumées.

[55] NF C 32-070, June 1979: Conducteurs et câbles pour installations, essais de classification des conducteurs et câbles du point de vue de leur comportement au feu.

[56] Testing for Public Safety. Underwriters' Laboratories Inc., 1978.

[57] UL 94, 2. Sept. 1973 Edition with supplements of May 1975, July 1976 and May 1978: Tests for flammability of plastic materials for parts in devices and appliances.

[58] A. J. Perkins: Comparative burning tests of common plastics. Underwriters' Laboratories Inc., Bulletin of Research 22, 1941.

[59] Communication from Underwriters' Laboratories Inc. of 22. 5. 79: Vertical burning test for thin materials as adopted for the second edition of the standard for tests for flammability of plastic materials for parts in devices and appliances, UL 94.

[60] UL 746C 2nd Edition, Mar. 1978: Standard for polymeric materials – use in electrical equipment evaluations.

[61] UL 746A, 2nd Edition from Dec. 1978: Standard for polymeric materials – short-term property evaluations.

[62] H. Reymers: Mod. Plast. 47 (1970) 10, p. 92.

[63] H. Reymers: Mod. Plast. 47 (1970) 9, p. 78.

[64] S. E. Goodall: ETZ-A 94 (1973), p. 314.

[65] R. Leber: Elektronorm 26 (1972), p. 513.

[66] R. Winckler, A. Warner: DIN-Mitt. 59 (1980), p. 446.

[67] H. Reichenbach: DIN-Mitt. 58 (1979), p. 35.

[68] U. Haier: DIN-Mitt. 59 (1980), p. 427.

[69] CEE Recommendation 5 May 1971, Document CEE (031-SEC) F 106 to E/72: Resistance of parts of insulating material to abnormal heat and to fire – provisional recommendations of the committee on general requirements.

[70] IEC-Document 15A (Central Office) 40, January 1980: Methods of test for the determination of the flammability of solid electrical insulating materials when exposed to an igniting source.

[71] VDE 0471, Part 100/...77, Draft 1, and DIN 57471, Part 100, Draft Oct. 1977: VDE-Bestimmung für die feuersicherheitliche Prüfung von elektrotechnischen Erzeugnissen, ihren Baugruppen und Teilen. Anleitung für Prüfverfahren und ihre Anwendung.

[72] VDE 0471, Part 101/...77, Draft 1, and DIN 57471, Part 101, Draft Oct. 1977: VDE-Bestimmung für die feuersicherheitliche Prüfung von elektrotechnischen Erzeugnissen, ihren Baugruppen und Teilen. Prüfung mit dem Glühdraht.

[73] VDE 0471, Part 102/...77, Draft 1, and DIN 57471, Part 102, Draft Oct. 1977: VDE-Bestimmung für die feuersicherheitliche Prüfung von elektrotechnischen Erzeugnissen, ihren Baugruppen und Teilen. Prüfung mit der Nadelflamme.

[74] VDE 0700, Part 101/...77, Draft 1, and DIN IEC 533, Draft Nov. 1977: Bericht über die Beurteilung nicht-metallener Gehäuse und anderer Teile von Haushaltsgeräten und ähnlichen Geräten im Hinblick auf ihre Beständigkeit gegen Feuer.

[75] CSA C 22.2 No. 63-1968, Revision Nov. 1969: Household refrigerators and freezers.

[76] ANSI/ASTM D 3713−78: Standard method for measuring response of solid plastics to ignition by a small flame.

8.5 Textiles

Dr. Martin Rieber

At first glance, textiles do not appear to belong in a book on the fire performance of plastics. There are, however, several reasons for including a short review on the burning behaviour of textiles at this point:

– Man is surrounded by textiles in the form of clothing and furnishings; burning behaviour and assessment of fire hazard are thus of major importance.
– Textiles can consist of natural or synthetic fibres or a mixture of both. Synthetic fibres are made of the same raw materials as plastics.
– Textiles are used in all the areas of application covered in this book. The regulations and test methods for textiles are therefore more or less identical to those for plastics.

It thus seems logical to round off the topic of fire performance with a section on textiles. The numerous applications of textiles are first introduced and the present situation is examined briefly. A review of the most important fire protection regulations relating to textiles follows together with an outline of the test methods. The section concludes with a look at future developments.

Only a short review of laboratory test procedures is given. Pilot scale or 1:1 scale methods are described in detail in Chapter 7 (see also Section 8.6 "Furniture and furnishings").

Due to the condensed nature of this contribution, topics specific to textiles such as flame retardants for fibres and applications such as working clothes are not discussed here. The reader is referred to the relevant technical literature.

Table 8.166 Fields of application for textiles

Clothing	private use professional use: work and protective clothing
Furnishing	floor covering wall and ceiling coverings curtains upholstery bedding
Industrial textiles	tarpaulins for lorries and containers, inflated structures and tents roofing conveyor belts non-wovens for insulation, soil stabilisation
Miscellaneous	toys decor ropes, nets awnings flags, etc.

8.5.1 Areas of application and fire hazards

Textiles are used in many applications, the most important of which are summarised in Table 8.166. The principal uses of textiles in clothing, furnishings and in industry are presented below taking into account the burning behaviour and potential fire hazards.

Clothing

For thousands of years Man has clothed himself with textiles made of natural materials such as wool, cotton, flax, linen and silk. In addition, leather and pelts have been used particularly as protection against cold. The manufacture of wholly or partly synthetic textiles suitable for clothing only started some 50 years ago. One of the most significant differences between wholly synthetic and natural fibres is that the latter do not melt on heating while the former do, usually undergoing decomposition. This results in considerable differences in their burning behaviour.

Ordinary clothing made of natural and synthetic fibres provides considerable protection of limited duration against heat and flames. Cotton clothing, for example, provides 2 to 5 s protection against a 25 cm long Bunsen flame while wool is effective for up to 20 s. This statement only holds, however, if certain structural characteristics of the textile are fulfilled. With clothing, the combination of various components as well as their cut and that of the whole must be taken into account.

Fire spread involving textiles is characterised by two features:

– Firstly the wearer would notice the fire relatively quickly and normally react immediately by removing the garments or attempting to extinguish them. A normal person thus limits the seat of the fire and the potential injuries.
– Secondly, the fire propagation of conventional clothing materials is so slow that relatively extended times are necessary for the fire to spread over a large area – if indeed this occurs at all and the fire does not extinguish on its own. Thus even if the wearer reacts incorrectly, his entire clothing does not generally catch fire in a disproportionately short time.

Protective clothing against flame and heat is a specialised topic and is not dealt with here.

The burning behaviour of clothing textiles is usually investigated by laboratory methods in which the specimen is positioned either vertically or at 45° to the vertical or horizontally. A flame usually between 2 and 5 cm long is applied either to the edge or the surface of the specimen. The ignitability, rate of spread of flame and/or surface destroyed are measured.

In the American "Mushroom" method the heat transfer is measured on a dummy leg. Comparative investigations are carried out on life-size dummies in order to ascertain whether a correlation exists between the laboratory test results and those of the "Mushroom" test.

Furnishing textiles

In the field of furnishing or household textiles distinctions must be made between applications involving quite different potential fire hazards. Increasingly popular *textile floor coverings*, for instance, can consist of the most diverse materials. While wall and ceiling coverings may be exposed to high heat levels in a fire, this does not occur with floorings since the hot combustion gases rise and cold air is drawn in from below. Even falling burning debris is not normally dangerous since the oxygen supply under it is restricted and the floor will thus usually char or melt rather than burn. Requirements and fire tests for floorings vary considerably. In many cases, floorings are governed by national building codes and are tested accordingly (for details see Section 8.2.2 to 8.2.17).

Wall and especially *ceiling coverings* are subjected to severe conditions in fires since they are exposed not only to flames but also to hot fire gases. Such coverings may be fabrics or linings coated with paper or foam. Their fire performance can be very different. If wall and ceiling claddings are firmly bonded to walls they are considered as building materials and are tested as such. Drapes and wallcoverings are generally not classified as building materials except in applications involving particular hazards such as conference halls.

The usual method is a small burner test with the flame applied to a vertically positioned specimen as in the German DIN 4102 Part 1 moderate flammability test for class B2 building materials (see Section 8.2.2).

Upholstered furniture with textile cushion covers is used in dwellings, places of work and in nearly all means of transport. Fire performance requirements vary considerably with the application. At present technical fire protection regulations covering the private sector are in force only in the USA and Great Britain; further details are given in Section 8.6.

Transportation seating is an important area of application for textiles. Aircraft seats are subject to Federal Aviation Regulations (FAR) while the FMVSS 302 (Federal Motor Vehicle Safety Standard) fire test is used practically worldwide in the automobile sector. Shipping is covered by the internationally adopted IMCO (Inter-Governmental Maritime Consultative Organization) recommendations. This subject is covered in detail in Section 8.3.

Fire testing of furniture is carried out with various ignition sources such as cigarette, small burner, waste-paper basket, wood cribs and newspaper. The requirements usually stipulate that no ignition or flame spread should occur with a defined ignition source. Since furniture is not counted as a building material and only has to comply with regulations when certain potential hazards are involved (e.g. in conference halls and theatres) it is difficult to set up meaningful tests to cover all permutations of materials and uses. The British and American regulations thus reflect the fact that burning cigarettes are the most frequent cause of fire. Moreover, if materials on ships and in planes are set alight by a low intensity ignition source such as a cigarette, match or paper, it must be ensured that this new and stronger secondary ignition source does not give rise to fire propagation or smoke development.

It is generally known that testing the burning behaviour of individual components of cushions does not enable meaningful predictions of the burning behaviour of the composites to be made. Consequently safety tests must always be carried out on upholstered furniture composites. Production checks on individual components are a different matter. In this case it is important to clarify which chemical and/or physical characteristics enable predictions of burning behaviour to be made and then test accordingly.

There is a world-wide consensus that comfort is an absolute priority where *bedclothes* and *bedding* are concerned. In order to feel comfortable, a range of physiological parameters must be fulfilled by selecting suitable fibre materials. If the burning behaviour of beds must meet certain requirements, considerable compromises usually have to be made on the physiological properties. Sometimes people act irresponsibly (e.g. smoking in bed) and this can harm others. Consequently, there has been a public demand for beds which are better able to withstand the effects of an ignition source. This is particularly important in hospitals, homes for the elderly and hotels. It is technically feasible to comply with such requirements, however the whole bed composite, not just the individual materials, must be considered.

British and American statistics show that bed fires have doubled over the last 10 years – a clear warning sign. The cause of fire is usually a cigarette. The victims, over half of whom are under the influence of alcohol or drugs, do not generally die of burns but in over 80% of cases from the effects of combustion products such as carbon monoxide liberated in large quantities by the smouldering fires typical of such incidents.

Curtain and *decorative fabrics* are used in many different way, mainly in the domestic sector. This makes a meaningful assessment of risks difficult. Here too, statutory requirements exist only for certain hazards such as conference halls, theatres and escape routes.

Curtains should be tested when hanging vertically, their normal position in use. In cases where curtains are considered as building materials (this only applies to high hazard areas) they are tested by the relevant procedures for such materials. Authorities, for example, may also insist on certain burning behaviour requirements when purchasing such fabrics. In the Federal Republic of Germany this can be classified according to DIN 66082 (tested to DIN 54336, specimen positioned vertically, flame applied to edge from below).

Under certain conditions, curtains can be a link in the chain of fire spread during the development of a fire. It is therefore important to know the burning behaviour of curtains and decorations particularly as many large fires have started with the ignition of the latter.

Industrial textiles

Industrial textiles include tarpaulins, tent material, packaging materials, filters, etc. Due to the heterogeneity of the materials, it is almost impossible to lay down uniform guidelines and test methods.

For instance, extended discussions have taken place on the requirements for *vehicle tarpaulins* for military use. Non-textile materials which do not ignite or immediately extinguish after the ignition source is removed usually have insufficient mechanical/physical properties. Consequently, pure or coated textiles, or to a limited extent plastic sheeting, are used. The burning test is usually carried out by applying a flame to the edge of a vertically positioned test specimen (DIN 54336 or DIN 53438). Although some materials meet the requirement of extinguishing immediately the ignition source is removed, a certain afterflame time is allowed for the reasons given above. This enables many technical properties to be optimised.

A further interesting area of application of awnings is for *inflatable* and *fabric structures*. Usually building regulations apply although they are oriented specifically to self-supporting building elements rather than to such special cases. It is therefore difficult to set standards ensuring adequate safety for the structure yet allowing variability in design. In the Federal Republic of Germany such tarpaulins must be of class B1 (low flammability) to DIN 4102 Part 1. It has been demonstrated that varying combinations of different materials do not necessarily result in similar courses of fire. This makes it difficult to determine the fire safety of the structure as a whole.

A similar situation exists with *camping tents*. Legal provisions are few and far between. In some countries, for instance, USA, Great Britain and shortly also in the Federal Republic of Germany a warning label is required. It should be reiterated that fire safety can be influenced by structural measures. Usually textile fire tests are used, mainly with a flame applied to the edge of a vertically positioned specimen (e.g. DIN 54336 or ISO/DP 6940 and 6941).

Legal provisions relevant to consumer protection exist for play tents. The test methods and limiting values are laid down in DIN-EN 71 Part 2.

The compilation attempted in this section shows the difficulties in considering the fire hazard for textiles on a uniform basis. Uniform conditions and test methods exist only when textiles are covered by regulations not as textiles but in conjunction with other materials used in specific applications e.g. building or transportation.

8.5.2 Regulations

Textiles, like plastics, are subject to certain regulations depending on the area of application. Other than clothing, the most important areas of application are building, transportation and mining.

Special fire protection regulations apply for *working* and *protective clothing* (e.g. fire protection clothing in foundries, working clothes in mines) and in public organisations (fire brigades, military units, etc.). In certain countries, regulations apply to the private use of clothing generally and for particularly vulnerable sections of the population such as children (night clothes) and the sick (hospital garments).

Such general regulations exist in the USA where the Department of Commerce requires testing to be carried out in accordance with CS 191 Flammability of clothing textiles. In many countries, including Australia, Finland, Great Britain, Ireland, Japan and the USA, proof of reduced fire hazard is required for childrens' night clothes. Hospital garments are covered by various provisions such as those in California.

The position regarding working and protective clothing is extremely unclear since each country applies different regulations laid down by various industries, authorities and officials (which may even vary at local level). Some states however are attempting to introduce general legal provisions binding on all areas in order to reduce the fire hazard of working clothes.

Import and consumer regulations relating to the flammability of *toys* exist in some states such as the Federal Republic of Germany, France and Great Britain. At present a directive is being finalised by the EEC for toys and this will also include burning behaviour. The ES 71/2 standard drawn up by the CEN will be incorporated substantially in this directive.

In the field of *furniture* and *furnishings*, various regulations exist for reducing the fire hazard of upholstery materials and furniture as well as bedding. Provisions for beds and bedding exist at present in Canada and the USA (test for burning behaviour of mattresses) and in Japan (burning behaviour of bedspreads). The burning behaviour of upholstery is tested in Great Britain and the USA in accordance with certain provisions (see Section 8.6).

Textiles used in *construction* are tested as building materials in most countries. Special tests are required for fabrics and films in some countries including Canada (ULC – S 109), Australia (AS 1530, Part 2), Japan (JIS A 1322), Sweden (SIS 65 00 82) and the USSR (GOST 12.1.017-80, Appendix 20). Typical applications include curtains and wall and ceiling linings.

Special test methods are being introduced on an increasing scale in the building sector for floor coverings. Test methods with vertically positioned specimens and small burners do not necessarily correspond to real conditions and are thus being gradually phased out in favour of procedures in which the back of the flooring material is covered. Tests are selected according to the definition of the fire hazard and either correspond to a small fire load as in the Methenamine pill test (see Section 8.2.14) or to a considerable fire load such as in the flooring radiant panel test (see Section 8.2.14 and 8.2.2). The latter test, which adequately reproduces the conditions occurring in a fire and thus correlates well with real fires, has been or will be incorporated in the test procedures for structural fire protection in many countries (further details are given in Section 8.2).

Normally no differentiation is made between materials used in *vehicle interiors* as far as burning behaviour is concerned. Almost everywhere materials used in civil aviation are governed by the regulations of the US Federal Aviation Administration (FAA) and, in this case by US FAR § 25853 and 25855 for aircraft interiors.

In the Federal Republic of Germany, the fire performance of materials used in rail vehicles is subject to the Federal Railways' regulations in DV 899/35 (for further details of these and other national provisions, e.g. for underground railways, see Section 8.3).

Shipping is governed by IMCO regulations; here again textiles are not singled out for special treatment.

In *mining*, the fire performance of conveyor belts with textile plies is tested by certain procedures laid down by the mining authorities.

8.5.3 Test methods

Depending on the area of application, the burning behaviour of textiles is determined by a multitude of tests involving various positions for the test specimen and ignition source and numerous types of the latter including matches, small burner, alcohol flame, wood crib, newspaper and waste-paper basket filled with newspaper.

A low or medium intensity small burner located in a combustion chamber is frequently used since this arrangement guarantees reproducible results and, under defined conditions, closely simulates ignition sources frequently found in practice such as cigarettes or matches. The test specimen is usually positioned horizontally, inclined at 45° or vertically while the flame may be applied to its edge or surface. The most onerous condition is when the flame is applied to the edge of a vertically positioned specimen.

Examples of the various specimen orientations are provided by the horizontal position in DIN 54333 (cf. FMVSS 302 in Section 8.3.1.2), 45° inclination in DIN 54335 and the vertical position in DIN 54336 (cf. similar test in Fig. 8.33 and Table 8.64 in Section 8.2.9 "Sweden", SIS 650082).

Table 8.167 contains a summary of some of the criteria for a selection of test procedures in use in the Federal Republic of Germany, France, Great Britain, Japan and the USA. These all involve a small burner as ignition source with specimens positioned horizontally, at 45° or vertically.

A review is given below of the most important standards in these five countries, relating to burning behaviour of textiles.

Federal Republic of Germany

Both the burning behaviour of textiles and their classification are covered by DIN Standards. In some instances the Standards relate to specialised applications such as floor coverings, protective clothing, mining (e.g. conveyor belts with textile plies and flameproof garments), automobile interiors and toys. Individual standards are:

- DIN 4842. 1977. Determination of the degree of thermal transmission of fabrics for heat protective clothing.
- DIN 4845. 1963. Flameproof fabrics consisting of cellulose fibres for protective clothes.
- Draft DIN 22 118. 1978. Conveyor belts with textile plies for coal mining. Burning characteristics and testing method.
- DIN 23 320 Part 1. 1980. Fireproof protective clothing for the mining industry.
- DIN 23 325. 1966. Flameproof protective clothing.
- DIN 54 331. 1974. Testing of textiles. Determination of the burning behaviour. Method of test by semi-circle.
- DIN 54 332. 1975. Testing of textiles. Determination of the burning behaviour of textile floor coverings.
- Pre-Standard 54 333. 1975. Testing of textiles. Determination of burning behaviour. Horizontal method – Edge ignition.

Table 8.167 Tests for determining the burning behaviour of textiles (ignition source: gas burner)

Country	Method	Specimen position	Flame application	Small burner Orientation	Flame length [mm]	Area of application
Federal Republic of Germany Pre-standard	DIN 75200–1980	hor[1]	Edge	ver[2]	38	Automotive interiors
	DIN 54333–1975	hor	Edge	ver	40	Textiles
	DIN 54334–1975	hor	Edge	ver	40	Textiles
	DIN 54335–1977	45°	Edge	ver	40	Textiles
	DIN 54332–1975	ver	Surface	45°	20	Floor coverings
	DIN 54336–1980	ver	Edge	60°	40	Textiles
France	NF G 07-099–1978	45°	Surface	135°	16	Textiles
	NF G 07-100–1978	45°	Edge	135°	16	Textiles
	NF G 07-113–1980	ver	Edge	ver	40	Textiles
Great Britain	BS 2963–1958; AMD 1968	45°	Surface	135°	16	Textiles
	BS 3119–1959	ver	Edge	ver	38	Textiles
	BS 5438–1976	ver	Surface	hor	40	Textiles
Japan	JIS L 1091–1973					
	Method A-1	45°	Surface	ver	45	Textiles
	Method A-2	45°	Surface	45°	65	
	Method A-4	ver	Edge	ver	45	
	Method C	45°	Edge	135°	16	
	Method D	45°	Surface	ver	40	
USA	FTMS 191 Method 5906	hor	Edge	ver	38	Textiles
	FMVSS 302–1970	hor	Edge	ver	38	Motor vehicle interior
	ASTM D 1230–1972[3]	45°	Edge	135°	16	Textiles
	FTMS 191					
	Method 5908 (1974)	45°	Edge	ver	16	Textiles
	Method 5903.2 (1971)	ver	Edge	ver	38	Textiles

1) hor = horizontal   2) ver = vertical   3) also corresponds to AATCC 32 – 1962 and CS 191 – 1953

- DIN 54 334. 1975. Testing of textiles. Determination of the burning behaviour. Ignition time, edge ignition.
- DIN 54 335. 1977. Testing of textiles. Determination of burning behaviour. 45° method, ignition on the edge.
- DIN 54 336. 1980. Testing of textiles. Determination of the burning behaviour. Vertical method, ignition at the lower edge of the specimen.
- DIN 66 080. 1976. Classification of burning behaviour of textile products. Principles.
- DIN 66 081. 1976. Classification of burning behaviour of textile products. Textile floor coverings.
- DIN 66 082. 1980. Classification of the burning behaviour of textile products. Drapery and curtain materials.
- Pre-Standard DIN 66 083. 1980. Classification of burning behaviour of textile products. Working and protective clothing.
- DIN 66 090 Part 1. 1980. Textile floor coverings. Requirements of construction. Burning behaviour.
- DIN 75 200. 1980. Determination of burning behaviour of interior materials in motor vehicles.
- DIN EN 71 Part 2. 1978. Safety of toys. Flammability of toys.

France

The French AFNOR G 07 Standards relating to textiles are given here. Additional internationally adopted standards exist but are not included in this summary (e.g. NF S 51-203. 1976. Flammability of toys, has been introduced as a European standard and corresponds to DIN EN 71 Part 2 mentioned above). Individual standards are:

- NF G 07-098. 1978. Textiles – Behaviour in fire – Data for choosing standardised methods of test to be used.
- NF G 07-099. 1978. Textiles – Burning behaviour – Estimation of the ease of flaming by determination of the probable duration of flaming.
- NF G 07-100. 1978. Textiles – Burning behaviour – Measurement of the speed of flame propagation.
- NF G 07-113. 1980. Textiles – Testing fabrics. Method of classification as a function of burning behaviour.
- NF G 07-128. 1980. Textiles – Behaviour in fire. Determination of the oxygen index.
- Norme expérimentale G 37-109. 1969. Textile supports covered with elastomers or plastics – burning behaviour (classification and test method).

Great Britain

In addition to the principal textile standards summarised here, there are numerous other standards relating to this class of material which are, nevertheless, not listed since they have been adopted internationally or are discussed elsewhere (e.g. BS 5852 Fire tests for furniture, in Section 8.6):

- BS 1547: 1959. Flameproof industrial clothing (materials and design).
- BS 2963: 1958 (incl. Amendments Nov. 1959 [PD 3563] and Nov. 1968 [AMD 128]). The flammability of fabrics.

- BS 3119: 1959. Method of test for flameproof materials.
- BS 3120: 1959 (incl. Amendment 1351 May 1974). Performance requirements of flame-proof materials for clothing and other purposes.
- BS 3121: 1959 (incl. Amendment 354 Oct. 1969). Performance requirements of fabrics described as of low flammability.
- BS 4790: 1972 (incl. Amendment 1847 Oct. 1975). Method for determination of flamma-bility of textile floor coverings.
- BS 4569: 1970. Surface flash in pile fabrics.
- BS 5438: 1976. Flammability of vertically oriented textile fabrics and fabric assemblies subjected to a small igniting flame.
- BS 5867: Part 2: 1980. Fabrics for curtains and drapes. Part 2. Flammability requirements.

Japan

The main methods relating to textiles are those of JIS L 1091-1973. Other tests include the "limiting oxygen index" (JIS K 7201-1972) and JIS D 1201-1973 (for car interiors, – for further details see Section 8.3).

– JIS L 1091-1973.	Testing methods for flammability of clothes.
A-1 and A-2 Methods.	45° Angle test
A-3 Method.	Horizontal test
A-4 Method.	Vertical test.
B,B' Method.	Surface burning tests.
C Method.	Burning rate test.
D Method.	Flame approach test for thermoplastic fabrics.

USA

A vast range of tests exists in the USA for determining the combustibility of textiles. Only the most important are listed here. Further methods are given elsewhere, e.g. Sections 8.2.14 and 8.6.

Federal Test Method Standards
- FTMS 191
  Method 5900 (1968). Flame resistance of cloth (horizontal).
  Method 5903.2 (1971). Flame resistance of cloth (vertical).
  Method 5904 (1968). Flame resistance of cloth (vertical, field).
  Method 5906 (1968). Burning rate of cloth (horizontal).
  Method 5907 (1972). Tablet flammability test for sleeping bag cloths.
  Method 5908 (1968). Burning rate of cloth (45° angle).
  Method 5910 (1968). Burning rate of cloth (30° angle).

Commercial Standard CS 191-53 (Revised). Flammability of clothing textiles.

American Society of Testing and Materials.
- ANSI/ASTM D 1230-61 (Reapproved 1972). Flammability of clothing textiles.
- ASTM D 3411-75 T. Flammability of textile materials.

American Association of Textile Chemists and Colorists.
- AATCC 32 (1962). Flammability of clothing textiles.
- AATCC 34 (1969). Fire resistance of textile fabrics.

National Fire Protection Association.
- NFPA 702 (1968). Wearing apparel flammability.
- NFPA 701 (1976). Flame resistant textiles and films.

Canvas Products Association International.
- CPAI-84 (1975). Flame resistant materials used in camping tentage.

8.5.4 Outlook

Due to the extremely varied areas of application of textiles and the many technical fire protection regulations and test procedures, it is difficult to make general observations on future developments.

In ISO, Technical Committee ISO/TC 38/SC 19 "Burning behaviour of textiles" is pushing ahead with the development of standards in accordance with the aim of this organisation of facilitating the international exchange of goods and services and encouraging mutual cooperation (see also Section 8.2.18).

Working Groups WG 1 "Terminology", WG 2 "Clothing", WG 3 "Household textiles", WG 4 "Industrial textiles", WG 5 "Textile floor and wall coverings", WG 6 "Analysis of fire incidents" and Sub-Committee SC 19 "Burning behaviour of textiles and textile products" have been active in various areas including:

- ISO/DP 6940. Textile fabrics – Determination of ease of ignition.
- ISO/DP 6941. Textile fabrics – Measurement of flame spread properties of vertically oriented specimens.
- ISO/DIS 4880/1. Burning behaviour of textiles and textile products – Vocabulary: Part 1.
- ISO/DP 7248. Fire data collection and presentation system.
- ISO/DIS 6925. Textile floor coverings – Burning behaviour – Tablet test at ambient temperature.
- Development of a method for surface flash effect with textile fabrics.
- Investigations on heat transfer and heat loss.
- Investigations on the burning behaviour of textiles for upholstered furniture, mattresses and bedding. This involves close cooperation with Sub-Committee ISO/TC 136/SC 1 (Furniture; test methods).

There is no intention of becoming involved in the problems of smoke development and toxicity of fire gases. Instead relevant developments are awaited from ISO/TC 92, the committee responsible for fire tests in building (see Sections 8.2.18 and 9.2.3).

8.6 Furniture and furnishings

8.6.1 Introduction

Furniture and furnishings include all moveable items used to equip a building such as cupboards, wardrobes, chests, tables, desks, seating, bedding, etc. Other building contents considered as furnishings such as household textiles (decorations, curtains) or floor coverings (the use of which is controlled by the building inspectorate in many countries, see Section 8.2) are not considered in this account. Upholstered furniture used in transportation (mainly as seating) is dealt with in Section 8.3.

Furniture and furnishings (henceforth referred to as furniture) pose differing fire hazards depending on the surroundings in which they are used. Decisive factors in considerations of hazard are type (private household or auditorium), size (single family dwelling or skyscraper) and purpose (barracks with young, highly trained soldiers or hospital with infirm patients) of a building as well as its contents (high or low fire load). The assessment of fire hazard is dealt with in greater detail in Chapter 7.

The different areas of a building are subject to varying fire hazard as American fire statistics show [1]. A summary is given in Fig. 8.115. In the USA over 50% of fatalities occur in private single- or two- family dwellings [2]. As can be seen from Fig. 8.115, particular hazards exist in living rooms, kitchens, cellars and bedrooms. Most fires in living-rooms and bedrooms are caused by smoking, i.e. by misuse of potential ignition sources such as glowing cigarettes or matches. The probability of fatalities is greatest in bedrooms since victims are usually taken by surprise in their sleep and are therefore unable to react quickly enough. The items of furniture most commonly set alight by the above ignition sources are armchairs, sofas and beds.

The course of such a fire is now illustrated using as an example the case of an upholstered piece of furniture and a cigarette or an open flame (e.g. a small burner to simulate a match). The cigarette ignition source can result in a smouldering fire as follows:

Depending on the material the cigarette on the upholstery composite (consisting of foam and cover material) causes the covering to melt or char near the glowing tip. In the first case, the cover material melts away from the incandescent region; the intensity of the cigarette ignition source is insufficient to make the cushion filling glow (if it consists of foam). Melting of the foam is endothermic and partially consumes the energy emanating from the embers which is thus insufficient to initiate the smouldering phase. In the second case, the cover material starts to char and incandesce in the vicinity of the cigarette embers. The underlying cushioning material is heated up and starts to smoulder thus liberating further heat which is partially trapped as a result of the insulating effect of the filling and thus causes the smoul-

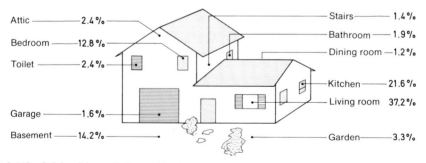

Fig. 8.115   Origin of domestic fire accidents

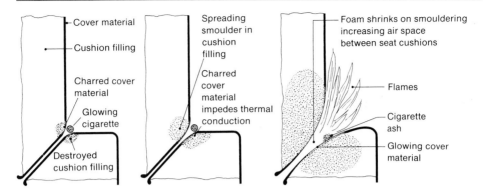

Fig. 8.116   Smouldering fire on an upholstery composite with a cigarette ignition source

dering to spread. Cushioning material can thus be made to glow and will suddenly burst into flame if enough air penetrates the void created. These processes are illustrated in Fig. 8.116 with polyurethane cushioning foam and a cotton cover [3].

Application of an open flame to an upholstery composite can result in the cover melting or glowing and charring. The cover material in such cases often catches fire if it does not incorporate a flame retardant. If the cover material ignites, it can act as a high intensity secondary ignition source and can ignite the cushion filling. In the worst case, the entire cushion combination burns up.

The ignition hazard of such upholstery composites can be considerably reduced by:

– shielding the cushioning from the heat of the ignition source with interliners,
– using upholstery fillings and cover materials with enhanced temperature resistance,
– the use of chemically and/or physically active flame retardants (see Chapter 5).

Numerous investigations have been carried out to ascertain the fire hazard of materials, combinations of materials and finished parts in upholstery. Laboratory tests on materials have proved to be least suitable for assessing the fire hazard of upholstered furniture. As in other areas (e.g. building, transportation, etc.) laboratory fire tests are most suitable for screening new materials under development and for quality control in manufacture. They also serve as a valuable extension of model fire tests where it is necessary to investigate the influence of certain material characteristics.

According to present understanding the most valuable tests appear to be those on combinations of cushioning material and covers. Such tests enable work to be carried out over a sensible time scale at moderate cost under conditions which are almost the same as those for tests on finished parts. This does not, of course, eliminate the need for model fire tests on finished parts or full scale tests in, for example, a fully furnished room since these show whether a correlation exists between the individual test methods and real fire situations (this topic is discussed further in Chapter 7).

Today, most investigations and test methods involve upholstery combinations made up in such a way that they correspond closely to the finished item such as an armchair or bed and are tested practically under finished part conditions. Numerous investigations have been carried out, particularly in the USA, Great Britain and Australia. These have covered the ignition hazards of upholstery composites with ignition sources of differing intensity such as a cigarette, match, small burner, methenamine tablet, wood cribs of various sizes, crumpled newspaper on its own or in a waste-paper basket, etc.

In the USA, *Damant* and *Young* have been particularly active in investigating the ignition hazard of covers and mattresses and cushions per se or in combinations. A selection of the more recent work is quoted here [4, 5]. *Lee* and *Wiltshire* [6] have also investigated this subject while *Rogers* et al. have been particularly concerned with the smouldering process of foams [7].

In Great Britain, comprehensive studies of the fire hazard of upholstery and covering materials have been carried out on behalf of the International Isocyanate Institute (III) on a suite consisting of two armchairs and a sofa as well as on a fully furnished room as *Prager* [1] and *Dawson* et al. [8] report. Other important investigations have been carried out at the Fire Research Station (FRS) by *Palmer* et al. [9–11] and *Woolley* et al. [12].

Finally, in Australia, *Moulen* and *Grubits* [13] and *Ramsay* and *Nicholl* [14] have published work on the fire performance of upholstery materials and foams.

8.6.2 Regulations and test methods

Few countries have regulations and provisions relating to the fire performance of furniture and furnishings since they form part of the mobile contents of buildings and are thus not subject to building codes. The authorities can demand performance requirements for furniture only in the case of buildings of special types and occupation. Due to the lack of suitable test methods these requirements must then be satisfied by passing the tests specified in the building regulations. In some Länder of the Federal Republic of Germany, for example, provisions relating to assembly rooms stipulate that seat covers must be class B1, low flammability, according to DIN 4102 Part 1.

In France, requirements exist for furniture for use in certain types of public building. Depending on the assessment of fire hazard these prescribe classification in classes M.3 or M.2 (for further details on French test and classification procedures, see Section 8.2.4). Such buildings are also subject to a regulation concerning the use of synthetic materials (insofar as an applications-related fire protection classification such as M.1 is not proven) which must exhibit only insignificant specified chlorine and nitrogen content so that any fire gases liberated do not contain a high level of hydrogen chloride or hydrogen cyanide.

At present the only countries in which regulations and test procedures for determining the fire hazard of furniture exist are the USA and Great Britain.

USA

In the USA, the use of certain furnishings is subject to mandatory regulations concerning their fire safety. For example, the US Department of Commerce has issued DOC FF 4-72 "Flammability standard for mattresses" [15] which was introduced in every American State in 1972. The fact that many fatalities are caused by mattress fires, started mainly by the effects of glowing smoking materials, led to this Standard. Mattresses complying with the Standard should make a contribution to reducing the hazards of a smouldering fire.

This test method for determining the ignition resistance of a mattress to a glowing cigarette is used for newly developed products not yet on the market as well as for quality control of commercially available mattresses.

The mattress meets specified performance requirements if glowing cigarettes, placed in certain spots on the horizontally positioned mattress illustrated in Fig. 8.117, do not cause charring of its surface extending more than 5.1 cm in any direction. The glowing cigarette is first laid on the bare mattress surface, then on the upper edge of the mattress where in the absence of a depression, it is held in place by three pins. Finally, various spots such as quilted surfaces are tested.

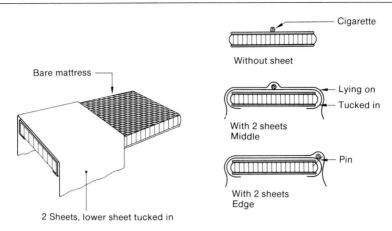

Fig. 8.117   Various arrangements for the DOC FF 4-72 flammability test for mattresses

The above tests are repeated using two sheets. The glowing cigarette is laid on a stretched sheet tucked under the mattress and a loose sheet laid immediately over it. An untipped cigarette 85 ± 2 mm long, weighing 1.1 ± 0.1 g is used.

In addition to this regulation which applies in the entire USA, the State of California also lays down certain requirements on the flame retardance of foams used as resilient filling materials in upholstered furniture. These are defined in Technical Information Bulletin 117 of the Californian Bureau of Home Furnishings [16] which specifies testing of individual upholstery materials by various means using an open flame as an ignition source (small burner, methenamine tablet). In addition the resistance of the materials to the effects of glowing cigarettes is also investigated. The following test methods are used:

– *Resilient Foams* are tested vertically with a Bunsen burner as in FTMS 191 Method 5903.2. This method is described in Section 8.3.3, as FAR Part 25, "Testing in vertical position". The specimen dimensions (305 mm × 76 mm × 12.7 mm), number of specimens (at least 10, five of which are conditioned at 104 °C for 24 h) and requirements of the present test are somewhat different from the FAR method. All five specimens of both test series must pass the test. If one specimen fails, five new specimens must be tested and pass. If one specimen still fails the test is considered as "not passed". The requirements are met if
   – the mean charred length of all specimens does not exceed 152 mm or 203 mm for any individual specimen,
   – the afterflame time of all specimens is not longer than 5 s on average (10 s for any individual specimen), and
   – the mean afterglow time does not exceed 15 s.
– *Shredded resilient foams* are tested by filling a cushion 330 mm × 330 mm, made of the intended covering material. The cushion is positioned horizontally 19 mm above a 38 mm long Bunsen flame so that an area of at least 254 mm diameter is exposed to the flame. In all, twenty specimens are tested; a flame is applied for 3 s and 12 s to five specimens each in both the warp and weft directions. The test is passed if the weight of the specimen does not decrease by more than 5% having applied the flame for 12 s.
– *Expanded polystyrene beads* used as fillings are tested in a wire mesh test basket 203 mm × 203 mm × 76 mm high filled to the top. The ignition source is a methenamine

tablet lit with a match and placed in the middle of the material with crucible tongs. The test is passed if the weight loss in five successive tests does not exceed 5%.

– *Non-synthetic upholstery fillings* are tested vertically by the method described above for resilient foams.
– *Feathers and down* must be contained in a flame retardant cover. The cover material is tested by a method based on FMTS No 191, Method 5903.2 under the conditions described above for resilient foams. However 20 specimens are tested in this case – five each are flamed for 3 s and 12 s in the warp and weft directions.
– *Synthetic fibres* used as cushion fillings are tested according to amended Standard CS 191-53 (see also Section 8.5.3 "Test methods, USA"). In this test a small flame (16 mm long) is applied for 5 s near the lower edge of five specimens (152 mm × 76 mm) inclined at 45° to the horizontal. The flame front must not reach the cotton thread attached to the top in less than 10 s on average (individual specimens ≧ 7 s). The time which the flames take to travel a distance of 127 mm or to extinguish is also noted.

The effect of glowing cigarettes is investigated by two methods. Cushioning materials are divided into resilient materials (excluding foams) and resilient foams. The testing of resilient cushioning materials is basically similar to the DOC FF 4-72 method described above. At least six specimens 305 mm × 305 mm are tested by burning cigarettes on their surface. In the case of three specimens, a piece of sheet is laid loosely over the cigarette. The test is passed if the maximum charred length does not exceed 51 mm in all directions measured from the cigarette.

The resistance of resilient foams to glowing cigarettes is assessed in a test rig which simulates an upholstered armchair. The test mock-up, illustrated in Fig. 8.118, is made of plywood. The foam parts which make up the cushioning are laid in to form a back rest (184 mm × 203 mm × 51 mm) and seat cushion (203 mm × 101 mm × 51 mm). Both parts are covered with a standard cotton fabric (back: 381 mm × 101 mm, seat: 280 mm × 101 mm). An untipped cigarette weighing 1.1 ± 0.1 g, 85 ± 2 mm long is used as an ignition source. A piece of cotton sheet (152 mm × 152 mm) is laid over the cigarette and upholstered composite.

After placing the foam parts in the test rig, the covering material is fixed to them using pins. A glowing cigarette is placed between the horizontal and vertical cushions so that it is in contact with both and the piece of sheet is laid over it. The test is terminated if no further combustion phenomena are visible for at least 5 min. The remaining foam is weighed. The

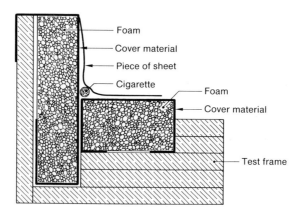

Fig. 8.118   Test mock-up for cigarette test on resilient foams

test is passed if in three successive runs at least 80% of the foam is undestroyed. If significant destruction occurs in one test, three further tests may be carried out. If all three give satisfactory results the test is considered passed.

Additional tests developed voluntarily by foam manufacturers serve as quality controls in the USA. These tests are being evaluated by the Consumer Product Safety Commission (CPSC). If they prove to be suitable, draft standard PFF 6-76 [17] will not be made mandatory in the USA as originally intended.

PFF 6-76 is a cigarette test for upholstered furniture in which the resistance of upholstered composites to glowing cigarettes is assessed. It is basically similar to Bulletin 117 mentioned above and the UFAC tests on upholstered combinations described below.

The Upholstered Furniture Action Council (UFAC) set up by furniture manufacturers has developed several tests for determining the resistance of materials used in upholstered furniture and composites to glowing smokers materials [18].

There are five tests for investigating

– polyurethane foams
– decking materials
– barrier materials (these are interliners for protecting PUR foams)
– fabric covers
– welt cords.

The tests on foams, barrier materials, fabric covers and welts are carried out with the apparatus illustrated in Fig. 8.119. Three tests on each are carried out with a glowing cigarette, 85 ± 2 mm long weighing 1.1 ± 0.2 g laid in the gap or on the welt between the back rest and seat cushion so that it is in contact with both. A piece of sheet, 125 mm × 125 mm is laid over the cigarette.

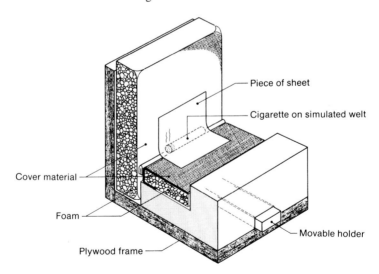

Fig. 8.119   UFAC cigarette test layout

The test rig shown in Fig. 8.119 is made of plywood. Polyurethane foam, 203 mm × 203 mm × 51 mm is used as cushioning for the back rest (in the case of the welt test a cotton filling is used). The seat cushion also consists of PUR foam and measures 203 mm × 127 mm × 51 mm (for the welt test 203 mm × 114 mm). The covering fabric used

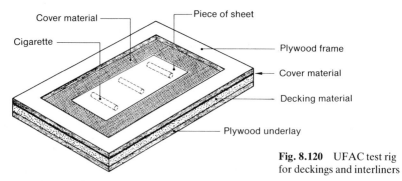

Fig. 8.120 UFAC test rig for deckings and interliners

in the tests is 203 mm × 381 mm for the back rest except with the PUR foam test and barrier test where it is 305 mm × 305 mm and 203 mm × 305 mm, respectively. The seat cushion cover is 203 mm × 203 mm.

The PUR foam and barrier tests are passed if the charred length above the cigarette does not exceed 50 mm. Depending on the test performance, covering materials are classified in classes I and II. The former is achieved if the charred length above the cigarette is less than 38 mm. If this length is exceeded, class II applies. In the welt test the cotton filling acting as a back rest must not be charred for more than 37 mm above the cigarette.

Deckings and interliners are tested using the apparatus illustrated in Fig. 8.120. The decking is laid on a plywood base and the cover fabric laid over it. The dimensions of all three components are 533 mm × 343 mm. A plywood frame with the same external measurements and internal dimensions of 406 mm × 216 mm is laid over this assembly. Three glowing cigarettes are placed on the remaining exposed surface of the cover fabric at equal intervals (see Fig. 8.120) and covered with a piece of sheet. The test is passed if the charred length on the base is less than 38 mm measured from each cigarette.

In addition to the American regulations and tests mentioned here, the New York Port Authority [19] insists that upholstered and plastic furniture used in its area passes certain fire tests. The plastics used must meet certain specifications based on the ASTM D 635 and ASTM E 162 tests (for further details see Section 8.2.14).

Finally, it is noteworthy that in Canada mattresses must meet the requirements of DOC FF 4-72 (see above). Textiles in consumer goods (including covering materials) must meet the requirements of the Hazardous Products Act based on ASTM D 1230 (this test largely resembles CS 191-53).

Great Britain

The Upholstered Furniture (Safety) Regulations introduced in 1980 in Great Britain [20] apply to upholstered seating sold commercially and stipulate that the specifications of BS 5852 must be met. Since October 1980 furniture which does not meet these specifications must carry a label warning of the potential ignition hazards of cigarettes or matches. All upholstered seating sold in Great Britain after 31. 12. 1982 must pass the BS 5852 cigarette test.

The tests for ignitability of upholstered seating described in BS 5852: Part 1 [21] consist of a test with a glowing cigarette and a small flame intended to simulate a match. The test apparatus is shown in Fig. 8.121 and consists of two steel frames hinged together, capable of being locked at right angles to each other. The frames are equipped with expanded metal mesh. The horizontal frame measures 450 mm × 150 mm while the vertical frame is 450 mm × 300 mm. The test apparatus can be opened out so that both parts are horizontal for inserting the covering material which is stretched over the entire frame with a retaining rod.

The covering material measures 800 mm × 650 mm. The upholstery fillings are laid under the cover and measure 450 mm × 150 mm × 75 mm and 450 mm × 300 mm × 75 mm for the seat and back, respectively. The cover material is held on the steel frames with clips. Finally the frames are returned to their original perpendicular positions.

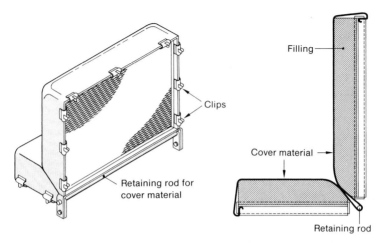

Fig. 8.121   Apparatus for testing the ignitability of upholstered seating according to BS 5852: Part 1

The glowing cigarette, (68 mm long, 8 mm diameter, mass 1 g) is placed at the junction between the seat and back rest at least 50 mm from the nearest side edge. If progressive smouldering or flaming occur within 1 h the test is failed. If no such phenomena occur, the test is repeated with a new cigarette placed at least 50 mm away from the position of the first cigarette. If no smouldering or flaming are observed a pass result is recorded.

The small flame test uses a 65 mm internal diameter tube, 200 mm long, connected to flexible tubing as a burner which is run on butane. The flame is approximately 35 mm long and the burner tube is usually positioned along the joint between the seat and back rest. The flame must be kept at least 50 mm from the nearest edge and is applied for 20 s to the material under test. If flaming or glowing continue for more than 120 s after removing the ignition source the test is failed. If this does not occur with the first and one repeat test, a pass result is recorded.

BS 5852: Part 1 is based on Draft for Development DD 58, 1978 [22]. Besides the ignition sources used in BS 5852, the latter also includes wood cribs of differing intensities (8.5 g, 17 g, 63 g and 126 g). The test rig is also of different dimensions with the seat and back of the same size i.e. 500 mm × 500 mm (see also Section 8.6.3).

In addition to the above tests, various other regulations relating to the burning behaviour of furniture and furnishings are used by the authorities. A series of test methods developed by the Department of the Environment (DOE) with the Property Services Agency (PSA) serves to check that furniture used in government offices meets certain requirements.

These test procedures are collected together in the DOE/PSA Fire Retardant Specifications. The most important relating to furniture are

– No. 3: Fire barrier standards for upholstery, i.e. seating and bedding.
– No. 4: Composite upholstery ignition standard (seating and bedding).
– No. 5: Flammability of beds and bedding.
– No. 6: Ignition standard for seating.

Test method No. 3 relates to fire barriers, i.e. interliners intended to protect the underlying foam from an ignition source.

Test method No. 4 is a procedure for screening materials prior to tests on finished assemblies by methods No. 5 (beds) and No. 6 (seating).

The use of various standardised ignition sources such as cigarette, match, small burner and wood cribs is common to all the above methods. Three tests are carried out on each material or finished part. In all cases, phenomena such as burning, glowing or smoke development should not be in evidence for more than 2 min after the ignition source is removed.

Finished parts fire tests Nos. 5 and 6 are carried out in a 30 m³ test room equipped to record time/temperature curves, smoke development, carbon monoxide concentration and temperature gradients (measured by thermocouples located at various distances from the specimen). Materials and finished parts meeting the above requirements should enable escape for up to 20 min after the start of a fire to be made.

Interliners for protecting underlying polyether foam are investigated in test No. 3 "Fire barrier standards". The foam block, 300 mm × 300 mm × 75 mm is completely enclosed by the protective interliner. The cushion so obtained is placed vertically in a test rig so that the various ignition sources (see above) are located 30 mm (10 mm in the case of a match) beneath the lower edge of the cushion and impinge on the edge. In the cigarette test the glowing cigarette is placed at the centre of the upper horizontal surface (300 mm × 75 mm).

Test No. 4 "Composite upholstery ignition standard" serves as a screening test for materials for bedding and seating. The materials must be retested by method 5 or 6 for finished parts depending on their use. The specimens are exposed to various ignition sources. In the case of intended use in seating, the dimensions of the test specimen are 450 mm × 300 mm for the seat and 450 mm × 600 mm for the back. In the case of mattresses samples 450 mm × 450 mm × usual thickness are used. Pillows are tested in their normal size.

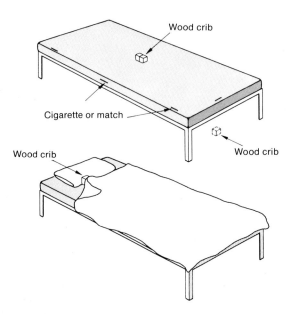

Fig. 8.122   Test rig for mattresses and bedding according to DOE/PSA No. 5

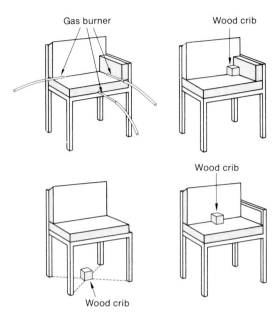

Fig. 8.123   Test rig for seating according to DOE/PSA No. 6

The test rig for seating for test No. 6 is illustrated in Fig. 8.123 while for mattresses a stoollike, 390 mm high rig with dimensions corresponding to those given above for the specimen is used.

Beds and bedding are tested to DOE/PSA No. 5 "Flammability of beds and bedding". The test apparatus is shown with bare mattress and with complete bedding in views A and B, respectively of Fig. 8.122. The tests are carried out using various ignition sources on the bare mattress and the combined bed and bedding (consisting of pillows, sheets, blankets, quilts, etc.).

Test No. 6 "Ignition standard for seating" is carried out with the rig illustrated in Fig. 8.123. The various ignition sources are placed at the points of highest fire hazard such as under the cushion and in the space between the seat and back or arm rests.

8.6.3 Future developments

Developments relevant to the fire performance of furniture are taking place primarily in the USA, Great Britain, Australia, within ISO and lately in the Federal Republic of Germany.

Investigations are in progress in the USA to ascertain whether the UFAC test methods introduced voluntarily and used for self-checking are suitable and adhered to by all furniture manufacturers. If the CPSC establishes that the UFAC self-checks are not effective, PFF 6-76 will probably become a statutory regulation across the USA.

Bulletin No. 121 published as a draft in April 1980 in California [23], describes a 1:1 test of the fire performance of mattresses used in buildings subject to high fire hazard such as prisons (danger of arson) or childrens' and welfare homes (fire hazard due to children playing with fire).

The bed frame and mattress are placed in a fire room, 3.0 m × 3.7 m × 2.4 m high. A metal bucket containing 10 double pages of crumpled newspaper is located under the bed. A thermocouple is fixed to the ceiling above the geometric centre of the mattress surface. The test is passed if after the ignition source has been consumed

- the mattress has not suffered a weight loss of more than 10% in the first 10 min from the start of the test
- the temperature at the thermocouple has not reached 260 °C
- the carbon monoxide concentration in the test chamber has not exceeded 1000 ppm.

Following the introduction of BS 5852: Part 1, work is being carried out on Part 2. In accordance with DD 58, ignition sources of increasing intensity (four wood cribs of increasing weight) will be used. Further parts of this test relating to fire performance of upholstered furniture are planned.

In Australia two draft standards for ignitability [24] and fire propagation [25] of upholstered seating have appeared. The test rig is based on British draft DD 58 and glowing cigarettes and Methenamine tablets (simulating the ignition energy of a match) are used. Work is also being carried out on four different wood cribs in accordance with DD 58 and newspaper ignition sources.

Within the framework of ISO, Working Group WG 4 Fire Tests in ISO/TC 136 (Furniture)/SC 1 is working on the development of methods for assessing the fire hazard of upholstered furniture (see also Section 8.2.18.1). Here it is hoped to test both individual components as well as composites. Tests of the latter will include the ignitability of mattresses and beds with bedding as well as of upholstered seating.

Ignition sources under consideration include a cigarette, match, small burner, methenamine tablet, wood cribs of varying intensity and crumpled newspaper in a wastepaper basket. In the future, radiation sources simulating electric fires will be examined. Considerable notice is being taken of the tests described in the British DD 58 draft in the development of these tests on composites.

In the Federal Republic of Germany, the Joint Committee NMP/NA Holz 854 "Testing the burning behaviour of upholstered furniture" has been set up in the Standards Committees "Materials Testing" and "Wood" to develop suitable methods for testing upholstered furniture. These methods will be submitted for discussion within the framework of ISO/TC 136.

Finally, it should be mentioned that, mainly at the instigation of Great Britain, discussions are taking place within the framework of the EEC on test methods for the burning behaviour of furniture.

References for 8.6

[1]   *F. H. Prager:* Untersuchungen zum Brandverhalten von Polstermöbeln. VFDB, 5th International Fire Protection Seminar, Karlsruhe 22–24. 9. 1976, Vol. I, p. 247.
[2]   *F. B. Clarke, J. Ottonson:* Fire Journal, 70 (1976) 3, p. 20.
[3]   *R. P. Marchant:* Cabinet Maker and Retail Furnisher, 7. 12. 1979, p. 12.
[4]   *G. H. Damant:* J. Consumer Product Flammability 2 (1975) 1, pp. 5/57; 3 (1976) 2, pp. 21/61; 3 (1976) 2, pp. 73/127; 3 (1976) 4, pp. 277/287.
[5]   *G. H. Damant, M. A. Young:* J. Consumer Product Flammability 4 (1977) 1, pp. 60/113; 4 (1977) 4, pp. 329/345.
[6]   *B. T. Lee, L. W. Wiltshire:* J. Fire & Flammability 3 (1972) 2, pp. 164/175.
[7]   *F. E. Rogers* et al.: J. Fire & Flammability 9 (1978) 1, pp. 5/13.

[8] *J. W. Dawson* et al.: Flexible polyurethane foam: Effects of covering materials on the behaviour of upholstered furniture. Report of the inter-company urethane panel, fire hazards subcommittee, 1973.

[9] *K. N. Palmer, W. Taylor:* Fire hazards of plastics in furniture and furnishings. Ignition studies. Building Research Establishment Current Paper CP 18/74, February 1974.

[10] *K. N. Palmer, W. Taylor, K. T. Paul:* Fire hazards of plastics in furniture and furnishings: Characteristics of the burning. Building Research Establishment Current Paper CP 3/75, January 1975.

[11] *K. N. Palmer, W. Taylor, K. T. Paul:* Fire hazards of plastics in furniture and furnishings: Fires in furnished rooms. Building Research Establishment Current Paper CP 21/76, February 1976.

[12] *W. D. Woolley* et al.: The ignition and burning characteristics of fabric covered foams. Building Research Establishment Current Paper CP 30/78, February 1978.

[13] *A. W. Moulen, S. Grubits:* Fire properties of some commonly used upholstery materials. Techn. Rec. 44/193/412, September 1973.

[14] *C. Ramsay, P. R. Nicholl:* The ignitability of flexible cellular plastics and their endproducts. CSIRO, Div. of Building Research, 1977.

[15] DOC FF 4−72. Mattresses. Flammability standard for mattresses. Federal Register 37, No. 110, 7. 6. 1972, pp. 11362/11367.

[16] Technical Information Bulletin 117. Requirements, Test procedure and apparatus for testing the flame retardance of resilient filling materials used in upholstered furniture. State of California, Department of Consumer Affairs, Bureau of Home Furnishings, January 1980.

[17] Proposed standard for the flammability (cigarette ignition resistance) of upholstered furniture (PFF 6−76). Part 1633. 1976.

[18] The Upholstered Furniture Action Council (UFAC) (PO Box 2436. High Point, NC 27261, USA). The following test methods were introduced by UFAC on 15. 3. 1979:
– Polyurethane foam test method.
– Decking materials test method.
– Barrier test method.
– Fabric classification test method.
– Welt cord test method.

[19] Flammability requirements of the New York Port Authority, Specifications governing the flammability of upholstery materials and plastic furniture.

[20] Consumer protection. The Upholstered Furniture (Safety) Regulations. Department of Trade. 1980.

[21] BS 5852: Part 1: 1979. Fire tests for furniture. Part 1. Methods of test for the ignitability by smokers' materials of upholstered composites for seating.

[22] DD 58: 1978. Draft for Development. Tests for the ignitability of upholstered seating.

[23] Technical Information Bulletin No. 121. Draft copy. Flammability test procedure for mattresses for use in high risk occupancies. State of California. Department of Consumer Affairs, Bureau of Home Furnishings, April 1980.

[24] DR 80123. Draft. Australian Standard. Method of test for the ignitability of upholstered seating. May 1980.

[25] DR 80124. Draft. Australian Standard. Fire propagation of upholstered seating of the low fire hazard type. May 1980.

9 Methods for Testing Secondary Fire Effects

9.1 Preliminary remarks

Secondary fire effects are those phenomena accompanying a fire which do not form part of the combustion process manifested by flames. They include smoke development, toxicity and corrosivity of fire gases and other phenomena such as burning or non-burning dripping or falling away of materials and finished parts.

Smoke production, toxicity and corrosivity of fire gases, which are the most important secondary fire effects, are dealt with in the following sections. Smoke production and its measurement are dealt with at some length since detailed investigations have already been carried out and many test methods have been incorporated in national and international regulations.

Smoke density testing of building materials is obligatory in many countries including the Federal Republic of Germany, the Netherlands, Austria, Switzerland, the Nordic countries, the USA, Australia and Japan.

In the field of transportation, prescribed test methods exist for motorised vehicles (Japan), rail vehicles (e.g. Federal Republic of Germany, France) and sea vessels (decking according to IMCO Resolution A.214 [VII], [see Section 8.3.4.2] and a Russian Proposal within IMCO), while aircraft are covered by the US Federal Aviation Regulations (FAR) which have been adopted by most countries.

Practically no methods for testing smoke production exist in electrical engineering – in France an experimental, i.e. non-obligatory, standard is on trial. Great efforts are being made to include smoke tests in large scale fire tests of cableways.

Theoretical aspects of smoke development are dealt with in Chapter 6 (the topics covered there are smoke generation, smoke production of plastics and smoke suppressants, and follow on directly from Chapters 4 and 5) and practical aspects are considered in Section 9.2. Toxicity and corrosivity of fire gases on the other hand, are dealt with entirely in Sections 9.3 and 9.4.

Systematic research into the theoretical and practical fundamentals of toxicity of fire gases has only just started. ISO Technical Report 6543 (see references for Chap. 7 [17]) enumerates the difficulties in developing tests for assessing the hazard of toxic gases. Basically two means of testing exist, chemical analysis of the fire gases and their effect on a biological system. The consensus of opinion is that the biological method most closely simulates the conditions in a real fire incident and chemical analysis can provide additional information to supplement the data obtained from the former method.

According to ISO two paths may be considered:

– identification of those materials which cause an exceptionally toxic environment,
– development of a standard for classifying all materials in regular use regarding the relative toxicity they cause.

Biological test methods have been developed in various countries and in some cases adopted as standards. DIN 53436 Parts 1 to 3 have appeared in the Federal Republic of Germany: Part 3, which describes the inhalation-toxicological investigation of thermal decomposition products, is available in draft form. This standard is intended to cover the toxicological testing of class A building materials which are required to carry a test mark (further details are given in 8.2.2). In Japan, certain building materials are tested to determine the toxicity of their decomposition products in accordance with Announcement No. 1231 of the Ministry of Building (see also 8.2.17). In the USSR, GOST 12.1.017-80 Appendix 21 contains a description of a method for testing the toxicity of decomposition products by biological means and by chemical analysis of certain components; the reader should consult 8.2.11 for further details.

In addition to the biological method, chemical analysis of individual fire gases has been introduced in various fields. This is particularly true in aviation where airline and manufacturers' material specifications place special restrictions on the toxicity of combustion products. Toxicity is tested parallel to smoke density measurements in a modified NBS smoke chamber by sampling smoke gas through special probes and determining the concentration of certain components (HF, HCl, HCN, SO_2, CO and NO_x) analytically (see also 8.3.3.3). The Japanese JIS draft is similar in principle (see 9.2.3.3). In France, test standard UTE C 20-454 covers the determination of the toxicity of fire gases from synthetic materials used in electrical engineering. The decomposition apparatus has certain similarities with the DIN 53436 equipment. The CO, CO_2, HF, HCl, HBr, HCN, SO_2 and NO_x components are determined by chemical analysis (for further details see 8.4.2.3). In addition, a French decree for the building industry states that synthetic materials which do not achieve class M.1 can only be used if they liberate less than 5 g of nitrogen and 25 g of chlorine as HCN or HCl per cubic metre of enclosed space. These quantities are calculated from the nitrogen and chlorine content of the material (further details are given in Section 8.2.4). For the reasons given in the introduction toxicologists consider that all the analytical techniques for determining the toxicity of individual components of fire gases mentioned here should be considered only as complementary to biological methods.

As far as corrosion caused by fire gases is concerned, the main interest is the cleaning and reinstatement necessary after a fire. Due to the many effective methods of clearing up, permanent damage to buildings and installations (including electrical and electronic equipment) has been considerably reduced and can even be repaired fairly rapidly on occasion. It is even possible to operate electronic equipment, which in the past would have been regarded as a complete write-off, after only a short interruption. With one exception in electrical engineering (see 8.4.1.2 and 8.4.2.3), no tests for ascertaining the corrosivity of fire gases have been introduced.

Besides the above secondary fire effects caused by fire gases, there are other phenomena, which have been the subject of much work such as flaming and non-flaming drippings of material. This risk factor (which should not be overrated) has been taken into account in various standards, and tests for determining burning drops have been introduced. As a result this hazard has been largely eliminated in the initial stages of a fire. It is in any case only of secondary importance in the fully developed fire.

Various methods of testing for burning drops exist in the building sector, e.g. in the Federal Republic of Germany as an addition to the DIN 4102 Part 1 small burner test (class B2, see 8.2.2) which involves placing a filter paper below the sample and observing if it is ignited. In Italy and Austria (see 8.2.6 and 8.2.7) the determination of burning drops is also based on the German small burner test and is included in the classification. In France the NF P 92-505 drop test in which the specimen is exposed to a radiator is used. Cellulose cotton wool placed under the sample must not ignite (further details are given in 8.2.4).

In the transportation field, the burning drop test in the so-called DB Brandschacht forms part of the requirements and classification of the Federal German Railways for rail vehicles (see 8.3.2.2). In aviation the burning time of falling drops is determined for materials tested to FAR Part 25 and included in the evaluation (see 8.3.3.2).

Burning drops also form part of the combustibility tests of UL Standard 94 in the electrical industry and are quoted as a classification characteristic (see 8.4.3.2).

9.2 Smoke development of fire gases

It is just as difficult to describe quantitatively the secondary effects accompanying a fire as the phenomenon of fire itself. The smoke gases occurring in a fire and the level of smoke production depend on a multitude of more or less interactive macroscopic parameters such as size of fire load, smoke production per unit weight of material, rate of fire propagation and combustion, ventilation, temperature reached, etc. To these must be added the various physical and chemical processes taking place on a microscopic scale during formation of smoke which impart certain characteristics to it (further details are given in Chapter 6). The smoke development in a fire is thus a non-reproducible individual event which can only be quantified with great difficulty, if at all, by measuring techniques.

A further problem is to develop techniques for measuring smoke density which correspond as closely as possible to the perception of the human eye or the vision obscured by smoke. Various investigations have shown that the product of visual range and smoke density is approximately constant. It is however, affected by the luminosity of the object and local light conditions. In the case of lacrimatory smoke, these relationships apply only to low smoke densities [1−3].

Photocells which cover the same range of wavelengths as the human eye are used in the photometric equipment available at present. However, they cannot measure human psychological or physiological reactions. It is hoped that such imperfect measuring techniques will nevertheless provide knowledge, for example on the use of certain materials, which when translated into practice will increase the chances of escape in a fire and thus improve safety levels.

In the following an introduction is given to the means of measuring smoke. Subsequently the techniques for measuring smoke density are presented and future developments are considered briefly.

9.2.1 Smoke measurement

Smoke density is measured by various techniques including purely visual recognition of smoke measuring rods in a room during a model fire test (see 8.2.10). The most frequently used tests are those based on optical methods i.e. attenuation of a light beam. There are also mechanical (separation of liquid and solid aerosol particles from the smoke gases) and electrical (generation of electrical charges in an ionisation chamber) methods. The latter methods are considered briefly below while the more important optical tests are discussed in detail subsequently. Various reviews of the subject have been published [4−6].

9.2.1.1 Mechanical methods

Smoke is measured mechanically by depositing liquid and solid aerosol particles from smoke gases on a surface, usually a filter. The deposited smoke particles are evaluated gravimetrically or optically. In 1967 *Cass* [7] presented a technique in which smoke from burning plastics is sucked through a filter. The amount of smoke (in %) deposited for a specific material is calculated from the weight of smoke deposited and the weight of the original material.

The "Arapahoe Smoke Box" [8] shown in Fig. 9.1 is a development of *Cass'* technique but has not achieved great practical importance and is used only as a laboratory screening test for plastics.

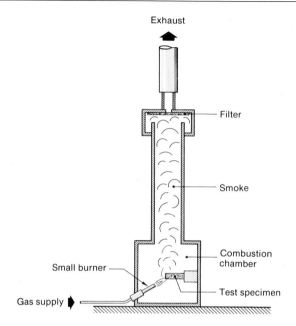

Fig. 9.1   Arapahoe smoke box

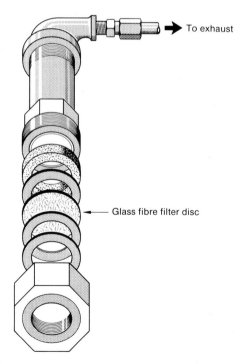

Fig. 9.2   Smoke sampling device

A further mechanical technique for measuring smoke development is an addition to the ASTM E 162-78 surface flammability of materials test.

A diagram of the apparatus and test specifications of this radiant panel test are given in Section 8.2.14. The smoke sampler is located in the exhaust hood and is shown in Fig. 9.2. It contains a glass fibre filter disc on which particles are trapped when smoke is drawn through it. Smoke emission is determined gravimetrically by weighing the filter before and after the test as well as photometrically. The latter method involves measuring the optical density of the smoke deposit area over a range of densities from 0 to 4.5 with a transmission densitometer and comparing it with the clean outer area of the disc.

The mechanical methods described here are not really suitable for evaluating smoke development in a fire incident and the associated hazards for humans since they give no prediction of sight obscuration. They can only be used for screening to eliminate certain materials and then only with great reservation.

9.2.1.2 Electrical methods

Smoke production may also be determined with ionisation chambers. This principle is widely used in smoke and fire detectors, particularly in industrial plants, public buildings and recently in private dwellings.

Ionisation chambers work on the following principle: oxygen and nitrogen molecules in the air between the electrodes are partially ionised by a radiation source (normally α-radiators such as radium [^{226}Ra]). The charge carriers give rise to a low current. If smoke particles penetrate the ionisation chamber, they combine with the ions whose mobility is then reduced thus lowering the flow of current. The smallest smoke particles, which are invisible, are ionised preferentially. Such ionisation chambers are thus used for detecting the very first stages of an initiating fire when no smoke is visible.

As with the mechanical methods, only a limited indication of sight obscuration is provided. Only those optical methods which show some correlation with the perception of the human eye are used in practice for the actual measurement of smoke density.

9.2.1.3 Optical methods

When light penetrates a smoke-filled room its intensity is reduced by absorption and scattering by smoke particles. The level of attenuation depends on particle size and shape, refractive index, wavelength and angle of incidence of the light. Such a complex system cannot be described mathematically and must thus be simplified as in the Beer-Lambert law:

$$F = F_0 \cdot e^{-\sigma \cdot L} \tag{1}$$

Where F = the light flux attenuated by the smoke layer
F_0 = the light flux at source
σ = the attenuation coefficient
L = the path length through the smoke.

The attenuation coefficient is defined as

$$\sigma = k \cdot \pi \cdot r^2 \cdot n \tag{2}$$

where k = a proportionality factor
r = the radius of the smoke particles
n = the number of particles per unit volume.

The optical density D can be derived from the Beer-Lambert law:

$$D = \log_{10}\frac{F_o}{F} = \frac{\sigma \cdot L}{2.303} \tag{3}$$

All smoke density test apparatus in practical use today operates on the Beer-Lambert principle. The photoelectric equipment registers extinction and does not differentiate between absorption and reflection of light. This differentiation can be of major importance in a fire incident since people trying to escape are probably more disorientated by strongly reflecting smoke than by reduced vision due to black absorbing smoke. Reflecting smoke consists principally of whitish, yellow, brown or grey fogs of condensed combustion gases. Black smoke is made up mainly of sooty solid components.

Various workers including *Bellisson* et al. [9] and *Teichgräber* and *Topf* within ISO/TC 92/WG 4 [10, 11] have been active in developing smoke density test equipment which determines smoke production by measuring contrast. Here the reflecting components of smoke are taken into account.

The principle of contrast measurement is explained below using the apparatus developed by *Teichgräber* and *Topf*.

A test specimen is decomposed by radiant heat in a chamber consisting of two interconnected sections – the decomposition and measurement compartments. The resultant smoke gases penetrate the measurement compartment which houses a photocell, two light sources A and B and a sector disc (Figs. 9.3 and 9.4). Incident light contrast is measured with light source A illuminating the black and white sectors of the disc. This results in values a and b respectively being measured by the photocell located opposite. Transmitted light extinction measurements are made through the third, transparent, sector of the disc after switching over to light source B giving value t. Values a and b (reflection, black and white sector) define the contrast as

$$K_1 = \frac{b}{a} \tag{4}$$

or

$$K_2 = \frac{b-a}{a} = \frac{b}{a} - 1 \tag{5}$$

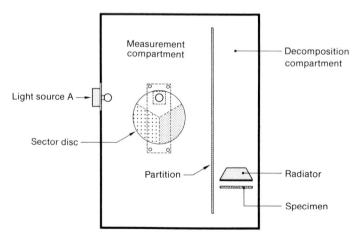

Fig. 9.3 Smoke measurement chamber

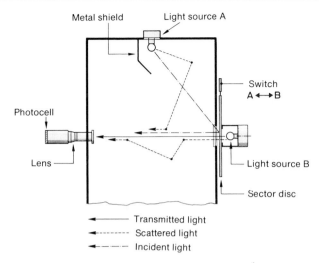

Fig. 9.4   Diagram of smoke density and contrast measurements after [10]

When both illumination intensities are equal ($a = b$) and there is no perceptible contrast, equation (5) results in the "correct" value of $K_2 = 0$ and $K_1 = 1$ [10].

Value t is evaluated according to the usual smoke density measurement procedure and quoted as extinction or as smoke density D according to equation (3).

The method described here for measuring contrast and extinction has been adopted in ISO/TC 92/WG 4 as the "ISO Smoke Test". Comprehensive round-robin tests have shown that the data obtained are easily distorted due to pronounced sooting of the sector disc. In the "ISO Smoke Test" in Technical Report TR 5924 [12] the contrast measuring device is no longer included (see Section 9.2.3.2). All important techniques for determining smoke production now under development and in practical use are thus based on extinction measurements.

9.2.2 The main optical methods of measuring smoke density

Although all the optical techniques for measuring smoke density described below are based on the principle of extinction measurements, they differ, in some cases considerably, as a result of special conditions laid down for each method. The test results are thus usually only valid and comparable for the particular method. Normally there is no correlation with other test methods.

The individual methods differ principally as follows:

- They can be carried out under static or dynamic conditions. In the former case, all the smoke generated is contained in a closed system (chamber) where it is measured. In the latter situation, the system is open; the smoke is measured as it escapes from the apparatus. Both procedures reflect a certain situation in a fire incident: the static method simulates smoke production in a closed room, while the dynamic method corresponds to smoke production in an escape route, for example.
- The length of the light path through the smoke layer varies in nearly all methods. The measuring device can be arranged horizontally or vertically although the former is usual in

Table 9.1   Principles of the most important techniques for measuring smoke density

Method according to	Light path horizontal/vertical	Length [mm]	Dynamic or static method	Specimen position horizontal/vertical	Energy supply by radiator/flame	Test conditions smouldering/flaming	Area of application *)
NBS	ver	914	sta	ver	R+F	s+f	B, TAV, E
ASTM D 2843	hor	308	sta	hor	F	f	B
DIN E 53437	hor	320	dyn	hor	R	s	B
NF T 51-073	hor	100	dyn	hor	R	s	–
Brandschacht to DIN 4102	hor	500	dyn	ver	F	f	B
SD/OI (s. 9.2.2.2)	hor	155	dyn	ver	F	f	–
NEN 3883	hor	220	dyn	ver	R+F	f	B
NT Fire 004	hor	230	dyn	hor+ver	F	f	B
NT Fire 007	hor	430	dyn	angle 30°	F	f	B
ASTM E 84	hor	914	dyn	hor	F	f	B
AS 1530, Pt 3	hor	305	dyn	ver	R	s	B
JIS A 1321	hor	250	dyn	ver	R+F	f	B
JIS A 1201	angle 80°	500	dyn	hor+ver	F	f	TA
DB-Smoke test	hor	160	dyn	ver	F	f	TRV
ISO Smoke Box	hor	360	sta	hor	R	s	B
modified Brandschacht to TGL 10685/11	hor	1000	dyn	ver	R+F	s+f	B
NBS-modified	ver	914	sta	hor	R	s	–
JIS-Draft	ver	variable (s. 9.2.3.3)	sta	hor	R	s	–
SU – to GOST 12.1.017-80	ver	800	sta	angle 45°	R	s+f	TS

*) B = building, T = transportation (AV = aviation, S = ship, A = automobile, RV = rail vehicle), E = electrotechnical

dynamic tests. In static tests it can be either, although there is a danger of stratification (i.e. the formation of smoke layers of differing optical density) and hence of distorted results. Stratification can be avoided by arranging the light path vertically or circulating the air.

- The dimensions of the test specimens, which may be positioned horizontally or vertically, vary according to the technique. With thermoplastics, vertical positioning is a disadvantage since the specimen withdraws from the flame or radiant heat source due to melting and flowing away.

- Energy can be applied to the test specimen by a radiant heat source and/or an open flame. Decomposition of the specimen takes place under smouldering or flaming conditions depending on the type and level of energy supply. Very different results can thus be obtained for the same material. Some methods involve smouldering and flaming conditions in order to take both these forms of smoke production, which almost always occur in fires, into account.

- Results are interpreted in different ways for each test procedure. For example, by calculating the maximum smoke density or percentage extinction. The methods of calculation are described for each test method below.

The principles of the main techniques for measuring optical smoke density discussed here are summarised in Table 9.1. Reviews and critical comparisons of the most important methods are contained in references [5, 6, 10, 13 and 14]).

As indicated in 9.2, it is not possible to describe smoke production in a fire incident quantitatively. In order to obtain defined information the numerous variables must be eliminated by working under standardised conditions. This can be achieved most conveniently by working on a laboratory scale. The conditions selected and laid down for a particular test method enable reproducible results to be achieved. It is thus possible, at least under test conditions, to obtain specific information on the smoke density of a material. It is impossible, however, to draw quantitative conclusions regarding the smoke generated from a material in a real fire. Nevertheless, limited predictions using laboratory results can be made on a purely empirical basis, i.e. from long experience of smoke development in real fires and in laboratory tests.

The techniques described in the following sections are divided into specific methods for determining smoke production only and multipurpose procedures carried out in conjunction with fire tests. They are used primarily in the building sector and are contained in relevant national regulations and codes. The other important area of application is transportation where requirements exist for smoke production of materials in passenger aircraft, ships, rail and motor vehicles (see Section 8.3).

For clarity, all smoke density test methods with the exception of the smoke density test of IMCO Resolution A.214 (VII) (see 8.3.4.3), are dealt with in this chapter and not in the chapters on building and transportation. Besides descriptions of the test methods, the smoke classes for classifying materials laid down in the various countries are also listed.

In the case of methods which are used in several fields (e.g. building and transportation) or in various countries where differing classifications apply, the commonest version is given. Changes or additions valid for other countries or areas of application are dealt with subsequently. All the test methods listed below are mandatory in the relevant area and are therefore in practical use.

9.2.2.1 Specific tests

Few methods exist for testing uniquely the smoke production of burning materials. The principal ones are the "NBS smoke box", "XP2 smoke density chamber", the Soviet method for determining the smoke formation coefficient to GOST 12.1.017-80 and the

German smoke density measuring apparatus given in the withdrawn DIN Draft E 53437. These are dealt with below. The decomposition apparatus used for generating fire gases specified in DIN E 53436 is used not only for determining smoke density but also, in its new version as DIN 53436, for toxicological testing (further details are given in 9.3).

Determination of specific optical smoke density with the NBS smoke chamber

This technique is the most frequently used method for measuring smoke generated by solid materials. It was developed in the USA by the National Bureau of Standards (NBS) and was later adopted for the building sector by ISO/TC 92/WG 4 as Draft Proposal DP 5659 [15]. It has also been introduced as an experimental standard in France [16] and was published in 1979 in the USA as ASTM E 662-79 [17]. The description of the "NBS Smoke Chamber" below is based on ASTM E 662-79. The NBS smoke density chamber is also used in aviation (passenger planes) and has also been accepted in electrical engineering (see below).

Diagrams of and test specifications for the NBS smoke density chamber to ASTM E 662-79 (previously NBS Technical Note 708 of Dec. 1971) are given in Figs. 9.5 and 9.6 and Table 9.2, respectively.

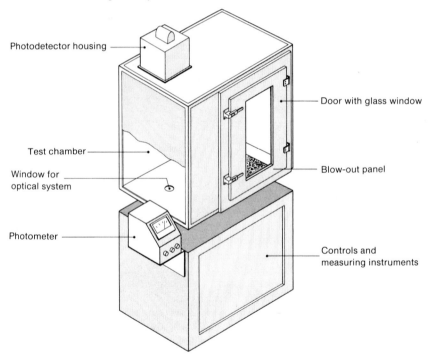

Fig. 9.5   General view of the NBS smoke chamber

The attenuation of a light beam caused by smoke collecting in the test chamber is measured. The smoke is generated by pyrolysis (smouldering conditions) or combustion (flaming conditions). The results are expressed as specific optical density derived from a geometric factor and the measured optical density, a measurement characteristic of the concentration of smoke. The specific optical density D_s is calculated from

$$D_s = \frac{V}{A \cdot L} \cdot \log_{10} \left(\frac{100}{T}\right)$$
(6)

where V = volume of the closed test chamber
     A = exposed area of the test specimen
     L = length of the light path through the smoke
     T = light transmittance (in %) read from the photosensitive instrument.

The expression $\frac{V}{A \cdot L}$ = 132 is constant for the NBS smoke density chamber.

D_m, the maximum specific optical density is calculated from Eq. (6) using the minimum light transmittance T obtained during the test. Further details and examples of calculations are given in ASTM E 662-79 (Section 10 and Appendix).

Table 9.2 Test specifications for determining specific optical smoke density to ASTM E 662-79

Specimens	at least six samples 76 mm × 76 mm × max. 25 mm, three of these samples are tested under flaming conditions and three under smouldering conditions
Test chamber	internal dimensions 914 mm × 610 mm × 914 mm
Specimen position	vertical, parallel to radiant heat source
Radiant heat source	vertical furnace with 76 mm diameter opening, radiation flux on specimen 2.5 W/cm² (smouldering conditions)
Ignition source	six tube propane micro burner positioned 6.4 mm away from and 6.4 mm above the lower edge of the specimen (irradiation and application of flame = flaming conditions)
Photometric system	light source with optics (colour temperature 2200 ± 100 K) vertical light beam, length 914 mm, photosensitive element
Test duration	max. 20 min or 3 min after minimum light transmission
Conclusion	determination of specific optical smoke density

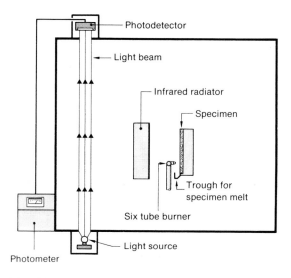

Fig. 9.6 Principle of the NBS smoke chamber

The NBS smoke density chamber is not mentioned in the various model building codes in the USA and, according to ASTM E 662-79, is only intended for use in research and development not as a basis for ratings for statutory purposes. In spite of this it is referred to in the HHS regulations for limiting the smoke density of interior finishes (see 8.2.14).

In the aviation industry, there are certain requirements in material specifications for evaluating smoke density, e.g. those prescribed by Airbus Industrie for the A 300 types. In this case the smoke density is determined with a modified NBS smoke density chamber while sampling is carried out to determine the toxicity of certain compounds (see 8.3.3.3). The specific optical densities listed in Table 9.3 must not be exceeded by aircraft components.

Table 9.3   Maximum permitted specific optical density for various aircraft components

Components	Test time [min]	Specific optical density D_s
Wall and ceiling claddings etc.	1.5 1.5−4.0	$\leqq 100$ $\leqq 200$
Textiles, curtains, cushion materials	4.0	$\leqq 100$
Electric cables	20	$\leqq\ 15$

In the field of electrical engineering in France, the NBS smoke density chamber is used to determine smoke density to UTE C 20-452 (further details are given in Section 8.4.2.3). Two quantities are calculated: VOF_4 ("Smoke Obscuration of Fire Gases" at 4 min) and IOF ("Smoke Density Index"). In the determination of the IOF, the time for the specific optical density D_s to reach a value of 16 is taken into account. This value corresponds to a light transmittance of 75% which is the limit of human vision. In transportation, UTE C 20-452 is used for testing various components like cables for rail vehicles, e.g. for the Paris Metro and French railways.

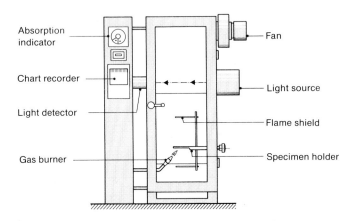

Fig. 9.7   Smoke density test apparatus as specified in the fire regulations directive

Determination of smoke density with the XP2 smoke density chamber

This method, developed in the USA, has been introduced as ASTM D 2843-77 [18]. It is used for determining the smoke production of plastics used in building. In Europe it is applied unchanged (Federal Republic of Germany) or in modified form (Austria, Switzerland) for determining the smoke density of burning building materials.

A diagram of the modified smoke density equipment used in Switzerland for testing smoke production is given below together with test specifications and classifications. This is followed by the version used in Austria, the USA and the Federal Republic of Germany.

In *Switzerland*, the testing of smoke production of building materials is carried out in accordance with the "Directive of the Fire Police Regulations" (1979) (chapter on "testing of building materials and elements, determination of smoke grade") (see also Section 8.2.8). A diagram of the test equipment and the test specifications are presented in Fig. 9.7 and Table 9.4, respectively.

Table 9.4   Test specifications for smoke formation

Specimens	six samples
	– solid materials: 30 mm × 30 mm × 4 mm
	– foams: 60 mm × 60 mm × 25 mm
	– coverings: 30 mm × 30 mm × original thickness
Test chamber	internal dimensions 790 mm × 308 mm × 308 mm
	air circulation 6.0 to 6.5 l/s
Specimen position	horizontal on wire grid 60 mm × 60 mm
Ignition source	propane gas pivotable burner, flame 150 mm long impinges on specimen at 45° to horizontal, distance of burner orifice to centre of specimen 45 mm
Photoelectric measuring device	light source with optics (colour temperature approx. 5500 K), horizontal light path, length 308 mm, photometer with narrow band photocell (max. sensitivity 550 nm)
Test duration	until specimen is consumed
Conclusion	depending on test result, classification in various smoke grades

At least three tests must be carried out and the arithmetic mean, on which the classification depends, calculated. The specimen is laid on the wire grid and the burner is pivoted away and lit. The intensity of the light beam is adjusted so that the photometer reads 0%. The burner pivots back automatically to the specimen and the light absorption is recorded as a function of time. The flame is applied until the specimen is consumed. The material is classified as per Table 9.5.

Table 9.5   Classification of the smoke grade of building materials (Switzerland)

Maximum light absorption [%]	Smoke grade	
>90	1	strong
>50–≦90	2	moderate
0–≦50	3	weak

In *Austria*, the smoke development of building materials is tested to ÖNORM B 3800 Part 1 (see 8.2.7). The equipment is the same as in Switzerland although the test specifications differ slightly. The Austrian test only lasts until smoke emission ceases or for a maximum of 15 min, not until the test specimen is consumed. The arithmetic mean, used to evaluate the smoke formation of the building material, is obtained from the five peak values of obscuration. Building materials are classified in the various smoke emission classes as per Table 9.6. According to ÖNORM B 3800 Part 1, Section 5, certain building materials are considered as weakly or moderately smoke emitting even without evidence.

Table 9.6   Smoke emission classes for building materials (Austria)

Maximum obscuration [%]	Smoke emission class
0–≦50	Q1 weakly smoke emitting
>50–≦90	Q2 moderately smoke emitting
>90	Q3 strongly smoke emitting

In the *USA*, the so-called XP2 smoke density chamber, originally introduced as ASTM D 2843 is specified for the determination of smoke production from plastics in the Uniform Building Code (UBC) and various other building codes. According to these codes only those plastics with a maximum smoke density rating of 50% or 75% (to UBC) are permitted (see below).

The original XP2 equipment and test specifications differ from the Swiss version (see Fig. 9.7 and Table 9.4) in minor respects summarised here:

– Equipment: the light source and fan are located on the left-hand side of the test chamber while the photometer is on the right. A 90 mm × 150 mm "EXIT" sign is fixed to the back of the inside of the chamber 480 mm above the floor.
– Test specifications: three specimens 25 mm × 25 mm × 6 mm are used. The test duration is 4 min.

The mean of three tests is obtained and the resultant mean light absorbance plotted as a function of time. The maximum smoke density is read off as the peak of the curve.

The smoke density is expressed in percent calculated from the area under the experimental curve divided by the total area (consisting of the interval 0–4 min multiplied by 0–100% light absorbance). The result is multiplied by 100 and is designated as the "Smoke Density Rating".

In the *Federal Republic of Germany*, only class A (i.e. non-combustible) building materials are tested for smoke development. Such building materials are inorganic but may contain organic binders. Smoke density is tested to ASTM D 2843-70, though the dimensions of the test specimens (30 mm × 30 mm × usual thickness, but max. 15 mm) are different from those in this 1970 American standard.

The test is passed according to the test principles for non-combustible (class A) building materials conforming to DIN 4102 subject to test marking (see 8.2.2) if light absorbance does not exceed 15% for an air flow of approx. 7 l/s. If evaluation according to ASTM D 2843 appears to be insufficient, additional tests may be carried out according to the withdrawn DIN Draft 53437 November 1966 (see below). This test which is performed under smouldering conditions is very elaborate and is thus seldom employed.

Testing smoke production of solid materials to GOST 12.1.017-80 (Soviet Union)

The Soviet GOST 12.1.017-80 [19] method for testing smoke development of solid materials was developed by the Central Scientific Institute for Fire Protection in Moscow. It has been proposed by the USSR within the framework of IMCO (Intergovernmental Maritime Consultative Organization) as an international test method. A diagram of the apparatus and test specifications for this procedure are presented in Fig. 9.8 and Table 9.7, respectively.

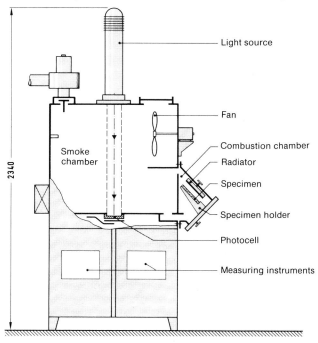

Fig. 9.8   GOST 12.1.017-80. Apparatus for determining smoke production

Table 9.7   Test specifications for determining smoke production

Specimens	10 samples 40 mm × 40 mm × ≦ 8 mm five samples are tested under smouldering and five under flaming conditions
Test chamber	internal dimensions 800 mm × 800 mm × 800 mm ≙ volume of 0.512 m^3
Specimen position	45° to horizontal and parallel to radiant heat source
Combustion chamber	volume 0.003 m^3, connected to test chamber via two openings: air inlet 20 mm × 160 mm at bottom and outlet 30 mm × 160 mm at top
Radiation source	electric radiator 120 mm × 120 mm 45° to horizontal, radiant flux up to 10 W/cm², conditions: – "smouldering" 2.5 W/cm², temperature on specimen surface 400 °C – "flaming" 9.6 W/cm², temperature on specimen surface 750 °C, ignition with 10 to 12 mm long gas flame
Photoelectric measuring device	light source emits vertical beam (length 800 mm) to photocell
Test duration	15 min
Conclusion	classification according to measured smoke generation coefficient

The method measures the attenuation of a light beam by smoke generated by smouldering or flaming decomposition of materials. The smoke generation coefficient is determined from the results of individual tests from:

$$D_m = \frac{V}{L \cdot m} \ln \frac{E}{E_{min}}$$ (7)

where V   = volume of test chamber in m^3
        m   = weight of specimen burnt in kg
        L   = length of light path in m
        E   = initial brightness at photocell
        E_{min} = minimum brightness at photocell

Materials are classified according to the magnitude of D_m into classes as follows:

$D_m \leqq 50$ Materials with slight tendency to generate smoke
$50 < D_m \leqq 500$ Materials with moderate tendency to generate smoke
$D_m > 500$ Materials with high tendency to generate smoke.

Smoke density measurements to Draft DIN 53436/DIN 53437 and to NF T 51-073

As indicated earlier, the smoke development of non-combustible (class A) building materials is tested in the Federal Republic of Germany to the withdrawn draft standards DIN 53436/53437 in those instances where the ASTM D 2843 test gives ambiguous results.

The building material is decomposed thermally in a quartz tube using an annular furnace. The apparatus is described in DIN 53436 Draft, August 1966 [20]. The smoke density is measured using the set up specified in DIN 53437 Draft, November 1966 [21]. The entire test rig is illustrated in Fig. 9.9 and a detailed diagram of the smoke density measuring apparatus is shown in Fig. 9.10. The test specifications are listed in Table 9.8.

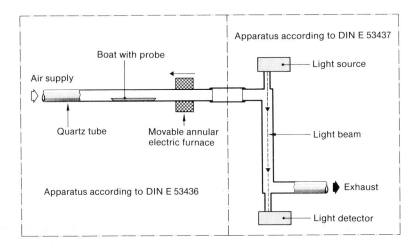

Fig. 9.9   DIN E 53436/53437. Smoke density measuring apparatus

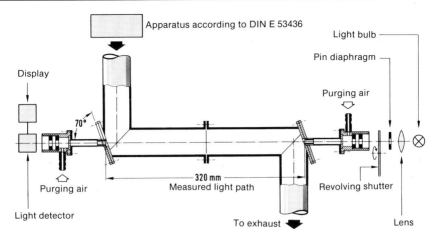

Fig. 9.10   DIN E 53437. Smoke density measuring apparatus

Table 9.8   Test specifications for smoke density measurements to DIN E 53436/53437

Specimens	dimensions: 270 mm × 5 mm × 2 mm, for each test temperature three (homogeneous material) or four (composite material) samples
Specimen position	horizontal in quartz glass boat
Test temperatures	250 °C, 300 °C, 350 °C, 400 °C, 450 °C, 550 °C, (if necessary also 200 °C and 500 °C)
Radiant heat source	annular furnace (100 mm long) around quartz tube (1000 mm long, outside diameter 40 mm) movable lengthways along the quartz tube with automatic advance operated at the above temperatures
Photoelectric measuring device	light source and detector, horizontal light beam, length of light path 320 mm
Test duration	15 min after switching on furnace advance, smoke density is recorded for 10 min
Conclusion	smoke density measurement is satisfactory if mean value of light absorption of three (or four) tests does not exceed 30% at any smouldering temperature

The annular furnace is heated to 250 °C and the air flow is adjusted (in the opposite direction to that of the motion of furnace) to 300 l/h. The specimen is placed in the quartz tube and the furnace advance mechanism switched on. After 15 min have elapsed, the smoke density is recorded for 10 min. If the first specimen gives a light absorption of less than 5% further tests can be dispensed with, otherwise two or three further specimens are tested at this temperature. The test temperature is subsequently increased to 300 °C, 350 °C, 400 °C, 450 °C and 550 °C (200 °C and 500 °C are additional temperatures which can be used).

The DIN E 53436/53437 method forms the basis for French standard NF T 51-073 [22]. This standard is not mandatory and serves only as a laboratory method for comparing plastics. The French standard specifies a 300 mm long annular furnace in the decomposition apparatus fixed in the middle of the quartz tube. Three specimens are tested at each of the temperatures 350 °C, 500 °C, 650 °C and 900 °C. The specimens are weighed into porcelain boats 80 mm × 10 mm × 6 mm. The measuring device in the French smoke density measurement apparatus is only 100 mm long.

The smoke index F, rate of increase of smoke density index V and intensity index I are determined as follows:

$$F = \frac{S}{m} \tag{8}$$

where S is the area obtained from the graphical plot of the maximum optical smoke density D_{max} against time (in min) and m is the mass of the specimen in g.

$$V = \frac{D_{max}}{m(t-t_o)} \tag{9}$$

where D_{max} is the optical smoke density, m is the mass of the specimen in g, t is the time required to reach D_{max} and t_o is the lag (time for the decomposition products from the boat to reach the smoke density measuring path).

$$I = \frac{D_{max}}{m} \tag{10}$$

A further rig for measuring smoke density based on DIN E 53437 is used in the Japanese JIS A 1321 standard (see 9.2.2.2).

9.2.2.2 Multipurpose tests

In the main, the methods listed here for determining the smoke production of materials are supplementary tests to techniques for determining fire performance or burning characteristics. Most of these supplementary tests are used in the construction field and are laid down in the relevant standards. Usually smoke production of materials is classified on the basis of test performance as laid down in the relevant regulations (particularly building codes).

With the exception of three methods used in the transportation sector (one of which, "Smoke density measurement during testing of deck coverings to IMCO Resolution A.214 (VII)" is discussed in 8.3.4.3), all the supplementary smoke density tests required in practice and listed below apply to building. Two further, non-mandatory tests are mentioned here for completeness:

A device for measuring smoke density (see Fig. 8.2) is located 100 mm above the thermocouple for determining smoke gas temperature in the "Brandschacht" used in the Federal Republic of Germany for testing non-combustible (class A2) and "low flammability" (class B1) building materials to DIN 4102 Part 1 (see 8.2.2). It consists of a light source which emits a horizontal beam of light (light path 500 mm) through the constricted upper part of the "Brandschacht" leading to the exhaust flue. The beam of light, attenuated by the smoke, is measured by a light detector. The smoke density determined in this way is not a prescribed criterion for classifying building materials but is quoted under special observations in the test report issued by the Materials Testing Institute as one of five categories (smoke development: none, very slight, moderate, strong, very strong).

Besides the accessory on the oxygen index apparatus described in the Japanese JIS D 1201 Standard, there is a further device for measuring smoke density viz the "Smoke Densitometer/Oxygen Index" (SD/OI) developed by Velsicol, an American company, and described in [23]. The system consists of a light source which emits a horizontal beam of light (path: 155 mm) and a light detector which measures the attenuated beam. In contrast to the Japanese apparatus, this device is not specified in any standard or regulation.

NEN 3883. Smoke test (Netherlands)

The Dutch test for smoke production of burning building materials (NEN 3883, Section 5, "Bepaling van de mate van rookontwikkeling bij brand") is carried out with the "Vlamoverslag" (flash-over) apparatus described in Section 8.2.3. The apparatus for measuring smoke density is shown in Fig. 9.11 while the complete "Vlamoverslag" equipment is illustrated in Fig. 8.8.

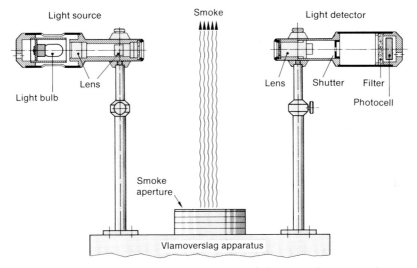

Fig. 9.11   NEN 3883. Set up for determining smoke production (Vlamoverslag apparatus)

The test specifications have already been summarised in Table 8.14 but the following changes are made in this case:

– at least 3×2 test specimens are required
– electrical input is 2250 W.

The attenuation of the light beam is monitored during the whole test by a chart recorder. The light transmission is defined as the quotient of the intensity of the smoke-attenuated light beam I and the original intensity I_0. The test lasts for a maximum of 30 min or is terminated 5 min after minimum light transmission has been clearly reached. Three runs are carried out.

Table 9.9   Mean smoke coefficient $\overline{R}$ as a measure of the contribution of burning building materials to smoke development

Mean smoke coefficient $\overline{R}$	Contribution to smoke development
$\leqq 5$	weak
$> 5 - \leqq 60$	moderate
$> 60 - \leqq 150$	strong
> 150	very strong

The smoke coefficient R is calculated from the minimum transmitted light intensity I_{min} from

$$R = 100 \log_{10} \left(\frac{I_o}{I_{min}} \right) \tag{11}$$

The arithmetic mean $\overline{R}$ is obtained from the values of R determined from three tests. The smoke development of building materials is divided into various categories based on $\overline{R}$ as shown in Table 9.9.

Various types of wood have been classified in the "moderate contribution to smoke development" category on this scheme. Building materials with a mean smoke coefficient $\overline{R}$ >150 do not meet the "basic requirements" of NEN 3891 (see 8.2.3 "Netherlands, classification") and must not be used on a large scale without protection.

The "Centrum voor Brandveiligheid TNO" (Technical Centre for Fire Protection) is at present investigating the influence of various factors such as type and quantity of material on smoke generation (see also 9.2.3).

Nordtest methods NT Fire 004 and NT Fire 007 for testing smoke development (Nordic countries)

Wall and ceiling linings

In the Nordic countries the smoke intensity of building materials such as wall and ceiling linings is tested by Nordtest method NT Fire 004, using the chamber described in Section 8.2.9 (Fig. 8.24 and Table 8.52). A diagram of the smoke intensity meter is shown in Fig. 9.12.

The test specifications have already been summarised in Table 8.52. A light source and photocell are located in the smoke outlet pipe on the side of the test apparatus such that a horizontal beam of light (length 230 mm) passes through the outlet pipe. The attenuation of the light beam due to the smoke gases is measured and recorded continuously as a function of time. The results are presented in a graph of smoke intensity against time.

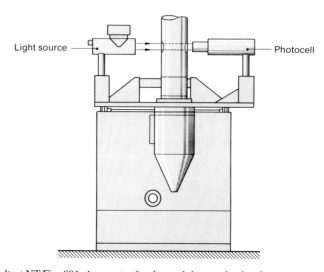

Light source   Photocell

Fig. 9.12   Nordtest NT Fire 004. Apparatus for determining smoke development

According to the NKB regulations, the contribution of wall and ceiling linings to smoke intensity is defined only for inside applications by classification in classes In 1 to 3. The following applies:

– Class In 1: Material does not contribute to smoke development, smoke density (maximum absorption $\triangleq$ 100): mean value $\leqq$ 10, individual values $\leqq$ 50.
– Classes In 2 and In 3: Material contributes moderately to smoke development, smoke density: mean value $\leqq$ 30, individual values $\leqq$ 95.

The overall classification of wall and ceiling linings is also described in Table 8.54.

Floorings

The smoke intensity from building materials used as floorings is tested by Nordtest method NT Fire 007. The apparatus and test specifications have been described in Section 8.2.9 (Fig. 8.26 and Table 8.55 respectively). The device for measuring smoke intensity is located at position A in the flue pipe in Fig. 8.26 and is illustrated in Fig. 9.13. The attenuation of a light beam (length 430 mm) passing horizontally through the flue pipe is measured continuously and the values are plotted as smoke intensity against time.

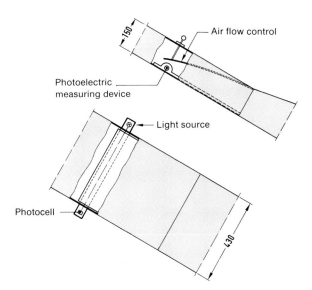

Fig. 9.13 Nordtest NT Fire 007. Device for measuring smoke intensity

According to the NKB the test is passed if the smoke density (maximum absorption $\triangleq$ 100) does not exceed 30 during the first 5 min of the test and is not greater than 10 subsequently (for further classifications see 8.2.9).

Testing of smoke development to ASTM E 84-79a (USA)

In the USA smoke production is usually tested to ASTM E 84 (other less frequently methods are ASTM E 162 [see 9.2.1.1], ASTM E 662 and ASTM D 2843 [see 9.2.2.1]).

Smoke development is measured at the "vent end" of the Steiner Tunnel (the complete apparatus is illustrated in Fig. 8.58 while the test specifications are summarised in Table 8.87

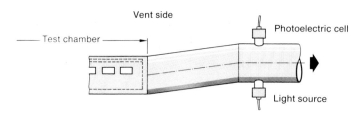

Fig. 9.14   ASTM E 84-79a. Apparatus for measuring smoke development

in Section 8.2.14); details are shown in Fig. 9.14. The light beam is aimed vertically up the vent pipe and the distance between the light source and photoelectric cell is 914 ± 102 mm. The measured absorption is recorded continuously and displayed graphically as a function of time. The time-absorption curve for the smoke density of red oak is shown in Fig. 9.15. The area under the test curve is divided by that under the curve for red oak and multiplied by 100. The resultant value for the material under test is compared with a scale on which asbestos-cement and red oak have been arbitrarily set at 0 and 100, respectively. According to the Uniform Building Code, the smoke density should not exceed 450.

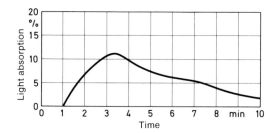

Fig. 9.15   Time-absorption curve for smoke density of red oak

AS 1530, Part 3. Smoke development test (Australia)

In Australia the smoke development of building materials is tested to AS 1530, Part 3-1976 using the "early fire hazard" test apparatus (see Fig. 8.67 and Table 8.101 in Section 8.2.16). The smoke density measuring device is illustrated in Fig. 9.16. The following additions to the test specifications given in Table 8.101 should be noted: a light source and photoelectric cell are mounted on the flue above the test apparatus such that a 305 mm long light beam is directed through the flue. The sensitivity of the photocell corresponds to that of the human eye (greatest sensitivity in the range 500−600 nm; only 50% of maximum sensitivity in the range <400 nm and >700 nm). The attenuation of the light beam due to smoke gases is recorded every 3 s during the test.

The test results are used to calculate the maximum smoke density for any 1 min period using the following formula:

$$D = \frac{1}{L} \log_{10} \frac{100}{100-R} \qquad (12)$$

where L is the length of the light path (305 mm) and R is the maximum value of the average reduction in percentage transmission of light for any 1 min period of the test. The mean of the optical densities so calculated is used to determine the "Smoke Developed Index" (Table 9.10). If some of the specimens do not ignite, the Index is calculated for each of the cases of ignition and non-ignition.

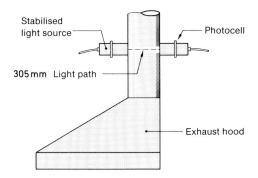

Stabilised light source

Photocell

305 mm Light path

Exhaust hood

Fig. 9.16   AS 1530, Part 3. Apparatus for determining smoke development

Table 9.10   "Smoke Developed Index"

Index number	Mean optical density $[\text{m}^{-1}]$	$[\text{m}^{-1}]$
0	< K*)	<0.0082
1	K – <2 K	0.0082–<0.0164
2	2 K – <2^2 K	0.0164–<0.0328
3	2^2 K – <2^3 K	0.0328–<0.0656
4	2^3 K – <2^4 K	0.0656–<0.131
5	2^4 K – <2^5 K	0.131 –<0.262
6	2^5 K – <2^6 K	0.262 –<0.525
7	2^6 K – <2^7 K	0.525 –<1.05
8	2^7 K – <2^8 K	1.05 –<2.10
9	2^8 K – <2^9 K	2.10 –<4.20
10	$\geqq 2^9$ K	$\geqq 4.20$

*) K = 0.0082

JIS A 1321 and JIS D 1201. Smoke production tests (Japan)

Building

In Japan the smoke density of building materials is measured by the JIS A 1321 "face test" in conjunction with fire performance. It is one of several parameters used for grading building materials in fire classes. A diagram of the apparatus and the test specifications for the face test are given in Section 8.2.17 (Fig. 8.68 and Table 8.107, respectively). A smoke collecting

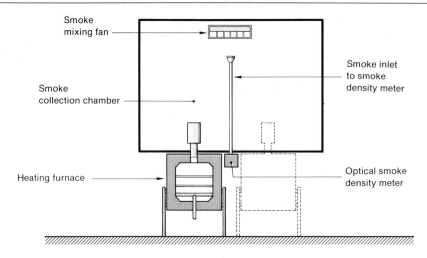

Fig. 9.17   JIS A 1321. Smoke collecting box

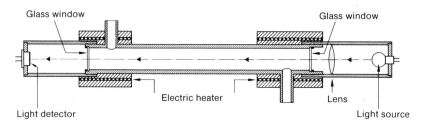

Fig. 9.18   Optical smoke density meter

Table 9.11   Classification of building materials according to smoke generation coefficients

Fire class	Smoke generation coefficient C_A per unit area
1	$\leqq$ 30
2	$\leqq$ 60
3	$\leqq$ 120

box is fixed on the face test equipment. The smoke collects in this box (Fig. 9.17) and is then drawn through an optical smoke density meter (Fig. 9.18).

The internal dimensions of the smoke collecting box are 1000 mm (height) × 1410 mm × 1410 mm. Smoke is drawn into the smoke density meter at approximately 1.5 l/m through an inlet located 300 mm below the centre of the ceiling of the box. The meter consists of a horizontal tube, 25 mm in diameter with a light source and light receiver at opposite ends protected by glass discs. The light path through the smoke is 250 mm.

The smoke generation coefficient (C_A) per unit area is obtained form

$$C_A = 240 \log_{10} \left(\frac{I_o}{I}\right) \tag{13}$$

where I_o is the light intensity (in lux) at the start of the heating test, and I is the minimum light intensity (in lux) during the test.

The resultant smoke generation coefficient C_A is used to classify the materials in individual fire classes (Table 9.11).

Transportation

JIS D 1201 contains a flammability test for organic materials for car interiors. Two methods are used:

- the "flammability test" similar to the American FMVSS 302 method (see Section 8.3.1.2) and
- the "fire retardant test" similar to the oxygen index method (see Section 8.2.9, Fig. 8.30 and Table 8.62).

A test for determining smoke density using the same apparatus fixed to the above equipment, is appended to both methods (Figs. 9.20 and 9.21). The smoke density meter is shown

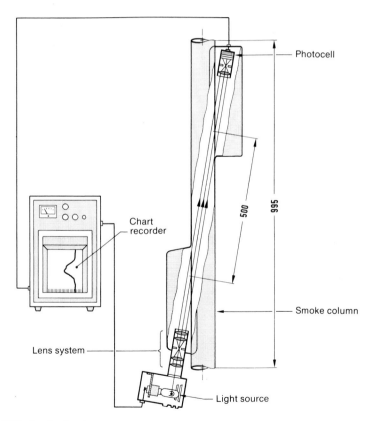

Fig. 9.19   JIS D 1201. Smoke density meter

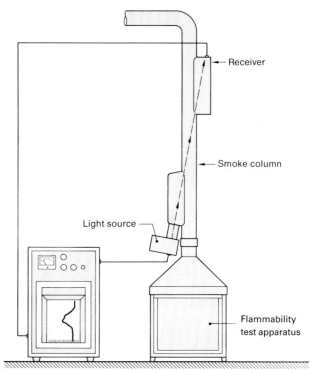

Fig. 9.20
Smoke density measurement
during flammability test

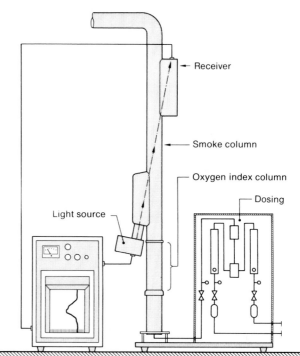

Fig. 9.21
Smoke density measurement
during fire retardant test

in Fig. 9.19. It consists of a light source, a smoke column traversed obliquely from bottom to top by a light beam, a photoelectric cell and a chart recorder. The smoke column is a 995 mm long steel tube with an internal diameter of 72 mm and the length of the light path in the smoke column is 500 mm.

The light attenuation coefficient C_S is used to classify materials in four smoke categories (Table 9.12).

Table 9.12 Classification of materials in smoke categories

Smoke category	Light attenuation coefficient C_S
1	<0.2
2	0.2−<1.0
3	1.0−<2.4
4	≧2.4

Testing smoke development with the German Federal Railways' Brandschacht (DV 899/35)

The smoke development of materials used by the German Federal Railways (DB) is tested in this organisation's Brandschacht equipment (for further details, diagram and test specification see 8.3.2.2). The smoke density meter is illustrated in Fig. 9.22.

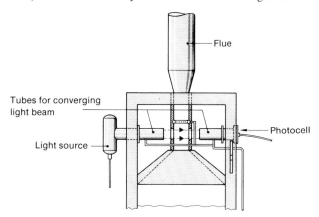

Fig. 9.22 Smoke density measurement in the DB Brandschacht

Table 9.13 Smoke development classes according to DV 899/35

Smoke development grade	Smoke development	Permitted sight obscuration in Brandschacht [%]
Q 4	smokes very little	≦10
Q 3	smokes and soots moderately	11− 40
Q 2	smokes and soots strongly	41− 70
Q 1	smokes and soots very strongly	71−100

Sight obscuration occuring during combustion is ascertained by means of a light path consisting of a bulb and photoelectric cell built into the exhaust flue of the DB Brandschacht. The attenuation of the light beam is recorded by a chart recorder in percent of initial value and designated sight obscuration and used for grading in smoke development classes as per the scheme given in Table 9.13.

9.2.3 Trends and developments in methods for measuring smoke density

Work is being carried out worldwide on the further development and perfection of existing procedures for determining the smoke density of fire gases. Particular efforts are being made in the fields of building, transportation and, increasingly, in electrical engineering.

Both national and international work is in progress with ISO prominent in the latter. Technical Committee ISO/TC 92 is particularly concerned with the fire performance of building materials and is working on the further development of the "ISO smoke box" (see 9.2.3.2). Additionally, in Europe, I-ILDA (Industry-Inter Laboratory Data Acceptance), a federation of European industrial fire laboratories is carrying out extended investigations and round-robin tests with this method and a modified "NBS smoke chamber" (see 9.2.3.1).

At national level, many countries are awaiting developments in the building sector from ISO and will adopt its methods in national regulations, often regardless of whether or not they already have a method for measuring smoke density.

Other countries are cooperating with ISO/TC 92 on techniques of smoke density measurement. The work at the Dutch TNO [24] is particularly comprehensive and includes development of the "ISO smoke box" within the framework of ILDA.

The "NBS smoke chamber" has been introduced in the USA as ANSI/ASTM E 662-79 [17]. In future the Nordic countries also intend to use this method which was introduced in 1980 as Nordtest method NT Fire 012. The Italians have considered this method for determining smoke density.

A smoke density measuring chamber resembling the NBS chamber has been developed in Japan and provides the additional facility of quantitative determination of certain gases (for further details see 9.2.3.3).

The CMEA countries including Czechoslovakia, Hungary and the GDR are also working hard on improving smoke density measuring methods. Investigations on a modified Brandschacht to TGL 10 685/11 have been carried out (see 9.2.3.4) in the GDR.

In electrical engineering, smoke development is increasingly determined at the same time as the fire performance of cables, for example by UTE C 20-452 for cables used by the French State Railways and Paris Metro. Smoke density of fire gases is also frequently measured during testing of cable bundles in large scale fire tests (such as IEEE 383 or SS 424 14 75; see 8.4.1.2).

Certain selected important developments of methods for measuring smoke density are given below. These include the modified "NBS smoke chamber", the "ISO smoke chamber", the JIS test method and the modified GDR Brandschacht.

9.2.3.1 Modified NBS smoke chamber

Modifications of the "NBS smoke chamber" are under development in order to overcome the disadvantages of the vertical specimen position (thermoplastics flow out of the range of the radiant panel and affect the smoke density measurement). A horizontal specimen position is being adopted and the sample is irradiated with a smaller version of the

ISO/DP 5657 ignitability radiator (see 8.2.18.2) without a pilot flame. In contrast to the conventional radiator which can only be operated at a single radiation intensity, there are several settings similar to the "ISO smoke box". Round-robin tests are being carried out with the modified "NBS smoke chamber" by Industry-ILDA.

9.2.3.2 Testing smoke development with the ISO smoke box

This method for measuring smoke density was developed by *Teichgräber* and *Topf* and adopted by ISO/TC 92/WG 4. The contrast measurement incorporated previously in the equipment (see 9.2.1.3) is deleted in Technical Report TR 5924 [12] discussed here. Diagrams of the smoke chamber and the optical measuring system are given in Figs. 9.23, 9.24 and 9.25; the test specifications are summarised in Table 9.14.

Table 9.14 ISO smoke box test specifications

Specimens	max. five specimens 165 mm × 165 mm × $\leqq$ 70 mm for each irradiation intensity 5, 4, 3, 2 and 1 W/cm^2
Specimen position	horizontal specimen is covered with aluminium foil so that a circular area 140 mm in diameter is irradiated
Test chamber	consists of decomposition chamber (in which specimen is decomposed with the help of the radiator) connected by an upper and lower duct to the measuring chamber in which the smoke density measuring system is located, total volume of both chambers 1.3 m^3
Irradiation source	ISO/DP 5657 ignitability radiator without pilot flame (see below) irradiance variable from 5 to 1 W/cm^2
Photoelectric measuring device	light source with optics, horizontal light path (length 360 mm), light detector and amplifier
Test duration	15 min
Conclusion	determination of maximum smoke density and where relevant time to specimen ignition

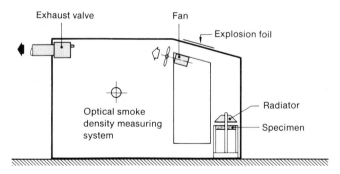

Fig. 9.23 General arrangement of ISO smoke box

The "ISO smoke box" consists of interconnected decomposition and measurement chambers (Fig. 9.24). The ignitability test device of ISO/DP 5657 described in 8.2.18.2 is located in the decomposition chamber and consists of a radiator cone with variable irradiance

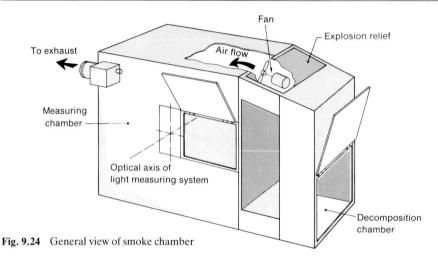

Fig. 9.24   General view of smoke chamber

(though here without a pilot flame) and a sample holder. The smoke produced in the decomposition chamber passes into the measurement chamber containing the smoke density measuring system via an upper and lower duct and is stirred with a fan (2000 r/min).

The smoke density measuring system consists of a tungsten halogen lamp light source with optics. It emits a horizontal light beam which passes through the chamber and impinges on a light receiver (consisting of optics and a photodiode) and is subsequently amplified. In order to shorten the light path to 360 mm, tubes project from the light source and receiver into the measuring chamber (see Fig. 9.25).

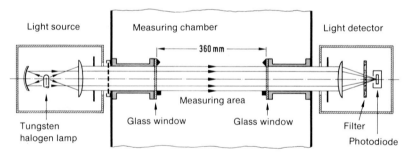

Fig. 9.25   Optical system for measuring smoke density

After calibrating the radiator, the irradiance is set to 5 W/cm^2 and the test specimen (covered with aluminium foil so that a circle 140 mm in diameter is irradiated) is placed in the sample holder. The test lasts for 15 min, during which the smoke density in the measurement chamber is monitored continuously. This procedure is repeated with four further specimens at the same irradiance. Subsequently the tests are repeated at lower irradiances down to 1 W/cm^2.

The mean smoke density D_{mm} is calculated from five tests at one irradiance from

$$D_{mm} = \frac{\Sigma D_m}{5} \tag{14}$$

The mean ignition time t_{im} of the five specimens is determined from

$$t_{im} = \frac{\Sigma t_i}{5}$$ (15)

9.2.3.3 Japanese JIS draft for testing the smoke development of plastics

The apparatus described in this draft consists of a smoke chamber in which materials are decomposed at three different temperatures with a radiator. The smoke density is measured with a vertical light beam in the chamber. In addition, the O_2, CO, CO_2, HCl and HCN contents of the decomposition gases are measured. A diagram of the apparatus and test specifications are given in Fig. 9.26 and Table 9.15 respectively.

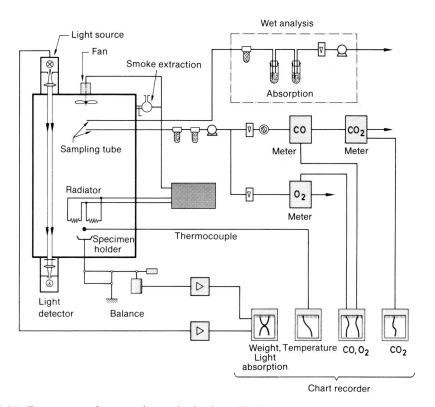

Fig. 9.26   Test apparatus for measuring smoke density to JIS draft

The radiator is calibrated before the test using an aluminium block with the same dimensions as the specimen. Tests are carried out with five samples at each of three furnace temperatures, 350 °C, 550 °C and 850 °C. The specimen holder enables the weight loss due to decomposition of the specimen to be continuously monitored and recorded. The light path can be set to suit smoke levels i.e. 250 mm or 500 mm for high smoke development and 1000 mm for low smoke development.

Table 9.15   Test specifications for determining gas composition and smoke density to JIS draft

Specimens	at least five samples 25.4 mm × 25.4 mm ×≦ 12 mm for each temperature 350 °C, 550 °C and 850 °C
Specimen position	horizontal on a specimen holder 50 mm × 50 mm which also acts as a balance
Test chamber	708 mm × 708 mm × 1000 mm high, volume 0.5 m³
Radiator	electric furnace run at 350 °C, 550 °C and 850 °C (at 550 °C, irradiance on the surface of the specimen must be 4.5 W/cm²)
Photoelectric measuring device	light source with optics, variable length (250 mm, 500 mm and 1000 mm) light path, light receiver
Gas analyser	infrared spectrophotometer for determination of CO and CO_2 O_2 determination HCl and HCN determined by absorption in aqueous solution and quantitative photometric analysis
Test duration	at least 20 min
Conclusion	determination of smoke density and other variables such as mass burning rate, type and quantity of combustion gases

The following pyrolysis gases are analysed and recorded continuously during the test: CO and CO_2 with an infrared spectrophotometer, HCl and HCN by absorption in aqueous solution and quantitative determination by the mercury-rhodanide or pyridine-pyrazolone methods. The oxygen content of the fire gases is also determined.

Note is made of whether and when the test specimen ignites and how long it burns. Irradiance is continued until the flames extinguish or for at least 20 min. The duration of afterglow is noted.

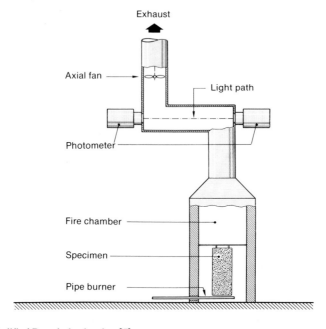

Fig. 9.27   Modified Brandschacht after [5]

The following are calculated from the results:

$$- \text{ Weight loss } (\%) = 100 \times \frac{\text{weight loss [g]}}{\text{initial specimen weight [g]}}$$

$$- \text{ Burning rate } = 60 \times \frac{\text{weight loss [g]}}{\text{burning time [min]}}$$

- Burning temperature (determined by measuring the maximum temperatures of the flame tip from the burning specimen with a thermocouple)
- Smoke attenuation coefficient C_S

$$C_S = \frac{1}{d} \log_{10} \left(\frac{F_o}{F} \right) [m^{-1}] \tag{16}$$

where
F_o = display reading before smoke development ($\triangleq 100\%$)
F = display reading during smoke development
d = length of light path

- Amount of decomposition products in ml per g of specimen and amount of HCl and HCN in g per g of specimen.

No further details on the calculations are given in the JIS draft.

9.2.3.4 Testing smoke development of building materials with the modified "Brandschacht" to TGL 10 685/11 (GDR)

Work has been carried out in the GDR on a method for determining the specific smoke emission of new types of materials, principally plastics [5]. The apparatus is based on the "Brandschacht". Only one sheet is tested since the smoke density can be more precisely determined than in the conventional "Brandschacht" with four sheets. The results from the latter are also affected by flames shooting upwards into the light path. This source of error is eliminated by the modified arrangement shown in Fig. 9.27 in which the flame is applied to the specimen with the line burner of the TGL 10 685/11 "Plattenrahmen" test (see 8.2.10). The smoke measurement area is 1 m long and the fire chamber is 0.45 m × 0.45 m × 1.25 m high. The specimen which is 0.2 m × 0.5 m is ignited over the line burner. The test can also be carried out under smouldering conditions using an infrared panel which can produce irradiance of up to 3 W/cm² on the specimen surface.

References for 9.2

[1] T. Jin: J. Fire & Flammability 9 (1978) 2, p. 135.
[2] ISO/TC 92/WG 4 N 180: DP 5659: Reaction to fire test – Smoke generated by solid materials. Annex F, December 1975.
[3] B. F. W. Rogowski: Flammability and smoke testing techniques. ERA Symposium, London, 6. 2. 1974.
[4] K. Maries: Measurement of smoke. QMC Instruments Ltd., 1976.
[5] P. Florschütz: Plaste Kautsch. 24 (1977) 9, p. 613.
[6] K. Pál: Muanyag és Gumi. 11 (1974) 4, p. 117 (Engl. translation in Intern. Polymer Sci. and Technol. 1 [1974] 7, p. T 103).

[7]   *R. A. Cass:* J. Cell. Plast. 3 (1967) 1, p. 41.
[8]   *J. Kracklauer* et al: Plast. Technol. 22 (1976) 3, p. 46.
[9]   *G. Bellisson, J. C. Tourette, E. Pot:* Mesure des fumées, méthode et premiers essais. Compte-Rendu No. 990 R 281, Paris, 1970.
[10] *R. Teichgräber, P. Topf:* Z. VFDB 23 (1974) 2, p. 52.
[11] ISO/TR 3814−1975. The development of tests for measuring "reaction to fire" of building materials.
[12] Technical Report TR 5924. Fire tests. Reaction to fire. Smoke generated by building materials ISO/TC 92/WG 4 N 528, 30. 4. 1980.
[13] *Y. Tsuchiya, K. Sumi:* J. Fire & Flammability 5 (1974) 1, p. 64.
[14] Fire performance of plastics. A review of RAPRA work. RAPRA of Great Britain. 1972. Part 1: Methods of test. Smoke tests. p. 33.
[15] ISO/TC 92/WG 4 N 212. Jan. 1977. DP 5659 (Edition-3). Reaction to fire test – Smoke generated by solid materials.
[16] Norme expérimentale X 10-702. Essai de mesure de la densité optique spécifique de la fumée. October 1976.
[17] ANSI/ASTM E 662−79. Specific optical density of smoke generated by solid materials.
[18] ANSI/ASTM D 2843−77. Standard test method for density of smoke from the burning or decomposition of plastics.
[19] GOST 12.1.017-80 Appendix 19. Method for the experimental determination of the smoke production coefficient of solid materials. 1980.
[20] DIN 53 436 Draft, August 1966. Gerät für die thermische Zersetzung von Kunststoffen unter Luftzufuhr.
[21] DIN 53 437 Draft, November 1966. Prüfung von Kunststoffen. Rauchdichtemessung.
[22] NF T 51-073. Matières plastiques. Comportement au feu. Méthode d'essai pour la mesure de l'opacité des fumées. September 1977.
[23] *C. A. Megal, A. F. Grand, J. F. Sabala:* J. Cell. Plast. 14 (1978) 6, p. 325.
[24] *H. A. L. Van Dijk, L. Twilt, H. Zorgman:* Smoke problems in buildings on fire. A TNO research project. Technical Centre for Fire Prevention. 1979.
[25] First Draft Proposal for JIS. Determination of the constituent of gas and smoke density resulted from the burning plastic materials. 1979.

9.3 Toxicity of fire gases

9.3.1 Introduction

The toxicity of fire gases is an extremely complex subject, the theoretical and practical foundations of which are only now starting to be systematically investigated. Because it would require the whole of this book to deal with physiological effects of fire gases and with further general questions of toxicity, only a short overview of current techniques of testing the toxicity of fire gases is given here. This is followed by the test methods which are required for satisfying specified toxicological demands in Federal German and Japanese building regulations.

9.3.2 Methods for assessing the hazard of toxic fire gases

The assessment of the hazard caused by toxic fire gases and the development of suitable test methods are described in ISO Technical Report 6543 [1]. The significance of and difficulties in working out such methods have been commented on by *Punderson* [2]. In Section 9.1 two

Table 9.16 Medical and toxicological terms

Term	Explanation
Anoxaemia	Low blood oxygen content
Anoxia	Oxygen deficiency in the tissues
Ataxia	Disruption of movement co-ordination
Cardio-vascular	Connected with heart and blood vessels
EEG	Electroencephalogram – recording of currents in the brain
ECG	Electrocardiogram – recording of the electrical activity (current and voltages) which occur with heart activity
Exposure	External conditions to which a biological system is exposed
Haemoglobin (Hb)	Colouring material of the red blood corpuscles which reacts with oxygen to give oxyhaemoglobin: $$Hb + O_2 \rightarrow O_2Hb$$ Oxyhaemoglobin transports the loosely bonded oxygen in the corpuscles and gives it up to the tissues in the capillaries. The affinity of haemoglobin for carbon monoxide is 300 times greater than its affinity for oxygen. If CO is present the reaction is: $$O_2Hb + CO \rightleftharpoons COHb + O_2$$ Haemoglobin combined with CO is not available for the transport of oxygen
Intoxication	Poisoning
Lethality	Ratio of the number of deaths to the total number of animals exposed
LC_{50}	Concentration of a material at which 50% of the animals die under specified conditions
LD_{50}	Single dose of a material with which 50% of the animals die within a few days
Relative acute inhalation toxicity	The capacity of a material to cause damage to the living organism by inhalation under fixed conditions
Toxicity	The capacity of materials to cause damage to the living organism by physical or chemical action
Ventilation	Lung ventilation

possibilities for examining fire gases were mentioned, either by chemical analysis or by the effects of the fire gases on a biological system. It is generally agreed that a toxicological study which relies entirely on chemical analysis of individual fire gas components does not permit a proper measure of the toxicological hazard. All the analytical methods which are listed in different standards in Section 9.1 are only meaningful if considered alongside toxicological inhalation methods.

In developing laboratory scale biological methods, criteria must be laid down for using the term "toxicity". The principal criterion today is that of lethality, that is to say the time needed until a particular animal reaches the point of death. Alongside this as a second toxicity criterion is the alteration in the physiological state of the animal under investigation. Such changes can be seen over a whole period of time before death occurs and are indicated by the word "incapacitation" in the following discussion. These problems, the work carried out and the methods developed by different research groups are investigated in [1] and also described in detail by *Jouany* and *Boudène* [3]. The meanings of the medical and toxicological terms used in this section are summarised in Table 9.16.

Even on a laboratory scale the toxic effects of the products of the thermal decomposition of a material on a living organism depend on a large number of parameters. These include the chosen temperature for decomposition of the material, whether decomposition products are produced by pyrolysis or flaming, the concentration and temperature of such decomposition products, the type of animal and the period of intoxication. This selection shows the multiplicity of the variables which influence the results and the difficulty in finding a correlation to the toxicity situation in an actual fire as this is influenced by quite different variables.

A frequent basis for judging the toxicity is that of comparing the material to be tested with a standard material, often a particular type of wood. This gives a measurement of whether the material being tested is more or less toxic than the reference material under the given test conditions and attempts are made to relate this to the "toxic reality". This method remains however in doubt because the problems in realistically estimating the fire hazard by testing – which have already been described in Chapter 7 – also exist in the field of toxicity.

9.3.2.1 Concept of lethality

As has already been stated, methods of testing materials toxicologically are based mainly on the concept of relative lethality. Lethality is determined under specified conditions on a statistical basis either as a function of the dose, LD_{50}, or as a function of concentration, LC_{50}. The time until the animals die is also considered. It is difficult to determine the exact point of death, various characteristic signs such as lack of breathing, absence of activity of the central nervous system or absence of heart activity are recommended.

Various workers have attempted to make statements about the toxicity of materials from a determination of the lethality [4–7]. The investigations were carried out using a pyrolysis apparatus based on DIN E 53436 [8] working under dynamic conditions in which an air/fire-gas mixture is passed through the exposure chamber. Newer investigations by *Klimisch* et al. [9, 10] were made using the modified method of DIN 53436 Parts 1–3. The advantages of such a dynamic system are the defined concentration of pyrolysis products during the investigation; thus it is possible to obtain the inhalation rate and the total inhaled quantity of the decomposed substance [9]. This method also allows the effects of the dose of the inhaled product on the animal to be determined. In addition the dynamic test procedure has the advantage that it can ensure that the animal is supplied with sufficient oxygen by adding air thus removing the danger of anoxia occurring from oxygen deficiency (less than 15% O_2) and avoiding stress phenomena arising from increased temperature of the surroundings. In addition to the lethality (specified as LC_{50}) the COHb content in the blood of the animal can be determined by biological measurement.

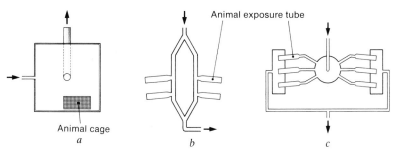

Fig. 9.28 Exposure systems

a: Whole body exposure (inhalation chamber)
b: Head and nose exposure (10 l chamber)
c: Tube exposure (1 l tube)

The animals used are mice or rats which can be put in various types of inhalation systems. Most commonly the animals are exposed to the decomposition products in a head-and-nose exposure system (tubes). Inhalation chambers in which complete body exposure is made are also common; volumes vary from 10–1,000 litres and the animals are put into separate cages in the chamber. Sketches which show the principles of these different exposure systems are given in Fig. 9.28.

Toxicological inhalation investigations have also been made in static systems in which the air/fire-gas mixture is led into an exposure chamber, e.g. the NBS smoke chamber (for details of the apparatus see Section 9.2.2.1, Figs. 9.5 and 9.6 and Table 9.2). Here the material under test is decomposed by a radiant panel with intensity 2.5 W/cm² under smouldering conditions or by the use of an additional pilot flame for flaming conditions. The animals are in cages which are spaced out in the NBS smoke chamber; thus the formation of the decomposition products and their inhalation occur simultaneously in one chamber. In addition, measurements of certain components of the air/fire-gas mixture (O_2, CO, CO_2, HCl, HCN, NO_x etc.) can be made by chemical analysis. The disadvantages of such a system are the concurrent effects of oxygen deficiency and heat release on the animal which make judgement of intoxication difficult.

9.3.2.2 Concept of incapacitation

This concept is based on the possibility of survival rather than that of death by intoxication and involves determining the point in a fire at which life-threatening incapacitation (e.g. the inability to flee) sets in. The research group of *Einhorn* [11, 12] has been particularly active with this problem. Using carbon monoxide, incapacitation has been investigated in a systematic study on test animals. Five intoxication stages were found ([3], p. 44):

– Stage 1. Onset of ataxia at COHb content in blood between 20 and 40% with animal's equilibrium being affected.
– Stage 2. Loss of the survival reaction (inability to flee) at COHb content between 40 and 50%.
– Stage 3. Motor collapse at about 65% COHb content.
– Stage 4. Anoxic shock, total unconsciousness, COHb content about 70%.
– Stage 5. Death, COHb content greater than 70%.

The animals were investigated in the NBS smoke chamber. They were placed in slings and were given electric shocks, signalled by light or sound signals, to determine their incapacitation. The principles of this test are illustrated in Fig. 9.29.

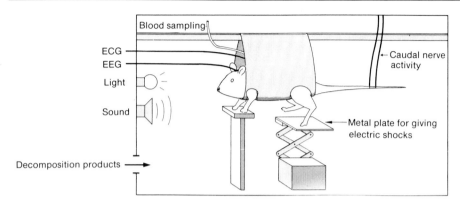

Fig. 9.29 Apparatus after *Einhorn*

Motor activities were measured in so-called "activity measuring cages" and in rotating wheels. *Kishitani* [13] has carried out investigations in activity measuring chambers; the activity of the animals (20 g mice) was measured by the movement which they caused. Other workers have measured the incapacitation time of animals using rotating wheels. This method forms the basis of the Japanese test described in Section 9.3.4.

9.3.2.3 Further methods

Investigators such as *Alarie* have studied the irritation of the bronchial tract. Here the changes in breathing frequency are measured as a function of the concentration of the inhaled irritant.

In addition to the above investigations, which were all made using the spontaneous breathing of the animal, the French group of *Jouany* and *Boudène* [3, 14] has carried out investigations involving controlled breathing of the animal. A rabbit was paralysed with curare and made to inhale toxic decomposition products in a controlled manner by means of a pump. The observations and measurements were made in three ways:

– the composition of the air/fire-gas mixture was continually analysed (O_2, CO, CO_2, HCl, HCN etc.),
– the condition of the blood of the animal was measured (pH value, O_2, CO_2, CO and COHb),
– the condition of the central nervous system was obtained by EEG, and of the cardio-vascular system by ECG and blood pressure.

"Physiograms" computed from these data were statistically evaluated and served as a base for the classification of the toxicity of the materials.

9.3.3 Testing the toxicity of thermal decomposition products according to DIN 53436

In the Federal Republic of Germany the measurement of the toxicity of thermal decomposition products is required in the tests laid down for class A2 non-combustible building materials [15] (see also 8.2.2). In this method the lethality of the test animals is determined as LC_{50}. The test follows Draft DIN 53436 from 1966 [8]. This Standard appeared in a new form as DIN 53436 Parts 1–3 in 1981 in which Part 2 was published as a pre-Standard and Part 3 as a draft [16]. A sketch showing the principles of the decomposition apparatus is

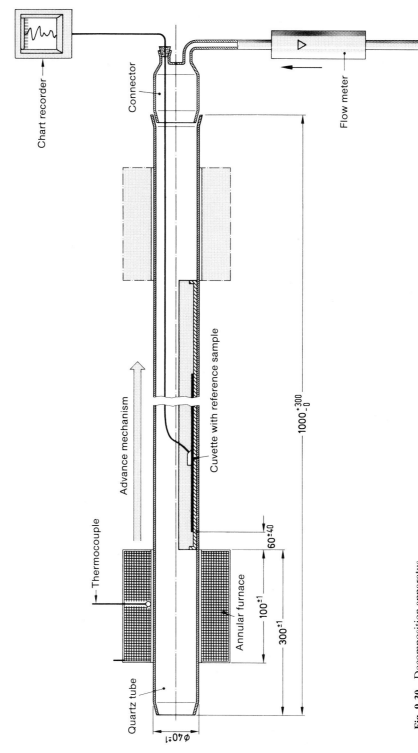

Fig. 9.30 Decomposition apparatus

given in Fig. 9.30. In the description below the test specifications are presented as given in reference [15]; the alterations introduced in [16] which are not yet applicable to building, are given in brackets.

The decomposition apparatus consists of a quartz tube 1,000 mm (1,000 mm–1,300 mm) long, 40 mm outside diameter and 2 mm wall thickness (a cuvette 400 mm long and 15 mm radius serves as the test container). Using a reference, temperatures of 300 °C and 400 °C are produced (additionally 500 °C and 600 °C). Twelve test specimens with dimensions 600 mm × 15 mm × maximum 20 mm (400 mm × 15 mm × 2 mm or other thicknesses are required for foams, films and textiles) are required. Air is passed into the decomposition apparatus at a rate of 300 litres per hour. According to [16] part 3, the air flow through the quartz tube is set at at 100 litres per hour and diluted either with 200 litres per hour of fresh air (method A) or with variable amounts of fresh air (method B) so that different concentrations of thermal decomposition products can be obtained causing variations in the death rates of the animals investigated. The thermal decomposition products are cooled (to 22 °C–30 °C) and led into inhalation chambers (nose or total body exposure systems).

In every test at least 5 rats (5 male and 5 female; body weight 160 g − 250 g; pedigree, weight and sex of the animals must be kept the same) are exposed for a minimum of 30 min. The test must be repeated at each temperature at least once. After the end of the investigation the COHb level in the animals' blood is determined as well as the death rate (number of deaths per total number of animals) observed within 14 days. According to [16] part 3, the concentrations of CO, CO_2 and O_2 are monitored during exposure in the inhalation chamber. In addition it is necessary to determine further gas components which are toxicologically important (e.g. HCN, HCl).

9.3.4 Testing of the toxicity of combustion gases according to Japanese Announcement No. 1231

Testing of the toxicity of combustion gases in the building field in Japan is laid down in Announcement No. 1231 of the 25th August 1976 [17] and relies on a determination of the incapacitation point of the test animals. A diagram of the test apparatus is given in Fig. 9.31. The decomposition furnace is identical with the apparatus used for the "face test" (see Section 8.2.17, Fig. 8.68). The decomposition products pass via a mixing chamber into the exposure chamber in which the test animals are situated. For every material to be tested two test specimens 220 mm × 220 mm × maximum 15 mm are used. The decomposition of the test specimens occurs in the "face test" furnace. The temperature of the gases leaving the furnace must show the characteristics given in Table 9.17.

The specimen in the furnace is decomposed over an area of 180 mm by 180 mm for six minutes. During the first three minutes it is exposed to the gas pilot flame (partial heat load)

Table 9.17   Temperature characteristics of decomposition gases

Time [min]	Temperature [°C]
1	70
2	85
3	100
4	170
5	190

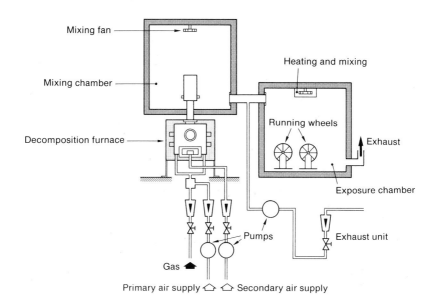

Fig. 9.31   Toxicological inhalation test apparatus according to Announcement No. 1231

and subsequently to the additional electric heater (full heat load). During the heating period 3 litres per minute of primary air and 25 litres per minute of secondary air are fed into the furnace from which 10 litres per minute are withdrawn via an outlet before the exposure chamber. Before heating, the temperature in the exposure chamber is 30 °C.

Eight cages each contain a running wheel and a 5 weeks old, female mouse, weighing between 18 g and 22 g. The running wheels are made from aluminium and weigh about 75 g. The time from the start of heating until incapacitation of the mice is registered automatically up to a total time of 15 minutes.

The mean standard incapacitation time for standard specimens of red lauan wood (Philippine mahogany) is determined. The mean incapacitation time is also determined for the material under investigation. Two separate investigations are carried out for each material. If the mean incapacitation time is longer than that of the standard specimen the material is permitted.

The mean incapacitation time X_s is obtained from

$$X_s = \overline{X} - \sigma$$

here $\overline{X}$ is the arithmetic mean and σ the standard deviation of the incapacitation times for the eight mice. If no incapacitation occurs the time is reckoned as 15 minutes.

References for 9.3

[1]   ISO Technical Report 6543–1979. The development of tests for measuring toxic hazards in fire.
[2]   *J. O. Punderson:* Fire and Materials 5 (1981) 1, p. 41.
[3]   *J. M. Jouany, C. Boudène,* in: G.P.C.P., Les plastiques et le feu. Journées d'étude. 24–16. 11. 1976, Compagnie Française d'Editions, Paris, 1978, p. 31.

[4] *H. Th. Hofmann, H. Oettel:* Kunststoff-Rundsch. 15 (1968) 6, p. 261.

[5] *H. Th. Hofmann, H. Sand:* Kunststoff-Rundsch. 21 (1974) 10, p. 413.

[6] *G. Kimmerle:* Methodology for toxicological analysis of combustion products. Intern. symp. on toxicity and physiology of combustion products, University of Utah, Salt Lake City, 22−26. 3. 1976.

[7] *C. Herpol:* Fire and Materials 1 (1976) 1, p. 29.

[8] DIN 53436 Draft. August 1966. Prüfung von Kunststoffen. Gerät für die thermische Zersetzung von Kunststoffen unter Luftzufuhr.

[9] *H. J. Klimisch, H. W. M. Hollander, J. Thyssen:* J. Combustion Toxicology 7 (1980), p. 209, 7 (1980), p. 243.

[10] *H. J. Klimisch:* J. Combustion Toxicology 7 (1980), p. 257.

[11] *I. N. Einhorn, M. M. Birky, M. L. Grunnet, S. C. Packham, J. H. Petajan, J. D. Seader:* The physiological and toxicological aspects of smoke produced during the combustion of polymeric materials. Annual Report Flammability Research Center/UU-12, UTEC 73-164 1973. Univ. Utah & National Science Foundation, Ranna Programme/GL 33650.

[12] *I. N. Einhorn, M. L. Grunnet, J. H. Petajan, R. C. Baldwin:* The physiological and toxicological aspects of combustion. VFDB 5. International Fire Protection Seminar, Karlsruhe, 22−24. 9. 1976, Vol. III Supplements, p. 23.

[13] *K. Kishitani:* Research in Japan on toxicity of combustion gases produced during fire. 2nd joint meeting US Japan panel on fire research and safety, UJNR, Tokio, 19−22. 10. 1976.

[14] *J. M. Jouany, C. Boudène, R. Truhaut:* The physiogram as a method for the evaluation of toxicity of combustion products in controled ventilation experiments. Intern. symp. on toxicity and physiology of combustion products, University of Utah, Salt Lake City, 22−26. 3. 1976.

[15] Prüfgrundsätze für prüfzeichenpflichtige nichtbrennbare (Klasse A) Baustoffe nach DIN 4102 Teil 1 – Edition July 1978. Mitt. IfBt 9 (1978) 5, p. 156.

[16] DIN 53436. Erzeugung thermischer Zersetzungsprodukte von Werkstoffen unter Luftzufuhr und ihre toxikologische Prüfung.
Part 1. April 1981. Zersetzungsgerät und Bestimmung der Versuchstemperatur.
Part 2. pre-Standard. April 1981. Verfahren zur thermischen Zersetzung.
Part 3. Draft. April 1981. Verfahren zur inhalationstoxikologischen Untersuchung thermischer Zersetzungsprodukte.

[17] Announcement No. 1231 of the Ministry of Construction, 25. 8. 1976. Semi-non-combustible and fire retardant building maerials conforming to the Building Standards Law.

9.4 Corrosivity of fire gases

Corrosion can be defined as the gradual destruction, starting from the surface, of metallic or non-metallic materials by chemical or electrochemical influences.

In a fire, gases which can corrode buildings and their contents are liberated from the combustible materials. The amount of corrosion damage depends mainly on the following factors: the type of material causing the corrosion, its concentration and duration of action, the temperature of the fire gases and of the surroundings, atmospheric humidity, the type of material, building component or contents attacked and, not least on the cleaning-up procedures which are applied.

The corrosion damage discussed here is concerned only with buildings and contents not subjected to direct fire effects, because corrosion effects are negligible compared with thermal damage in the direct region of influence of the fire.

Corrosion damage can be roughly divided into two types [1]:

- Damage to buildings, caused by the corrosive effect of fire gases on building materials and components.
- Damage to equipment, caused by the corrosive gases attacking machinery, stored metallic products, production equipment and electrical and electronic installations.

In principle, all organic materials can liberate corrosive gases on pyrolysis. Investigations have shown that even materials such as chipboard, wool and cotton can lead to corrosion effects on metals on combustion [1]. However, the primary corrosion effects result from the decomposition of PVC, followed by those from plastics with a high halogen flame retardant content, and arise from the effect of acidic hydrogen halides (e.g. HCl). For plastics with a low flame retardant content the corrosion damage is markedly less.

One must be careful not to equate high chlorine content of a material with high corrosion risk, because, in a fire, it is unusual for full-scale combustion to occur. For example, floor coverings are, in practice, only partially destroyed because of their position. Densely packed stored materials are also less affected due to the formation of a charred layer which protects the underlying material.

Bromine-containing plastics are less corrosive than those containing chlorine; in addition, the same effective fire protection can be obtained with a lower bromine content.

Investigations of corrosion damage are mainly limited to the effects of PVC fire gases. It was first thought that there might be a danger to the strength of reinforced concrete structures from these gases but many investigations have shown that these fears are unfounded [2−5].

In recent years there have been ongoing investigations into corrosion damage to metallic materials and to equipment made from them, such as machines and electrical and electronic appliances. The results have shown that, contrary to earlier beliefs, such plant does not usually become a total write-off but that, with the exception of precision components, there is no impairment of functional efficiency. After appropriate cleaning such plant can usually be used again without loss [1, 2, 6−9].

A short explanation of the principle of corrosive attack on building materials and metals will now be given followed by a summary of the methods of cleaning usually applied to buildings, equipment and to electrical and electronic plant. This seems an appropriate place to note the work carried out on this topic by *Grupp* whose more recent publications [7, 8] give the present state of the art and contain more than 100 references. An introduction to fundamentals and types of corrosion can be found in two comprehensive expositions [10, 11].

The corrosive attack of fire gases on metals will be illustrated using PVC as an example. The HCl produced from PVC in the region of the fire combines with the ample supply of water vapour to give hydrochloric acid which then condenses on the cooler metallic parts away from the immediate region of the fire. The actual corrosion occurs as a phase-boundary reaction between the solid metal phase and the liquid condensate phase. A "corrosion element" results in which the anodic process of metal dissolution and the cathodic process of reduction of hydrogen ions to hydrogen and of oxygen to hydroxyl ions occur. The following reactions take place:

– Anodic process (metal dissolution; oxidation)

$$M \longrightarrow M^{2+} + 2e^- \tag{1}$$

– Cathodic process (reduction)

$$2\,H^+ + 2e^- \longrightarrow H_2 \quad (H^+ \text{ reduction}) \tag{2}$$
$$O_2 + 2\,H_2O + 4e^- \longrightarrow 4\,OH^- \quad (O_2 \text{ reduction}) \tag{3}$$

Depending on whether the dissolution of the metal occurs by hydrogen-ion reduction (Equation 2), or by oxygen reduction (Equation 3) the process is termed acid or oxygen corrosion. If the HCl produced from PVC fire gases impinges on a steel surface, acid corrosion takes place formally according to the following reactions:

$$Fe + 2\,HCl \longrightarrow FeCl_2 + H_2 \tag{4}$$
$$FeCl_2 + 2\,H_2O \longrightarrow Fe(OH)_2 + 2\,HCl \tag{5}$$

However, the HCl condensate always contains dissolved atmospheric oxygen and oxygen corrosion (equation 6) occurs simultaneously:

$$2\,Fe + O_2 + 2\,H_2O \longrightarrow 2\,Fe(OH)_2 \tag{6}$$

The actual rust formation process is complicated and can be formulated as follows ([10], page 12):

$$Fe \longrightarrow Fe^{2+} + 2e^- \tag{7}$$
$$2\,Fe^{2+} + O \longrightarrow 2\,Fe^{3+} + O^{2-} \tag{8}$$
$$O + 2e^- \longrightarrow O^{2-} \tag{9}$$
$$O^{2-} + H_2O \longrightarrow 2\,OH^- \tag{10}$$
$$Fe^{2+} + 2\,OH^- \longrightarrow Fe(OH)_2 \tag{11}$$
$$2\,Fe(OH)_2 + O + H_2O \longrightarrow 2\,Fe(OH)_3 \tag{12}$$
$$Fe(OH)_3 \longrightarrow FeO(OH) + H_2O \text{ (rust)} \tag{13}$$

The extent of corrosion depends in the main on the prevailing atmospheric humidity; as Fig. 9.32 shows, there is a sudden increase in corrosion rate in the region between 40 and 70% relative humidity. For HCl the critical relative humidity is 56%, for HBr it is 39.5%.

After a fire two consecutive methods of cleaning must be implemented in order to minimize the corrosion damage; they are fully described in [7] and will be given here briefly:

– immediately after the fire, measures must be taken to stop the corrosion attack,
– subsequently the fire condensates and any corrosion products must be removed.

In the light of the data described above, an obvious immediate measure is the lowering of atmospheric humidity to limit corrosion attack. Essentially this can be done either by raising the temperature of the surroundings or by the use of certain substances as drying agents.

Table 9.18 Cleaning agents (after [7] Part I, p. 26)

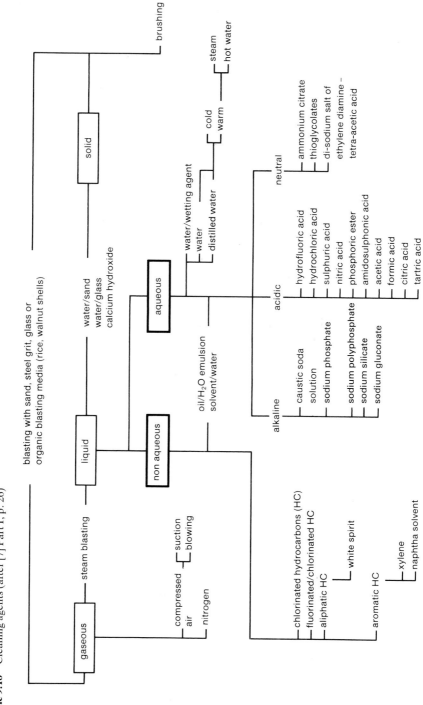

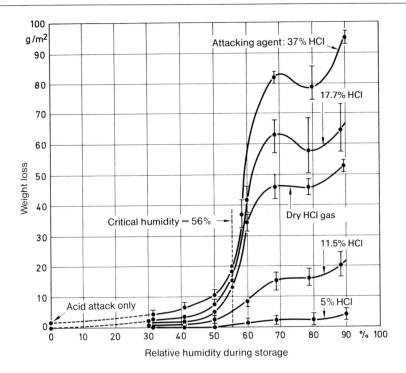

Fig. 9.32 Corrosion rate of non-alloyed steel stored over different HCl concentrations as a function of atmospheric humidity (After *Längle*) ([7] part I, page 23)

The first method, which involves heating the enclosed air, is often not feasible in large buildings. Powerful de-humidifiers are therefore preferred. These can lower the relative atmospheric humidity to about 30% (i.e. below the critical point of 56% for HCl condensates) in a few hours even in large buildings. Silica gel and calcium chloride are used as drying agents; silica gel is preferred because of its easy regenerative properties, while calcium chloride is less commonly used because of its restricted regenerative ability and its tendency to fuse and cake.

A further immediate measure consists in the application of anti-corrosion oils as rust inhibitors which work by chemically inhibiting corrosion attack and also by repelling water. The oil flows under the moisture film and so keeps it away from the metal surface; this is known as the "dewatering effect". The disadvantages are the high cost of such oils and also the fact that their removal is labour intensive.

In addition to the immediate cleaning measures outlined here there are further long term methods. The most important cleaning materials are summarised in Table 9.18. Table 9.19 shows the various areas in which different types of cleaning may be used.

Various measures are used for cleaning machinery and electrical and electronic plant depending on whether the plant has suffered corrosion damage.

Where corrosion has not occurred it is usually sufficient to wash off smoke gas condensates and soot. This is done with "cold" or "neutral' cleaning materials. "Cold" cleaning agents are either solvents like chlorinated or fluorinated hydrocarbons or water/solvent mixtures. "Neutral" cleaners are simply commercially available non-ionic or anion-active

Table 9.19   Cleaning methods (after [7], part I, p. 28)

Application		Cleaning method
Buildings,	dry	Brushing Mechanical removal (scraping, chiselling) Sand blasting
	wet	Wiping High pressure hot water Steam cleaning
	dry/wet	Chalk slurry (paste)
Electronics,	dry	Blowing/sucking
	wet	Petroleum spirit Freon Water
Machines,	not corroded	Cold cleaners Neutral cleaners Protecting materials Protecting oil
	already corroded	Acid cleaners (e.g. phosphoric acid) Neutral cleaners (complexing agents) Alkaline cleaners (sodium hydroxide)

detergents which are added to water in small quantities and dissolve the condensates. However, when using aqueous systems care must be taken to ensure immediate and complete drying.

In plant where corrosion damage has occurred acid, neutral or alkaline rust-removing agents must be applied. The different aqueous systems are given in Table 9.18. The acid rust removers usually contain phosphoric acid as their active ingredient while the alkaline ones are based on sodium hydroxide and the neutral ones on complexing agents.

These measures enable machines and plant (especially electronic plant) which would previously have been totally written-off to be quickly returned to full operation. An indication of the progress in this field is that cleaning measures are no longer simply in the development stage but are already offered by firms as a commercial service [9].

For the sake of completeness it should be mentioned here that attention is being given to tests for determining the corrosivity of fire gases, especially in the field of electrical engineering. In the Federal Republic of Germany, draft VDE 0472 Part 813 describes testing of the corrosivity of fire gases from cables and insulated conductors. Corrosivity is determined by absorbing the gases from pyrolysed test specimens in water and measuring the pH value.

This problem has also been tackled in France: fire gas corrosivity is determined according to UTE C 20-453 by burning the specimen in a closed glass vessel and measuring the increase in the electrical resistance arising from the effects of the corrosive fire gases on an oxide-free copper wire (more details about these methods are given in Sections 8.4.1.2 and 8.4.2.3). No further test methods for measurement of the corrosivity of fire gases in these and other areas such as building and transport have yet been developed.

In cleaning buildings a distinction is made between wet and dry methods. Before a decision is made as to the method to be adopted it is necessary to determine the distribution of chloride arising from the corrosive fire gases in the structure. This is done by taking test borings and determining the water soluble chloride content. If the chloride content exceeds a certain value, cleaning must be undertaken. The cheapest method is application of steam or high pressure hot water by means of which it is possible to remove completely the corrosive condensate which has penetrated up to a depth of 5 mm.

Sand blasting allows cleaning only to a depth of 2 mm without the cost becoming excessive, so that the methods with water are always cheaper and more effective. A further method is by chalk cleaning. A layer of calcium hydroxide is sprayed onto the concrete to remove the hydrochloric acid. This must be repeated five to ten times in order to obtain the desired effect; because of this the method is very expensive and is only to be recommended if high chloride concentrations are to be removed from great depth.

The most expensive and therefore least used method is "Torcreting" which involves removing the chloride-containing concrete section and replaceing it by spraying concrete of appropriate quality (further details about the methods described here are given in [7], part II, p. 56−57). There is no general rule as to which of the methods described here would be applied in a particular case. This depends on the requirements of the particular restoration.

References for 9.4

[1] *K. Fischer:* Schadenprisma 5 (1976) 4, pp. 61/80.
[2] *P. H. Effertz, H. Grupp, W. Jach:* Der Maschinenschaden 43 (1970) 3, pp. 89/99.
[3] *K. Fischer:* Zeitschrift VFDB 20 (1971) 4, pp. 140/144; 21 (1972) 1, pp. 1/11.
[4] *W. A. Morris, J. S. Hopkinson:* Fire International 47 (1973), pp. 71/81.
[5] *C. Reiter:* Versicherungswirtschaft 28 (1973) 9, pp. 492/497.
[6] *P. H. Effertz, H. Grupp:* Der Maschinenschaden 45 (1972) 1, pp. 7/19.
[7] *H. Grupp:* Der Maschinenschaden 53 (1980) 1, pp. 20/28; 53 (1980) 2, pp. 56/63.
[8] *H. Grupp:* Brandschutzausgerüstete Kunststoffe und ihre Brandfolgeschäden sowie Brandschutz-maßnahmen. Symposium "Kriechstromfestigkeit und Brennbarkeit von Kunststoffen", Haus der Technik, Essen, 6. 5. 1981.
[9] *F. K. Behrens, H. Renz, H. Grupp:* Der Maschinenschaden 54 (1981) 3, pp. 77/86.
[10] *H. Gräfen, E. M. Horn, U. Gramberg:* Korrosion, in Ullmanns Encyklopädie der technischen Chemie, 4. Ed., Vol. 15, pp. 1/59, Verlag Chemie, Weinheim, 1978.
[11] *R. T. Foley, B. F. Brown:* Corrosion and corrosion inhibitors, in Kirk-Othmer (Eds.): Encyclopedia of Chemical Technology. 3. Ed., Vol. 7, pp. 113/142. John Wiley & Sons, New York, London, 1979.

10 Appendix

10.1 Suppliers of flame retardants and smoke suppressants

Manufacturers and suppliers	Products
North America	
Aluminum Company of America, 1501 Alcoa Bldg., Pittsburgh, PA 15219, USA	Aluminium hydroxide
Americhem Inc., 2038 Main St., Cuyahoga Falls, OH 44222, USA	Dispersions of phosphate esters, chlorinated paraffins, zinc borate, aluminium hydroxide, antimony oxide
Ampacet Corp., 250 S. Terrace Ave., Mount Vernon, NY 10550, USA	Dispersions of chlorinated paraffins, antimony oxide
Asarco Inc., 120 Broadway, New York, NY 10005, USA	Antimony oxide
Borg-Warner Chemicals, Borg-Warner Corp., International Center, Parkersburg, WV 26101, USA	Phosphorus/nitrogen intumescent compounds
Buckman Laboratories Inc., 1256 N. McLean Blvd., Memphis, TN 38108, USA	Barium metaborate
C-I-L Inc., P. O. Box 200, Station A, Willowdale, ON M2N 5S8, Canada	Chlorinated paraffins
Claremont Polychemical Corp., 501 Winding Rd., Old Bethpage, NY 11804, USA	Antimony oxide, zinc borate
Climax Molybdenum Co., 1600 Huron Pkwy., Ann Arbor, MI 48106, USA	Molybdenum compounds
Diamond Shamrock Corp., 351 Phelps Court, P. O. Box 2300, Irving, TX 75061, USA	Chlorinated paraffins
Dover Chemical Corp., sub. ICC Industries Inc., 720 Fifth Ave., New York, NY 10019, USA	Chlorinated paraffins, organic halogenated compounds

Manufacturers and suppliers	Products
Dow Chemical Co., 2020 Dow Center, Midland, MI 48640, USA	Organic brominated and chlorinated compounds
East Coast Chemicals Co., P . O. Box 160, Cedar Grove, NJ 07009, USA	Phosphate esters, halogenated phosphorus compounds, chlorinated paraffins, antimony oxide
Emery Industries Inc., 1300 Carew Tower, Cincinnati, OH 45202, USA	Organic brominated compounds
FMC Corp., Industrial Chemicals Div., 2000 Market St., Philadelphia, PA 19103, USA	Phosphate esters
Ferro Corp., Chemical Div., 7050 Krick Rd., Bedford, OH 44146, USA	Organic brominated compounds
Great Lakes Chemical Corp., P . O. Box 2200, W. Lafayette, IN 47906, USA	Organic brominated compounds
Harshaw Chemical Co., 1945 E. 97th St., Cleveland, OH 44106, USA	Antimony oxide
Harwick Chemical Corp., 60 S. Seiberling St., Akron, OH 44305, USA	Phosphate esters, halogenated phosphorus compounds, chlorinated paraffins, aluminium hydroxide, antimony oxide, zinc borate
Hooker Chemicals & Plastics Corp., 345 Third St., Niagara Falls, NY 14303, USA	Organic chlorinated and brominated cycloaliphatic compounds
Isochem Resins Co., 99 Cook St., Lincoln, RI 02865, USA	Phosphonate esters, halogenated phosphorus compounds, zinc borate
Kaiser Chemicals, div. Kaiser Aluminum & Chemical Corp., 300 Lakeside Dr., Oakland, CA 94643, USA	Aluminium hydroxide
Keil Chemical Div., Ferro Corp., 3000 Sheffield Ave., Hammond, IN 46320, USA	Organic chlorinated compounds
M & T Chemicals Inc., P. O. Box 1104, Rahway, NJ 07065, USA	Antimony oxide
Mobay Chemical Corp., Penn Lincoln Pkwy. West, Pittsburgh, PA 15205, USA	Phosphate esters
Mobil Chemical Co., Phosphorus Div., P. O. Box 26683, Richmond, VA 23261, USA	Phosphate esters, halogenated phosphorus compounds

Manufacturers and suppliers	Products
Monsanto Co., 800 N. Lindbergh Blvd., St. Louis, MO 63166, USA	Phosphate esters, organic chlorinated compounds, halogenated phosphorus compounds
Neville Chemical Co., Neville Island, Pittsburgh, PA 15225, USA	Organic chlorinated compounds
Nyacol Inc., Megunco Rd., P. O. Box 349, Ashland, MA 01721, USA	Antimony oxide
Olin Corp., Chemical Div., 120 Long Ridge Rd., Stamford, CT 06904, USA	Phosphate esters, halogenated phosphorus compounds
PPG Industries Inc., P. O. Box 66251, Chicago, IL 60666, USA	Antimony oxide, organic brominated compounds
Pearsall Chemical Div., Witco Chemical Corp., P. O. Box 437, Houston, TX 77001, USA	Organic chlorinated and brominated compounds, chlorinated paraffins
Podell Industries Inc., 3 Entin Rd., Clifton, NJ 07014, USA	Dispersions of phosphate esters, chlorinated paraffins, antimony oxide
Saytech Inc., 25 Kimberly Rd., East Brunswick, NJ 08816, USA	Organic brominated and chlorinated compounds
Sherwin-Williams Co., Chemical Div., P. O. Box 6506, Cleveland, OH 44101, USA	Molybdenum compounds
Solem Industries Inc., 3400 Oakcliff Rd., Atlanta, GA 30067, USA	Aluminium hydroxide
Stauffer Chemical Co., Specialty Chemicals Div., Westport, CT 06880, USA	Phosphate esters, halogenated phosphorus compounds
U. S. Borax, 3075 Wilshire Blvd., Los Angeles, CA 90010, USA	Zinc borate
Velsicol Chemical Corp., 341 E. Ohio St., Chicago, IL 60611, USA	Organic brominated and chlorinated compounds
Ware Chemical Corp., 1525 Stratford Ave., Stratford, CT 06497, USA	Phosphate esters, antimony oxide, barium metaborate, zinc borate
White Chemical Corp., East 22nd St., Bayonne, NJ 07002, USA	Organic brominated compounds

Manufacturers and suppliers	Products

Europe

Albright & Wilson Ltd., 1 Knightsbridge Green, London SW1X 7QD, Great Britain	Phosphate esters, phosphorus compounds
Anzon Ltd., Cookson House, Willington Quay, Wallsend, Tyne & Wear, NE28 6UQ, Great Britain	Antimony oxide, antimony sulphide, zinc and magnesium oxides
BA Chemicals Ltd., Chalfont Park, Gerrards Cross, Bucks., SL9 OQB, Great Britain	Aluminium hydroxide
Bayer AG, D-5090 Leverkusen, Germany	Phosphate esters
Bleiberger Bergwerksunion AG, Postfach 43, A-9601 Arnoldstein, Austria	Antimony sulphide
Borax Holdings Ltd., Borax House, Carlisle Place, London, SW1P 1HT, Great Britain	Zinc borate
Chemische Fabrik Grünau GmbH, Postfach 120, D-7918 Illertissen, Germany	Antimony-containing compounds
Chemische Fabrik Kalk GmbH, Postfach 910210, D-5000 Köln 91, Germany	Organic brominated compounds, phosphate esters
Chemische Werke Hüls AG, Postfach 1320, D-4370 Marl, Germany	Chlorinated paraffins
Chemische Werke München Otto Bärlocher GmbH, Postfach 500108, D-8000 München 50, Germany	Inorganic masterbatches for PVC, borates
Ciba-Geigy AG, CH-4002 Basel, Switzerland	Phosphate esters, halogenated phosphorus compounds
Condea Petrochemie GmbH, Mittelweg 13, D-2000 Hamburg 13, Germany	Phosphate esters
Hoechst AG, Postfach 800320, D-6230 Frankfurt 80, Germany	Organic phosphorus compounds, chlorinated paraffins
Imperial Chemical Industries PLC, Mond Division, P. O. Box 13, Runcorn, Cheshire, Great Britain	Chlorinated paraffins

Manufacturers and suppliers	Products
ISC Chemicals Ltd., St Andrew's Road, Avonmouth, Bristol BS11 9HP, Great Britain	Organic brominated compounds
Martinswerk GmbH, Postfach 1209, D-5010 Bergheim, Germany	Aluminium hydroxide
Metallgesellschaft AG, Reuterweg 14, D-6000 Frankfurt 1, Germany	Aluminium hydroxide, organic brominated compounds, masterbatches
Produits Chimiques Ugine Kuhlmann, Tour Manhattan, Place de l'Iris, Cédex 21, F-92087 Paris La Défense, France	Aluminium hydroxide, organic brominated compounds, phosphorus compounds, chlorinated paraffins
Riedel-de-Haën AG, Wunstorferstr. 40, D-3016 Seelze, Germany	Organic brominated compounds
Société Industrielle et Chimique de l'Aisne, B. P. 46, F-02301 Chauny, France	Antimony oxide
Süddeutsche Kalkstickstoffwerke AG, Postfach 1150/1160, D-8223 Trostberg, Germany	Nitrogen-containing compounds
Vereinigte Aluminium Werke AG, Postfach 2468, D-5300 Bonn, Germany	Aluminium hydroxide
Vieille Montagne, 19, rue Richer, F-75442 Paris, Cédex 09, France	Zinc oxide

Asia

Asahi Denka Kogyo KK, Furukawa Building 8, 2-chome, Nihonbashi-Murmachi, Chuo-ku, Tokyo, Japan	Organic halogenated compounds, phosphate esters
Asahi Glass Co. Ltd., Chiyoda Building, 2-1-2 Marunouchi, Chiyoda-ku, Tokyo 100, Japan	Organic halogenated compounds
Chisso Co., 7-3 Marunouchi 2-chome, Chiyoda-ku, Tokyo 100, Japan	Phosphorus and nitrogen compounds
Daihachi Chemical Industry Co. Ltd., 3-54, Chodo, Higashi Osaka City, Osaka Pref. 577, Japan	Phosphate esters, phosphorus compounds, borates

Manufacturers and suppliers	Products
Dai-ichi Chemical Industries Ltd., 2-2-1, Higashi Sakashita, Itabashi-ku, Tokyo 174, Japan	Organic brominated compounds
Dead Sea Bromine Co. Ltd., P. O. Box 180, Beer Sheba, Israel	Organic brominated compounds
Hitachi Chemical Co. Ltd., Shinjuku Mitsui Building, 2-1-1, Nishi-Shinjuku, Shinjuku-ku, Tokyo 160, Japan	Organic brominated compounds
Kyowa Hakko Kogyo Co. Ltd., Ohtemachi Building, 6-1 Ohte-machi 1-chome, Chiyoda-ku, Tokyo 100, Japan	Phosphate esters
Marubeni Co., Fine Chemicals Sec., Osaka (A 777), C. P. O. Box 1000, Osaka 530-91, Japan	Organic brominated compounds
Mitsui Toatsu Chemicals Inc., 2-5 Kasumigaseki 3-chome, Chiyoda-ku, Tokyo 100, Japan	Phosphate esters, organic brominated compounds
Nippon Chemical Industrial Co. Ltd., 15-1, Kameido 9-chome, Koto-ku, Tokyo 136, Japan	Organic phosphorus compounds
Nippon Kayaku Co. Ltd., Tokyo Kaijo Building, 2-1, Marunouchi, 1-chome, Chiyoda-ku, Tokyo 100, Japan	Organic brominated compounds, organic phosphorus compounds
Nissan Chemical Industries Ltd., Kowa-Hitotsubashi Building, 7-1, Kanda-Nishiki-cho 3-chome, Chiyoda-ku, Tokyo 101, Japan	Organic halogenated compounds, nitrogen-containing compounds
Otsuka Chemical Co. Ltd., 10 Bungo-machi, Higashi-ku, Osaka 540, Japan	Organic halogenated compounds
Sanko Chemical Co. Ltd., 16 Toori-cho 8-chome, Kurume City, Fukuoka 830, Japan	Organic phosphorus compounds
Sumitomo Chemical Co. Ltd., New Sumitomo Building, 15 5-chome, Kitahama, Higashi-ku, Osaka, Japan	Antimony oxide, organic phosphorus compounds, organic halogenated compounds
Teijin Chemicals Co. Ltd., 6-21, 1-chome, Nishishinbashi, Minato-ku, Tokyo, Japan	Organic brominated compounds

10.2 Abbreviations for plastics*

Plastic	Abbreviation	Plastic	Abbreviation
Thermoplastics			
polyethylene	PE		
high density polyethylene	HDPE	– hexamethylene diamine	
low density polyethylene	LDPE	and adipic acid	PA 66
polypropylene	PP	– laurinolactam	PA 12
polystyrene	PS	polymethyl methacrylate	PMMA
styrene butadiene		polyethylene terephthalate	PETP
copolymer	SB	polybutylene terephthalate	PBTP
acrylonitrile butadiene		polycarbonate	PC
styrene copolymer	ABS	polyoxymethylene	POM
acrylonitrile styrene			
acrylic ester copolymer	ASA	**Thermosets**	
styrene acrylonitrile		polyurethane	PUR
copolymer	SAN	polyisocyanurate	PIR
polyvinyl chloride	PVC	phenol formaldehyde resin	PF
chlorinated polyvinyl chloride	PVCC	urea formaldehyde resin	UF
polyvinylidene chloride	PVDC	melamine formaldehyde resin	MF
polytetrafluoroethylene	PTFE	epoxy resin	EP
perfluoroethylene propylene	FEP	unsaturated polyester resin	UP
ethylene tetrafluoroethylene			
copolymer	ETFE	**High temperature resistant**	
polyvinyl fluoride	PVF	**plastics**	
polyvinylidene fluoride	PVDF	polyphenylene oxide	PPO
polychlorotrifluoroethylene	PCTFE	polyphenylene sulphide	PPS
polyamide	PA	polyether sulphone	PES
based on		polysulphone	PSO
– ε-caprolactam	PA 6	polyimide	PI
		polybenzimidazole	PBI

* as in DIN 7728 Part 1 or *Hj. Saechtling:* Kunststoff-Taschenbuch. 21st Edition, Carl Hanser Verlag, Munich, 1979.

10.3 Terminology of fire protection

The definitions and terms listed in Sections 10.3.1 and 10.3.2 are based on the ISO 3261, AFNOR X 65-020, ASTM E 176−79a and DIN E 50060 standards [1−4] and numerous discussions by the author with English, French and German colleagues. The fire protection standards described in this book and relevant specialised literature have also been taken into account.
The definitions of fire protection terms given in 10.3.1 have been taken from ISO 3261 but have been altered where necessary.
The three language glossary in Section 10.3.2 is considerably more extensive than the above standards and contains expressions which are not specific to fire protection but are widely used in the field. The glossary is not claimed to be complete but is intended to assist the reader acquainting himself with the subject as well as those consulting literature in other languages. It is hoped that it will provide the impetus for a Thesaurus of fire protection terminology in several languages.

References

[1]   ISO 3261−1975. Fire tests − Vocabulary.
[2]   Norme expérimentale X 65-020. Essais de comportement au feu. Vocabulaire. December 1978.
[3]   ASTM E 176−79a. Standard definitions of terms relating to fire tests of building construction and materials. August 1979.
[4]   Draft DIN 50060. February 1981. Brennverhalten von Werkstoffen und Erzeugnissen. Begriffe.

10.3.1 Definitions of terms connected with fire protection

Term	Definition
Afterflame	Persistence of flaming of a material under specified test conditions after removal of the ignition source
Afterglow	Persistence of glowing of a material after cessation of flaming or after removal of the ignition source
Burn	Undergo combustion
Burning behaviour	All the physical and/or chemical changes that take place when materials or products are exposed to controlled flames
Calorific potential	Calorific energy per unit mass which could be released by the complete combustion of a material
Char (n.)	Carbonaceous residue from pyrolysis or incomplete combustion
Char (v.)	Form carbonaceous residue during pyrolysis or incomplete combustion
Combustible	Capable of burning
Combustion	Exothermic reaction of a combustible substance with an oxidising agent, accompanied by flames and/or glowing and/or smoke
Damaged area	Total of the area of a material permanently affected by thermal phenomena under specified test conditions, e.g. by loss of material, shrinking, softening, melting, charring, combustion, pyrolysis, etc.
Ease of ignition	Ease with which a material can be ignited under specified test conditions
Fire	a) Combustion process characterised by the emission of heat and smoke and/or flame b) Combustion spreading uncontrolled
Fire behaviour	All the physical and/or chemical changes that take place when materials or products are exposed to fire and burn in an uncontrolled manner
Fire effluent	Total gaseous, particulate or aerosol effluent from a fire or pyrolysis
Fire load	Calorific potential of all the combustible contents in a space, including facings of walls, partitions, floors and ceilings
Fire performance	See fire behaviour
Fire resistance	Ability of an element of building construction, component or structure, to fulfil for a stated period of time the required stability, integrity, thermal insulation and/or other specified duty, in a standard fire test
Fire retardance	Property of a substance or a treatment applied to a material which markedly reduces its combustibility
Flame (n.)	Zone of combustion in the gaseous phase with emission of light
Flame (v.)	Undergo combustion in the gaseous phase with emission of light
Flame retardance	Property of a substance or treatment applied to a material of retarding markedly the propagation of flame
Flame retardant	Substance that markedly retards the propagation of a flame
Flame spread	Propagation of a flame front

Term	Definition
Flame spread rate	Distance travelled by a flame front in unit time under specified test conditions
Flame spread time	Time taken by a flame on a burning material to travel a specified distance or surface area under specified test conditions
Flammability	Ability of a material or product to burn with a flame under specified test conditions
Flammable	Capable of burning with a flame under specified test conditions
Flash-over	Sudden transition to a state of total surface involvement in a fire of combustible materials in a compartment
Flash point	Minimum temperature at which, under specified test conditions, a material gives off sufficient flammable gas to produce a flash on applying an ignition source
Full fire development	Transition to a state of full involvement of combustible materials in a fire
Fully developed fire	State of total involvement of combustible materials in a fire
Glowing combustion	Combustion of a material in the solid phase without flame but with emission of light from the combustion zone
Heat of combustion	See calorific potential
Heat release rate	Amount of calorific energy released per unit time by a material during combustion under specified test conditions
Ignite (vt)	Initiate combustion
Ignite (vi)	Catch fire with or without the application of an external heat source
Ignition temperature/ point	Minimum temperature of a material at which sustained combustion can be initiated under specified test conditions
Incandescence	Glowing produced without combustion or other chemical reaction, e.g. by electrical heating of a tungsten filament
Light (v.)	Initiate combustion in the gaseous phase
Lighted (a.)	State of a material after appearance and during persistence of a flame
Lighting (n.)	Nascence of a flame
Mass burning rate	Mass loss per unit time under specified test conditions
Melting behaviour	Phenomena accompanying the softening of a material under the influence of heat (including shrinking, dripping and burning of molten material)
Optical density of smoke	Measure of the degree of opacity of smoke: expressed as the negative common logarithm of transmittance
Pyrolysis	Irreversible chemical decomposition of a material due to an increase in temperature without oxidation
Pyrophoric material	Material which ignites spontaneously in air
Radiation	Transfer of thermal energy without the necessity of an intervening medium
Reaction to fire	Response of a material in contributing by its own decomposition to a fire to which it is exposed under specified test conditions
Scorch (v.)	Modify the surface of a material by limited carbonisation
Self heating	Exothermic reaction within a material causing a rise in temperature of the material

Term	Definition
Self ignition	Ignition arising from self heating
Self propagation of flame	Propagation of a flame along a solid without externally applied heat
Smoke	Visible suspension of solid and/or liquid particles in gases resulting from combustion or pyrolysis
Smoke obscuration	Reduction in luminous intensity due to passage through smoke
Smouldering	Slow combustion of a material without light being visible and generally characterised by smoke and a rise in temperature
Soot	Finely divided particles, mainly carbon, produced and deposited during the incomplete combustion of organic materials
Spontaneous ignition temperature	Minimum temperature at which a material will ignite spontaneously under specified test conditions without externally applied heat
Time temperature curve	Conventional time related variation in temperature during a standard fire test
Wicking	Transmission of a combustible fluid through a particulate or fibrous material thus promoting ignition and/or combustion

10.3.2 English, German and French terms frequently used in connection with fire protection

English	German	French
actual calorific value	effektive Verbrennungs-wärme (f)	valeur (f) calorifique réelle
ad-hoc fire experiment	Ad-hoc-Brandversuch (m)	essai (m) au feu ad hoc
afterflame	Nachbrennen (n) mit Flamme	flamme (f) persistante
afterflame time	Nachbrenndauer (f)	durée (f) de persistance de flammes
afterglow	Nachglimmen (n)	incandescence (f) résiduelle
alcohol flame	Alkoholflamme (f)	flamme (f) d'alcool
to apply a flame	beflammen	appliquer une flamme
approval	Anerkennung (f)	homologation (f)
arc	Lichtbogen (m)	arc (m) électrique
area burning rate	Flächenabbrenngeschwindig-keit (f)	vitesse (f) de combustion en surface
arson	Brandstiftung (f)	incendie (m) criminel
arsonist	Brandstifter (m)	incendiaire (m)
ash	Asche (f)	cendre (f) or cendres (f pl.)
building	Bauwesen	bâtiment (m) or construction (f)
building component	Bauteil (n)	élément (m) de construction
building material	Baustoff (m)	matériau (m) de construction
building regulations	Bauvorschriften (f pl.)	réglementation (f) (bâtiment)
building structure	Bauwerksteil (n)	structure (f)
to burn	brennen	brûler
burned area	verbrannte Flächen-anteile (m pl.)	surface (f) or zone (f) brûlée
burner	Brenner (m)	brûleur (m)
burning behaviour	Brennverhalten (n)	comportement (m) à la flamme
to burn out	ausbrennen, ausglühen	calciner, réduire en cendres
Bunsen burner	Bunsenbrenner (m)	brûleur (m) or bec (m) Bunsen
calorific potential	Heizwert, spezifische Ver-brennungswärme	pouvoir (m) calorifique
char	Verkohlungsrückstand (m)	charbon (m) or résidu (m) charbonneux
to char	verkohlen	carboniser or charbonner
chimney	Rauchabzug (m)	conduit (m) de fumée
combustibility	Brennbarkeit (f)	combustibilité (f)
combustible	brennbar	combustible
combustion	Verbrennung (f)	combustion (f)
combustion chamber	Brennkasten (m)	chambre (f) de combustion
combustion products	Verbrennungsprodukte (n pl.)	produits (m pl.) de combustion
composite building materials	Verbund-Baustoffe (m pl.)	matériaux (m pl.) de construction composites or matériaux multicouches
conveyor belt	Fördergut (m)	courroie (f) transporteuse
to cool	abkühlen, kühlen	refroidir
corrosion	Korrosion (f)	corrosion (f)

English	German	French
corrosivity	Korrosivität (f)	corrosivité (f)
course of fire	Brandverlauf (m)	déroulement (m) de l'incendie
damaged area	beschädigte Fläche (f)	surface (f) or zone (f) endommagée
damaged length	Länge der Beschädigung (f)	longueur (f) endommagée
decomposition	Zersetzung (f)	décomposition (f)
decreasing fire	abklingender Brand (m)	incendie (m) décroissant
degradation	Abbau (m)	dégradation (f)
thermal -	thermischer -	- thermique
oxidative -	oxidativer -	- oxidative
diffusion flame	Diffusionsflamme (f)	flamme (f) de diffusion
edge application of flame	Kantenbeflammung (f)	action (f) de la flamme sur la tranche (de l'éprouvette)
exposure time	Einwirkungsdauer (f)	temps (m) d'exposition
(of an ignition source)	(einer Zündquelle)	(d'une source de feu)
extinction	Verlöschen (n)	extinction (f)
to extinguish	löschen	éteindre
fire	Brand (m), Schadenfeuer (n), Feuer (n)	feu (m), incendie (m) or sinistre (m)
fire behaviour	Brandverhalten (n)	comportement (m) au feu or tenue (f) au feu
fire-brigade	Feuerwehr (f)	sapeurs-pompiers (m pl.)
fire development	Brandentwicklung (f)	développement (m) de l'incendie
fire effluents	flüchtige Brandprodukte (n pl.)	produits (m pl.) volatils de combustion
fire experiment	Brandversuch (m)	essai (m) au feu
fire exposure	Feuerbeaufschlagung (f)	exposition (f) au feu
fire gases	Brandgase (n pl.)	gaz (m pl.) de combustion
fire hazard	Brandrisiko (n)	risque (m) d'incendie
fire insurance	Feuerversicherung (f)	assurance (f) incendie
fire load	Brandlast (f)	charge (f) calorifique
fire-load density	flächenbezogene Brandlast (f) (Brandbelastung)	densité (f) de charge calorifique
fire loss	Brandschaden (m)	dommage (m) causé par l'incendie
fire performance	Brandverhalten (n)	comportement (m) au feu or tenue (f) au feu
fireplace	Brandherd (m)	foyer (m) de l'incendie
fire precaution	vorbeugender (baulicher) Brandschutz (m)	prévention (f) incendie (bâtiment)
fire propagation	Brandausbreitung (f)	propagation (f) de l'incendie
fire protection	Brandschutz (m)	sécurité (f) or protection (f) contre l'incendie
fire resistance	Feuerwiderstandsfähigkeit (f)	résistance (f) au feu
fire retardant	abbrandverzögernd	ignifuge
fire-retardant treatment	Brandschutzausrüstung (f)	ignifugation (f)
fire room	Brandraum (m)	local (m) pour essais au feu
fire safety	Brandschutz (m)	sécurité (f) or protection (f) contre l'incendie
fire scenario	Brand-Fallstudie (f) (Szenario [n])	scénario (m) d'incendie
fire test	Brandprüfung (f)	essai (m) au feu

English	German	French
flame	Flamme (f)	flamme (f)
to flame	brennen (mit Flamme)	flamber
flame application	Beflammung (f)	application (f) de la flamme
flame front	Flammenfront (f)	front (m) de flammes
flame height	Flammenhöhe (f)	hauteur (f) de la flamme
flameless combustion	Verbrennung (f) ohne Flammenerscheinung	combustion (f) sans flamme
flame retardant	Flammschutzmittel (n)	ignifugeant (m) or retardateur (m) de flammes
flame spread	Flammenausbreitung (f)	propagation (f) de flammes
flame-spread rate	Flammenausbreitungs-geschwindigkeit (f)	vitesse (f) de propagation de flammes
flame-spread time	Flammenausbreitungs-dauer (f)	durée (f) de propagation de flammes
flame tip	Flammenspitze (f)	pointe (f) de la flamme
flammability	Entflammbarkeit (f)	inflammabilité (f)
flammable	entflammbar	inflammable
flash-over	Feuerüberschlag (m), Feuerübersprung (m)	embrasement (m) généralisé
flash point	Entflammungspunkt (m)	point (m) d'éclair
flooring	Fußbodenbelag (m)	revêtement (m) de sol
fuel	Brennstoff (m)	combustible (m)
	Kraftstoff (m)	carburant (m)
fully developed fire	vollentwickelter Brand (m)	incendie (m) en pleine extension
furnace	Ofen (m)	four (m)
gas	Gas (n)	gaz (m)
gas burner	Gasbrenner (m)	brûleur (m) à gaz
to glow	glimmen	brûler sans flamme
glowing combustion	Glimmen (n)	combustion (f) sans flamme
heat	Wärme (f)	chaleur (f)
heating	Erwärmung (f)	échauffement (m)
heat of combustion	spezifische Verbrennungswärme (f)	pouvoir (m) calorifique
heat release rate	Wärmeabgabe-geschwindigkeit (f)	débit (m) calorifique
ignitability	Entzündbarkeit (f)	facilité (f) d'allumage
to ignite	entzünden, sich entzünden	allumer, prendre feu
ignition	Zündung (f)	allumage (m)
ignition device	Zündvorrichtung (f)	dispositif (m) d'allumage
ignition point	Entzündungspunkt (m)	point (m) d'allumage
ignition source	Zündquelle (f)	source (f) de feu
ignition temperature	Entzündungstemperatur (f)	température (f) d'allumage
ignition time	Zünddauer (f)	temps (m) d'allumage
incandescence	Glühen (n)	incandescence (f)
to be incandescent	glühen	être incandescent
initiating fire	Entstehungsbrand (m)	incendie (m) naissant
intumescence	Intumeszenz (f)	intumescence (f)
intumescent	intumeszierend	intumescent
irradiation	Bestrahlung (f)	irradiation (f)
laboratory test	Laborprüfverfahren (n)	essai (m) en laboratoire
to light	anzünden	mettre le feu or enflammer
light absorption	Lichtabsorption (f)	absorption (f) de lumière

English	German	French
lighting	Aufflammen (n) Entflammung (f)	inflammation (f)
light source	Lichtquelle (f)	source (f) lumineuse
luminous flame	leuchtende Flamme (f)	flamme (f) lumineuse
mass burning rate	Abbrandgeschwindigkeit (f)	vitesse (f) massique de combustion
to melt	schmelzen	fondre
melting behaviour	Schmelzverhalten (n)	comportement (m) thermo-fusible
method of test	Prüfmethode (f)	méthode (f) d'essai
model fire test	Modellbrandversuch (m)	essai (m) d'incendie en ma-quette
multiple flame burner	Reihenbrenner (m)	brûleur (m) multiflamme
non-combustibility	Nichtbrennbarkeit (f)	incombustibilité (f)
non-combustible	nicht brennbar	incombustible
optical smoke density	optische Rauchdichte (f)	densité (f) optique de la fumée
photocell	Photozelle (f)	cellule (f) photo-électrique
pilot flame	Zündflamme (f)	flamme-pilote (f)
premixed flame	vorgemischte Flamme (f)	flamme (f) prémélangée
post-combustion	Nachverbrennung (f)	post-combustion (f)
to put out	löschen	éteindre
pyrolysis	Pyrolyse (f)	pyrolyse (f)
pyrophoric material	pyrophorer Stoff (m)	pyrophore (m)
radiant flux	Strahlungsfluß (m)	flux (m) de rayonnement
radiant panel	Strahlerplatte (f)	panneau (m) radiant
radiation	Wärmestrahlung (f)	rayonnement (m) thermique
radiation intensity	Strahlungsintensität (f)	intensité (f) de rayonnement
radiator	Strahler (m)	radiateur (m)
radiometer	Radiometer (n)	radiomètre (m)
rate of burning	Brenngeschwindigkeit (f)	vitesse (f) de combustion
reaction to fire	Rückwirkung auf das Feuer (or: Brandverhalten)	réaction (f) au feu
recognition	Anerkennung (f)	homologation (f)
regulations	Vorschriften (f pl.)	réglementation (f)
sample	Probekörper (m)	éprouvette (f)
to scorch	versengen	roussir
self-heating	Selbsterwärmung (f)	auto-chauffage (m)
self-ignition	Selbstentzündung (f)	allumage (m) spontané
self-propagation of flame	selbständige Flammenausbreitung (f)	autopropagation (f) de flamme
short-circuit	Kurzschluß (m)	court-circuit (m)
smoke	Rauch (m)	fumée (f)
smoke chamber	Rauchkammer (f)	chambre (f) à fumée
smoke density	Rauchdichte (f)	densité (f) de fumée
smoke development	Rauchentwicklung (f)	développement (m) or dégagement (m) de fumée
smoke generation	Rauchentwicklung (f)	développement (m) or dégagement (m) de fumée
smoke layer	Rauchschicht (f)	couche (f) de fumée
smoke obscuration	Verdunkelung durch Rauch	obscurcissement (m) par la fumée
smoke particles	Rauchteilchen (-partikel) (n pl.)	particules (f pl.) de fumée

English	German	French
smoke production	Rauchentwicklung (f)	développement (m) or dégagement (m) de fumée
smoke retarder	Rauchverminderer (m)	agent (m) réducteur de fumée
smoke suppressant	Rauchverminderer (m)	agent (m) réducteur de fumée
smouldering	Schwelen (n)	feu (m) qui couve
to soften	erweichen	ramollir
soot	Ruß (m)	suie (f)
spark	Funke (m)	étincelle (f)
specific optical density	materialbezogene optische Rauchdichte (f)	densité (f) optique spécifique
specimen	Prüfstück (n)	échantillon (m)
specimen holder	Probenhalterung (f)	porte-éprouvette (m)
spontaneous ignition	Selbstentzündung (f)	allumage (m) spontané
spontaneous ignition temperature	Selbstentzündungstemperatur (f)	température (f) d'allumage spontané
spread of flame	Flammenausbreitung (f)	propagation (f) de flammes
structural fire precautions	vorbeugender, baulicher Brandschutz	prévention (f) incendie (bâtiment)
surface burn	oberflächiges Abbrennen (n)	combustion (f) en surface
surface flame action	Flächenbeflammung (f)	action (f) de la flamme sur la surface
surface flash	oberflächiges Abflammen (n)	effet (m) éclair
temperature resistant	temperaturbeständig	thermostable
testing laboratory	Prüflaboratorium (n)	laboratoire (m) d'essais
test report	Prüfbericht (m)	procès-verbal (m) or compte-rendu (m) d'essais
test results	Prüfergebnis (n)	résultats (m pl.) d'essais
thermal	thermisch	thermique
thermocouple	Thermoelement (n)	thermocouple (m)
time-temperature curve	Temperatur-Zeit-Kurve (f)	courbe (f) température temps
toxicity	Toxizität (f)	toxicité (f)
to vaporise	verdampfen	volatiliser
wicking	Dochtwirkung (f)	effet (m) mèche
wood crib	Holzkrippe (f)	foyer (m) de bois

10.4 International and national standards organisations

International Organisations

International Electrotechnical Commission (IEC)
1—3, rue de Varembé
CH-1211 Geneva 20

International Organization for Standardization (ISO)
1—3, rue de Varembé
CH-1211 Geneva 20

National Organisations

From ISO-Catalogue 1980. International Organization for Standardization.

Australia

Australien/Australie (SAA)
Standards Association of Australia
Standards House
80—86 Arthur Street
North Sydney – N.S.W. 2060

Austria

Österreich/Autriche (ON)
Österreichisches Normungsinstitut
Leopoldgasse 4
Postfach 130
A-1021 Wien 2

Belgium

Belgien/Belgique (IBN)
Institut belge de normalisation
Av. de la Brabançonne, 29
B-1040 Bruxelles

Brazil

Brasilien/Brésil (ABNT)
Associação Brasileira de Normas Técnicas
Av. 13 de Maio, n° 13—28° andar
Caixa Postal 1680
CEP: 20.003 – Rio de Janeiro-RJ

Bulgaria

Bulgarien/Bulgarie (DKC)
State Committee for Standardization
at the Council of Ministers
21, 6th September Street
Sofia

Canada

Kanada/Canada (SCC)
Standards Council of Canada
International Standardization Branch
2000 Argentia Road, Suite 2–401
Mississauga, Ontario
L5N 1V8

Czechoslovakia

Tschechoslowakei/Tchécoslovaquie (ČSN)
Uřad pro normalizaci a měřeni
Václavské náměsti 19
11347 Praha 1

Chile

Chile/Chili (INN)
Instituto Nacional de Normalización
Matias Cousino 64–6° piso
Casilla 995 – Correo 1
Santiago

China

China/Chine (CAS)
China Association for Standardization
P.O. Box 820
Beijing

Denmark

Dänemark/Danemark (DS)
Dansk Standardiseringsråd
Aurehøjvej 12
Postbox 77
DK-2900 Hellerup

Finland

Finnland/Finlande (SFS)
Suomen Standardisoimisliitto r.y.
P.O. Box 205
SF-00121 Helsinki 12

France

Frankreich/France (AFNOR)
Association française de normalisation
Tour Europe
Cedex 7
F-92080 Paris La Défense

German Democratic Republic

Deutsche Demokratische Republik/République Démocratique Allemande
(not a member of ISO)
Amt für Standardisierung, Meßwesen und Warenprüfung (ASMW)
Wallstr. 16
DDR-102 Berlin

Germany, F.R.

Bundesrepublik Deutschland/Allemagne, R.F. (DIN)
DIN Deutsches Institut für Normung
Burggrafenstraße 4−10
Postfach 1107
D-1000 Berlin 30

Greece

Griechenland/Grèce (ELOT)
Hellenic Organization for Standardization
Didotou 15
Athens 144

Hungary

Ungarn/Hongrie (MSZH)
Magyar Szabványügyi Hivatal
Budapest
Pf. 24.
1450

India

Indien/Inde (ISI)
Indian Standards Institution
Manak Bhavan
3 Bahadur Shah Zafar Marg
New Delhi 110002

Indonesia

Indonesien/Indonésie (YDNI)
Badan Kerjasama LIPI-YDNI
(LIPI-YDNI Joint Standardization Committee)
Jln. Teuku Chik Ditiro 43
P.O. Box 250
Jakarta

Ireland

Irland/Irlande (IIRS)
Institute for Industrial Research and Standards
Ballymun Road
Dublin-9

Israel

Israel/Israël (SII)
Standards Institution of Israel
42 University Street
Tel Aviv 69977

Italy

Italien/Italie (UNI)
Ente Nazionale Italiano di Unificazione
Piazza Armando Diaz 2
I-20123 Milano

Japan

Japan/Japon (JISC)
Japanese Industrial Standards Committee
c/o Standards Department
Agency of Industrial Science and Technology
Ministry of International Trade and Industry
1−3−1, Kasumigaseki, Chiyodaku
Tokyo 100

Mexico

Mexiko/Mexique (DGN)
Dirección General de Normas
Tuxpan No. 2
Mexico 7, D.F.

Netherlands

Niederlande/Pays-Bas (NNI)
Nederlands Normalisatie-Instituut
Polakweg 5
P.O. Box 5810
2280 HV Rijswijk ZH

New Zealand

Neuseeland/Nouvelle-Zélande (SANZ)
Standards Association of New Zealand
Private Bag
Wellington

Norway

Norwegen/Norvège (NSF)
Norges Standardiseringsforbund
Haakon Vll's gate 2
N-Oslo 1

Poland

Polen/Pologne (PKNiM)
Polski Komitet Normalizacji, Miar i Jakości
Ul. Elektoralna 2
00-139 Warszawa

Portugal

Portugal (DGQ)
Direcção-Geral da Qualidade
Serviço de Normalização
Rua José Estêvão, 83−A
1199 Lisboa Codex

Romania

Rumänien/Roumanie (IRS)
Institutul Român de Standardizare
Căsuta Postală 63−87
Bucarest 1

South Africa, Rep. of

Südafrika, Rep./Afrique du Sud, Rép. d' (SABS)
South African Bureau of Standards
Private Bag X 191
Pretoria 0001

Spain

Spanien/Espagne (IRANOR)
Instituto Nacional de Racionalización y
Normalización
Zurbano 46
Madrid 10

Sweden

Schweden/Suède (SIS)
SIS – Standardiseringskommissionen i Sverige
Tegnérgatan 11
Box 3 295
S-10366 Stockholm

Switzerland

Schweiz/Suisse (SNV)
Association suisse de normalisation
Kirchenweg 4
Postfach
CH-8032 Zürich

United Kingdom

Vereinigtes Königreich/Royaume-Uni (BSI)
British Standards Institution
2 Park Street
London W1A 2BS

USA

USA (ANSI)
American National Standards Institute
1430 Broadway
New York, N.Y. 10018

USSR

UdSSR/URSS (GOST)
USSR State Committee for Standards
Leninsky Prospekt 9
Moskva 117049

Yugoslavia

Jugoslawien/Yougoslavie (JZS)
Jugoslovenski zavod za Standardizaciju
Slobodana Penezića-Krcuna br. 35
Pošt. Pregr. 933
11000 Beograd

10.5 Organisations concerned with structural fire safety

The list of important organisations involved with fire safety in buildings given here is intended to supplement Section 8.2.1. Further organisations – in particular national test institutes – will be found in Sections 8.2.2 to 8.2.18. The reader is also referred to Section 10.8, "Abbreviations".

Conseil International du Bâtiment pour la Recherche et la Documentation (CIB) (International Council for Building Research, Studies and Documentation).
This independent organisation has approximately 50 members. Structural fire precautions are discussed in CIB W 14 "Fire Commission" by 14 countries. (See also Section 8.2.18).

International Laboratories Data Acceptance (ILDA).
This European association of state fire safety laboratories has no official status; members exchange experience particularly on correlation of national fire test methods.

Réunion Internationale des Laboratoires d'Essais et de Recherche sur les Matériaux et les Constructions (RILEM) (International Association of Test and Research Laboratories for Building Materials and Structures).
An important function of this organisation is the interchange of information on experimental research. There is also cooperation on fire tests for building materials and components.

Union Européenne pour l'Agrément technique dans la construction (UEAtc) (European Union for Technical Approval in Building).
This organisation is made up of 11 countries who are represented mainly by national test institutes.

10.6 Abbreviations for Countries

Country	Abbreviation
Australia	AUS
Austria	A
Belgium	B
Canada	CDN
Czechoslovakia	ČS
Denmark	DK
Finland	SF
France	F
German Democratic Republic	GDR
Germany, Federal Republic of	D
Great Britain	GB
Hungary	H
Iceland	IS
Italy	I
Japan	J
Luxemburg	L
Netherlands	NL
Norway	N
Soviet Union	SU
Spain	E
Sweden	S
Switzerland	CH
United States of America	USA

10.7 Electrotechnical safety and standards organisations in Europe and overseas

EEC:

CENELEC-General Secretariat
2, Rue Bréderode
B-1000 Bruxelles

Belgium:

CEBEC
B.P. 11
B-1640 Rhode-St.-Genèse

Denmark:

DEMKO
8 Lyskaer
DK-2730 Herlev

Eire:

IIRS
Ballymun Road
Dublin 9

France:

LCIE
33, Av. du Général-Leclerc
F-92260 Fontenay-Aux-Roses

UTE
12, Place des Etats-Unis
F-75783 Paris Cedex 16

Great Britain:

BEAB, Mark House The Green
9/11 Queen's Road
Hersham/Walton-on-Thames
Surrey KT12 5NA

BSI/THE
Maylands Avenue
Hemel Hempstead
Herts HP2 4SQ

Italy:

IMQ
Via dei Pestagalli, 1
I-20138 Milano

Netherlands:

KEMA
Utrechtseweg 310
Arnhem

Other CENELEC member states:

Austria: ÖVE
                  Eschenbachgasse 9
                  A-1010 Wien 1

Finland: SETI
                  Särkiniementie 3
                  SF-00210 Helsinki 21

Greece: ELOT
                  Didotou 15
                  GR-Athens 144

Norway: NEMKO
                  Gaustadelléen 30
                  Blindern
                  Oslo 3

Portugal: Comissão Electrotécnica
                  Portuguesa
                  Rua Artilharia Um, 104-2° Esq.
                  P-1000 Lisboa 1

Spain: Asociación
                  Electrotécnica Española
                  Francisco Gervás, 3
                  Madrid 20

Sweden: SEMKO
                  Box 30049
                  S-104 25 Stockholm

Switzerland: SEV
                  Seefeldstr. 301
                  CH-8008 Zürich

Rest of Europe:

Czechoslovakia: Elektrotechnický
                  Zkušební ústav
                  Troja, Pod lisem 129
                  ČS-17102 Praha 7

Hungary: MEEI
                  Váci út 48/a−b
                  H-1132 Budapest XIII

Iceland: The State Electrical
                        Inspection
                        Sidumuli 13
                        IS-105 Reykjavik

Poland: Centralne Biuro
                        Jakości Wyrobów
                        ul. Swietokrzyska 14
                        PL-00-050 Warszawa

Roumania: ICPE
                        Bd. T. Vladimirescu Nr. 45−47
                        Sectorul 6
                        Bucarest

Yugoslavia: JEK
                        Trzaska 2
                        Ljubljana

North, Central and South America:

Argentina: S.G.S. Argentina S.A.
                        Cerrito 1136−5° Piso
                        Casilla de Correo 4290
                        1010 Buenos Aires

Brazil: Associação Brasileira
                        de Normas Técnicas
                        Av. Alma Barosse 54−Gr. 1505
                        Rio de Janeiro

Canada: CSA
                        178 Rexdale Boulevard
                        Rexdale/Ontario M9W 1R3

Mexico: DGN
                        Av. Cuauhtémoc Nr. 80
                        Mexico 7 D.F.

USA: UL / Follow-Up Services
                        1285 Walt Whitman Rd.
                        Melville, Long Island, N.Y. 11746

                        UL / Follow-Up Services
                        333 Pfingsten Road
                        Northbrook
                        Illinois 60062

Asia and Australia:

Australia:	Regulatory Authorities Approvals Committee 1 Castlereagh Street Sydney 2000
Hongkong:	Hong Kong Standards and Testing Centre Eldex Industrial Bldg., 12th Floor, Unit A 21, Ma Tau Wei Road, Hung Hom, Kowloon Hong Kong
India:	Indian Standards Institution Manak Bhavan 9 Bahadur Shah Zafar Marg New Delhi 110 002
Iran:	ISIRI P.O. Box 2937 Teheran
Israel:	The Standards Institution of Israel (S.I.I.) 42, University Street Tel Aviv 69 977
Japan:	JCII 25, Ichiban-cho, Chiyoda-ku Tokyo 102
	JET 14−12, Yoyogi 5-chome, Shibuya-ku Tokyo 151
	JMI-Lab 1-21-25 Kinuta, Setagaya-ku Tokyo

10.8 Abbreviations

The following list contains the principal abbreviations used for plastics, fire safety and associated fields. It is arranged alphabetically without regard to individual topics or a logical relationship. The field and application as well as the section of this book where the abbreviation appears are given.

Abbreviation	Meaning	Field	Application	Section
ABNT	Associação Brasileira de Normas Técnicas	standards organisation	Brazil	10.4
ABS	Acrylonitrile butadiene styrene copolymer	plastics		4.2.1.2, 10.2
AEA	Asociación Electrotécnica Española	electrotechnical standards organisation	Spain	10.7
AFNOR	Association Française de Normalisation	standards organisation	France	8.2.4, 10.4
AIA	American Insurance Association	building	USA	8.2.14
ANSI	American National Standards Institute	standards organisation	USA	8.2.14, 10.4
AS	Australian Standard	standards	Australia	8.2.1, 8.2.16
ASA	Acrylonitrile styrene acrylic ester copolymer	plastics		4.2.1.2, 10.2
ASMW	Amt für Standardisierung, Meßwesen und Warenprüfung	standards organisation	GDR	8.2.10, 10.4
ASTM	American Society for Testing and Materials	standards	USA	8.2.1, 8.2.14
BAM	Bundesanstalt für Materialprüfung	materials testing	Federal Republic of Germany, building, etc.	8.2.2
BBC	Basic Building Code	building	model building code, USA	8.2.14
BOCA	Building Officials & Code Administrators International, Inc.	building	model building code, USA	8.2.14
BRE	Building Research Establishment Fire Research Station, Borehamwood, Hertfordshire WD6 2BL	building	fire testing, Great Britain	8.2.5

Abbreviation	Meaning	Field	Application	Section
BRI	Building Research Institute, Ministry of Construction	building	Japan	8.2.17
BS	British Standard	standards	Great Britain	8.2.5
BSI	British Standards Institution	standards organisation	Great Britain	8.2.5, 10.4
BVD	Brand-Verhütungs-Dienst für Industrie und Gewerbe	fire protection	Switzerland, building, etc.	8.2.8
BZA	Bundesbahn-Zentralamt	transportation (railways)	Federal Republic of Germany	8.3.2.2
CAS	China Association for Standardisation	standards organisation	China	10.4
CCE	Commission des Communautés Européennes	international organisation	economics incl. fire protection	8.2.18
CCFT	Coordinating Committee for Fire Tests	fire protection	ISO	7.3, 8.2.1, 8.2.18
CEE	Commission for Conformity Certification of Electrical Equipment	electrical engineering	recognition of test results	8.1.1, 8.4.4
CEN	Comité Européen de Normalisation	standardisation	Europe	8.1.1
CENELEC	Comité Européen de Normalisation Electrotechnique	electrotechnical standardisation	Europe	8.1.1, 8.4.4
CEP	Comissão Electrotécnica Portuguesa	standards organisation	electrical engineering, Portugal	10.7
CIB	Conseil International du Bâtiment pour la Recherche et la Documentation. General Secretariat: 704 Weena, P.O. Box 20704, Rotterdam, Netherlands	building	International Council for Research and Documentation	8.2.18, 10.5
CMEA	Council for Mutual Economic Assistance	international organisation	Eastern Countries, inter alia trade	8.1.1

Abbreviation	Meaning	Field	Application	Section
CNR	Consiglio Nazionale delle Ricerche	research institute	Italy, fire protection	8.2.6
CPSC	Consumer Product Safety Commission	consumer protection	USA	8.2.14
CS	Commercial Standard	standardisation	USA	8.5.3
CSA	Canadian Standards Association	standards organisation	Canada	8.2.15
CSE	Centro Studi ed Esperienze dei Vigili del Fuoco	research institute	fire brigade, fire protection, Italy	8.2.6
CSIRO	Commonwealth Scientific and Industrial Research Organisation Division of Building Research, CSIRO, Graham Road, Highett, Vic. 3190	research institute	Australia, building, fire protection, etc	8.2.16
ČSN	Czech State Standards Organisation	standards organisation, building	Czechoslovakia	8.2.13
CSTB	Centre Scientifique et Technique du Bâtiment	building	France, materials testing, inter alia fire protection	8.2.4
DB	Deutsche Bundesbahn	transportation (railways)	Federal Republic of Germany	8.3.2
DGN	Dirección General de Normas	standards organisation	Mexico	10.4
DGQ	Direcção-Geral da Qualidade	standards organisation	Portugal	10.4
DIN	Deutsches Institut für Normung	standards organisation	Federal Republic of Germany	8.2.2, 10.4
DIS	Draft International Standard	standardisation	ISO	8.2.18
DKE	Deutsche Elektrotechnische Kommission	electrical engineering, standardisation	Federal Republic of Germany	8.4.1.1
DOC	Department of Commerce	governmental	USA, ministry of trade	8.6
DOE	Department of Environment	governmental	Great Britain	8.2.5
DP	Draft Proposal	standardisation	ISO	8.2.18

Abbreviation	Meaning	Field	Application	Section
DS	Dansk Standardisering-sråd	standards organ-isation	Denmark	8.2.9, 10.4
DSC	Direction de la Sécurité Civile	governmental	France, inter alia fire protection	8.2.4
EBS	Experimental Building Station	building	Australia, mate-rials testing, inter alia fire protec-tion	8.2.16
ECE	Economic Commission for Europe	international organisation	economics (United Nations)	8.1.1
EDF	Electricité de France	electrical engineering	France	8.4.2
EEC	European Economic Community	international organisation	inter alia trade	8.1.1
ELOT	Hellenic Organisation for Standardisation	standards organ-isation	Greece	10.4
EMI	Epitésügyi Minőségel-lenőrzó Intezet	building	Hungary (Insti-tute for quality control in building)	8.2.12
EMPA	Eidgenössische Materialprüfungs- und Versuchsanstalt	materials testing	Switzerland, inter alia fire protec-tion (federal test institute)	8.2.8
EP	Epoxy resin	plastics		4.2.3.3, 10.2
ES	European Standard	standardisation	published by CEN and CENELEC	8.1.1
ETB	Ausschuß für Einheit-liche Technische Baubestimmungen	building	Federal Republic of Germany (committee for uniform building regulations)	8.2.2
ETFE	Ethylene tetra-fluoroethylene copolymer	plastics		4.2.1.4, 10.2
FAA	Federal Aviation Administration	aviation	USA, govern-mental	8.3.3
FAR	Federal Aviation Regu-lations	aviation	USA, regulations	8.3.3

Abbreviation	Meaning	Field	Application	Section
FEP	Perfluoroethylene propylene	plastics		4.2.1.4, 10.2
FIRTO	Fire Insurers' Research & Testing Organisation	fire protection	Great Britain	8.2.5
FIT	Flash-Ignition Temperature	test method	USA, plastics according to ASTM D 1929	4.1.3, 8.2.14
FKT	Fachausschuß Kraftfahrzeugtechnik	transport (motor vehicles)	Federal Republic of Germany	8.3.1.2
FMVSS	Federal Motor Vehicle Safety Standards	transport	USA	8.3.1.2
FNK	Fachnormausschuß Kunststoffe im DIN	standardisation (plastics)	Federal Republic of Germany	8.4.2.2
FNM	Fachnormausschuß Materialprüfung im DIN	standardisation (materials testing)	Federal Republic of Germany	8.4.2.2
FR	Federal Register	legal	USA, official gazette	8.3.1.1
FRS	Fire Research Station	fire protection	Great Britain	8.2.5
FSC	Flame Spread Classification	test method	USA, building ASTM E 84	8.2.14
FTMS	Federal Test Methods Standards	standardisation	USA	8.3.3.2, 8.5, 8.6
GOST	USSR State Committee for Standards	standards organisation	USSR	8.2.11, 10.4
HDPE	High density polyethylene	plastics		4.2.1.1, 10.2
HET-acid	Hexachloroendomethylene tetrahydrophthalic acid	flame retardant		5.2
HEW	Department of Health, Education and Welfare	governmental	USA	8.2.14
HHS	Department of Health and Human Services	governmental	USA	8.2.14
HUD	Departement of Housing and Urban Development	governmental	USA	8.2.14
IATA	International Air Transportation Association	transport	aviation	8.3.3

Abbreviation	Meaning	Field	Application	Section
IBN	Institut Belge de Normalisation	standards organisation	Belgium	8.2.3, 10.4
ICAO	International Civil Aviation Organization	transport	aviation	8.3.3
ICBO	International Conference of Building Officials	building	USA	8.2.14
IEC	International Electrotechnical Commission	electrical engineering	standardisation	8.1.1, 8.4.4
IfBt	Institut für Bautechnik	building	Federal Republic of Germany	8.2.2
IIRS	Institute for Industrial Research and Standards	standards organisation	Eire	10.4
ILDA	International Laboratories Data Acceptance	fire protection	association of test institutes	10.5
I-ILDA	Industry-ILDA	fire protection	association of industrial test laboratories	8.2.1
IMCO	Inter-Governmental Maritime Consultative Organization	transport	sea transport	8.3.4
INN	Instituto Nacional de Normalización	standards organisation	Chile	10.4
IRANOR	Instituto Nacional de Racionalización y Normalización	standards organisation	Spain	10.4
IRS	Insitutul Român de Standardizare	standards organisation	Roumania	10.4
ISI	Indian Standards Institute	standards organisation	India	10.4
ISO	International Organization for Standardization	standards organisation		8.2.18
JIS	Japanese Industrial Standards	standardisation	Japan	8.2.17
JISC	Japanese Industrial Standards Committee	standards organisation	Japan	8.2.17, 10.4
JO	Journal Officiel	legal	France, official gazette	8.2.4

Abbreviation	Meaning	Field	Application	Section
JZS	Jugoslovenski zavod za Standardizaciju	standards organisation	Yugoslavia	10.4
KOMO	Stichting voor Onderzoek, Beoordeling en Keuring van Materialen en Constructies	building	Netherlands	8.2.3
LBO	Landesbauordnung	building	Federal Republic of Germany	8.2.2
LCPP	Laboratoire Central de la Préfecture de Police	test institute	France, building, fire tests, etc	8.2.4
LDPE	Low density polyethylene	plastics		4.2.1.1, 10.2
LNE	Laboratoire National d'Essais	test institute	France, building, fire tests, etc	8.2.4
LOI	Limiting Oxygen Index	test method	USA: ASTM D 2863	8.2.9
MBO	Musterbauordnung	building	Federal Republic of Germany, model building code	8.2.2
MCSR	Motor Carrier Safety Regulations	transport	USA	8.3.1.1
MF	Melamine formaldehyde resin	plastics		4.2.3.4, 10.2
MPA	Materialprüfanstalt	test institute	Federal Republic of Germany, materials	8.2.2
MSZH	Magyar Szabványügyi Hivatal	standards organisation	Hungary	8.2.12, 10.4
NABau	Normenausschuß Bauwesen im DIN	standardisation (building)	Federal Republic of Germany	8.2.2
NATA	National Association of Testing Authorities	test institutes	Australia, fire testing, etc	8.2.16
NBC	National Building Code	building	USA, model building code	8.2.14
NBC	National Building Code of Canada	building	Canada	8.2.15
NBN	Normes Belges – Belgische Normen	standardisation	Belgium	8.2.3

Abbreviation	Meaning	Field	Application	Section
NBS	National Bureau of Standards	standardisation	USA, test methods, fire protection, etc	8.2.1, 8.2.14, 9.2.2.1
NCSBCS	National Conference of States for Building Codes and Standards	building	USA, model building code	8.2.14
NEN	Nederlandse Norm	standardisation	Netherlands	8.2.3
NFPA	National Fire Protection Association	fire protection	USA	8.2.14
NHTSA	National Highway Transport Safety Association	transport	USA, governmental	8.3.1.1
NKB	Nordiska Kommitten för Byggbestämmelser	building	Nordic countries	8.2.9
NMP	Normenausschuß Materialprüfung im DIN	standardisation (materials testing)	Federal Republic of Germany	8.2.1
NNI	Nederlands Normalisatie-Instituut	standards organisation	Netherlands	8.2.3, 10.4
NPRM	Notice of Proposed Rule Making	legal	USA	8.3.3
NS	Norsk Standard	standardisation	Norway	8.2.9
NSF	Norges Standardiseringsforbund	standards organisation	Norway	8.2.9, 10.4
NT	Nordtest	test method	Nordic countries	8.2.9
ON	Österreichisches Normungsinstitut	standards organisation	Austria	8.2.7, 10.4
OTSZ	Országos Tűzvédelmi Szabályzat	fire protection building regulations	Hungary	8.2.12
PA	Prüfzeichen mit Auflagen	building (test mark)	Federal Republic of Germany	8.2.2
PA	Polyamide	plastics		4.2.1.6, 10.2
PBI	Polybenzimidazole	plastics		4.2.4.1, 10.2
PBTP	Polybutyleneterephthalate	plastics		4.2.1.7, 10.2
PC	Polycarbonate	plastics		4.2.1.8, 10.2
PCTFE	Polychlorotrifluoroethylene	plastics		4.2.1.4, 10.2

Abbreviation	Meaning	Field	Application	Section
PE	Polyethylene	plastics		4.2.1.1, 10.2
PES	Polyether sulphone	plastics		4.2.4.1, 10.2
PETP	Polyethylene tere-phthalate	plastics		4.2.1.7, 10.2
PF	Phenol formaldehyde resin	plastics		4.2.3.1, 10.2
PI	Polyimide	plastics		4.2.4.1, 10.2
PIR	Polyisocyanurate	plastics		4.2.2.3, 10.2
PKNiM	Polski Komitet Nor-malizacji, Miari Jakości	standards organ-isation	Poland	10.4
PMMA	Polymethyl methacry-late	plastics		4.2.1.5, 10.2
POM	Polyoxymethylene	plastics		4.2.1.9, 10.2
PP	Polypropylene	plastics		4.2.1.1, 10.2
PPO	Polyphenylene oxide	plastics		4.2.4.1, 10.2
PPS	Polyphenylene sulphide	plastics		4.2.4.1, 10.2
PS	Polystyrene	plastics		4.2.1.2, 10.2
PSA	Property Services Agency	governmental	Great Britain, DOE	8.6
PSO	Polysulphone	plastics		4.2.4.1, 10.2
PTFE	Polytetrafluoroethylene	plastics		4.2.1.4, 10.2
PUR	Polyurethane	plastics		4.2.2.3, 10.2
PVC	Polyvinyl chloride	plastics		4.2.1.3, 10.2
PVCC	Chlorinated polyvinyl chloride	plastics		4.2.1.3, 10.2
PVDC	Polyvinylidene chloride	plastics		4.2.1.3, 10.2
PVDF	Polyvinylidene fluoride	plastics		4.2.1.4, 10.2
PVF	Polyvinyl fluoride	plastics		4.2.1.4, 10.2
RbBH	Richtlinien für die Ver-wendung brennbarer Baustoffe im Hochbau	building (guidelines for the use of flam-mable materials)	Federal Republic of Germany	8.2.2
RILEM	Réunion Internationale des Laboratoires d'Essais et de Recherche sur les Matériaux et les Con-structions	building	association of test laboratories	10.5

Abbreviation	Meaning	Field	Application	Section
SAA	Standards Association of Australia	standards organisation	Australia	8.2.16, 10.4
SABS	South African Bureau of Standards	standards organisation	South Africa	10.4
SAN	Styrene acrylonitrile copolymer	plastics		4.2.1.2, 10.2
SANZ	Standards Association of New Zealand	standards organisation	New Zealand	10.4
SB	Styrene butadiene copolymer	plastics		4.2.1.2, 10.2
SBC	Standard Building Code	building	USA, model building code	8.2.14
SBCC	Southern Building Code Congress International, Inc.	building	USA, model building code	8.2.14
SBG	Seeberufsgenossenschaft	shipping	Federal Republic of Germany	8.3.4
SBN	Svensk Byggnorm	building	Sweden, building regulations	8.2.9
SC	Sub-Committee	standardisation	ISO and IEC	8.2.18, 8.4.4
SCC	Standards Council of Canada	standards organisation	Canada	8.2.15, 10.4
SFS	Suomen Standardisoimisliitto r.y.	standards organisation	Finland	8.2.9, 10.4
SIA	Schweizerischer Ingenieur- und Architektenverein	private organisation	Switzerland, fire protection standards, etc	8.2.8
SII	Standards Institution of Israel	standards organisation	Israel	10.4
SIS	Standardiseringskommissionen i Sverige	standards organisation	Sweden	8.2.9, 10.4
SIT	Self-Ignition Temperature	test method	USA, plastics ASTM D 1929	4.1.3, 8.2.14
SNCF	Société Nationale des Chemins de Fer	transport	France, railways	8.3.2
SNiP	Sovetskie Normy i Pravila	standardisation	USSR	8.2.11
SNPE	Société Nationale des Poudres et Explosifs	test institute	France, building, fire tests, etc	8.2.4

Abbreviation	Meaning	Field	Application	Section
SNV	Schweizerische Nor-menvereinigung	standards organ-isation	Switzerland	8.2.8, 10.4
SOLAS	International Conven-tion for the Safety of Life at Sea	shipping	regulations	8.3.4.1
SPV	Statens Planverk	governmental	Sweden, building	8.2.9
SSV	Schiffssicherheits-verordnung	shipping	Federal Republic of Germany (safety regula-tions)	8.3.4.1
StBA	Staatliche Bauaufsicht	building	GDR (state building inspecto-rate)	8.2.10
STG	Schiffsbautechnische Gesellschaft	shipping	Federal Republic of Germany	8.3.4
TC	Technical Committee	standardisation	ISO and IEC	8.2.18, 8.4.4
TGL	Technische Güte- und Lieferbedingungen	standardisation	GDR	8.2.1, 8.2.10
TNO	Toegepast Natuur-wetenschappelijk Onderzoek	research institute	Netherlands, building, fire pro-tection, etc	8.2.3
TOSCA or TSCA	Toxic Substances Con-trol Act	legal	USA	2.
TR	Technical Report	standardisation	ISO	8.2.18
UBC	Uniform Building Code	building	USA, model building code	8.2.14
UEAtc	Union Européenne pour l'Agrément technique dans la construction	building	Europe, technical certification	10.5
UF	Urea formaldehyde resin	plastics		4.2.3.4, 10.2
UFAC	Upholstered Furniture Action Council	furniture	fire protection	8.6
UIC	Union Internationale des Chemins de Fer	transport	rail vehicles	8.3.2
UL	Underwriters' Laboratories Inc.	test institute	USA, fire tests, electrical engineering, building, etc.	8.4.3.1, 8.2.14

Abbreviation	Meaning	Field	Application	Section
ULC	Underwriters' Laboratories of Canada	test institute	Canada, fire tests, electrical engineering, building etc.	8.2.15
UMTA	Urban Mass Transportation Administration	transport	USA, governmental	8.3.2
UNI	Ente Nazionale Italiano di Unificazione	standards organisation	Italy	8.2.6, 10.4
UP	Unsaturated polyester resin	plastics		4.2.3.2, 10.2
UTE	Union Technique de l'Electricité	electrical engineering	France	8.4.2
VDE	Verband Deutscher Elektrotechniker e.V.	electrical engineering	Federal Republic of Germany	8.4.1.1
VFDB	Vereinigung zur Förderung des Deutschen Brandschutzes e.V. Hertzstr. 16, 75 Karlsruhe 21	fire protection association	Federal Republic of Germany, building	
VKF	Vereinigung kantonaler Feuerversicherungen	building (fire insurers' association)	Switzerland	8.2.8
VTT	Valtion Teknillinen Tutkismuskeskus	test institute	Finland, fire tests, building, etc.	8.2.9
VÚPS	Výzkumný Ústav Pozemních Staveb	building	Czechoslovakia, research institute, building, etc.	8.2.13
WG	Working Group	standardisation	ISO, IEC	8.2.18, 8.4.4
YDNI	Badan Kerjasama LIPI-YDNI	standards organisation	Indonesia	10.4

10.9 Journals and books

The following list contains only those journals and monographs devoted exclusively to fire protection. No claim is made regarding completeness and sources concerned with fire fighting and the fire services have been disregarded. For relevant papers in plastics journals and pertinent sections in monographs on plastics the reader should consult the references at the end of each section in this book.

Journals

CA (Chemical Abstracts) Selects: Flammability. Fortnightly. American Chemical Society, 2540 Olentangy River Rd., Columbus Ohio 43202, USA.

Combustion and Flame. Three volumes per annum each consisting of three issues. Elsevier North-Holland, Inc., 52 Vanderbilt Avenue, New York, N.Y. 10017, USA. Vol. 41 (1981) (first volume for 1981).

Fire and Materials. Quarterly. Heyden & Son Ltd., Spectrum House, Hillview Gardens, London NW4 23Q, England. Vol. 5 (1981).

Fire International. Quarterly. Unesas House, Dudley Road, Tunbridge Wells, Kent, England. Issue 70, March 1981.

Fire Safety Journal (previously Fire Research). Quarterly. Elsevier Sequoia S.A., P.O. Box 851, CH-1001 Lausanne 1, Switzerland. Vol. 4 (1981).

Fire Technology. Quarterly. National Fire Protection Association (NFPA), 470 Atlantic Avenue, Boston, MA 02210, USA. Vol. 17 (1981).

Journal of Fire and Flammability. Quarterly. Technomic Publishing Company, Inc., 265 Post Road West, Westport, CT 06880, USA. Vol. 13 (1981).
The following associated journals also appear quarterly:
Journal of Combustion Toxicology. Vol. 8 (1981).
Journal of Consumer Product Flammability. Vol. 8 (1981).
Journal of Fire Retardant Chemistry. Vol. 8 (1981).

Rubber and Plastics. Fire and Flammability Bulletin. Monthly. Elsevier Sequoia S.A., P.O. Box 851, CH-1001 Lausanne 1, Switzerland. Vol. 2 (1981).

VFDB-Zeitschrift, Forschung und Technik im Brandschutz (Fire protection research and engineering). Quarterly. W. Kohlhammer GmbH, Stuttgart, Federal Republic of Germany. Vol. 30 (1981).

Books

M.W. Alexejev, M. J. Roitman, P. G. Demidov, N. A. Tarasov-Agalakov: Grundlagen des Brandschutzes (Fundamentals of fire protection). Translated from the Russian, Staatsverlag der DDR, Berlin, 1976.

C. J. Hilado: Flammability Handbook for Plastics. 2nd ed., Technomic Publishing Co., Inc., Westport, 1974.

W. C. Kuryla, A. J. Papa (Editors): Flame Retardancy of Polymeric Materials. Five volumes (Vols. 1 and 2 1973, Vol. 3 1975, Vol. 4 1978, Vol. 5 1979). Marcel Dekker, Inc., New York.

M. Lewin, S. M. Atlas, E. M. Pearce (Editors): Flame Retardant Polymeric Materials. Two volumes (Vol. 1 1975, Vol. 2 1978). Plenum Press, New York.

J. W. Lyons: The Chemistry & Uses of Fire Retardants. Wiley-Interscience, John Wiley, New York, 1970.

V. T. Monachov: Methods for Investigating the Fire Hazard of Materials (Russ.). 2nd revised ed., Moscow, Chimija publishing house, 1979.

National Materials Advisory Board: Fire Safety Aspects of Polymeric Materials. Ten volumes. Technomic Publishing Company, Inc., Westport, USA.
Vol. 1: Materials: State of the Art. 1977.
Vol. 2: Test Methods, Specifications and Standards. 1979.
Vol. 3: Smoke and Toxicity (Combustion Toxicology of Polymers). 1978.
Vol. 4: Fire Dynamics and Scenarios. 1978.
Vol. 5: Elements of Polymer Fire Safety and Guide to the Designer. 1979.
Vol. 6: Aircraft: Civil and Military. 1977.
Vol. 7: Buildings. 1979.
Vol. 8: Land Transportation Vehicles. 1979.
Vol. 9: Ships. 1980.
Vol. 10: Mines and Bunkers. 1980.

K. Pál, H. Macskásy: A Műanyagok Éghetősége (Combustibility of plastics). Műszaki Könyvkiadó, Budapest, 1980.

M. J. Roitman: Grundlagen der Brandschutz-Normierung im Bauwesen (Fundamentals of fire protection standardisation in building). Translated from the Russian, Staatsverlag der DDR and Verlagsgesellschaft Rudolf Müller, Köln-Braunsfeld, 1974.

R. Thater: Brennverhalten von Plastformstoffen (Burning behaviour of plastics). VEB Verlag für Grundstoffindustrie, Leipzig, 1968.

P. Thiéry: Fireproofing. Elsevier Publishing Company Ltd., Amsterdam, 1970.

H. Vogel: Flammfestmachen von Kunststoffen (Flameproofing of plastics). Dr. Alfred Hüthig Verlag, Heidelberg, 1966.

Index to Standards

* = Experimental Standard

* Draft Spanish Standard

Author Index

Key Word Index

In order to assist the reader, terms occuring frequently in the book are qualified with abbreviations indicating the relevant section as follows:

building = *bui*
transportation = *tra*
motor vehicles = *mot*
rail vehicles = *rail*
aircraft = *air*
ships = *sea*
hazardous materials = *haz*

electrical engineering = *el*
textiles = *tex*
furniture and furnishings = *fur*
smoke = *smo*
toxicity = *tox*
corrosion = *cor*

Countries are abbreviated as per Table 10.6

HANSER BOOKS

Braun
Simple Methods of Identification of Plastics: With the Plastics Identification Table by Hansjürgen Saechtling.
96 pages. 8 illustrations. 14 tables. 1982.
ISBN 3-446-13573-1.

Gaechter/Mueller
Plastics Additives Handbook
Approx. 570 pages, illustrations, tables, trade-name register. 1983.
ISBN 3-446-13662-2.

Gastrow
Injection Molds: Design and Construction.
Approx. 320 pages, 540 illustrations. 1983.
ISBN 3-446-13663-0.

Hummel/Scholl
Atlas of Polymer and Plastics Analysis
Vol. 1: Polymers: Structures and Spectra. 740 pages, 1903 spectra, numerous illustrations and tables. 1978. ISBN 3-446-12590-6.
Vol. 2: Plastics, Fibres, Rubber, Resins. Part 1: Text; Part 2: Spectra.
ISBN 3-446-12591-4 (in preparation).
Vol. 3: Additives and Processing Aids. 720 pages. 1355 spectra. 46 figures. 124 tables. 1981. ISBN 3-446-12592-2.
In coproduction with Verlag Chemie

Johannaber
Injection Molding Machines
200 pages. 166 illustrations. 29 tables. 1983.
ISBN 3-446-13575-8.

Krause/Lange/Ezrin
Plastics Analysis Guide: Chemical and Instrumental Methods.
190 pages. 34 tables. 1983.
ISBN 3-446-13587-1.

Rao
Designing Machines and Dies for Polymer Processing with Computer Programs
FORTRAN and BASIC
208 pages. 87 illustrations. 22 tables. 1981.
ISBN 3-446-13500-6.

Saechtling
International Plastics Handbook.
Approx. 520 pages, 150 illustrations, 126 tables, trade-name register. 1983.
ISBN 3-446-13668-1.

Schnabel
Polymer Degradation: Principles and Practical Applications.
220 pages. 80 illustrations. 1981.
ISBN 3-446-13264-3.

Troitzsch
International Plastics Flammability Handbook: Principles, Regulations, Testing & Approval. 506 pages. 168 illustrations. 198 tables. 1983. ISBN 3-446-13571-5.

Ulrich
Introduction to Industrial Polymers.
154 pages. 51 illustrations. 43 tables. 1982.
ISBN 3-446-13561-8.

Welling
Plastics Engineering Dictionary: German-English.
278 pages. 2nd edition. 1982.
ISBN 3-446-12931-6.

Wittfoht
Plastics Technical Dictionary

Part 1: Alphabetical Dictionary: English-German.
550 pages. Numerous illustrations. 1981.
ISBN 3-446-11522-6.

Part 2: Alphabetical Dictionary: German-English. 1983. ISBN 3-446-12583-3

Part 3: Reference Volume. Illustrated Systematic Groups.
508 pages. 26 groups. More than 500 illustrations and explanatory drawings. 1981. ISBN 3-446-12582-5.

Hanser Publishers, P.O.Box 86 04 20, D-8000 Munich 86, Fed. Rep. of Germany